Praise F[illegible] ed

One of the untold [illegible] ne US is the role of medical and public health professionals in spreading disinformation, pushing for policies that exacerbate the virus' spread, and drive people away from important interventions, particularly vaccines, which blunt the deadly effects of SARSCOV2. Because of professional courtesy, solidarity or just sheer cowardice, many inside the professions have refused to take on these frauds, egomaniacs, purveyors of sickness and suffering in white coats. Jonathan Howard's book We Want Them Infected, though, names names. In painstaking detail, he builds an indictment of these men and women who have blood on their hands, abusing the trust of millions to peddle lies and falsehoods. This book is one for the ages, making it hard to sweep the complicity of these individuals with the virus under the carpet, leaving a record for the future, a cautionary tale for all of us.

—Gregg Gonsalves, PhD, Associate Professor, Yale School of Public Health, Associate Professor (adjunct), Yale Law School

The legacy of the COVID-19 pandemic will haunt our nation (United States) for many years. This is true not only because of the horrific toll of more than one million American deaths, and those who lost loved ones, but also several failed public health policies that contributed to America's suffering. In "We Want Them Infected" Dr. Howard tells a dark story of how spurious concepts of herd immunity may have contributed to the spread of COVID-19 in the United States (and perhaps globally). His book provides important information about how we might limit the death and destruction of future virus pandemics.

—Dr. Peter Hotez, MD, PhD, DSc (hon), FASTMH, FAAP , Texas Children's Hospital: Endowed Chair of Tropical Pediatrics, Co-Director, Texas Children's Hospital Center for Vaccine Development Baylor College of Medicine: Dean, National School of Tropical Medicine, Professor, Departments of Pediatrics, Molecular Virology & Microbiology, Health Policy Scholar Rice University, Baker Institute Fellow in Disease & Poverty Texas A&M University, Faculty-Senior Fellow, Hagler Institute for Advanced Study & Scowcroft Institute of International Affairs

The Hippocratic Oath enjoins us to "first do no harm". Yet, throughout the COVID-19 pandemic, some very prominent doctors have done immense harm. While others were struggling to understand the virus and save lives, a few were spreading what we describe as disinformation, but might equally call lies. By aligning with populist politicians they undermined public health responses and cost many lives. Everyone who has suffered from COVID-19, losing friends and relatives or experiencing Long COVID, or who cared for them, owes a debt of gratitude to Jonathan Howard. By cataloging in detail the ways in which the words and actions of those who, for whatever reason, distorted the science, he must surely have destroyed any remaining credibility they possess.

—Dr. Martin McKee, President, British Medical Association, Professor of European public health at the London School of Hygiene and Tropical Medicine

A comprehensive and sober fact-checking of a disturbing phenomenon: the rise of the COVID contrarian doctor. We Want Them Infected deconstructs the revisionist history and failed predictions of the physicians repeatedly caught prioritizing wishful thinking over data. Dr. Howard has kept the receipts that show these contrarian doctors' crystal balls are badly broken.

—Jonathan Jarry, MSc, Science Communicator for McGill University's Office for Science and Society

Jonathan Howard's important book sheds light on a crucial issue: how previously mainstream doctors became mouthpieces of misinformation, promoting claims as false as those of anti-vaccine activists, and making controlling COVID-19 that much harder. The book is gripping, hard to put down, full of evidence and the personal experience of frontline doctors, and thoroughly explains both the problems with the doctors' claims and the way they affected the fight against the virus. It is a valuable addition to understanding how misinformation spread during the pandemic, and I would encourage policy makers, doctors, and academics to read and share it.

—Dorit Reiss, Professor of Law and the James Edgar Hervey '50 Chair of Litigation at UC Hastings College of Law.

We Want Them Infected

How the failed quest for herd immunity led doctors to embrace the anti-vaccine movement and blinded Americans to the threat of COVID

Jonathan Howard MD

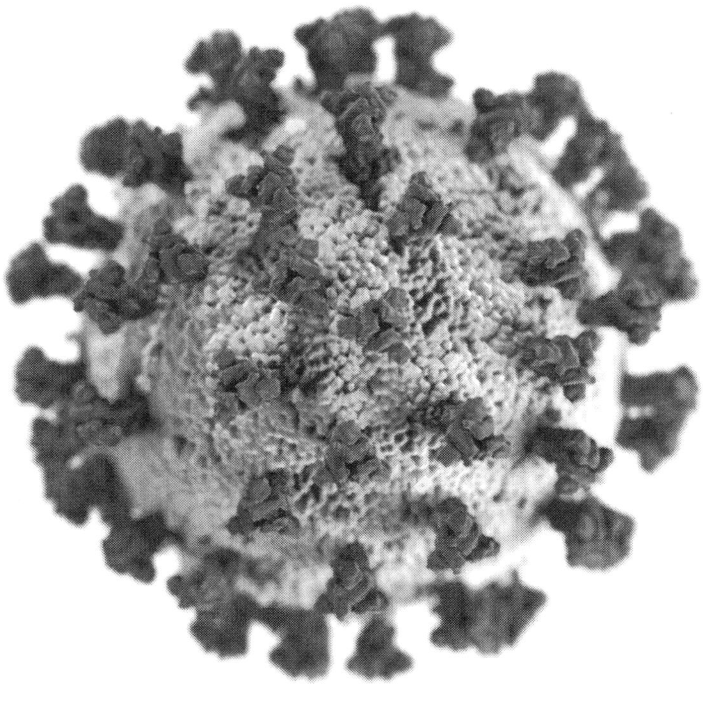

REDHAWK
PUBLICATIONS

Redhawk Publications
The Catawba Valley Community College Press
2550 US Hwy 70 SE
Hickory NC 28602

ISBN: 978-1-959346-03-6

Library of Congress Number: 2023935828

Layout and edit by Robert Canipe and Melanie Johnson Zimmermann

Cover by Ashlyn Blake

Printed in the United States of America

redhawkpublications.com

Freedom itself cannot exist when the truth is buried under trash-heaps of sensational lies and emotionally-appealing half-truths. It is fundamentally impossible to make good choices in one's own self-interest, the essence of freedom, based on bad information.

—Twitter User: @aggualaqisaaq (account since suspended)

The next question in regard to quarantine is somewhat different, because in the state of, sense of a quarantine, if someone has a contagious disease, against which there is no inoculation, then the government will have the right to require quarantine. What is the principle here? It's to protect those people who are not ill, to protect the people who, to prevent the people who are ill from passing on their illness to others. Here you are dealing with a demonstrable physical damage.

Remember that in all issues of protecting someone from physical damage, before a government can properly act, there has to be a scientific, objective demonstration of an actual physical danger. If it is demonstrated, then the government can act to protect those who are not yet ill from contracting the disease, in other words to quarantine the people who are ill is not an interference with their rights, it is merely preventing them from doing physical damage to others.

—Ayn Rand

Disclaimer

The opinions expressed in this book are mine alone and do not necessarily represent my employer. All of the information is as accurate as possible as of January 2023. I regret any errors that inevitably slipped through.

Table of Contents

Foreword

The problem with pandemics is that people want to forget them. One year a million Americans are killed by a deadly new virus; the next everyone else is back rooting for the Georgia Bulldogs. The impulse to move on from this particular kind of tragedy is more than a little odd. The United States contains less than five per cent of the world's population and experienced more than twenty percent of its COVID deaths. If we don't spend time figuring out why we did such a poor job of protecting ourselves against the last deadly pathogen, how will we protect ourselves any better from the next? Beneath the impulse, I think, is a kind of fatalism--a feeling that there was never much we could have done to save ourselves. That all those people who died were going to die no matter how the rest of us behaved, and so why worry very much about how we behaved?

Now here comes Jonathan Howard to tell us why. A neurologist and psychiatrist in New York City, Dr. Howard served on the front lines in COVID's first wave. He witnessed a lot of preventable death and suffering. And then he watched, with growing incredulity, as influential scientists attempted to deny or minimize what he had seen with his own two eyes. As members of his own profession violated its deepest principles—and were rewarded with fame and political influence. Dr. Howard wrote a series of compelling essays about his experience—which is how I first learned of his existence. His writing was the first I'd seen that explored how and why a handful of prominent doctors and scientists staked out a position hostile to evidence-based medicine, and got a lot of people killed.

Now Dr. Howard has expanded those essays into this book. It's an important book, for a couple of reasons. It shows how much damage can be caused, in a society that has trouble figuring out who is and who is not an expert, by a corrupt or phony expert. It also hints at what we might do, to prevent that damage from happening all over again. I urge you to read it.

—Michael Lewis

Introduction

The title of this book is astonishing. *We Want Them Infected.* Those four words come not from some random crackpot, but from Dr. Paul Alexander, an epidemiologist and official in the U.S. Department of Health and Human Services during the Trump administration. On July 4, 2020, before anyone had been vaccinated, he said:

> *Infants, kids, teens, young people, young adults, middle aged with no conditions etc. have zero to little risk....so we use them to develop herd...we want them infected....*

In the middle of a raging pandemic, with a new, poorly understood virus that was capable of overwhelming hospitals and morgues, Dr. Alexander wanted it to spread rapidly amongst hundreds of millions of unvaccinated, young Americans.

He was not alone. Doctors and scientists from our most prestigious universities convinced millions of Americans that COVID was only dangerous for the elderly and infirm They influenced powerful politicians, who also wanted the virus to spread widely. While overwhelmed frontline doctors begged the public to avoid the virus, other doctors, completely sheltered from the consequences of their words, worked to undermine these efforts.

Though they spoke in euphemisms, unlike Dr. Alexander, they too supported the mass infection of unvaccinated children and young adults. To achieve their goal, they spoke about SARS-CoV-2 the exact same way anti-vaxxers speak about measles or HPV. The arrival of vaccines did nothing to dampen their enthusiasm to spread the virus. In fact, doctors led a successful campaign to undermine pediatric vaccination. The anti-vaccine movement is now mainstream.

In this book, I will toggle back and forth between an imaginary world, where the pandemic ended many times, and the real world where COVID remains the third leading cause of death in the U.S. In the imaginary world, COVID only threatened the old and infirm. In the real world, tens of thousands of children and young adults were seriously harmed or killed by COVID. In the imaginary world, pediatric vaccines were dangerous and useless. In the real world, the vaccines are imperfect, but much safer than the virus for children. In the imaginary world, all it took to protect nursing homes and open schools was to say "protect nursing homes" and "open schools". In the real world, this was impossible when the virus was allowed to spread freely. In the imaginary world, contrarian doctors were silenced and suppressed. In the real world, they were loud and influential.

All this had real world costs, though not everyone paid the price.

Over a million people are now dead in the country that had been previously ranked first out of 195 countries on its pandemic preparedness. It's not over yet.

—Jonathan Howard – January 2023

Chapter 1: "We have protected the vulnerable by vaccinating the older population."

"We have protected the vulnerable by vaccinating the older population."

~ Dr. Jay Bhattacharya

On July 26, 2021, Dr. Jay Bhattacharya, a medical school graduate turned health economist at Stanford University, participated in a roundtable discussion with Florida Governor Ron DeSantis. Dr. Bhattacharya had very good news for the Governor and the citizens of Florida. He said:

> *We have protected the vulnerable—by vaccinating the older population, we have provided them with enormous protection against severe disease and death. That's why you see, even as the cases have risen in Sweden in the past wave, or in the UK in this past wave, and in Florida in this past wave, the number of deaths have not risen proportionally. Why? Because we protected the vulnerable.*
>
> *The key thing to me is hospitalizations and deaths from COVID. While we've done an incredible job at decoupling the cases from the deaths, the public focus on cases at this point, I think, only serves to panic people without actually serving any other public health purpose.... I don't think the delta variant changes the calculus or the evidence in any fundamental way.*[1]

On August 1, 2021, Governor DeSantis blasted Dr. Bhattacharya's optimistic message on both *Twitter* and *Facebook*. He quoted Dr. Bhattacharya as saying:

> *We have protected the vulnerable by vaccinating the older population.*[2]

Reality would soon prove otherwise. Although Dr. Bhattacharya claimed that Florida had "protected the vulnerable," in fact, fewer than 50% of Floridians were fully vaccinated at the time.[3] Florida ranked 44th in vaccinating 18- to 64-year-olds and 46th for vaccinating those between 12- to 17-years and those older than 65-years.[4] Anyone actually concerned with protecting rather than pacifying the vulnerable would have recognized that Florida was a disaster waiting to happen.

A disaster is exactly what happened.

Despite Dr. Bhattacharya's casual dismissal of the Delta variant, it changed the calculus in a very fundamental way. In August and September 2021, the Delta variant ripped through the state, causing unprecedented death and suffering. Just four days after Floridians were told the vulnerable had been protected, Dr. Marc Napp, the chief medical officer for Memorial Healthcare System in Hollywood, Florida, said:

> *We are seeing a surge like we've not seen before in terms of the patients coming. It's the sheer number coming in at the same time. There are only so many beds, so many doctors, only so many nurses.*[5]

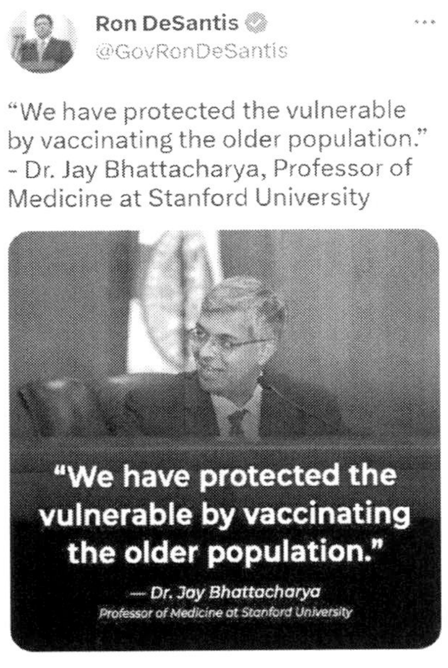

Tweet by Florida Governor Ron DeSantis on August 1, 2021.[73]

Though Florida fared well during the pandemic's first year, since April 2021 when vaccines became available to those 16-years and older, Florida has the highest COVID death rate among the country's six most populated states, double the rate of New York and California.[4] More Floridians died of COVID *after*

Dr. Bhattacharya's "we protected the vulnerable" comment than died before it, and 20,000 people died in August and September 2021 alone.[6]

As with New York City during its initial wave, mobile morgues were needed to store the corpses.[7] 17,200 Floridians were hospitalized with COVID during the August 2021 peak.[8] The mayor of Orlando asked citizens to conserve water to help maintain a supply of liquid oxygen. Just three weeks after Dr. Bhattacharya assured Floridians that the vulnerable had been protected, the American Association of Retired People (AARP) reported "Florida led the nation in nursing home resident and staff deaths in the four weeks ending Aug. 22."[9] Fifteen educators in Miami-Dade County Public Schools District died in a 10-day period.[10] Overwhelmed healthcare workers suffered too. "We are exhausted," said Dr. Rupesh Dharia, an internist.[8] "Our patience and resources are running low."

Much of this was avoidable. One study from October 2021, estimated that if Florida had vaccinated 74% of its citizens, as many other states had done, by the end of August that year, it would have had 61,327 fewer hospitalizations and 16,235 fewer deaths.[11]

Tragically, Delta's victims were not all elderly people with multiple medical comorbidities, only days away from dying of these diseases when they happened to contract COVID. According to one news report:

> *Dr. Chirag Patel, assistant chief medical officer of UF Health Jacksonville, said the patients hospitalized with the virus during this latest surge tend to be younger and had fewer other health issues, but were nearly all unvaccinated. Of those who have died, including patients ranging in age from their 20s to their 40s, more than 90 percent were not immunized.*[8]

"We've had more patients this time around that have passed away at a younger age with very few, if any, medical problems," Dr. Patel said. "They simply come in with COVID, and they don't make it out of the hospital."

The Delta variant did not spare children either, many of whom were old enough to be vaccinated by that time. During the peak of the Delta wave, 68 children were being hospitalized daily in

Florida.[12] Some of them were sick enough to need mechanical ventilation in the ICU and several died.[13] A headline from *Politico* on September 9, 2021, declared "Child COVID Deaths More Than Doubled in Florida as Kids Returned to the Classroom."[14] Doctors on the ground spoke of the suffering. Dr. Mobeen Rathore, a Florida pediatrician, said:

> *Kids do get sick. Kids do get hospitalized. Kids do get sick and go to the ICU, get intubated, be on a ventilator and even be on ECMO which is a heart lung machine, sort of a last ditch effort to support these children. Unfortunately children do die. In fact many of you probably heard the news, there's a 17-year-old who died in St. Johns County just in the last few days so I think we have to be very sure and understand that kids can get serious illness. And I can tell you that in the almost 18 months ending in June we had three deaths in our area in children. That's one death every six months. And just in July and August we had four deaths in children so that's two deaths a month.*[15]

As the Delta wave receded, the *Tampa Bay Times* reported "4 Kids Among Florida's COVID Death Toll as State Sets Another Record for Fatalities." The article quoted a pediatric ICU nurse manager who said:

> *The delta variant really kind of changed the game for us, because we weren't seeing that many children — now we're starting to see them in the ICU. Families are just reeling from this. These are normal healthy children who are suddenly just really struck down with this disease.*[16]

It also quoted a neuropsychologist who described the virus's impact on children as "relentless, unforgiving and terrifying.... You have patients who are air hungry – they're struggling for breath. As scary as that is for adults, imagine what that is like for kids to go through that."

Predictably, parents expressed their regret for not vaccinating their children. One headline from September 2021 read, "Florida Dad Regrets Not Getting COVID Vaccine After 15-Year-Old Daughter's Death." According to the article:

> *Victoria tested positive for COVID-19 almost two weeks ago. She had a fever and body aches. Later she was sent home from the hospital, but then her dad, Hector, had to take her back. "Within four or five days, her breathing started getting worse and worse," he said. Doctors told Hector she had COVID pneumonia. Just after she started to get better, she stopped breathing. Hector had to leave the room while they tried to resuscitate her. "About 15, 20 minutes later, they couldn't bring her back," Hector said as he held back tears.*[17]

"She was so beautiful and so smart," her father said.

> *Hector Ramirez says he's now thinking of getting vaccinated. He didn't get the shot for his daughter, and he regrets it. "It's something that's going to be stuck with me for my whole life, thinking maybe I should have done that sooner," he said. "Maybe I could've done something to help prevent this." He says Victoria was healthy, but that changed quickly.*

The sad truth is that Mr. Ramirez absolutely could have done something to prevent this. Victoria should still be alive.

It's likely that Mr. Ramirez believed his daughter had no risk of COVID and therefore saw no need to vaccinate her. It's possible he heard this from Dr. Bhattacharya, who opposed vaccinating children and young adults against COVID. Along with his ideological twin, Dr. Martin Kulldorff, he wrote an article in June 2021 titled "The Ill-Advised Push to Vaccinate the Young," which argued that young people should be left vulnerable to COVID because "the old have a thousand-fold higher mortality risk than the young."[18] Based on such illogical arguments and pure myths spread by these and like-minded doctors, Florida would later become the only state to advise against the COVID vaccine for healthy children.[19] As Governor DeSantis said:

> *I would say we are affirmatively against the COVID vaccine for young kids. These are the people who have zero risk of getting anything.*

While the Delta wave eventually subsided, the virus wasn't done with Florida yet. The winter Omicron wave of 2021-2022 killed over 200 Floridians per day at its peak.[4] Even a year after Dr. Bhattacharya's false reassurance that Florida was protected, COVID continued to kill and injure Floridians. A news report from June 2022 said:

> *The latest COVID-19 wave in Florida may be cresting, hospital reports indicate, while the weekly statewide death toll spiked by more than 1,000 residents for the first time in more than three months.*[20]

Clearly, Florida had not "protected the vulnerable." In fact, its citizens had been misled and purposefully exposed. Dr. Bhattacharya did not treat any COVID patients in Florida, or anywhere else for that matter.

"At least every second person who died from COVID-19 since vaccines became available might have been saved by getting the shot."
~ Brown School of Public Health

Prior to the pandemic, the Johns Hopkins Center for Health Security ranked the U.S. as the first out of 195 countries on their pandemic preparedness.[21] Reality would soon prove otherwise. A million Americans died of COVID in two years, and a headline from *The New York Times* on August 31, 2022, read "U.S. Life Expectancy Falls Again in 'Historic' Setback."[22] For now at least, China has a higher life expectancy than the US.[23] According to an article in the *Journal of the American Medical Association* (*JAMA*) from October 2022:

US life expectancy dropped to about 73 years for men and to about 79 years for women, the lowest levels since 1996. Three-quarters of overall life expectancy lost during this period was attributed to COVID-19 deaths, according to a CDC statement.[24]

Had America controlled the virus like New Zealand, Japan, or South Korea, over 800,000 Americans would be alive today. Why did the country that was supposed to be the best prepared to handle a pandemic fail so completely?

While there's no single answer to this question, I think Dr. Bhattacharya's false reassurance to Floridians provides an important clue as to what went wrong. Americans let their guard down and surrendered to the virus because highly credentialed doctors at prestigious universities reassured them the virus posed no threat to them and the worst was over. Americans were told fear of the virus was worse than the virus itself. Doctors mocked people who tried to avoid it, saying they were mentally unstable.

Influential scientists successfully pushed for unvaccinated children and young adults to contract SARS-CoV-2. They became cheerleaders for the virus, writing articles titled "The Triumph of Natural Immunity"[25] and tweeting "Natural Immunity wins again."[26] Doctors even said it was "natural and healthy" for unvaccinated children to get sick with COVID. Experts who were supposed to level with the public about the dangers of a deadly virus instead repeatedly minimized its threat and encouraged tens of millions of people to leave themselves defenseless against it, even after a safe and effective vaccine was available to them.

Many people heard their message. An analysis by the Brown School of Public Health estimated that between January 2021 and April 2022, at least 318,000 COVID deaths could have been prevented had every eligible American been vaccinated.[27] According to this report:

This means that at least every second person who died from COVID-19 since vaccines became available might have been saved by getting the shot.

This was a national tragedy. As vaccine-expert Dr. Peter Hotez said:

> *The number of Americans who lost their lives because they refused the COVID vaccine is just staggering. It's the greatest self-immolation in American history.*[28]

Kevin and Misty Mitchem would almost certainly be alive today had they been vaccinated. The unvaccinated couple was in their 40s when they died of COVID 15-days apart, leaving behind five children.[29] According to a news report:

> *"He had the pain of not only being sick, but the pain of his wife being gone," Kevin's brother Mike Mitchem said. "The pain of wondering, 'what's going to happen to my kids?'"*
>
> *The couple's youngest children are living with family in South Carolina, but the Mitchem family is now on a mission: to share Kevin and Misty's story, in the hopes that it convinces other unvaccinated people to change their mind.*
>
> *In his last phone call with his mother Terry Mitchem, Kevin went as far as to say, "Mom, I love you, and I wish I would've got the shot."*
>
> *"His last words were a rebuttal to him not getting the vaccine," Mike Mitchem said. "It was regret; you could hear the regret in his voice."*

"Am I convinced that this is true, that there are little invisible pathogens that randomly jump around from person to person and have the capacity to really harm, injure and even kill?"

~ Dr. Kelly Brogan

Unfortunately, there has always been a small cadre of doctors who spread misinformation about viruses and vaccines, though prior to the pandemic, they were pariahs in the medical community. A doctor I trained with, Dr. Kelly Brogan, is a prime example of such a doctor. She promotes herself as a "holistic psychiatrist" and most people would instantly recognize her as a quack, though a charismatic one who gained a large following and was platformed by the South by Southwest festival, Joe Rogan, and Gwyneth Paltrow's Goop conference.

During the pandemic, Dr. Brogan was named as one of the Disinformation Dozen. According to Center for Countering Digital Hate, which compiled the list:

> *The Disinformation Dozen are twelve anti-vaxxers who play leading roles in spreading digital misinformation about COVID vaccines. They were selected because they have large numbers of followers, produce high volumes of anti-vaccine content or have seen rapid growth of their social media accounts in the last two months.*[30]

Though it's hard to believe such doctors exist, Dr. Brogan is a germ-theory denier who does not believe viruses cause illness. In 2017 she received attention for promoting the myth that HIV does not cause AIDS.[31] In a now deleted *Facebook* post, she wrote:

> *FACT: You can have a microbe in your body and not be sick*
> *FACT: You can be sick and not have a microbe in your body*
> *FACT: GERM THEORY IS DISPROVEN*

This is breathtakingly absurd. Unsurprisingly, she opposes all vaccines and blames them for all assortments of maladies, including sudden infant death syndrome (SIDS). She even wrote an article titled "HPV Vaccine Maker's Study Proves Natural HPV Infection Beneficial, Not Deadly," which argued HPV vaccination is unnecessary since "HPV infection itself confers protection against HPV reinfection."[32] In reality, HPV-related cancers cause thousands of deaths every year in the U.S.

The idea that potentially deadly viruses are actually beneficial is widespread in anti-vaccine circles. Dr. Brogan clearly articulated her pro-virus stance in her article "Vaccination: Your Body. Your

Baby. Their Flu" when she said:

> *This better way embraces periodic sickness as part of comprehensive wellness. The only way to truly protect ourselves and our infants is through natural immunity bolstered by wild-type exposure in the community. Once you have a particular flu strain, when it comes around again, you will be uniquely protected, and you will pass on this protection to your newborn. There is no replacement for this.*[33]

Obviously, vaccines are a replacement for "this." Getting infected with a virus to gain immunity makes as much sense as giving away your money to avoid being robbed. Yet, many doctors embraced this absurd logic with regards to SARS-CoV-2, using the exact same pro-virus language as Dr. Brogan.

To her credit, Dr. Brogan does not pretend all her beliefs are grounded in science and evidence. She explicitly rejects the scientific method in favor of mystical knowledge and intuition. She wrote:

> *There are paths to a kind of human experience that we know, in our hearts, is our birthright. We are finding each other, touching our own souls, and healing inside and out. ... It's time to decide what you believe. And make no mistake, it's about belief, not about facts, not about science as the final objective.*[34]

It was no surprise at the pandemic's start when Dr. Brogan spread conspiracies to avoid admitting SARS-CoV-2 was responsible for mass illness and death. She claimed COVID deaths were "likely being accelerated by the fear"[35] of SARS-CoV-2, rather than the virus itself. In one video she said:

> *Am I convinced that this is true, that there are little invisible pathogens that randomly jump around from person to person and have the capacity to really harm, injure and even kill? That's a really hard way to live.*[36]

She would later add, "There are other theories about what's going on that have nothing to do with a virus spreading. That literally suggests, there is potentially no such thing as a coronavirus."

"We are, indeed, at war. It is good versus evil. Dark versus light."
~ Dr. Christiane Northrup

Doctors are highly trusted people. Our words carry great weight. As such, I've always been particularly perturbed by anti-vaccine doctors. Parents who are legitimately confused by anti-vaccine misinformation deserve sympathy and support. In contrast, anti-vaccine doctors learned the facts, but actively labored to reject them. An anti-vaccine doctor is like an arsonist firefighter, a trusted figure spreading the exact danger they are obligated to prevent.

I've also been fascinated by anti-vaccine doctors. I can't figure them out. Why have they devoted so much of their energy to trashing medicine's greatest achievement? How do they feel justified doing this when they have no real-world responsibility for treating children sickened by vaccine-preventable diseases? While I don't really know what motivates anti-vaccine doctors, here's how I've come to think about them.

Anti-vaccine doctors are motivated by narcissism. They are supremely confident and believe themselves to be unappreciated geniuses. They feel they are ahead of their time and history will prove them right. They compare themselves to famous doctors who were disbelieved in their time, but who turned out to have brilliant insights (the Semmelweis Reflex[37]). They never admit error, even as they boast of their own humility. They hold themselves in very high regard, even though they last entered a hospital 10 years ago.

They feel everyone else should similarly hold them in high regards. They want to be celebrated with nightly cheers like those frontline healthcare workers received at the start of the pandemic. They are compelled to let their audience know they are more "enlightened" than doctors who actually treat sick people. They feel it's cool, edgy, and "heterodox" to "challenge the conventional wisdom" on vaccines. In contrast, nothing is more boring and unexceptional than a doctor who says "vaccinate your children." One gets the sense that if mainstream doctors were against vaccines, these doctors would (rightly) call them a "suppressed miracle cure." Pharma makes more money from treating diseases than preventing them, after all.

Anti-vaccine doctors want to be famous. They enjoy making speeches and being interviewed. They all have a large number of *YouTube* videos. A doctor who turns against vaccines can gain a lot of attention for doing so. They can become heroic figures. Their social media feeds are filled with fans praising them for their "courage" and "independence."

However, having an audience to please means anti-vaccine doctors have a public image to maintain. Most have carefully curated websites and newsletters. There are often photos of them meditating, doing yoga, or exercising. They strive to seem perfect and natural. It seems to be a lot of work.

It's all about being *different* from other doctors. However, this need – above all else – to differentiate oneself, means that anti-vaccine doctors have to continually escalate their rhetoric to keep the spotlight focused on them. Anti-vaccine doctors are leaders, but they are also followers, who are beholden to their audience.

When I first encountered the anti-vaccine movement, anti-vaccine doctors could gain attention by claiming vaccines caused autism. That was once cool and edgy. After a few years, however, this bogus claim was merely the price of entry into Anti-Vaxx World, and Dr. Brogan and others were forced to blame vaccines for all manners of maladies, such as the "epidemic" of SIDS[38] (even though SIDS rates have decreased markedly). Other anti-vaccine doctors have compared vaccines to rape, and anti-vaccine activist Robert F. Kennedy, Jr. compared vaccinations to the Holocaust.[39] Attacking pediatricians and medical organizations became commonplace. Mr. Kennedy also compared vaccine expert Dr. Paul Offit to a Nazi war criminal.

Anti-vaccine doctors are impervious to evidence. A million corpses didn't dent Dr. Brogan's COVID denialism. Even as late as November 2022 she promoted a video titled "Debunking the Nonsense" that she described as her "favorite presentation on the dismantling of germ theory." According to the video:

> *This field of so-called science is the foundation for which every tyrannical, inhumane measure was*

> *justified during the COVID-19 era. The lockdowns, the social distancing, the masking, the experimental vaccines, the mandates, the business closures, the job loss, the severe depression, the economic impact, the censorship, the centralization of power, the increased government control, the segregation, the discrimination, the harmful hospital protocols, the unnecessary death, and every other piece of the official COVID-19 narrative rests on the shoulders of the completely unproven concept of pathogenic disease causing particles that are passed from person-to-person.*[40]

Though there are many studies showing vaccines are safe and effective, no amount of evidence will convince anti-vaccine doctors. They summarily reject all studies showing vaccines are safe and effective. They readily accept all studies that purport to show vaccine harm. They've created a brand, and being anti-vaccine is at the center of it all. Admitting that vaccines are safe and effective in any way would destroy their image.

Many anti-vaccine doctors geared up to fight COVID vaccines well before they even existed. One analysis, which included the Facebook page of anti-vaccine doctor Sherri Tenpenny, found that:

> *Major anti-vaccine groups were sowing seeds of doubt on Facebook weeks before the US government launched its vaccine development program 'Operation Warp Speed'.*[41]

This is why it's a waste of time to engage with anti-vaccine doctors. They are against hypothetical vaccines that don't even exist, and they always will be.

Anti-vaccine doctors don't handle criticism well. They are certain they know the "truth", and it bothers them that their genius is unappreciated. They claim to be censored and suppressed. They block dissenters on social media, even as they purport to value "healthy debate." They perceive themselves as victims, constantly under attack. Some of them take this very literally. The suicide of an anti-vaccine doctor Jeffrey Bradstreet in 2017 sparked a widespread conspiracy that holistic doctors were being murdered.[42]

Indeed, anti-vaccine doctors see conspiracies *everywhere*. They claim that anyone who contradicts them is lying, especially prominent vaccine scientists. Since they "know" vaccines are unsafe and ineffective, only a cover-up can explain why the scientific literature doesn't support them. Those perpetuating this cover-up always have a nefarious agenda, such as depopulating the world. Prior to the pandemic, Dr. Brogan shared a now deleted video titled "Vaccine Conspiracy or Racist Population Control Campaign" on *Facebook* and wrote articles titled "CDC: You're Fired. Autism Cover-up Exposed."[72]

These conspiracies were easily repurposed for COVID, and several anti-vaccine doctors took a very dark turn during the pandemic. According to one news article about anti-vaccine obstetrician Dr. Christiane Northrup, who was elevated by Oprah Winfrey and named as one of the 100 most trusted people in America by *Reader's Digest* in 2013:

> *For much of the pandemic, there has been a tidy pattern to Christiane Northrup's days.*
>
> *A retired celebrity doctor with a New Age fandom, she would take her position at a sunny desk in coastal Maine, snap on a camera, and hold forth on spiritual topics such as chakra alignment and energy fields. With a flowery dress and glittering jewelry, she sometimes serenaded her online audience of half a million or so by plucking an enormous harp.*
>
> *Then Northrup would land on a gloomier theme: COVID-19. Northrup would claim that the virus was part of a plot involving Deep State brainwashing and treacherous depopulation schemes. She encouraged fans to check out QAnon, called the a "COVID death cult," and described the vaccines as crimes against humanity.*
>
> *"We are, indeed, at war," she said in one recent dispatch. "It is good versus evil. Dark versus light."*[43]

At the pandemic's start, Dr. Brogan warned that the government was planning to "link our passports with our vaccination records"[36] in order to achieve "totalitarian governmental control not unlike the divide-and-conquer dehumanization agendas that preceded the Holocaust." In an article titled "Health as Spiritual Warfare," Dr. Brogan wrote about a "war between the energy of sovereign human vitalism and dehumanizing parasitism."[44] She said her enemies were "vampires" and "parasites." In a wink to the QAnon crowd, she warned of "the human child predator, i.e., the abuser/molester/victimizer," and wrote:

> *We are entering a post-science world.*
>
> *And like when wars were fought and blood was shed over seeming differences in religious doctrine, ideology, and faith—we are now in a spiritual war, and your body is the battlefield.*
>
> *What is being ushered in under the cover of a "pandemic" is the fulfillment of what was initiated with Homeland security under the cover of "terrorist attacks"...protection from an unseen enemy justifying the stripping of liberties and ever-expanding surveillance and control of the people for our "safety." In order to actualize this digital police state, we must be convinced that our bodies — including our childrens' — are not our own responsibility and that they (especially the most vulnerable to adverse effects among them) should be offered up for the greater good. Medical tyranny imposes unconsented medical interventions on the populace as a strategic form of bio-power and bio-governance. And these medical interventions — be they masks, compulsory vaccination, social distancing, mandated chemotherapy, or court-ordered injected psychotropics — represent more than simply the preferred and popularly accepted way of responding to illness. This entire system is preying on your devotion, compliance, complicity,*

> *and allegiance for it to exist. Remove that, and it withers and dessicates like the parasite it is.*

Naturally, she claimed vaccines were "the ultimate parasite on human biology" and asked:

> *Could it be that this vaccine is the ultimate gesture of spiritual capture and transhumanistic abandonment of human biology? If we are no longer genetically human, do we still have human rights?*

There were significant costs to this type of paranoia, though doctors who worked with COVID patients paid the price. This reveals another core feature of anti-vaccine doctors. They are sheltered from the consequences of their words. Anti-vaccine doctors can be found talking on a stage or in a podcast booth. However, I can't think of a single anti-vaccine doctor who might care for a child hospitalized with a vaccine-preventable disease. Such children seem to be mere abstractions for them.

Finally, anti-vaccine doctors are in it for the grift. Whether it's supplements or a subscription to their online content, nearly all of them have an online store. These hustles can be extremely lucrative. In 2017, America's leading anti-vaccine doctor, Dr. Joseph Mercola, filed an affidavit stating his net worth was "in excess of $100 million."[45] Dr. Brogan charges $400 per year to be part of her "Vital Life Project," which she ironically pitches as "a one-stop-shop for you to step into self-ownership."[46] The anti-vaccine movement is an industry, and anti-vaccine doctors always have ways to let strangers send them money.

Despite these red flags, anti-vaccine doctors have titles and credentials. Some, like Dr. Brogan, are incredibly compelling public speakers. Their ability to use medical jargon gives them a legitimacy that makes them more pernicious than the average anti-vaxxer on *Facebook*. They can be ridiculous, but they are also persuasive and therefore dangerous.

Doctors who were stars of the anti-vaccine movement before the pandemic doubled their efforts when COVID arrived. Their misinformation has undoubtedly cost lives. However, for the most part, their media footprint shrank. They didn't influence powerful politicians and they lacked the imprimatur conferred by prestigious universities. Many were kicked off social media platforms and no credible news organization asked for their views. Dr. Andrew Wakefield, the world's most infamous anti-vaccine doctor, was essentially invisible. Though they spread dangerous conspiracies, they were likely preaching to the already converted. Most people who heeded their messages weren't going to get vaccinated in the first place.

While the disinformation put forth by the Disinformation Dozen was appalling, it was not surprising. It would have been a shock if they had been honest about COVID's threat, encouraged vaccination, and refrained from pushing bogus cures. As such, I will discuss these quacks and hucksters only to point out how their methods and ideas gained widespread acceptance during the pandemic. Unfortunately, they will appear frequently in that role.

"It's not about health, it's about contrarianism."
~ Dr. Carl Bergstrom

Prior to 2020, the idea that it was beneficial when unvaccinated children got sick with a potentially fatal virus was relegated to the fringes of the anti-vaccine movement. A doctor who spoke about the "natural benefits" of measles or HPV was immediately and appropriately branded as a dangerous quack. However, during the pandemic, these ideas became mainstream and influenced parents, regulatory agencies, and politicians. A diverse group of doctors, none of whom had reputations for spreading misinformation previously, adopted many of the ideas put forth by Dr. Brogan and other members of the Disinformation Dozen.

In realizing this, I had a flashback to when I first encountered the anti-vaccine movement. The first few times I read anti-vaccine articles, I found them superficially plausible. I lacked the background knowledge to spot their flaws and was blissfully ignorant of the mendaciousness that characterizes the anti-vaccine movement. It was only when I dug further that I realized their grave flaws.

For example, in a collection of articles titled "200 Evidence Based Reasons NOT To Vaccinate,"[47] Sayer Ji, the founder of the anti-vaccine site *GreenMedInfo* and Dr. Brogan's ex-husband, listed an article titled "A Measles Outbreak Was Reported in a Highly

Vaccinated Population, San Diego, 2008." Sounds bad, right?

However, the actual title of the article, which was published in the journal *Pediatrics* in 2010, was "Measles Outbreak in a Highly Vaccinated Population, San Diego, 2008: Role of the Intentionally Undervaccinated." The article concluded that "measles outbreaks can occur among clusters of intentionally undervaccinated children, at major cost to public health agencies, medical systems, and families."[48] In attempting to convince people vaccines don't work, Mr. Ji distorted the titles of articles that showed vaccines work quite well.

As a gullible naïf, this level of deception was astonishing to me. I knew moving forward that I had to verify every "fact" I read in anti-vaccine articles. Usually these "facts" were blatantly false or crucial information was purposefully left out. I now expect such deception from anti-vaxxers and can spot the errors and omissions in anti-vaccine articles from a mile away. It's often not that hard.

Before the pandemic, I didn't apply this level of scrutiny to the work of highly credentialed doctors at renowned medical schools. I believed such doctors made dedicated efforts to be both accurate and thorough, especially when communicating with the public. If they said a vaccine trial didn't measure a clinical outcome or that no healthy children died from a particular virus, I wouldn't rush to confirm this myself. I assumed the author had carefully researched these claims and was accurately reporting their findings. Now, as with traditional anti-vaccine content, I can no longer assume that many doctors accurately report basic facts or make a diligent effort to be nuanced and thorough, including all relevant information.

While some of the doctors and scientists I will discuss were unknown prior to the pandemic, others were world-famous advocates for evidence-based medicine. One is a mathematician; another is a Nobel Prize winner. Some are liberal, while others have clear right-wing, libertarian proclivities. Several have found employment at the Brownstone Institute, a think tank founded by a man who is an outspoken proponent of child labor with previous connections to White supremacist groups.[49]

Some have expertise in infectious diseases, though most do not. Some treated COVID patients, though few were on the front lines, and most did not see patients at all. While they've written extensively on pediatric COVID, only one is a pediatrician. Some are in private practice and others work at Stanford, Harvard, John Hopkins, and the University of California, San Francisco. Some, such as the authors of the Great Barrington Declaration, are formally linked to each other through their collaboration. Others are connected through their frequent podcast appearances, co-authoring of articles, and *Substack* entrepreneurship.

Aside from Dr. Brogan, I've not met any of these doctors. I have no personal grudges against them, and I even quoted several of them favorably in a book I wrote on cognitive biases in medicine.[50] Though I'm not a mind reader, I'm convinced many of their statements, while highly irresponsible, were made in good faith. Other times, I'm less sure. Some of the doctors I will discuss truncated graphs in very misleading ways or blamed COVID vaccines for a case of polio in a man who should have been vaccinated 15 years ago.[51]

Despite their diverse backgrounds, all the doctors I discuss in this book share several key traits. First, unlike Dr. Brogan, they don't embrace mystical sources of knowledge. They purport to be men and women of science and data. They speak in measured tones using medical jargon and referencing scientific papers. They often claim to be "nuanced" or "in the middle," implying an absurd equivalence between those who think COVID is caused by 5G and those who object to millions of unvaccinated children getting COVID. They are not easily identifiable as untrustworthy, and to the average person, they sound eminently reasonable. There was no indication prior to the pandemic that some of them would embrace a philosophy that advocated purposefully exposing unvaccinated children and young adults to a new, dangerous virus. The fact that they all suggested protecting vulnerable people made this message seem more credible.

Second, while they all unequivocally acknowledge the virus is dangerous for the elderly and infirm, they feel that for everyone else, it was fear of the virus and measures to contain it that posed a greater threat than the virus itself. Like Dr. Bhattacharya's claim the vulnerable had been protected in Florida, they falsely pacified millions of Americans about the dangers of COVID. They relentlessly minimized the virus for young people and trashed any and all measures to limit infections in this population. They've repeatedly underestimated the virus, declaring the pandemic over and downplaying the risks of infection just before a new variant ripped through the population.

They mostly favor routine childhood vaccinations, and they support vaccinating older, vulnerable people against COVID, at least with the first two doses. As such, they take great umbrage at being called anti-vaccine simply because they are against COVID vaccines for children. Like Dr. Tenpenny, several opposed the pediatric COVID vaccine before a single child had been vaccinated. They feel COVID is a categorically different disease than the measles, though they can never explain exactly why. Doctors, who were upset by measles outbreaks where no children died, said that we should accept dead children as a "matter of course", so long as they were killed by COVID.

Most importantly, these doctors have had large platforms and great influence. They made many widely seen *YouTube* videos and hosted popular podcasts. Most have large social media followings. They told many people what they wanted to hear, and commentators praised their "relentless optimism and positivity,"[52] without regard for whether or not what they were reading was true.

They have been frequent guests on Fox News,[53] CNN, and CNBC. Their articles have appeared in *The Atlantic*, *Wall Street Journal*, *USA Today, NPR*, *The New York Times*, and *The Washington Post*, to name a few. Journalists regularly seek them out for "expert" commentary. Their views have been published in prestigious medical journals and online medical publications, such as *Medscape* and *MedPage Today*. Their work has also been featured at less prestigious outlets, such as the *Epoch Times*, described as a "far-right international multi-language newspaper and media company affiliated with the Falun Gong new religious movement"[54] and a "global-scale misinformation machine."[55] Their work has been published and favorably profiled in *The Defender*, a newsletter published on the website of Robert F. Kennedy, Jr., who is perhaps America's leading anti-vaxxer and himself a member of the Disinformation Dozen.[30]

These doctors wanted their words to impact the real world and they succeeded. Many of them spoke directly to parents, providing them with "toolkits"[56] they could use to oppose any and all measures to limit the spread of the virus in schools. They wrote articles titled "Kids don't need COVID-19 Vaccines to Return to School",[57] "The Downsides of Masking Young Students Are Real",[58] and "The Case

Against COVID Tests for the Young and Healthy."[59] Some have testified before Congress and in court cases. Others worked behind the scenes to convince powerful politicians to adopt their ideas. Some advised the Governors of Florida and Virginia. Others worked for and influenced President Trump, helping to set COVID policy for the entire country.

While overwhelmed frontline doctors begged the public to keep cases low, other doctors worked equally hard to spread the virus among most of the population. Dr. Paul Alexander, an epidemiologist and official in the U.S. Department of Health and Human Services in the Trump administration was channeling their voice when he wrote on July 4, 2020:

> *Infants, kids, teens, young people, young adults, middle aged with no conditions etc. have zero to little risk....so we use them to develop herd...we want them infected....*[60]

Dr. Alexander would later appear on conspiracy-theorist Alex Jones's program *InfoWars* and say the COVID mRNA vaccines were a "bioweapon."[61] He would also warn that vaccines tainted the blood supply, writing:

> *Unvaccinated Blood: It is your right to demand and source unvaccinated blood now for yes, Igor is right, the blood supply is damaged now and high risk; I won't want blood from a vaccinated person.*[62]

Predictably, Dr. Alexander encourages strangers to send him money for his "COVID research stipend support."[63]

Of course, the only doctors with unblemished records are those who had the wisdom to keep their thoughts to themselves. Nearly everyone underestimated COVID at various times. Infectious-disease expert Dr. Paul Offit, for example, predicted on March 2, 2020, that COVID would cause less than "one-tenth of the damage that influenza causes every year in the United States."[64] He acknowledged his error soon thereafter saying, "If you're going to be wrong, be wrong in front of millions of people. Make a complete ass of yourself".[65]

I made an ass of myself several times during the pandemic, though usually to an audience of dozens. To pick one example, I said in August 2020:

> *Given that COVID is benign in the vast majority of young children, I doubt it will become a major killer for decades in the future like measles. Young kids will likely develop natural immunity and hopefully a vaccine will create immunity in adults.*[66]

That aged horribly, and I've since written volumes refuting such nonsense. However, my aim is not to collect quotations from doctors who made good faith errors in the middle of a rapidly changing pandemic only to later recognize their mistake. The doctors I will discuss haven't just minimized COVID in an errant tweet or two. The errors and omissions I will describe are not isolated events.

Rather, they are part of a consistent pattern where the harms of the virus as well as the efficacy and safety of the vaccine were repeatedly minimized. None of these doctors made an error overestimating COVID. All of their errors served their belief that the virus isn't dangerous to young people, but the vaccine is.

On social media, they are collectively referred to as "COVID Contrarians", meaning they don't say crazy things, like blaming Bill Gates for purposefully unleashing COVID, but by claiming to be "data-driven", "balanced", and "nuanced", they've undermined our pandemic response in more subtle, and more damaging ways. As biologist Dr. Carl Bergstrom said about a doctor who advocated for the mass infection of unvaccinated children and then opposed the COVID vaccine:

> *How can you advocate for herd immunity in October but oppose vaccination in March? Sadly predictable: many those previously opposed to non-pharmaceutical interventions are now positioning themselves against vaccination as well. It's not about health, it's about contrarianism.*[67]

My quarrels with these doctors are not just matters of opinion about policy choices. Reasonable people can disagree about gray areas of trifling importance, such as the appropriateness of booster mandates in college students. Rather, my disagreements with contrarian doctors are much more basic than this. In their relentless quest to minimize the virus, they regularly used bogus statistics, made nonsensical arguments, and refused to share crucial information that would undercut their position. Some even helped inspire conspiracies that would later become gospel truth amongst QAnon adherents.

Indeed, several doctors discussed in this book have associated themselves very closely with dangerous, reality-denying conspiracy theorists who are unabashedly anti-vaccine and claim that COVID was a hoax. They seem to share a similar philosophy. Some contrarian doctors are hostile to the entire concept of public health. One even authored an article, titled "How Democracy Ends: COVID19 Policy Shows a (Potential) Path to the End of America" in which he said a future Hitler could use a pandemic to seize power.[68] Dr. Brogan said the same thing.

Large portions of this book are merely quotes by contrarian doctors. Please read them carefully and judge for yourself whether they aged well or not. Also pay close attention to the tone and language these doctors use. Watch some of their *YouTube* videos. What words do they use to describe the virus? What words do they use to describe the vaccine and other measures to control COVID? Are they willing to share bad news about the virus? Are they willing to share good news about the vaccine?

Doctors do not need to see eye-to-eye on every issue. We need to leave room for good faith disagreement. Indeed, the doctors I discuss don't agree about every issue. Some are virulently anti-vaccine for children, while one authored an excellent defense of pediatric COVID vaccination. However, basic facts are not up for debate and doctors have a responsibility to be very careful when communicating with millions of people.

Debating pandemic policy requires some semblance of a shared reality. It's impossible to have a meaningful conversation with a misinformed interlocutor – and there are many – who insist COVID is just the flu, that it poses a "negligible" risk to a healthy person younger than 65, and the pandemic ended long ago. As Dr. Steven Goodman, a Stanford epidemiologist said:

Debates among scientists about the evidence are healthy. But if conducted in public the rules change. They can confuse people and undermine the consistent messaging needed for public health. Politicians can also misuse these debates to undermine public health policies they don't like. The result? Our complete failure to contain COVID-19.[69]

He's right. This book is fundamentally about the obligations doctors have when communicating with the public about a deadly virus.

This book is also about the real-world consequences of doctors' failure to meet those obligations. It's important to remember that there was a real person behind every statistic on a government website. According to one news report about an unvaccinated teen:

Nineteen-year-old Breanna Gray was going to start college to get her associate's degree this year at Navarro College before dying from COVID-19. Her parents, Tabatha and Brandon, say burying their child is something no parent should have to do. "We don't want parents to have to watch their kid through a window or through a phone crying for them and begging, 'Mommy, I need you, mommy I can't do this.' That's the hardest part and we just want to get it out there that this is not a game. This is not a joke."[70]

Her mother said Breanna had "No underlying health conditions whatsoever. Nothing. Healthy."[71]

We'll never know exactly why Breanna believed that COVID was a game or a joke, but it's possible she listened to famous doctors and scientists who told her she had no risk from COVID, only from the vaccine.

Chapter 2: "It was an unimaginable hell to be quite honest."

"COVID Vaccines for Children Should Not Get Emergency Use Authorization." ~ Drs. Vinay Prasad, Stefan Baral, Wesley Pegden

What qualifications do I have to write this book? I am a neurologist and psychiatrist at New York University Langone Health and Bellevue Hospital in New York City. I treat patients with multiple sclerosis and work as a consulting neurologist in the hospital, as well as in Bellevue's psychiatric emergency room. While I am not an expert in viruses or vaccines, I've written textbook chapters on infections of the nervous system. I've published on COVID outcomes in patients with multiple sclerosis[1] and on neurological disorders in patients hospitalized with COVID.[2] I published one study on vaccines in patients with multiple sclerosis.[3] My study on the COVID vaccine in this population will be presented at the Americas Committee for Treatment and Research in Multiple Sclerosis annual meeting in February 2023.

I've also treated patients with vaccine-preventable diseases. I saw a woman from Mexico die of subacute sclerosing panencephalitis, a complication of measles,[4] and I've treated a handful of older polio survivors and those from overseas. These cases, though exceptionally rare, were especially poignant knowing their suffering could have been prevented if they had been born a few years later or in a different country. Very few medical problems have a solution as simple as a vaccine.

Shingles is the only vaccine-preventable disease I've seen regularly, and it can be horrible. I've seen it cause strokes,[5] spinal cord inflammation,[6] and blindness.[7] Everyone has a painful rash, and the pain can linger long after the rash disappears. One of my immunosuppressed patients had shingles over her entire body during the pandemic and had to be admitted for antiviral therapy. Shingles taught me that "benign childhood diseases" aren't always so benign. I am vulnerable to it. Thankfully, my vaccinated children aren't.

Most importantly, I am very familiar with the techniques used to minimize viruses and spread fear about vaccines. I became fascinated by the anti-vaccine movement after my old friend Dr. Kelly Brogan morphed into an anti-vaccine celebrity. After seeing her anti-vaccine *Facebook* posts, I learned everything I could about the anti-vaccine movement and the refutations to their arguments. I spent many hours arguing with anti-vaxxers on social media. I befriended vaccine-advocates throughout the country, led seminars on the anti-vaccine movement, and worked at vaccine information sessions for the Orthodox Jewish community in Brooklyn. In 2018, I co-wrote a book chapter with law professor Dorit Reiss titled "The Anti-Vaccine Movement: A Litany of Fallacy and Errors"[8] and in 2019, I published a book titled *Cognitive Errors and Diagnostic Mistakes: A Case-Based Guide to Critical Thinking in Medicine.*[9]

I was always less interested in vaccines themselves than in the cognitive biases that led smart people – Dr. Brogan graduated from MIT and Cornell – to reject medicine's greatest achievement. I was never that afraid of vaccine-preventable diseases. My children are vaccinated, as are all of their friends. However, I feared the mindset behind anti-vaccine movement, writing in 2019:

> *The biggest danger to my kids isn't the measles, but the thought process that leads people to reject the vaccine in the first place.*[10]

Little did I know.

As soon as the virus hit, I knew Dr. Brogan and other members of the Disinformation Dozen[11] would spew a nonstop deluge of nonsense about it, as well any eventual vaccine against it. That was an easy prediction to make, and the only thing I got right about this.

However, I greatly underestimated the strength and durability of anti-vaccine myths. I thought once anti-vaxxers saw their family and friends die of COVID, they would prefer a needle to a coffin. Instead, many doubled down on their denial, claiming COVID is harmless with their last breath. One headline from October 2021, after vaccines were available, declared "In the Last Three Months, Five Conservative Talk Show Hosts Have Died From COVID." They had all "urged their audiences to avoid vaccines for COVID-19."[12] Not only were people willing to die to maintain their allegiance to anti-vaccine propaganda, but some seemed determined to take as many people with them as possible.

I also underestimated the appeal of the anti-vaccine movement, which has grown this pandemic, sweeping up previously respectable doctors and scientists in its path. I've been writing about the spread of anti-vaccine beliefs in mainstream medicine since the spring of 2020. I started writing after I read an editorial by Drs. Vinay Prasad, Stefan Baral. and Wesley Pegden, a mathematician, titled "COVID Vaccines for Children Should Not Get Emergency Use Authorization," which was published in the *BMJ*. Its central thesis was that "severe outcomes or death associated with COVID-19 infection is very low for children, undermining the appropriateness of an emergency use authorization for child COVID-19 vaccines."[13]

Even though around 450 children had died of COVID and tens of thousands more had been hospitalized by the time the *BMJ* editorial was published, it neglected to mention any of these sad facts. It also did not mention a Pfizer press release that the vaccine was 100% effective in preventing pediatric COVID in a randomized controlled trial.[14] This trial data was published in *The New England Journal of Medicine* two months later.[15] The article in the *BMJ* had but a single reference, about the swine flu debacle of 1976.[13] Aside from this, it was entirely fact-free.

The article also did not consider variants and its authors were explicitly not concerned about their possibility. On February 8, 2021, Dr. Baral tweeted:

> *I don't think variants are going to cause a third wave of #COVID19 in the coming weeks or months across Northern Europe or North America.*[16]

They thought COVID was going away. On June 23, 2021, Dr. Prasad tweeted:

> *First, let us all remember cases are FALLING PRECIPITOUSLY...The raw number of adolescent cases is the point THAT IS FALLING...The actual numbers show both COVID and MIS-C (Multisystem Inflammatory Syndrome in Children) is plummeting with adult vaccination.*[17]

Unfortunately, the Delta and Omicron variants arrived soon thereafter. Pediatric COVID cases stopped "FALLING PRECIPITOUSLY," and more children were infected than ever before. Nearly 1,000 more children died of COVID in the year after the *BMJ* editorial was published,[18] and tens of thousands more were hospitalized, some very sick in the ICU. There are now over 20 studies showing the vaccine has already protected millions of children from rare but grave harms. There would have been many more injured and dead children if there had been no emergency use authorization for the pediatric COVID vaccine, an authorization the *BMJ* article advocated against.

I knew the article in the *BMJ* omitted crucial facts and I felt it was poorly argued. Though it was published in a top-notch medical journal and written by three credible authors, its refusal to state basic facts reminded me of anti-vaccine articles I'd read before the pandemic. Indeed, when the vaccine was fully approved for adolescents a year later, the authors did not promote adolescents receiving it. Though its blasé attitude towards sick children was standard by that point in the pandemic, it revealed how many doctors have come to think about pediatric COVID: *Nearly all kids are low risk, so why bother trying to save a few with a vaccine?*

I disagree with this. Whether we're talking about measles, polio, or COVID, I don't think that any child should suffer or die for lack of a vaccine. I wrote two rebuttals to the *BMJ* editorial, both of which stated the basic facts about how COVID had impacted children thus far, as well as the recent news of a successful vaccine trial. I thought my readers deserved to know these key facts. One of my rebuttals, written with several other doctors, was published in the *BMJ* itself. Readers learned that "from the start of the pandemic to the start of June 2021 there have been 441 COVID-19 pediatric deaths."[19] That's not a small number of dead children.

My other rebuttal also contained a warning. It said:

> *It is not inconceivable that a COVID-19 variant could significantly affect children and spread widely before we could widely vaccinate children.*[20]

This rebuttal was published at *Science-Based Medicine*, a website devoted to critical thinking in medicine and captained by Drs. David

Gorski and Steven Novella. I've since posted 100 articles there, many detailing the many similarities between "old school" and "new school" anti-vaccine doctors, as Dr. Gorski phrased it.[21] My articles reflect my disbelief that prominent doctors could publish fact-free articles in reputable journals arguing that unvaccinated children should be allowed to or even encouraged to contract COVID.

Incredibly, neither overwhelming evidence of COVID's risk to some children nor evidence of the vaccine's ability to keep them safe dissuaded many doctors from this belief. As the pandemic progressed, their unwillingness to abandon the belief that unvaccinated children should contract COVID forced them to adopt extreme, even pro-virus positions. Those of us who were familiar with anti-vaccine misinformation witnessed Dr. Brogan's pre-pandemic, pro-virus talking points get recycled regarding COVID. Every anti-vaccine argument we'd heard previously about the MMR and HPV vaccines was repurposed with regards to the COVID vaccine by influential, reputable doctors with access to powerful politicians. Anti-vaccine ideas are now mainstream.

"It was an unimaginable hell to be quite honest." ~ Dan Gustafson, nurse on COVID unit

I also witnessed New York's horrific first wave. COVID hit us like a tsunami, though anyone who paid attention to what was happening abroad knew what was coming. I don't know if it exists, but I had pre-traumatic stress disorder, as I was plagued by nightmares of mass death just before COVID arrived in full force. I started taking medication to help me sleep for the first time in my life. My fears were not misplaced. One nurse described her experience by saying, "It was just complete chaos. It was like a medical war zone."[22] Another said, "It was an unimaginable hell to be quite honest."

I started the pandemic thinking I would be most useful in my familiar role as a consulting neurologist at Bellevue Hospital. However, very few patients needed neurological care during that first wave, and the few that did had catastrophic strokes or encephalitis, which they did not survive. After a week of mostly sitting on the sidelines I volunteered to work in the ICU, though truthfully, I was only marginally more helpful than a medical student.

The ICU was an eerie place. IV poles were placed outside the rooms to minimize exposure to staff. Almost all the patients were Black or Hispanic. Some were Asian. Very few were White. Guards from the Department of Corrections kept watch over dying inmates. There were two patients in a room meant for one. There were just bodies of motionless people, intubated, sedated, and alone. Some lived. Most died. I would occasionally gaze out a window to glimpse the crumbling ruins of the Renwick Smallpox Hospital on Roosevelt Island, reminding myself that humanity had defeated viruses before.

After realizing I had more to contribute elsewhere, I spent the rest of that first wave working on the medicine floors treating patients who weren't well enough to go home, but who weren't sick enough to need mechanical ventilation in the ICU. Sadly, there wasn't much to do for these patients either.

Bellevue is located in a relatively well-off area of Manhattan, and our ER was never too overwhelmed. However, every day, dozens of the sickest patients were transferred from other city hospitals in Brooklyn and Queens that were deluged with patients.[23] Of course, every hospital was deluged with COVID patients. All New Yorkers heard the wails of the ambulances, day and night. Hospital workers also heard the nonstop "code blue" pager, summoning the airway team to yet another room. I would often arrive in the morning to learn that half of the people I left the night before had died or been transferred to the ICU. Though we came very close, Bellevue never totally ran out of space, as many people died daily, making space for new arrivals.

At its peak in the middle of April, up to 800 people were dying of COVID every day in New York City.[24] As the morgues became overwhelmed, massive refrigerated trucks were brought in to store the bodies.[25] Over 135 such trucks were used throughout the city.[26] Even that was not enough. According to news reports, "Shelves were placed in the trailers, doubling their capacity, as funeral directors ran out of storage room. Cemeteries and crematories could not handle the load." Several hospitals needed forklifts to move all the dead bodies.[27] Finding space to bury the bodies was difficult,[28] a problem faced by many countries.

Deaths spiked not just in hospitals, but in homes as well. According to news reports:

About 120 morgue workers and soldiers from the

> *U.S. Army, the National Guard and the Air National Guard are working in shifts around the clock, driving rented vans around the city to pick up the bodies of as many as 280 people a day who have died at home and have probably not been part of the official death count.*[29]

While not all of these people died of COVID, many certainly did.

Overall, I saw more people die in a few weeks than I had in my entire career. One of the first was an elderly man who worked as a carpenter at Bellevue for several decades, though he retired before I arrived. I also saw plenty of middle-aged people and several young people die.

The youngest person I saw die was a 23-year-old man with no underlying conditions. He was able to breathe when I first met him, but was completely obtunded, unable to speak or move. Several days before his death, I made him suffer by clumsily placing a nasogastric tube so he could be fed. We didn't know he would die, and he needed nutrition. I still think about that a lot. I wonder what kind of person he was and what his future might have held. His aunt said that he was a loner, and it makes me sad that only a few people might have mourned his passing. He wasn't in touch with his mother, who had substance abuse issues, I was told. I promised myself to remember his name, and I think about him often. I've often wondered if I should call his aunt to see how she is doing, to tell her that I still remember her nephew and that we did everything we could for him. She was an emergency medical technician and knew she gave him the virus. I hope she doesn't blame herself.

I can't imagine what our patients and their families went through. Many older patients were delirious, paranoid, and hallucinating. It must have been terrifying when we approached with our faces hidden by masks and goggles. Many others did not speak English, and it was impossible to communicate with them, especially with our PPE and the loud air purifiers, which had been installed in every room.

No one died with a loved one by their side, which greatly compounded the tragedy for everyone involved. The father of a 35-year-old man screamed at us that we hadn't done enough to save his son. Had he been there, he would have seen we did everything we could. His son died of blood clots throughout his body. COVID was never just another respiratory virus. It was never just the flu. This was clear to anyone who worked in a hospital.

This was also clear to anyone who read a newspaper. The headlines from the start of the pandemic were horrific. "Shocking Video Shows the Bodies of NYC Coronavirus Victims Being Forklifted Into A Refrigerated Truck Used As A Temporary Morgue"[30] said one. "Bodies Of 750 COVID-19 Victims In New York City Remain in Refrigerated Trucks"[31] said another. There are many videos and photos documenting all this.[32] Prisoners were asked to dig graves.[33] Children who lost their parents described their loss.[34] COVID's threat was hardly some well-kept secret.

While we lost a staggering number of patients, many more were discharged home, thanks in part to the care they received. The condition of these survivors varied widely. Some left without symptoms and were seemingly back to normal. Many survivors had been intubated and bed bound for weeks or months. They didn't die, but were quite debilitated, barely able to move after experiencing prolonged immobility.[35] With the focus on deaths, these survivors often get overlooked. I wonder how they are doing now. Others left in the middle of their disease course, as they had somewhere to go or simply didn't want to be in the hospital. One man left to attend the funeral of his brother who had died of COVID. We tried to make people stay, especially if they didn't have housing, but we couldn't force them to do anything. I wonder how many of these patients were willing and able to isolate themselves.

It was also a terrifying time to work in a hospital. Not only were many health care workers traumatized by the mass death, but we also worried about getting sick ourselves or bringing the virus home to our families. I'll never forget the first time a COVID patient coughed all over me, though this would soon become routine. This patient, an older Hispanic man, would be dead two days later.

We now know that PPE works very well. Working with COVID patients was safer than eating in the workroom with colleagues. But we didn't know that back then, and PPE was often in short supply. Early on, some healthcare workers had to improvise and use everyday items, such as trash bags and snorkel masks, to try to protect themselves.[36] We all had to wear a single-use N95 mask for a week or longer. Our administration worked hard to get us PPE, but they couldn't create masks out of thin air.

It was also a time of powerlessness, and none of us had felt so helpless at such a large scale before. COVID was a brand-new disease, and we had no idea how to treat it. Doctors were understandably desperate to try anything to save lives. However, I tend to be fairly conservative and often embrace the idea that the best treatment is no treatment. As such, I made sure none of my patients received unproven treatments, such as hydroxychloroquine, unless I felt their death was imminent and there was nothing to lose.

However, many questions had no easy answers. Was it worth it to amputate an older man's leg after he had developed a blood clot? What was his chance of survival? We had no evidence to guide us through decisions like this, and I pushed for one of my patients, the former Bellevue carpenter, to have his leg amputated several days before he died. I still think about that a lot too. What a horrible thing. However, even with the knowledge and treatments available today, many of these patients still would have died. It's much better to get COVID now than in the spring of 2020, but doctors are still unable to save many patients.

The trauma made many healthcare workers reconsider their careers.[37] One traveling nurse, who served in Iraq and Afghanistan, estimated that he saw 3,000 people die of COVID. "War doesn't even compare to this," he said, "I would rather die, any other way of dying, than dying with coronavirus."[38] A doctor at Elmhurst Hospital in Queens also used a war metaphor to describe his experience at the pandemic's start. He said:

> *If you watch a war movie to see people shooting from all over, that's what this almost felt like. One thing after the next after next, you can't even catch up with what has to happen.*[39]

Consumed by fear, grief, and powerlessness, some healthcare workers took their own lives.[40] I know too many doctors who contracted COVID to count during that first wave. Some were really sick for weeks. Thousands of frontline workers died, and some of them were very young.[41] I knew several of them.

Despite the carnage, it was also an inspirational time. We tried to keep the oldest doctors out of harm's way, but almost everyone was eager to help however they could. Ambulance crews came from all over the country, their sirens wailing constantly throughout the otherwise quiet city streets. Field hospitals were set up in several places and a massive naval hospital, the USNS *Comfort* arrived, though it only treated 182 patients due to strict admission criteria.[42] Children's hospitals and pediatricians cared for adults,[43,44] and gynecologists treated men. Medical schools graduated students several months early so they could care for patients.[45] Medical students who were earlier in their training were properly shielded from patients. Instead, they reviewed patients' charts and called families to keep them informed about their loved ones. So did radiologists and pathologists. The news was often not good. Other students helped make plastic face shields. Everyone did what they could. People sent us food, small gifts, and kind cards. We really appreciated it.

Our city was saved by doctors and nurses who traveled from around the country to help. I heard deep southern accents at the hospital that I normally heard only from tourists in Times Square. The city cheered for us every night at 7PM, even though many of us didn't really feel we deserved it given how many people we lost daily.

As an attending doctor I had to make some tough decisions, but even during a pandemic, much of the work was delegated to younger doctors. Residents, interns, nurses, EMTs, respiratory techs, pharmacists, custodial, kitchen, and maintenance staff were the unsung heroes of that horrific first wave. They kept the hospital running and the patients well-cared for, day and night. Our incredible facilities staff managed to install ventilation in every room in a very short amount of time. There were people whose sole job was to bring bodies to the overflowing morgue. I can't imagine how they managed to do this every day. One article from that time read, "'Somebody's Got To Do It': Forklift Driver Moves Bodies of Coronavirus Victims."[46] I wonder how that person is doing today.

Our hospital director, Dr. Nate Link, kept everyone calm with his cool demeanor during daily briefings, even when he was informing us that 50 more critically ill patients were on their way. The administration and countless others toiled behind the scenes to ensure the hospital was properly staffed and PPE was delivered. I'm certain we saved many lives, though we all wish we could have done more.

Looking back on the whole thing, I'm not really sure I did a lot. But I saw a lot.

While New York City was hit hard and early, our experience didn't turn out to be an extreme outlier, unfortunately. We all remember headlines such as "Coronavirus Kills 70 Veterans at Massachusetts Care Home."[47] When the refrigerated trucks left New York, they were needed in other states, even after vaccines were available.[48] Children's hospitals elsewhere opened their doors to adults.[49] Spain had to convert an ice rink into a morgue[50] and coffins piled up in Italian churches.[51] In India, "hundreds of corpses have been found floating in the [Ganges] river or buried in the sand of its banks."[52] Images of innumerable funeral pyres there are unforgettable. In Ecuador, bodies were simply left in the street.[53] Variations of these scenes played out all over the world.

Overall, I think we had it easy in New York City. I don't envy doctors who worked elsewhere. While New York City's COVID experience was indeed a tsunami, it receded fairly rapidly. By the end of May, fewer than 100 people were dying daily, which is still a high number, of course. But once that first wave ended, COVID never overwhelmed our city again. In contrast, many other parts of the country experienced COVID like a slow-moving flood, with periodic waves of overwhelming disease.

However, instead of receiving cheers from a grateful city, healthcare workers elsewhere were reviled and attacked for their work. Our patients were horrifically unlucky. Elsewhere, they were horrifically misinformed. Sadly, millions of people were told the virus posed no threat to them, while the risks of the vaccine were real and significant. Many people begged to get vaccinated just before COVID killed them.[54] Others lashed out at the doctors trying to save their life.[55] They had been told COVID only killed elderly people, and they reacted violently towards those who told them unwanted truths. I never treated such a patient, fortunately. No one threatened to punch me unless I gave their loved one ivermectin.

"Doctors who have cared for #COVID19 patients will never underestimate what this virus is capable of."
~ Dr. Abraar Karan

I bring all this up for three reasons. First, my quirky interest in the anti-vaccine movement prepared me well for this moment.

Second, while my experience didn't allow me to predict the course of the pandemic better than anyone else, it gave me plenty of respect for the virus and some humility too, I hope. As Dr. Abraar Karan, an infectious disease expert at Stanford, said:

> *One thing I guarantee you will notice if you pay attention, doctors who have cared for #COVID19 patients will never underestimate what this virus is capable of. The antivaxx, antimask pundits who have been tweeting from the safety of their home for the past two years often will.*
>
> *I have yet to meet a fellow physician who has spent the majority of their time caring for these cases who would claim to know exactly what to expect from #SARSCoV2 — because we continue to be surprised. Surprised by people who die that shouldn't. People who suffer for longer than we would expect. People who seem to get better & then suddenly turn for the worse. People who are doing poorly & who end up surviving.*
>
> *Medicine humbles us as clinicians; this virus has too. Hearing non-clinicians downplay it after long days/weeks/months where we are working hard to try & save people's lives Honestly- eventually you can't help but feel like half of the people on here who claim to know what the right answer is or what's "safe enough" are full of BS.*[56]

Dr. Karan is right, and he ended with a crucial point: frontline healthcare workers have skin in the game. He said:

> *Because if you get sick, they won't be responsible for it. They won't be accountable to you, your family, your loved ones Your doctors will be at your bedside. Your antimask, antivaxx saviors will not. A common response I hear from sick patients once it's too late —*

"I wish I had listened."

A frontline healthcare worker might be wrong about everything, but if they minimize the virus and successfully convince large numbers of people to not take it seriously, they'll be creating more tragic work – and risk – for themselves. There's a reason no ICU doctors encouraged unvaccinated young people to contract COVID simultaneously.

In contrast, some other doctors, those who never treated a COVID patient, never grasped what the virus could do. From the pandemic's first days, they drastically underestimated SARS-CoV-2 and treated it as a well-known, predictable entity. They spoke with extraordinary confidence about an entirely new disease, one they experienced exclusively as an online event. They were also sheltered from the consequences of their words. They never heard an unvaccinated patient say "I wish I had listened" as she lay dying of COVID.

Third, people who – to this day – deny what the virus can do, or even blame doctors for the carnage, dishonor the supreme sacrifice many healthcare workers made. According to one news article from May 2020:

> *Dr. James Mahoney was a pulmonary specialist and ICU doctor at University Hospital in Brooklyn. He was 62 and supposed to retire, but when the pandemic hit New York, he decided to keep working. He died from COVID-19 after treating patients with the condition, which is caused by the coronavirus. As a longtime doctor at an underfunded Brooklyn hospital that served the poor and black community, medical students, colleagues, and patients looked at Mahoney as a hero.*[57]

Unlike the doctors discussed in this book, such voices have truly been silenced.

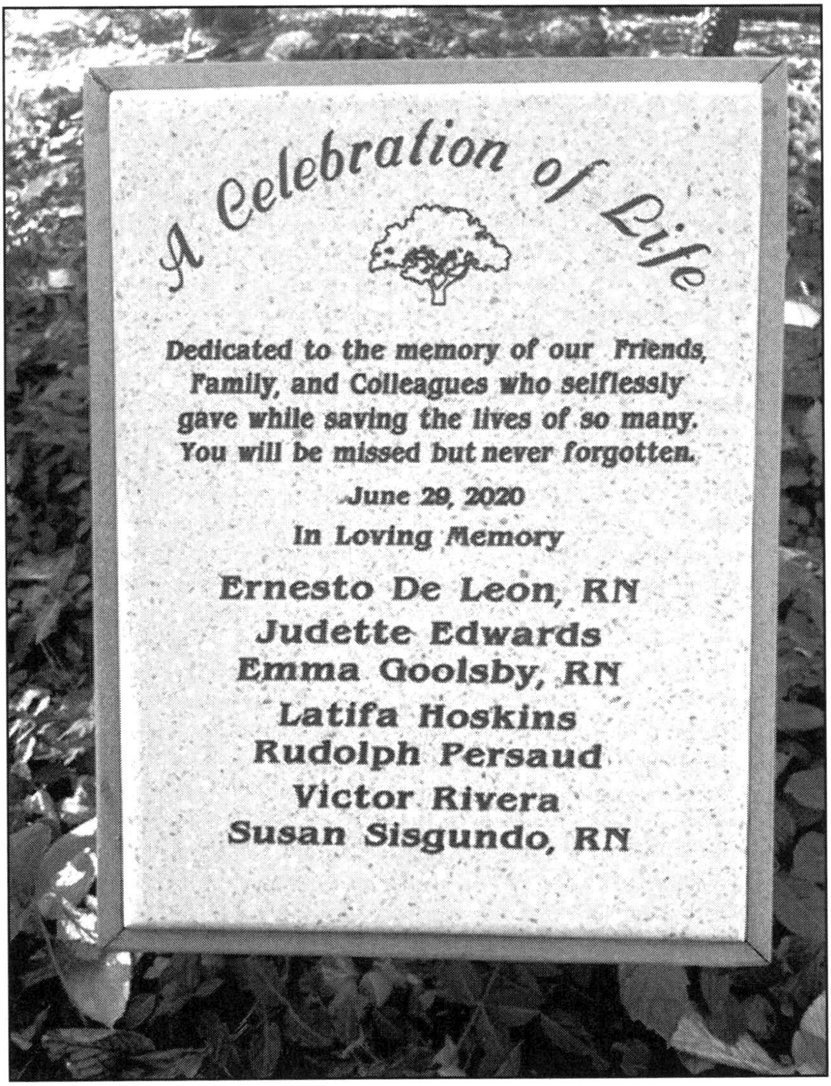

A memorial to Bellevue Hospital employees who died in COVID's first wave. Source: author's personal archive

Chapter 3: "This would translate to about 10,000 deaths."

"Why Most Published Research Findings Are False" ~ Dr. John Ioannidis

I peaked early. My first public comment about COVID was my wisest. It occurred on February 24, 2020, when I responded on *Twitter* to a doctor who asked: "#medtwitter—are you nervous about corona?"[1]

Indeed, I was nervous. I saw the drastic measures China used to contain the virus and I saw what was happening in Italy. I remember hearing one young Italian woman warn the world that the virus was coming for their grandparents too. I believed her so I replied:

> *This seems much more contagious than the flu. So yes, very concerned. Hope I'm wrong.*[2]

Though I acknowledged there was nothing individual doctors could do to stop the virus, I added "This has the potential to be an [*sic*] worldwide disaster."[3]

Not everyone saw it that way. While many doctors shared my concern, many others thought that COVID's threat was greatly exaggerated. However, few doctors voiced this opinion more confidently and publicly than Dr. John Ioannidis, an epidemiologist at Stanford University.

Dr. Ioannidis doesn't conduct much primary research himself, but rather studies science itself, something he calls meta-research. He examines the work of other scientists and tells them what they are doing wrong and how they might improve. According to his *Wikipedia* page:

> *Ioannidis has defined meta-research to include "thematic areas of methods, reporting, reproducibility, evaluation, and incentives (how to do, report, verify, correct, and reward science)". He has performed large-scale assessments of the presence of reproducible and transparent research*

> *indicators such as data sharing, code sharing, protocol registration, declaration of funding and conflicts of interest in biomedical sciences, social sciences, and psychology. He has led or co-led efforts to define and improve reproducibility in science, e.g. computational reproducibility, and to reduce research waste in study design, conduct, and analysis. Ioannidis has co-authored the Manifesto for Reproducible Science, an eight-page document illuminating the need to fix the flaws in the current scientific process and mitigate the "reproducibility crisis" in science.*[4]

Dr. Ioannidis is a paragon of evidence-based medicine and one of the most cited scientists alive. His most famous paper, "Why Most Published Research Findings Are False," was the most-accessed article in the history of *Public Library of Science* (*PLoS*) as of 2020, with nearly three million views.[5] Dr. Ioannidis has received elected membership to the National Academy of Medicine, the European Academy of Sciences and Arts, the European Academy of Cancer Sciences, the American Epidemiological Society and Vice-president of the Association of American Physicians. This is but a small sample of his achievements. Though Dr. Ioannidis may not exactly be a household name, he's about as famous as a scientist can be. I was a fan and quoted him several times in my book on cognitive errors in medicine.

I think examining Dr. Ioannidis' early pandemic statements help explain how our response got off to such a horrible start, the consequences of which linger to this day.

"This would translate to about 10,000 deaths."
~ Dr. John Ioannidis

On March 17, 2020, Dr. Ioannidis wrote an essay in *STAT* titled "A Fiasco in The Making? As The Coronavirus Pandemic Takes Hold, We Are Making Decisions Without Reliable Data." It contained the following paragraph:

> *If we assume that case fatality rate among individuals*

> *infected by SARS-CoV-2 is 0.3% in the general population — a mid-range guess from my Diamond Princess analysis — and that 1% of the U.S. population gets infected (about 3.3 million people), this would translate to about 10,000 deaths. This sounds like a huge number, but it is buried within the noise of the estimate of deaths from "influenza-like illness." If we had not known about a new virus out there, and had not checked individuals with PCR tests, the number of total deaths due to "influenza-like illness" would not seem unusual this year. At most, we might have casually noted that flu this season seems to be a bit worse than average. The media coverage would have been less than for an NBA game between the two most indifferent teams.*[6]

This all seems pretty straightforward. Based on an outbreak on a cruise ship, the *Diamond Princess*, Dr. Ioannidis calculated a case fatality rate with the limited information that was available at that time and assumed 1% of Americans would get infected. Combining these metrics, he calculated that about 10,000 people would die. He thought if we didn't test for it, we might not notice the virus at all. He felt that "at most we might have casually noted" its impact, and that overall, it would be as significant as a dull basketball game.

Dr. Ioannidis' article acknowledged that others made more dire predictions, though he did not agree with them. "Some worry that the 68 deaths from COVID-19 in the U.S. as of March 16 will increase exponentially to 680, 6,800, 68,000, 680,000," he wrote. "In the most pessimistic scenario, which I do not espouse, if the new coronavirus infects 60% of the global population and 1% of the infected people die, that will translate into more than 40 million deaths globally, matching the 1918 influenza pandemic," he added. Even if these dire predictions proved true, he felt the virus would not rob people of many years of life. He wrote:

> *The vast majority of this hecatomb would be people with limited life expectancies. That's in contrast to 1918, when many young people died.*

As governments took drastic steps to slow the virus, Dr. Ioannidis worried the cure would be worse than the disease. He feared that:

> *Locking down the world with potentially tremendous social and financial consequences may be totally irrational. It's like an elephant being attacked by a house cat. Frustrated and trying to avoid the cat, the elephant accidentally jumps off a cliff and dies.*

He was concerned that "the majority of the extra deaths may not be due to coronavirus but to other common diseases and conditions such as heart attacks, strokes, trauma, bleeding, and the like that are not adequately treated…," and warned that "unpredictable evolutions may ensue, including financial crisis, unrest, civil strife, war, and a meltdown of the social fabric."

He reiterated these beliefs in a paper published two days later titled "Coronavirus Disease 2019: The Harms of Exaggerated Information and Non-Evidence-Based Measures."[7] In this paper, Dr. Ioannidis wrote about "exaggerated pandemic estimates", "exaggerated case fatality rate", and "exaggerated exponential community spread." He felt the case fatality rate was "probably higher than seasonal flu (CFR = 0.1%), but not much so." Dr. Ioannidis stated a claim that 20%-60% of adults would be infected was "substantially exaggerated" and that "China data are more compatible with close contact rather than wide community spread being the main mode of transmission." He said that "even if COVID-19 is not a 1918-recap in infection-related deaths, some coronavirus may match the 1918 pandemic in future seasons. Thus, we should learn and be better prepared." Though he later said his critics were "isolating single sentences out of context, distorting the meaning of others and using misleading slogans (eg 'COVID-as-flu')."[64] he felt at the pandemic's start that SARS-CoV-2 was much less concerning that the flu. He wrote that:

> *If only part of resources mobilized to implement extreme measures for COVID-19 had been invested towards enhancing influenza vaccination uptake, tens of thousands of influenza deaths might have been averted.*[7]

He felt SARS-CoV-2 was a false alarm, saying that "this year's coronavirus outbreak is clearly unprecedented in amount of attention received," not in the threat it posed. Dr. Ioannidis stated that other coronaviruses receive scant attention, and it is "only this year that every single case and every single death gets red alert broadcasting in the news."

Dr. Ioannidis published this paper March 19, 2020. Here's a small sample of headlines from that day from around the world:

> *In Italy, the military is deployed to the city of Bergamo, Lombardy, the Italian city worst hit by COVID-19, to collect and transport the bodies of dead residents to crematoriums in other cities, as Bergamo's authorities say their facilities can no longer process the large number of fatalities. The city's mayor Giorgio Gori says the true number of dead could be much higher than what's been reported.*
>
> *Iran's Ministry of Health and Medical Education reports 149 more COVID-19 deaths and an additional 1,046 cases, bringing the death toll in the country to 1,284 and its total number of cases to 18,407.*
>
> *Spain's Ministry of Health says the country's COVID-19 death toll has risen to 767, with 169 more deaths and 3,431 new confirmed cases, for a total of 17,147 cases.*[8]

Several countries were a few weeks ahead of the U.S. in their pandemic experience, and it was obvious why SARS-CoV-2 received an "unprecedented" amount of attention. COVID's threat was no secret, and news from the U.S. on March 19, 2020, said:

> *More than 14,200 people have now tested positive in the U.S. and at least 187 have died. Experts warn those numbers will continue to spike as more people are tested.*[9]

Indeed, those numbers continued to spike. Over 100,000 Americans would be dead of COVID by the end of May 2020. Those experts were right. However, millions of Americans had been told not to trust them.

"Multiply your 'lost in the noise' 10,000 influenza-like deaths by 20+"
~ Will, *STAT* commenter

Others were more clear-eyed at the pandemic's start. In a prescient article from February 2020 called "You're Likely to Get the Coronavirus," Dr. James Hamblin recognized the features that made SARS-CoV-2 such a worrisome foe. He wrote:

> *With its potent mix of characteristics, this virus is unlike most that capture popular attention: It is deadly, but not too deadly. It makes people sick, but not in predictable, uniquely identifiable ways. Last week, 14 Americans tested positive on a cruise ship in Japan despite feeling fine—the new virus may be most dangerous because, it seems, it may sometimes cause no symptoms at all.*[10]

He also quoted Harvard epidemiology professor Dr. Marc Lipsitch as saying, "I think the likely outcome is that it will ultimately not be containable."

The day after Dr. Ioannidis published his *STAT* article, Dr. Lipsitch penned a rebuttal on the same website titled "We Know Enough Now to Act Decisively Against COVID-19. Social Distancing is a Good Place to Start." Dr. Lipsitch said:

> *In Italy, coffins of COVID-19 victims are accumulating in churches that have stopped holding funerals. In Wuhan, at the peak of the epidemic there, critical cases were so numerous that, if scaled up to the size of the U.S. population, they would have filled every intensive care bed in this country. That is what happens when a community waits until crisis hits to try to slow transmission.*[11]

Dr. Lipsitch added that "it is crucial to emphasize that a pandemic like this does not dissipate on its own, as Ioannidis suggested as a possibility," and that "waiting and hoping for a miracle as health systems are overrun by COVID-19 is not an option." He would later say in an interview:

> *We had enough evidence to see that uncontrolled spread was very dangerous. The idea that we should just sort of sit by and gather data calmly struck me as incredibly naïve.*[12]

Dr. Lipsitch was not the only critic who noted that Dr. Ioannidis neglected what had already happened overseas. One of Dr. Ioannidis' critics tweeted at the time:

> *Do you not see what is happening in Italy? This virus quickly almost crashed their healthcare system. The same thing happened in Wuhan - people were dying at home because they couldn't get a hospital bed. This is absolutely not the flu.*[13]

Indeed, COVID was absolutely *not* the flu, and this was obvious

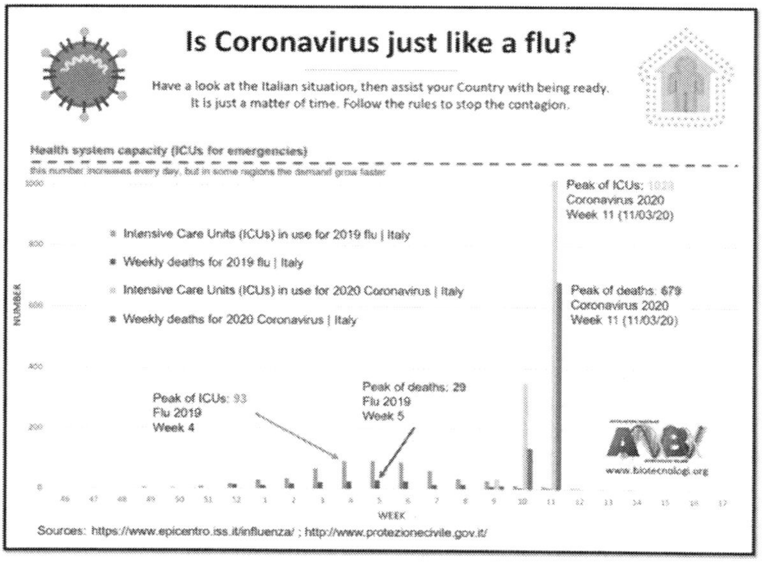

Dr. Tal's data from March 12, 2020

early on. On March 12, 2020, immunologist Dr. Michal Tal posted data from Italy that showed COVID had put 1,028 people in the ICU and killed 679 compared to 92 ICU admissions and 29 deaths for the flu in 2019.[14]

While Dr. Lipsitch took issue with Dr. Ioannidis' pandemic philosophy, others noted more basic problems with his calculations. Epidemiologist Dr. Hilda Bastian noticed flaws in his estimation that 0.3% of people who contract COVID will die, writing "the 0.3% CFR (case fatality rate) seems likely to be too low".[15] Presently, COVID's death rate is at 0.3% of the total U.S. population, proving Dr. Bastian's criticism was correct.

Dr. Bastian also said that "the 1% rate of people infected, however, is likely to be very wide off the mark. It's far lower than the infection rate on the Diamond Princess (which was more like 20%)." Others noticed this as well. One commenter on Dr. Ioannidis' *STAT* article wrote:

> *In the same article that you use the Diamond Princess cruise ship as a case study for fatality rates, you estimate that 1% of the U.S. population might be infected. The Diamond Princess cruise ship saw nearly 25% of the ship's passengers infected. Perhaps multiply your "lost in the noise" 10,000 influenza-like deaths by 20+.*[16]

Even this would turn out to be a gross underestimate. Over 200,000 Americans – "*10,000 influenza-like deaths by 20+*" – would be dead by the end of September 2020.[17]

"If I were to make an informed estimate based on the limited testing data we have, I would say that COVID-19 will result in fewer than 40,000 deaths this season in the USA."

~ Dr. John Ioannidis

A month later, Dr. Ioannidis would partially adopt his critics' position and completely reverse his assumption that just 1% of the U.S. would contract COVID. Based on a controversial antibody study from Santa Clara County in California,[18] Dr. Ioannidis and other Stanford researchers estimated the virus was 50-85 times more common than previously thought.[19] No longer did he speak of "exaggerated exponential community spread."[7] Instead, he spoke of *unrecognized* exponential community spread. He felt the virus was "very common" and that the number of known COVID cases was merely the "tip of the iceberg."[20]

The notion that the virus could spread rapidly and silently was a potentially very worrisome development. It implied that only drastic measures would be able to contain it. For example, Dr. Anthony Fauci said on March 19, 2020:

> *We are getting more and more information that someone can transmit even when they are asymptomatic. So in order to protect oneself, society and particularly the vulnerable people, we've really got to adhere to the physical separation.*[21]

In contrast, Dr. Ioannidis thought the virus's ability to easily spread undetected was extremely reassuring. If large numbers of people had been infected without even realizing it, that meant COVID's impact would be much less severe than initially feared. As Dr. Ioannidis put it, this would mean the "probability of dying if you are infected diminishes by 50-85 fold."[22] COVID is "not the apocalyptic problem we thought,"[23] he said. He felt that most people had no or mild symptoms and that this was a cause for "optimism" about reopening society. He called COVID a "common and mild infection"[20] for most people. He said, "the infection fatality rate for this new coronavirus was likely to be in the same ballpark as the seasonal influenza."[22] He stated that "for someone who is less than 65 and has no underlying diseases, the risk is completely negligible…these deaths are extremely exceptional." Elsewhere, Ioannidis would say that "for people younger than 45, the infection fatality rate is almost 0%."[24] In reality, 45,000 Americans younger than this have died of COVID thus far.

On April 9, 2020, after 22,000 Americans were already dead,[17] Dr. Ioannidis made another optimistic prediction. He said:

> *If I were to make an informed estimate based on*

> *the limited testing data we have, I would say that COVID-19 will result in fewer than 40,000 deaths this season in the USA.*[25]

That quote appeared in an article by Fareed Zakaria, who wrote:

> *A group of Stanford University scholars believe that the basic reason that estimates of deaths have had to be revised downward is because without widespread testing from the start, we didn't realize how many mild or asymptomatic cases there would be. That means the denominator — those who have been infected — is larger than initial estimates and the fatality rate for COVID-19 is lower. (If two out of 100 people with the virus die, the fatality rate is 2 percent; if two out of 1,000 die, it is 0.2 percent.) In March, the World Health Organization announced that 3.4 percent of people with the virus had died from it. That would be an astonishingly high fatality rate. Fauci suggested a week later that the actual rate was probably 1 percent, which would still be 10 times as high as the flu. Since then, we have learned that many people, perhaps as many as half, don't have any symptoms. Some studies find that 75 to 80 percent of people infected could be asymptomatic. That means most people infected with the virus never get to a clinic and never get counted.*
>
> *Stanford's John Ioannidis, an epidemiologist who specializes in analyzing data, and one of the most cited scientists in the field, believes we have massively overestimated the fatality of COVID-19. "When you have a model involving exponential growth, if you make a small mistake in the base numbers, you end up with a final number that could be off 10-fold, 30-fold, even 50-fold," he told me.*

This was exactly what we all wanted to hear, myself included. If the virus was already widespread and most people had minimal or no symptoms, it meant that we were closer to the middle, or even the end, of the pandemic than to its start. Indeed, Dr. Ioannidis felt there was a decent chance the worst was close to over, saying on April 17, 2020:

> *Acknowledging for the fact that the epidemic is still evolving, and we cannot be sure whether we will hit even higher peaks in the future, although this doesn't seem to be the case, at least for the European countries, and it seems to be that even in the US, in most states we're very close to the peak, if not past the peak, the risk is something that should be manageable as opposed to the panic and horror stories that are circulating about.*[22]

Dr. Ioannidis' optimism wasn't just limited to medical journals and niche publications. He was a ubiquitous media presence early in the pandemic. As Stephanie Lee reported, Dr. Ioannidis' optimistic predictions:

> *Caught the eye of many conservative commentators, from Ann Coulter to Fox News personality Lisa Boothe. Bret Stephens cited it in a New York Times column titled "It's Dangerous to Be Ruled by Fear." It also circulated among West Wing aides, Bloomberg reported.*[26]

Dr. Ioannidis was not camera shy himself. He took his hopeful message to podcasts and the airwaves, appearing on CNN and programs hosted by far-right Fox News firebrands like Laura Ingraham and Mark Levin. According to *The Washington Post*, by December 2020, Dr. Ioannidis "had appeared at least 18 times on major cable news networks, repeatedly questioning the severity of the pandemic."[12]

During some of these appearances, Dr. Ioannidis told the viewers to distrust everything they've heard so far. He told Mr. Levin that "the evidence we had early in the pandemic was utterly unreliable."[27] He said predictions that millions of Americans would die were "completely off, it is just an astronomical error." This was almost certainly a reference to epidemiologist Dr. Neil Ferguson, who predicted COVID would kill over two million Americans. Importantly, Dr. Ferguson's estimate applied only "in the (unlikely) absence of any control measures or spontaneous changes in individual behavior."[28] In other words, Dr. Ferguson projected that two million Americans would die only if no one did anything at all to control the virus, a key fact Dr. Ioannidis did not mention.

Dr. Ioannidis then told viewers he had newer and better data. This data was incredibly good news. Again, it was what we all wanted to hear: COVID isn't *that* bad. According to Dr. Ioannidis, "the vast majority" of people "don't even realize that they have been infected, they are asymptomatic, they have no symptoms, or they have very mild symptoms that they would not even bother to do anything about."[27] He said the risk of dying from COVID was high for elderly people, especially those in nursing homes and those with serious underlying diseases, but "most of the population has minimal risk, in the range of dying while you're driving from home to work and back."

Dr. Ioannidis would tell Mr. Levin that the infection fatality rate is "probably in the range of 1 in a 1,000." Mr. Levin repeated the good news by saying, "You say one in a thousand. You're saying well under 1%, is that one-tenth of 1% of the population that actually has the virus will pass away as a result of the virus, or in connection to the virus." Dr. Ioannidis responded in an interesting way by saying, "This is as open question…99% of people (in Italy) who die with this virus have other reasons as well to die."

Whether he was assuming that only 1% of the population would get COVID or that it was already widespread, Dr. Ioannidis' message was loud and clear: though COVID can devastate older, ill people, for everyone else the virus was only as dangerous as "driving to work and back." He felt its overall impact would be as significant as a February contest between the New York Knicks and the Sacramento Kings.[6] Many people believed him.

"I think the authors of the above-linked paper owe us all an apology"

~ Dr. Andrew Gelman

However, as with Dr. Ioannidis' initial prediction that only a small percentage of Americans would contract COVID, his calculation that the virus was already widespread also met with fierce criticism. Critics noted that the Santa Clara antibody study recruited subjects through *Facebook* ads, which could have created a skewed sample if people who thought they had COVID jumped at the chance to get tested.[29] Moreover, according to the reporting of Ms. Lee, subjects were invited to enroll in the study by Dr. Jay Bhattacharya's wife. Ms. Lee wrote:

> *[She] invited parents in a wealthy enclave of Northern California to sign up for her husband's coronavirus antibody study this month, falsely claiming that an "FDA approved" test would tell them if they had immunity and could "return to work without fear."*[30]

Even if the study population had been entirely random and unbiased, many other problems emerged. Stanford statistician John Cherian noted that, unless the antibody test was close to 100% perfect, "nearly all of the positive results can be explained away as false positives (and we know next to nothing about the true prevalence of COVID-19 in Santa Clara County)."[31] Indeed, Dr. Taia Wang, an infectious disease expert at Stanford who was charged with validating the accuracy of their antibody test, refused to have her name on the final publication. She didn't trust the antibody test, saying it "alarmed" her and that it "performed very poorly on samples with lower antibody"[32] levels. Again, according to the reporting of Ms. Lee, Dr. Wang sent an email to fellow faculty members, including Drs. Bhattacharya and Ioannidis, several days before the Santa Clara data was published. Dr. Wang wrote:

> *I declined authorship on any manuscript because, based on our testing, I do not believe that the [Premier Biotech] kit is a robust readout for the presence [receptor-binding domain] antibodies.*[32]

Statistician Andrew Gelman similarly eviscerated the Santa Clara study and concluded:

> *I think the authors of the above-linked paper*

> *owe us all an apology. We wasted time and effort discussing this paper whose main selling point was some numbers that were essentially the product of a statistical error.*
>
> *I'm serious about the apology. Everyone makes mistakes. I don't think they authors need to apologize just because they screwed up. I think they need to apologize because these were avoidable screw-ups. They're the kind of screw-ups that happen if you want to leap out with an exciting finding and you don't look too carefully at what you might have done wrong.*[33]

Dr. Ioannidis would later defend his study by saying, "It's not perfect, but it's the best science can do."[34]

However, it didn't take complicated statistics or immunology to realize the fatal flaws in Dr. Ioannidis' claims. All it took was elementary school math and knowledge of basic pandemic facts. New York City had already recorded over 10,000 COVID deaths[35] when Dr. Ioannidis told Fox News viewers the death rate was "probably in the range of 1 in a 1,000."[27] If 10,000 people had already died, and if only 1 in a 1,000 people died overall, this would require 10 million New Yorkers to have been infected. Only 8.3 million people live there. This is one of several times he and other doctors made calculations that require more people to have contracted COVID in a given area than actually exist in that area.

Sadly, more than 1 in a 1,000 people who contract COVID will die from it. In fact, by some estimates, the 1 in a 1,000-fatality rate is accurate only for 25-year-olds.[36] Given that over one million Americans have died of COVID thus far, a fatality rate of one in 1,000 people would require over a billion total infections, though the entire population of the U.S. is only 330 million people. Moreover, a study published in May 2020 would find that only about 16% of COVID infections were truly asymptomatic.[37] Studies of asymptomatic individuals would find that 80% of them eventually develop symptoms.[38] Such individuals are more accurately described as pre-symptomatic.

"I never said that I knew that the death toll was going to be '10,000 deaths in the US'."
~ Dr. John Ioannidis

Unfortunately, COVID turned out to be more consequential than "an NBA game between the two most indifferent teams."[6] As the death toll rose in the spring of 2020, doctors who felt the flu would be worse than COVID had two choices: admit they were wrong or back-pedal and double-down. Infectious-disease expert Dr. Paul Offit, who predicted that COVID would cause less than "one-tenth of the damage that influenza causes every year in the United States,"[39] chose to admit he was wrong.

Dr. Ioannidis did the opposite. His first strategy was to claim he didn't say what he said. When asked in July 2020 about his statement that "this would translate to about 10,000 deaths," Dr. Ioannidis said:

> *I never said that I knew that the death toll was going to be "10,000 deaths in the US". How could I, in a piece where the message was "we don't know"! The 10,000 deaths in the US projection was meant to be in the most optimistic range of the spectrum and in the same piece I also described the most pessimistic end of the spectrum, 40 million deaths. The point I wanted to emphasize was the huge uncertainty.*[40]

Dr. Ioannidis would later say his critics were guilty of "the 10,000 strawman."[41] Defending himself against accusations he said only 10,000 people would die, he wrote:

> *Another gross distortion propagated in social media is that the op-ed had supposedly predicted that only 10,000 deaths will happen in the USA as a result of the pandemic. The key message of the op-ed was that we lack reliable data, that is, we do not know. The self-contradicting misinterpretation as "we don't know, but actually we do know that 10,000 deaths will happen" is impossible. The op-ed discussed two extreme scenarios to highlight the tremendous uncertainty absent reliable data: an overtly optimistic*

> *scenario of only 10,000 deaths in the US and an overtly pessimistic scenario of 40,000,000 deaths.*[42]

It's true that Dr. Ioannidis never said he "knew" the death toll was going to be 10,000 people. However, any fair reading of his *STAT* article, as well as everything else he said at the time, shows that he felt COVID's danger was greatly exaggerated.

Despite this, Dr. Ioannidis would claim his *STAT* article presented two equally plausible scenarios – one overtly optimistic and one overtly pessimistic – and that he merely said we need to collect more data to determine which of these is more accurate. It's possible that Dr. Ioannidis *meant* for his "10,000 deaths" statement to be "the most optimistic range of the spectrum," but that's not what he wrote. It's also not what very influential people heard.

Similarly, it's true that Dr. Ioannidis discussed more pessimistic scenarios. He wrote in March 2020:

> *Some fear an analogy to the 1918 influenza pandemic that killed 20-40 million people... Importantly, this year we are dealing with thousands, not tens of millions deaths.*[7]

In a different article that month he wrote:

> *In the most pessimistic scenario, which I do not espouse, if the new coronavirus infects 60% of the global population and 1% of the infected people die, that will translate into more than 40 million deaths globally, matching the 1918 influenza pandemic.*[6]

So, while Dr. Ioannidis did discuss pessimistic scenarios, he only did so to say that he did not believe them. He compared COVID to the 1918 flu pandemic only as a foil for his belief that COVID's threat was greatly exaggerated. While he expanded on the most "optimistic scenario," saying it would matter as much as an "NBA game between the two most indifferent teams," he never elaborated on the potential consequences of the pessimistic scenario. Why would he? He thought these pessimistic scenarios were "completely off, just an astronomical error." Millions of Americans would come to share this belief.

"There were additional contributing reasons."
~ Dr. John Ioannidis

While Dr. Ioannidis' attempts to rewrite his initial pandemic predictions were indecorous, they were rather benign. However, his second strategy to avoid admitting he underestimated COVID was far more pernicious. In an article ironically titled "Forecasting for COVID-19 has Failed," which was published online August 25, 2020, when COVID's death toll was 177,693 Americans,[17] Dr. Ioannidis discussed the pandemic as if it was over and his initial optimism had been vindicated. He wrote:

> *Very few hospitals were eventually stressed and only for a couple of weeks. Most hospitals maintained largely empty wards, expecting tsunamis that never came… Tragically, many health systems faced major adverse consequences, not by COVID-19 cases overload, but for very different reasons.*[42]

Over 850,000 Americans died of COVID in the ensuing two years.[17]

In this article, Dr. Ioannidis also revisited his prediction "that COVID-19 will result in fewer than 40,000 deaths this season in the USA."[25] He acknowledged this prediction was "so wrong" and he called himself a "fool" for having made it. However, he listed "additional contributing reasons"[42] as to why his prediction was incorrect. He wrote:

> *When I made that tentative quote, I had not considered the impact of the new case definition of COVID-19 and of COVID-19 becoming a notifiable disease, despite being aware of the Italian experience where almost all counted "COVID-19 deaths" also had other concomitant causes of death/comorbidities. "COVID-19 death" now includes not only "deaths by COVID-19" and "deaths with COVID-19", but even deaths "without COVID-19 documented". Moreover, I had not taken seriously into account*

> *weekend reporting delays in death counts. Worse, COVID-19 had already started devastating nursing homes in the USA by then, but the nursing home data were mostly unavailable. I could not imagine that despite the Italian and Washington state experience, nursing homes were still unprotected. Had I known that nursing homes were even having COVID-19 patients massively transferred to them, I would have escalated my foolish quote several fold.*

Of course, the simplest reason why Dr. Ioannidis' prediction aged so poorly so quickly is that he drastically underestimated COVID. His prediction "that COVID-19 will result in fewer than 40,000 deaths this season in the USA"[25] was made on April 9, 2020. By that day, 22,000 Americans had already died of COVID, and 2,000 more died that day.[17] Yet, Dr. Ioannidis was predicting that only 18,000 more people would die of COVID "this season", and he did so on a day when 799 people died in New York State alone, breaking the record for daily COVID deaths for the third straight day.[43] Over 7,000 New Yorkers had died already. Unless COVID vanished *instantly*, Dr. Ioannidis' prediction would age poorly within a few days. Indeed, by April 17, 2020, America's COVID death toll was 39,581 and 2,197 people died that day.[17]

Though his prediction of 40,000 deaths was obliterated in just 8 days, Dr. Ioannidis was unfazed. In fact, on the very day his prediction was proven wrong – April 17, 2020 – he gave an interview in which he said that, based on his Santa Clara antibody study:

> *We realize that the number of infected people is somewhere between 50 and 85 times more compared to what we thought, compared to what had been documented. Immediately, that means that the infection fatality rate, the chance of dying, the probability of dying, if you are infected, diminishes by 50-85 fold, because the denominator in the calculation becomes 50-85 fold bigger. If you take these numbers into account, they suggest that the infection fatality rate for this new coronavirus is likely to be in the same ballpark as seasonal influenza.*[22]

He said that if society did not reopen soon, "the consequences will be far worse than coronavirus."

Over a million Americans have died since, and none of Dr. Ioannidis' "additional contributing reasons" explain the enormous gap between his prediction of 40,000 fatalities and the actual death toll. COVID's death toll was high because morgues were literally overflowing with bodies, not because it had been made a "notifiable disease."

Moreover, it's true that many nursing homes were poorly managed early in the pandemic. Most notoriously, New York Governor Andrew Cuomo issued a disastrous order on March 25, 2020, that no "resident shall be denied re-admission or admission to the NH [nursing home] solely based on a confirmed or suspected diagnosis of COVID-19."[44] After an investigation, New York State added 6,500 deaths to its tally of long-term care residents who died of COVID.[45] While this is a substantial number of fatalities, they do not come close to accounting for Dr. Ioannidis' underestimation of the virus.

Additionally, no reasonable person expected that overwhelmed, under-resourced nursing homes and care facilities would both recognize COVID's danger and be able to hermetically seal off vulnerable residents in a couple weeks' time. We still haven't figured out how to do this. A headline from November 2022 read "COVID Deaths Still Loom Over NH Nursing Homes as Outbreaks Continue."[46] Yet at the pandemic's start, when no one was vaccinated and testing was scarce, with a virus that spread asymptomatically – a point Dr. Ioannidis stressed – he "could not imagine…nursing homes were still unprotected."[42]

I could imagine why many nursing homes were unprotected. No one says nursing homes handled COVID flawlessly, but it's not their fault Dr. Ioannidis expected them to be perfectly protected instantly everywhere for the duration of the pandemic. Perhaps some nursing home directors believed the worst was over. Maybe they listened to Dr. Ioannidis when he said in April 2020 that:

> *It seems to be that even in the US, in most states we're very close to the peak, if not past the peak, the risk is something that should be manageable as opposed to the panic and horror stories that are circulating about.*[22]

Doctors who lacked real world responsibility for protecting vulnerable people spent much of the pandemic portraying this as a trivial task, one that wasn't done to perfection because those with actual responsibility were incompetent or indifferent. The notion that it would be easy to protect tens of millions of vulnerable people became one of the pandemic's most damaging myths. In reality, protecting this population was infinitely harder than contrarian doctors made it out to be in their podcasts, editorials, and *Twitter* feeds.

"On average they are 80-years-old with other comorbidities, as we say, and there's quite some debate on whether these people would have died anyhow, if not immediately, you know, perhaps in a few days or in a few weeks or a few months."
~ Dr. John Ioannidis

Beyond this, Dr. Ioannidis' defense of his poor prediction contained the glimmer of some of the pandemic's most dangerous and enduring myths. When Dr. Ioannidis said to Fox News host Mark Levin, "This is as open question…99% of people who die with this virus have other reasons as well to die,"[27] he was signaling that the COVID death toll was exaggerated and couldn't be trusted.

As the death toll dwarfed his optimistic predictions, Dr. Ioannidis worked extremely hard to convince people that large swaths of victims died *with* COVID, not *from* COVID, that death certificates were unreliable, that COVID's only true victims were on their deathbed anyway, and that lockdowns likely killed many people, not the virus. His core message was this:

> *The number of person-years lost is very small and you're not even sure that SARS-CoV-2 really did contribute to their death substantially.*[22]

He first expressed these sentiments in his March 2020 *STAT* article when he wrote that "A positive test for coronavirus does not mean necessarily that this virus is always primarily responsible for a patient's demise" and that "the vast majority of this hecatomb would be people with limited life expectancies."[6] Though he stressed there was much still to learn, these beliefs remained a constant feature in his interviews and publications in the pandemic's first few months.

March 23, 2020

> *The number of deaths hopefully is captured with more accuracy, even though for that number there can be some debate, for example, whether these deaths are with SARs-CoV-2 or by SARS-CoV-2...*
>
> *Based on what we know now, many people who are infected with this coronavirus, they present with very little, either no symptoms or mild, moderate symptoms, that are very difficult to distinguish from the common cold or flu...so what we know is just the tip of the iceberg...*
>
> *Another observation that has emerged is that many of these people (in Italy) probably would have had very limited life expectancy in the absence of that infection, and it still remains to be decided how many of these infections are deaths with SARS-CoV-2 versus deaths by SARS-CoV-2, meaning that the virus has the key influence on the outcome rather than just giving a final kick or participating among many other factors in shaping the outcome, but these people having multiple other reasons that they would have a very poor endpoint and eventually die, many of them.*[47]

April 7, 2020

> *Finally, a major question that should be answered is the causal contribution of SARS-CoV-2 infection to related deaths. It is difficult to differentiate between deaths with SARS-CoV-2 infection and deaths caused by SARS-CoV-2 infection because the vast majority of patients who have died had 1 or more other major pathologies (98.8% with at least 1 comorbidity, and 48.6% having 3 or more diseases) that contributed to their death.*[48]

April 17, 2020

There is some contentious issue about what exactly should count as a COVID-19 death. For example, in the last few days (in New York City) we have seen a very large number of probable COVID-19 deaths being added to the figures, and these are deaths where we have not documented with laboratory testing the presence of the virus, so they are pretty presumptive in terms of whether these are deaths that were caused by COVID-19, COVID-19 was present, but not really a key player in the demise of the patient.

So, I think we need to wait and see some mature data on what exactly the contribution of the virus has been in different deaths that we have documented. In Italy, where we have some more mature data, we see that close to 99% of people have underlying diseases, actually in most cases multiple underlying diseases and underlying causes that could also have led them to death. In the US, it seems to be less, but we would need to get some more in-depth analysis of what exactly is killing these people and how…

So, the data in Italy suggest that it's very difficult to differentiate between deaths by SARS-CoV-2 and deaths with SARS-CoV-2. Since we had close to 99% of people dying have other causes that may have contributed to their demise, it's very difficult to dissociate and say that these people specifically died because they were infected. It's very likely that many of them would have died anyhow, if not immediately within a very short period of time, because of these other causes of death that they had. I think this is an ongoing debate…

Countries use very different systems of recording deaths, and we know, not just from the COVID-19 era, but also from the past, that filling out death certificates can be very tricky. We know that death certificates often are pretty inaccurate, and if you create an environment where people believe that this is the cause of death, that is really the most prominent at the moment, they may subconsciously or unconsciously prefer to list COVID-19 as a major cause of death in the certificate, even though it may be less significant contributor if not an innocent bystander in some cases. This is very difficult to tell at the moment because, as you realize, the battle is still ongoing. But at some point, we need to go back and check very carefully and try to understand what exactly did the virus do to all these people.

If we do that, we will also be able to estimate how many years of life were really lost, because it's not just the number of deaths, it's the number of person-years lost that matters the most. If you have someone who is young and healthy and has no other problems and suddenly dies in their twenties, this is a very large number of person-years lost compared to someone who is very old and has multiple reasons to die, and is already dying from something else and you just happen to find a PCR positive test for SARS-CoV-2 in a nasal swab. The number of person-years lost is very small and you're not even sure that SARS-CoV-2 really did contribute to their death substantially.[22]

April 19, 2020

So, this is also an open question. Because for the data that we have more mature and detailed information, like the data from Italy that has already through the peak of their epidemic wave, we realize that 99% of people who die with this virus have other reasons as well to die. On average, they have close to three other reasons to die. On average they are 80-years-old with other comorbidities, as we say, and there's quite some debate on whether these people would have died anyhow, if not immediately, you know, perhaps in a few days or in a few weeks or a few months. In our country we see a fairly similar picture.

We see that people who are disadvantaged, poor people, creating even further inequality in the population through COVID-19, seem to be very hard hit. We see that the age of death on average is a little bit lower compared to European countries, in the range of 73 or 74-years-old, and we see again lots of comorbidities in people who die with COVID-19. It's very hard to say how many of these people would have died anyhow and how much is the direct contribution of the virus.

These data are evolving, but if anything they suggest that the burden of disease as we call it, the number of person-years lost, how many years of life are being lost, is much less than even what the number of deaths would suggest. This is not to minimize the problem. It is a serious problem.[27]

June 27, 2020

COVID-19 has become a notifiable disease, so it is readily recorded in death certificates. What we do know, however, is that the vast majority of people who die with a COVID-19 label have at least one and typically many other comorbidities. This means that often they have other reasons that would lead them to death. The relative contribution of COVID-19 needs very careful audit and evaluation of medical records.

The number of COVID-19 deaths can be both undercounted and overcounted, and the relative ratio of over- and under-counting varies across different locations. In most European countries and the USA it is more likely to be overcounted, especially if we are talking about "deaths by COVID-19"...For COVID-19 we are in early days, and we need to be careful to dissociate deaths from COVID-19 versus deaths that happened because of the disruption induced by lockdown.

In terms of numbers of lives lost, so far the COVID-19 impact is about 1% of the 1918 influenza. In terms of quality-adjusted person-years lost, the impact of COVID-19 is about 0.1% of 1918 influenza, since the 1918 influenza killed mostly young healthy people (average age 28), while the average age of death with COVID-19 is 80 years, with several comorbidities.[24]

July 15, 2020

Now, your point that we're literally counting, as opposed to estimating, deaths from coronavirus is correct. But I'll push back that this may not yield mortality figures as accurately as people think. Because of the attention on coronavirus, we're better at knowing that a deceased person had coronavirus than had the flu. This means we're good at knowing when someone died with coronavirus — but not necessarily that they died from the infection. We assume that dying with coronavirus is dying from coronavirus.[40]

Though these quotes are from early in the pandemic, Dr. Ioannidis would continue to resist the idea that COVID was responsible for mass death. In an article titled "Over- and Under-estimation of COVID-19 Deaths," published on July 28, 2021, he repeated familiar themes. He said, "Even before the major reshuffling of death causes due to COVID-19, death certificates were known to be notoriously error-prone"[49] and that "certain deaths are also clinically attributed to COVID-19 despite negative test results or without any testing."

However, his most inflammatory charges in this article were that doctors weren't competent enough to know what killed their patients and they had "financial incentives" to improperly put COVID on death certificates. He wrote that:

Death certificates have always been inaccurate, but COVID-19 maximizes the challenge of prioritizing multiple comorbidities. In the USA, chain-of-event and contributing factor information in COVID-19 deaths seem congruent in most COVID-19 death

> *certificates. However, congruence does not prove accuracy. In many other countries, death certificates are even more unreliable. Some financial incentives may promote coding for COVID-19. The unavoidable alert that a lethal infectious disease is circulating may also affect death cause attribution.*

While Dr. Ioannidis spoke of inaccurate death certificates and "financial incentives", he provided no evidence COVID's death toll was exaggerated because doctors filled out death certificates inaccurately due to errors in "prioritizing multiple comorbidities" or for "financial incentives".

"Just going crazy, and intubating people who did not have to be intubated"
~ Dr. John Ioannidis

Unfortunately, the idea that doctors had "financial incentives" to inappropriately put COVID on death certificates was not the most provocative charge Dr. Ioannidis would level against frontline doctors. During an appearance on Dr. Vinay Prasad's *Plenary Session* podcast on February 9, 2021, Dr. Ioannidis said, "There is an effect of what we did, mostly wrong, in the first wave."[50] Obviously, Dr. Ioannidis was not referring to himself when he said, "what we did, mostly wrong," but rather to overwhelmed doctors dealing with a completely new disease at the pandemic's start. Dr. Ioannidis then said that "a lot of lives" were lost at that time in part because of doctors "not knowing how to use mechanical ventilation, just going crazy, and intubating people who did not have to be intubated." Dr. Ioannidis provided no evidence for this claim.

It's worthwhile to remember what doctors were facing at that time. One article quoted Dr. Stuart Kessler, Director of the Emergency Department at Elmhurst Hospital in Queens, New York. It said:

> *"We are always preparing for emergency situations, but I don't think anyone in the country could have been prepared for what happened in March and April," Dr. Kessler began. "We knew something was*

> *different fairly early in March but there were a few days when we just had an overwhelming volume of patients coming to the emergency department and we saw almost double the volume, but not just double the volume, ten times the level of illness."*
>
> *It was a horrifying new experience for the entire Elmhurst staff, Dr. Kessler recalled — unlike anything they had seen before.*
>
> *"So, it was early in March we realized this was going to be different. This was all brand new to everyone, there was really no predicting. You expected it would stop, then there were days when you just had no idea how much longer it could go," Dr. Kessler said, recalling the overwhelming number of individuals admitted.*[51]

Dr. Ioannidis accused Dr. Kessler and his colleagues of "just going crazy, and intubating people who did not have to be intubated"[50] and the cost was "a lot of lives."

Dr. Ioannidis would later repeat this accusation in an article titled "COVID-19 in Children and University Students," in which he said that the "future infection fatality rate may decrease with better protection of vulnerable children, more effective treatments, and avoidance of harmful treatments (e.g. improper mechanical ventilation strategies.)"[52] Again, Dr. Ioannidis provided no evidence that children were dying from "improper mechanical ventilation strategies" rather than from COVID.

"They claim five hundred thousand people have died from COVID-19. Bullshit."

~ Ted Nugent

All of this had consequences in the real world. Dr. Scott Atlas, who would become President Trump's COVID advisor, shared Dr. Ioannidis' optimism and reached out to the White House to share the good news with his future employers. According to the House Select Subcommittee on the Coronavirus Crisis:

> *On March 21, 2020, Dr. Atlas sent an email to CMS Administrator Seema Verma to advocate against "the need for lockdown and even the frantic need for urgent testing," calling the federal government's approach to combating the virus "a massive overreaction" that was "inciting irrational fear" in Americans. Dr. Atlas stated that the early data showed the "virus would cause about 10,000 deaths"—a number that he claimed "would be unnoticed" in a normal flu season—and argued that "[t]he panic needs to be stopped."*[53]

Dr. Atlas would tell the House Select Subcommittee that Dr. Ioannidis was the source of his figure that COVID would likely kill "about 10,000" people, a number that "would be unnoticed" in a normal flu season.[54] According to Dr. Deborah Birx, the White House Coronavirus Response Coordinator under President Trump, Dr. Ioannidis' Santa Clara antibody study influenced Dr. Atlas and the information he passed on to White House leaders. She said that Dr. Atlas:

> *Probably had been providing information to senior leaders in the White House since late March, around his hypothesis and around his belief and his fundamental belief using some biased antibody data out of California that the virus was much more widespread, and came back to that full circle that the disease was no worse than flu in his conceptual framework.*[55]

The notion that COVID's death toll was greatly inflated, that its only victims were sick elderly people, and that many people died because doctors were "just going crazy" intubating them, became powerful myths amongst right-wing COVID deniers and conspiracy theorists. Though they used less formal diction than Dr. Ioannidis, their underlying premises were identical. To pick one example amongst many, the right-wing rocker Ted Nugent said:

> *They claim five hundred thousand people have died*

> *from COVID-19. Bullshit. I believe that medical examiners in all 50 states have gone, 'I put down on the death certificate that he died of asphyxiation, but they made me put COVID.' 'Well, this guy was stabbed to death, but they made me put down COVID.' 'This guy was run over by a tandem gravel truck doing a four-wheel drift and the crows be pecking at your flesh, but they made me put down COVID-19.'*[56]

President Trump also spread this message on *Twitter* in the summer of 2020 when he retweeted QAnon influencer, Mel Q.[57] Mel Q claimed the CDC had "quietly updated the COVID number to admit that only 6% of all the 153,504 deaths recorded actually died of COVID," since "the other 94% had 2-3 other serious illnesses & the overwhelming majority were of advanced age." Dr. Ioannidis' interviewer on Fox News, Mr. Levin, would also promote Mel Q's conspiracy that COVID deaths are inflated by tweeting "THE U.S. DID NOT SURPASS 200,000 COVID-19 DEATHS."[58]

Luminaries of the anti-vaccine movement, such as Dr. Kelly Brogan, similarly cast doubt on the dangers of the virus and the accuracy of death certificates saying at the pandemic's start. Sounding eerily like Dr. Ioannidis, she said:

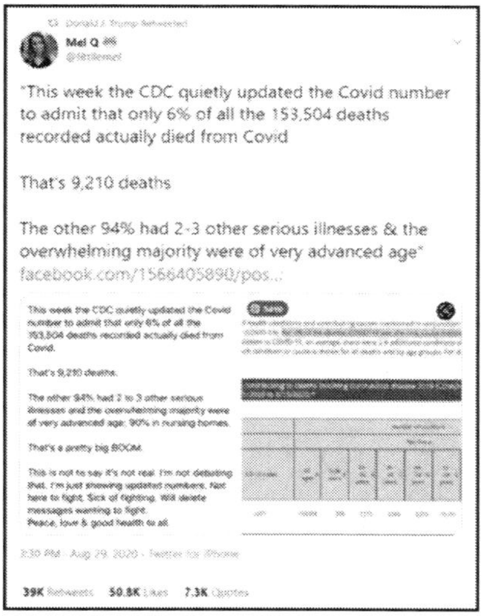

President Trump's retweet of (now deleted) Mel Q tweet – Source: Public domain

> *There is a tremendous lack of vigilance around the declaration of cause of death in hospitals... Cardiorespiratory collapse' was the phrase I was encouraged and taught to put on a death certificate if we didn't immediately know the cause of death.*[59]

President Trump would also promote similar themes, saying at a October 2020 rally:

> *Our doctors get more money if somebody dies from COVID. You know that, right? I mean, our doctors are very smart people. So what they do is they say, 'I'm sorry, but, you know, everybody dies of COVID.'*[60]

Among the most widely believed COVID conspiracies is that the death rate of the virus … has been "deliberately and greatly exaggerated"
~ Survey results

Perhaps now at least some previously perplexing behavior is a bit more understandable. Those who denied COVID's threat with their last breath *really* believed the chance of dying was "completely negligible" or "almost 0%" for everyone but grandma. Angry mobs who harassed public health officials *really* believed warnings about COVID were "completely off, just an astronomical error." Those who mocked social distancing guidelines *really* believed the "vast majority" of people "don't even realize that they have been infected." Anti-vaxxers *really* believed "death certificates often are pretty inaccurate."

And why wouldn't they *really* believe these things? They heard it all from a highly respected scientist, associated with a highly respected university, who spoke with great conviction as he told them just what they wanted to hear.

Unfortunately, false beliefs travel around the world with the click of a button and the US has become a main exporter of pandemic myths. According to one survey:

> *Among the most widely believed COVID conspiracies is that the death rate of the virus, which according to the Johns Hopkins University tracker has so far killed nearly 1.1 million people worldwide, has been "deliberately and greatly exaggerated". Nearly 60% of respondents in Nigeria said this was definitely or probably true, along with more than 40% in Greece, South Africa, Poland and Mexico. About 38% of Americans, 36% of Hungarians, 30% of Italians and 28% of Germans felt the same.*[61]

"What really caused 2,600,000 COVID-19 deaths" ~ Dr. John Ioannidis

As the pandemic progressed Dr. Ioannidis eventually accepted that millions of people actually died from the virus, but with some key caveats. In a talk from March 2021, he listed the following reasons as "what really caused 2,600,000 COVID-19 deaths":[62]

- *Social injustice, inequalities, racism, poverty*
- *Smoking*
- *Other modifiable risk factors/lifestyle (e.g., see obesity)*
- *Poor protection of nursing homes*
- *Poor adoption of effective public health measures*
- *Adoption of harmful, pro-contagion public health measures (e.g., foolish blind lockdowns)*
- *Suboptimal and harmful treatments and medical care*
- *Lack of vaccination*

From doctors to "foolish blind lockdowns" to nursing home directors to COVID victims themselves, Dr. Ioannidis felt there was a lot of blame to go around. He even said a "lack of vaccination" was at fault. Almost everyone was to blame it seems, except the virus itself and influential scientists who repeatedly minimized it in public. In fact, in an interview from July 2022, Drs. Prasad and Ioannidis had the following exchange:

> ***Dr. Prasad**: Early in the pandemic you were viciously attacked for expressing a policy viewpoint and intuition that is different from others. In a number of ways your core thesis was: in an effort—well intentioned—to control the coronavirus, we may inflict great damage on ourselves. That lesson appears to be borne out in a number of historical and recent events. How do you judge you original intuition?*

***Dr. Ioannidis**: I wish I had been wrong on this point. Unfortunately, I am afraid I might have been correct.*[63]

Chapter 4: "What can be asserted without evidence can also be dismissed without evidence"

The Claim: "It's very likely that many of them would have died anyhow, if not immediately within a very short period of time, because of these other causes of death that they had."
~ Dr. John Ioannidis

Christopher Hitchens famously said, "What can be asserted without evidence can also be dismissed without evidence." It would be perfectly legitimate to dismiss many of Dr. John Ioannidis' statements on these grounds alone. However, since some of the pandemic's most powerful and enduring myths were given credence by one of the world's most famous scientists, it's important to understand what Dr. Ioannidis got wrong and what the truth actually is.

It's a truism that extraordinary claims require extraordinary evidence. This is especially true for an influential scientist with a large megaphone making substantial allegations in public against overwhelmed frontline doctors treating patients infected with an entirely new virus. One of Dr. Ioannidis' most extraordinary claims at the pandemic's start was that "it's very likely that many of them would have died anyhow, if not immediately within a very short period of time, because of these other causes of death that they had" and that "a positive test for coronavirus does not mean necessarily that this virus is always primarily responsible for a patient's demise."[1] In other words, *these people didn't die of COVID.*

As evidence for this, Dr. Ioannidis cited a study that said "an autopsy series that tested for respiratory viruses in specimens from 57 elderly persons who died during the 2016 to 2017 influenza season."[2] The study found that "influenza viruses were detected in 18% of the specimens, while any kind of respiratory virus was found in 47%." Of course, it does not follow from this that a new and different virus, namely SARS-CoV-2, would be an "innocent bystander" in the deaths of people in 2020. If so, it would be impossible to attribute a large number of deaths to a new respiratory virus ever again.

Dr. Ioannidis was correct that nearly all COVID victims, especially during the first wave, were older people with multiple medical comorbidities. According to the National Center for Health Statistics, "for over 5% of these deaths, COVID-19 was the only cause mentioned on the death certificate. For deaths with conditions or causes in addition to COVID-19, on average, there were 4.0 additional conditions or causes per death."[3] This can make it difficult, in very limited circumstances, to tell when someone dies *with* the virus or *from* the virus.

None of this is new. Prior to the pandemic when people with underlying conditions died of natural causes, their death certificates almost always listed multiple comorbidities. How could they not? As Dr. Scott Braunstein said:

> *Any clinician who has had experience deciding on what to list as cause of death on a death certificate, as I have had to do for the past 15-plus years, understands that the diagnoses chosen involve a great deal of discretion and judgment. In most cases, there are multiple contributing diagnoses, and it is common practice to list more than one factor. Underlying diabetes or coronary artery disease are common diseases that contribute to mortality, even when the immediate trigger for death was pneumonia, influenza, or some other infectious process.*[4]

In contrast, someone who got struck by lightning and happened to test positive for SARS-CoV-2, would almost certainly not have COVID listed on their death certificate. Dr. Jeremy Faust examined over a million COVID death certificates and found that just 5,368 (0.5%) "had some kind of unnatural event (like trauma or overdose, which we call "external" deaths) listed as the underlying cause."[48] Even many of these cases were falls in elderly people, and it is entirely possible COVID was to blame. However, common sense is the most powerful refutation to the notion that large numbers of people died from mundane causes like cancer and heart disease with SARS-CoV-2 acting as an "innocent bystander."

While few COVID victims were young and healthy, it's ludicrous to expect a large percentage of the deceased would have died "immediately" or "perhaps in a few days or in a few weeks or a few months"[5] had they not contracted COVID. They were not "already dying from something else" when doctors just happened "to find a PCR positive test for SARS-CoV-2 in a nasal swab."[1] The virus did not just give a "final kick"[6] to people who were days or weeks away from dying of other causes.

Most frail 85-year-olds will still be alive in one month. That's how we get 86- and 87-year-olds. Similarly, most people with hypertension, diabetes, and obesity won't die in the next month. Though these diseases shorten lifespans, they are considered chronic conditions precisely because people live with them for many years. Of course, anyone who worked on a COVID unit saw some young and healthy people die from the virus. No demographic was completely spared during that first wave. By May 2020, 73 children in New York State alone had developed a severe COVID complication that would later be named Multisystem Inflammatory Syndrome in Children (MIS-C) and three children had already died of MIS-C in the state.[7] COVID did not completely spare children, and this was widely discussed in the news.

Moreover, if large numbers of COVID victims were just old people dying of cancer and heart disease, then hospital life would have continued as normal. It did not. There are not normally refrigerated trucks behind my hospital to store dead bodies – indeed, they are gone now. Pediatricians don't normally treat seniors and gynecologists don't normally treat men. Medical schools don't normally graduate students early to work on overflowing hospital wards. The overhead "airway team" page doesn't normally go off dozens of times per day. Dozens of people don't normally die in a single nursing home in the span of several days. The military is not normally needed to retrieve dead bodies from homes. It's normally not a challenge to find space to bury dead bodies. Hospitals don't normally need forklifts to move them. Skating rinks in Spain and rivers in India are not normally full of dead bodies. Bodies aren't normally left in the streets of Ecuador. *Something* abnormal happened. There's only one conclusion: COVID killed these patients.

When Dr. Ioannidis said that "you're not even sure that SARS-CoV-2 really did contribute to their death substantially,"[1] he could only have been referring to the fortunate people who experienced the pandemic exclusively from their laptop. Clinicians who worked with COVID patients were certain what killed them – it was COVID. He was wrong to say, "it's very hard to say how many of these people would have died anyhow and how much is the direct contribution of the virus."[5] In fact, it was *very easy* to say how many of our patients who we saw die from COVID would have "died anyhow." Virtually none of them would have "died anyhow." We know what it looks like when patients die of cancer and heart disease. It was very easy to say, "how much is the direct contribution of the virus." The virus was directly responsible for killing our patients. Everyone who worked in a hospital during this pandemic will say the same thing.

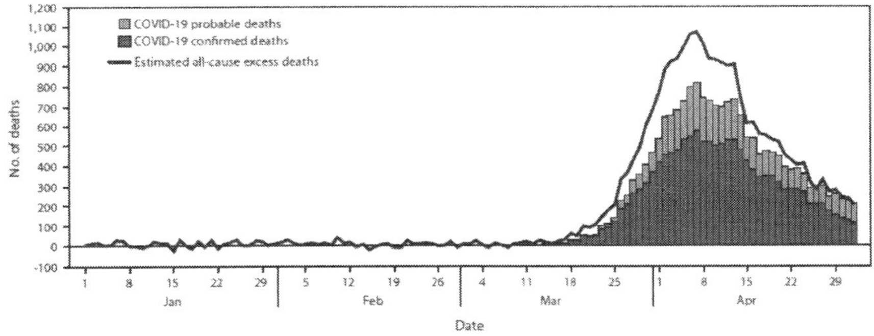

Number of laboratory-confirmed and probable COVID-19–associated deaths and total estimated excess deaths – New York City, March 11–May 2, 2020[49]

Studies of death certificates confirm the unsurprising news that most people who are said to have died of COVID actually died of COVID. According to a CDC report:

> *Among death certificates from calendar year 2020 listing COVID-19 and at least one other co-occurring diagnosis, the documentation is consistent with these deaths being attributable to COVID-19. Specifically, in 97% of 357,133 death certificates with COVID-19 and at least one other diagnosis, the documented chain-of-event and significant contributing conditions were consistent with those reported in clinical and epidemiologic studies to occur among patients with severe COVID-19–associated outcomes.*[8]

Additionally, in every state and country throughout the pandemic, excess mortality – the number of deaths from all causes above and beyond what is expected under usual conditions – perfectly mirrored COVID deaths. This again demonstrates that nearly everyone who was said to have died of COVID, almost certainly died of COVID. In fact, this suggests that COVID deaths are undercounted.

The Claim: "Death certificates have always been inaccurate, but COVID-19 maximizes the challenge of prioritizing multiple comorbidities"
~ Dr. John Ioannidis

As evidence for his claim that "Death certificates have always been inaccurate, but COVID-19 maximizes the challenge of prioritizing multiple comorbidities,"[9] Dr. Ioannidis cited two papers written before the pandemic. He never provided any evidence COVID death certificates were particularly inaccurate, nor did he provide any evidence that "financial incentives may promote coding for COVID-19." His reference for that extraordinary claim was an article from India, which merely noted that the families of frontline workers who died of COVID while on duty were given financial compensation for their sacrifice.[10] His paper contained no evidence that anyone falsified death certificates, especially in the U.S.

Dr. Ioannidis was right that "filling out death certificates can be very tricky"[1] at times, though the situation is not nearly as dire as depicted. To understand how death certificates work, let's consider a woman with a brain tumor who has a seizure while driving and gets into a nasty car crash. She undergoes several surgeries and seems to be making a good recovery. However, she later dies from a wound infection. Did she die of the wound infection, the car crash, a seizure, or her brain tumor? Of course, all of these contributed to her demise. Death certificates account for this complexity, allowing clinicians to select several causes of death in an ordered manner. According to the CDC:

> *The cause-of-death section consists of two parts. Part I is for reporting a chain of events leading directly to death, with the immediate cause of death (the final disease, injury, or complication directly*

causing death) on Line a and the underlying cause of death (the disease or injury that initiated the chain of morbid events that led directly and inevitably to death) on the lowest used line. Part II is for reporting all other significant diseases, conditions, or injuries that contributed to death but which did not result in the underlying cause of death given in Part I. The cause-of-death information should be YOUR best medical OPINION...When a number of conditions resulted in death, the physician should choose the single sequence that, in his or her opinion, best describes the process leading to death.[11]

Additionally, the CDC along with the National Center for Health Statistics put out specific guidelines to help standardize death certificates during the pandemic. They said:

An accurate count of the number of deaths due to COVID–19 infection, which depends in part on proper death certification, is critical to ongoing public health surveillance and response.[12]

It's true, though, that there's a degree of subjectivity when determining the chain of events leading directly to death. Two doctors may not fill out a death certificate in the exact same way. Though death certificates allow doctors to distinguish between a patient with terminal cancer who incidentally tested positive for SARS-CoV-2 and those who actually die of COVID, some errors have certainly been made. Moreover, during the pandemic's peak in New York City, when morgues were overwhelmed, Dr. Oxiris Barbot, the commissioner of the city's Department of Health said, "Any patient who has had a positive coronavirus test and then later dies – whether at home or in a hospital – is being counted as a coronavirus death."[13] Though there's no evidence the number is large, assuredly the COVID death tallies include *some* individuals who contracted SARS-CoV-2 and died immediately thereafter of a disease that would have killed them regardless.

Governmental agencies were aware of this problem, and many cared about getting the numbers right. The UK, for example, initially counted anyone who died at any time after a positive test, regardless of cause, as a death due to COVID. After restricting this time period to 28-days, an arbitrary time-frame, they reduced their death toll by 12%.[14] Several American municipalities also lowered their death tallies. According to a statement from one California county that lowered its death totals:

> *It is important to accurately report deaths due to COVID-19 so that residents and health officials have a more precise understanding of the impact of the pandemic and response actions in our community. Using the older definition of COVID-19 deaths, a resident who had COVID-19 but died due to another cause, like a car accident this person would be included in the total number of reported COVID-19 deaths for Alameda County. Under the updated definition of COVID-19 deaths, this person would not be included in the total because COVID-19 was not a contributing factor in the death.*[15]

It's good that governments cared about reporting accurate data and were willing to adjust their tallies when appropriate.

Dr. Ioannidis' statement that doctors who fill out death certificates "may subconsciously or unconsciously prefer to list COVID-19 as a major cause of death in the certificate, even though it may be less significant contributor if not an innocent bystander in some cases"[1] implies that doctors weren't competent enough to distinguish between someone who died from COVID and someone who was on their deathbed for another reason when they happened to test positive for SARS-CoV-2.

No one who worked on a COVID unit would agree with this. Our patients all lived in areas where the virus was spreading. They came in with the same signs, symptoms and lab results. This is the opposite of a medical mystery. They all had COVID. They didn't all die in the same way though. Some died immediately, while others lingered for months. None of our patients were deathly ill with other causes when the virus tickled their nose. They were mostly just average, older people living perfectly normal lives when they got COVID.

The vast majority would still be alive today were it not for SARS-CoV-2.

The Claim: "COVID-19 death" now includes not only "deaths by COVID-19" and "deaths with COVID-19", but even deaths "without COVID-19 documented".

~ Dr. John Ioannidis

While the majority of Americans who are said to have died of COVID tested positive for the virus, Dr. Ioannidis was correct that some patients who are listed as having died of COVID are categorized "without COVID-19 documented."[16] In other words, the death tally includes people who never tested positive for SARS-CoV-2. In NYC's first wave, for example, of the 18,879 COVID deaths, 13,831 (73%) were laboratory-confirmed COVID–associated deaths and 5,048 (27%) were probable COVID–associated deaths.[49]

While this sounds nefarious, a trip down memory lane to spring 2020 reveals this isn't as big a problem as it sounds. Though testing soon became widely available, early in the pandemic it was available for only a small fraction of patients.[17] It was never available for people who died at home and is still not widely available in many parts of the world. However, this does not necessarily mean doctors were wrong to categorize certain deaths as due to COVID without testing.

Like many viruses, SARS-CoV-2 produces a characteristic set of signs and symptoms.[18] In the words of Dr. David Oliver, "Doctors treating patients with COVID-19 over the past 12 months recognise a very different clinical syndrome in the sickest patients and a tide of cases of a kind, severity, and clinical course that we have not seen before."[19] Indeed, this novelty is what allowed Chinese ophthalmologist Dr. Li Wenliang to recognize COVID as a new disease in the first place. Dr. Wenliang, who tragically died from the virus himself,[20] was reprimanded by hospital administrators and formally admonished by the police in Wuhan for his honesty as he bravely warned the world of a new virus.

Doctors were right to put COVID as the cause of death when someone who lived where the virus was circulating developed signs of symptoms of COVID and then died gasping for air. This is true even if that person was not tested for SARS-CoV-2. As the CDC stated in its death certificate guidelines, "Ideally, testing for COVID–19 should be conducted, but it is acceptable to report COVID–19 on a death certificate without this confirmation if the circumstances are compelling within a reasonable degree of certainty."[12]

The argument that a positive test is required to diagnose COVID implies that the disease cannot exist without the test, which would be nice if it were true. It's the same logic employed by President Trump when he said, "Cases are up because we have the best testing in the world and we have the most testing."[21] Obviously, countless millions of people died of viruses before anyone even knew that viruses existed.

The Claim: "We need to be careful to dissociate deaths from COVID-19 versus deaths that happened because of the disruption induced by lockdown." ~ Dr. John Ioannidis

New York City had its first confirmed case of COVID March 1, 2020.[22] When we locked down three weeks later, an average of 16 people were dying of COVID per day. Three weeks later, hospitals were overwhelmed and 829 people were dying daily. Gradually, the deluge receded. The refrigerated trucks left and slowly the hospital returned to normal. By the middle of May, the daily death toll fell below 100 people daily. *Something* abruptly stopped the spread of the virus in New York City, and those who feel the lockdowns deserve no credit are obligated to provide a better explanation.

Dr. Ioannidis even suggested that lockdowns might have been to blame for the carnage, saying "we need to be careful to dissociate deaths from COVID-19 versus deaths that happened because of the disruption induced by lockdown."[23] He provided no evidence that lockdowns, rather than the virus, killed people *en masse* and his premise raises some challenging questions.

Why did the deaths peak just three weeks after the lockdown started? Why did the deaths decline precipitously as the lockdown dragged on, instead of rising further? What exactly, besides COVID, killed thousands of people who were asked only to stay at home. If New York City had locked down in 2019 as part of a bizarre experiment, would these nightmarish scenes of death have occurred in just three weeks? If so, what *exactly* would kill all these people in such a short period of time? Why did the deceased all have nearly identical symptoms, X-rays, and lab values? Why did people who were able to isolate rarely die? Why did the deaths come in waves, as with previous pandemics? Why did Florida's deadliest waves come in the summer of 2021 and winter of 2022, well after lockdowns ended? Why are unvaccinated people much more likely to die than vaccinated and boosted people?[24] Why was China, which had nearly 3 years of exceedingly strict lockdowns, spared horrific scenes of mass death until they ended their Zero COVID approach in December 2022? What about New Zealand, which had 7 weeks of a national stay-at-home order?[25] Why did New Zealand's excess mortality *decline* during their lockdown while this metric spiked in countries with uncontrolled spread of the virus?[26]

Again, the answers to these questions all point in the same obvious direction: the virus, not lockdowns, killed a lot of people. In fact, one analysis from May 2020 found:

> *36,000 fewer people would have died if social distancing measures had been put in place across the U.S. just one week earlier.*[27]

The Claim: "The number of person-years lost, how many years of life are being lost, is much less than even what the number of deaths would suggest."
~ Dr. John Ioannidis

Even when Dr. Ioannidis acknowledged that the virus killed people, he minimized this loss of life saying, "the number of person-years lost, how many years of life are being lost, is much less than even what the number of deaths would suggest."[5] While most COVID victims were elderly, doctors who worked with COVID patients know many others had their lives shortened by several decades. As Dr. Nina Shapiro said:

> *Those who are in terrific shape, are young and have no prior illness can, indeed, become critically ill from COVID. Many have died and many will die.*[28]

Research supports the observations of frontline doctors. One study from October 2020 calculated that the virus had stolen 2.5 million years of potential life in the US.[29] Just under half of these years were taken from people younger than 65 years. As the paper's author, Dr. Stephen J. Elledge said, "COVID-19 has wiped out millions of years of productive, active, and happy existence."[30] Later variants would pose a greater risk to younger people, especially the Delta variant. In fact, the number of years of life lost for each COVID death increased by 36% in 2021 compared to 2020.[50]

Another study published March 2022 calculated the virus had stolen 3.9 million years of life away from Americans and the average COVID-19 victim lost over 9 years of life.[31] Not all COVID victims were 90-year-olds with advanced cancer, only days away from dying, when they happened to test positive for SARS-CoV-2. In the words of Dr. Utibe Essien, "These are everyday people who are dying. They're losing time with their kids, their grandkids, their opportunities to build their futures."[29]

He's right. Beyond that, the casual dismissal of deaths in elderly people doesn't square well with the philosophy of "protecting the vulnerable".

The Claim: Doctors were "just going crazy, and intubating people who did not have to be intubated" ~ Dr. John Ioannidis

During his interview with Dr. Prasad on the *Plenary Session* podcast in February 2021, Dr. Ioannidis said ventilators were instrumental in the death of COVID patients, stating doctors were "just going crazy, and intubating people who did not have to be intubated"[32] leading to their demise. However, he never provided evidence supporting this claim, because no such evidence exists.

There are two reasons why people blamed excessive intubations for the death of COVID patients. The first of these was Dr. Cameron Kyle-Sidell, an emergency medicine and critical care doctor from New York City. He felt during New York's first wave that his patients "looked a lot more like they had altitude sickness than pneumonia,"[33] and reasonably wondered if old ventilation strategies might need to change for this new virus. Dr. Kyle-Sidell did not spread any conspiracy theories, but he gained a lot of attention early in the pandemic, leading many people to think doctors were intubating too many patients.

The second reason why intubations were blamed for patients' dying was the sad fact that so few ventilated patients survived that first wave. A study of 2,634 COVID patients from April 2020 found that many intubated patients died, sadly.[34] Dr. Muriel Gillick, a geriatric and palliative care doctor, said that "contrary to the impression that if extremely ill patients with COVID-19 are treated with ventilators they will live and if they are not, they will die, the reality is far different."[33]

That people on ventilators often died does not mean ventilators killed patients, obviously. Some patients with diabetes believe insulin causes blindness and leads to amputations.[35] Of course, they are reversing cause and effect. Patients with severe diabetes are more likely to need insulin and they are more likely to suffer complications from their disease such as vision loss and amputations.

This logical failure repeated itself during the pandemic. The first wave found the most vulnerable people, many of whom became gravely ill with COVID. These patients were intubated and most died. It's tragic, but without a vaccine these people never stood a chance. Most of the world found that out over the next few months, and the pandemic's deadliest month came eight months after the first wave in New York City, when doctors supposedly killed patients through premature intubations. Imagine if the only thing doctors needed to do to save millions of lives around the world was to not intubate people. I think we would have figured that out and the pandemic would have unfolded very differently.

More formal evidence of the safety of intubation in COVID patients is available. A meta-analysis of 12 studies found:

> *The synthesized evidence of almost 9000 patients suggests that timing of intubation may have no effect on mortality and morbidity of critically ill patients with COVID-19. These results might justify a wait-and-see approach, which may lead to fewer intubations.*[36]

Though this meta-analysis was published after Dr. Ioannidis made his accusation, all 12 studies it reviewed were published beforehand.

A subsequent study unsurprisingly found that intubated patients died at a higher rate, but "there was not a significant association between mortality and timing of intubation."[37] Another study found that "early intubation is associated with improved survival rates" in patients with severe COVID.[38] One study that compared COVID pneumonia with other causes of severe pneumonia concluded that:

> *Mechanically ventilated patients with severe COVID-19 pneumonia had similar mortality rates as patients with other causes of severe pneumonia but longer times to liberation from mechanical ventilation. Mechanical ventilation use in COVID-19 pneumonia should follow the same evidence-based guidelines as for any pneumonia.*[51]

Dr. Kyle-Sidell might have been on to something in those pandemic's first days. Maybe some patients could have been spared intubation, but there's no evidence that anyone lost their lives because of it.

Even if it had turned out that intubating COVID patients was detrimental, this does not imply that doctors could have known it at the time. Doctors cannot be blamed for not knowing how to perfectly combat a new virus from the first instant it swamped their hospital. This is like expecting all nursing homes to perfectly protect their residents from day 1. Of course, there was going to be a learning curve. That's why it would have been a disaster had the virus been allowed to spread more widely at the pandemic's start. Remember, you had a neurologist-psychiatrist like myself, making decisions about whether or not to amputate an ischemic leg.

Though the notion that COVID patients were dying of premature intubations was scarcely more than an internet rumor, it had real world consequences. Dr. Alison Pittard, an intensivist in the UK, spoke about the effect conspiracies had on her patients saying:

> *They think if they do not go on a ventilator, they have got a better chance of surviving, because once they go on a ventilator they are going to die irrespective. And of course that is not correct because if you are faced with a patient who needs to go on a ventilator*

> *... if they don't go on a ventilator then the chances are that they will die. So, that is almost saying there is a 100% chance of dying. Whereas if they go on a ventilator then they will have a 40% chance of dying.*[39]

Frontline doctors certainly can't be blamed for the deaths of one class of patients. According to the New York City Fire Department, "in the first five days of April, 1,125 people were pronounced dead in their homes or on the street in New York City, more than eight times the deaths recorded during the same period in 2019."[13] While not all of these were COVID victims, many certainly were. Perhaps some could have lived had they made it to the hospital. Maybe they stayed away because they feared doctors would go "crazy" intubating them.

"It's entirely possible that there are millions of uncounted COVID-19 deaths."
~ Dr. Gideon Meyerowitz-Katz

Of course, undercounting COVID deaths is a significant problem too, and some states have added thousands of deaths to their tallies to address this problem. Undercounting was particularly a problem early in the pandemic when healthcare systems were overwhelmed, large numbers of people died at home, and testing was scarce or nonexistent.

In some parts of the country, doctors may have been reluctant to attribute deaths to COVID under these circumstances. One funeral home director said about the death certificates of likely COVID victims, "I've seen it many times where the doctors will just leave it off. They're exhausted, they're busy, and they have a funeral director hounding them."[40] One coroner from Louisiana said families have discouraged him from putting COVID on the death certificate. He said, "In 2020, getting COVID, or dying from COVID, or being a family member that had COVID, was a scarlet letter. It was shunned."[41] He admitted to not putting COVID on the death certificate at times saying:

> *I can recall a guy who had COVID symptoms; his*

> *X-ray looked like COVID because I saw it. And the guy says, 'You're not sticking a swab in my nose,' and he died a few days later. That guy had COVID, but I didn't call it COVID.*

One study that looked at excess mortality found that, due to both "pervasive underreporting," and deaths caused by "indirect mechanisms," there are many deaths missing from the official numbers.[42] The study found that:

> *Deaths during the COVID-19 pandemic have been primarily monitored through death certificates containing reference to COVID-19. This approach has missed more than 170,000 deaths related to the pandemic between 2020 and 2021.*

Additionally, to this day, some COVID deaths may go unrecognized. Even mild cases can elevate the risk of heart attacks and strokes.[43] The risk of blood clots remains elevated for nearly a year after infection.[44] How many people who died of these mundane causes would still be alive were it not for their SARS-CoV-2 infection?

Undercounting deaths is likely a much more significant problem in other parts of the world. As epidemiologist Gideon Meyerowitz-Katz wrote:

> *We probably aren't overcounting deaths on a global scale by very much. While there are almost certainly some deaths that are being inappropriately counted as being caused by COVID-19 that were really due to something else, the number is probably enormously outweighed by undercounting. It's plausible that the true global toll of COVID-19 is 10% lower than we think, but it's quite likely to be 50% higher or more. Given the data from some developing nations, it's entirely possible that there are millions of uncounted COVID-19 deaths.*[45]

In December 2022, the World Health Organization, published a paper in *Nature* that COVID and its secondary consequences caused

13.3-16.6 million excess deaths from 2020 to 2021, which was 2.74 times more than that been reported previously.[46] According a news article on this paper:

> *The 20 countries with the highest estimated excess deaths represent almost half of the global population and account for 80 per cent of the estimated global excess deaths from 2020 to 2021.*
>
> *These countries are Bangladesh, Brazil, Colombia, Egypt, India, Indonesia, Iran, Italy, Mexico, Nigeria, Pakistan, Peru, the Philippines, Poland, the Russian Federation, South Africa, the United Kingdom, Turkey, Ukraine and the United States of America.*[47]

In the end, COVID turned out to be more consequential than "an NBA game between the two most indifferent teams."[2]

Chapter 5: "By rebuilding population immunity among the least at-risk, moreover, we help buffer risk for those most vulnerable."

Even accounting for the fact that New Zealand is an island, it took a very different approach to the pandemic compared to the U.S. and most of the world. For two years, New Zealand used periodic lockdowns to squelch cases, allowing them to avoid major outbreaks until most of their citizens were vaccinated. COVID cases exploded there after Omicron forced them to abandon their Zero COVID policy and people started dying of COVID. However, their overall death rate is much less than the U.S. If the U.S. had New Zealand's death rate, over 800,000 people would still be alive today.

Though many people are still alive in New Zealand today because they postponed the inevitable, some doctors feel their approach was completely wrong. I'll revisit New Zealand at the end of this chapter.

"When most of a population is immune to an infectious disease, this provides indirect protection – or population immunity (also called herd immunity or herd protection) – to those who are not immune to the disease."

~ Johns Hopkins University

First, it's necessary to understand the concept of herd immunity. An article from Johns Hopkins University describes herd immunity as "When most of a population is immune to an infectious disease, this provides indirect protection – or population immunity (also called herd immunity or herd protection) – to those who are not immune to the disease".[1] The article gives examples of measles, mumps, polio, and chickenpox as diseases for which herd immunity exists in the U.S. Outbreaks of these diseases can still occur in pockets of unvaccinated people, but due to herd immunity, they fade away and don't spiral out of control.

Herd immunity marks a slowdown in the transmission of a virus in a population, where a single case results in less than one new case, versus a single case resulting in more than one new case. Notably, if the infection prevalence is high, there will still be significant onward transmission, just fewer cases tomorrow than today on average. The pathway to herd immunity has the potential to be very ugly.

The herd immunity threshold depends on both the virus and the population. A more contagious virus will have a higher herd immunity threshold. The road to herd immunity shortens with every person who becomes immune, either through the virus or a vaccine, so long as the immune response is robust and durable. Of course, newborns will continue to be vulnerable, and no population has ever achieved herd immunity to a virus through natural infection alone.

People's behavior also matters. A community where choirs regularly gather in small, poorly ventilated rooms will have a higher herd immunity threshold than a village of isolated hermits. In the words of Dr. James Hamblin, "if we all sealed ourselves in isolation pods today," COVID could not spread and "there would be no more deaths."[2]

We'll know the U.S. has reached herd immunity for COVID when there are sporadic, limited outbreaks here and there, but no sustained transmission of the virus, as is currently the case for measles and chickenpox. We're not close to this situation now with COVID. A headline from December 5, 2022, read "Thanksgiving Kicked Off a COVID Surge, and It's Slamming U.S. Hospitals Already Battling the Tripledemic: 'It's the Perfect Storm for a Terrible Holiday Season.'"[3] Many scientists believe herd immunity is not possible for SARS-CoV-2.

"I'm not sure how to convey this message in a half-acceptable way. But, if the objective were to send SARCoV2 into endemicity, then healthy kids have to be exposed to the virus, ideally earlier than later. This is not 'eugenism'; it is bog-standard infection disease epidemiology."

~ Dr. Francois Balloux

The notion that children should contract vaccine-preventable diseases to protect vulnerable adults precedes COVID and was one of the main arguments anti-vaxxers used against the chickenpox vaccine. According to their logic, children with chickenpox provide an "immune boost" to adults, who are then less likely to get shingles, a painful and potentially devastating disorder that can cause blindness[4] and cardiovascular disease.[5] For this reason, anti-vaxxers claim it is good when unvaccinated children contract chickenpox, generation after generation, forevermore.

The evidence on whether or not children with chickenpox protect adults against shingles is conflicting. One study found that adults exposed to children with chickenpox had a moderately lower rate of shingles,[6] while several other have found that vaccinating children against chickenpox did not lead to a higher rate of shingles in adults.[7] However, even if children sick with chickenpox perfectly protect adults against shingles, infecting children to protect their older relatives is a moral abomination, especially since safe and effective vaccines are available for both chickenpox and shingles. Children have the right to be protected against diseases that can harm them. This didn't used to be controversial amongst doctors.

While very few children suffer serious consequences from chickenpox, in the U.S. it killed about 100 people per year[8] and hospitalized 10,500 more before the vaccine.[9] Moreover, the chickenpox vaccine drastically lowers children's risk of developing shingles later in life.[10] Children who have been vaccinated against chickenpox won't need their infected grandchildren to protect them from shingles.

Could you imagine having to explain to a child with a horrible case of chickenpox that she was left unvaccinated to possibly reduce her grandmother's risk of shingles by a small amount? Indeed, young children have died of chickenpox because their governmental health agencies felt they should be used as shields for adults. In an article titled "Could the Death of My Daughter Have Been Prevented?" a nurse, Angie Bunce-Mason, described the death of her 3-year-old daughter from chickenpox.[11] "I had the impression until Elana became ill that chickenpox was never dangerous," she said. The UK, where Elana lived, is one of few countries where the chickenpox vaccine is not part of the routine pediatric vaccine schedule. Ms. Bunce-Mason concluded by saying:

> *My goal now is to talk with other parents about the*

> *potential complications of chickenpox and to let people know that there is a vaccine that helps protect against the disease. As a mum, I don't want the death of Elana to be wasted – I want others to be able to benefit from our experience.*

The U.S. has vaccinated children against chickenpox since 1995, meaning the vaccine has saved around 2,700 lives.[12] Future generations of doctors will see chickenpox and shingles as often as I've seen measles and polio. That's a big deal, and if vaccinating children slightly increases my risk of shingles, I am happy to take that risk to protect future generations.

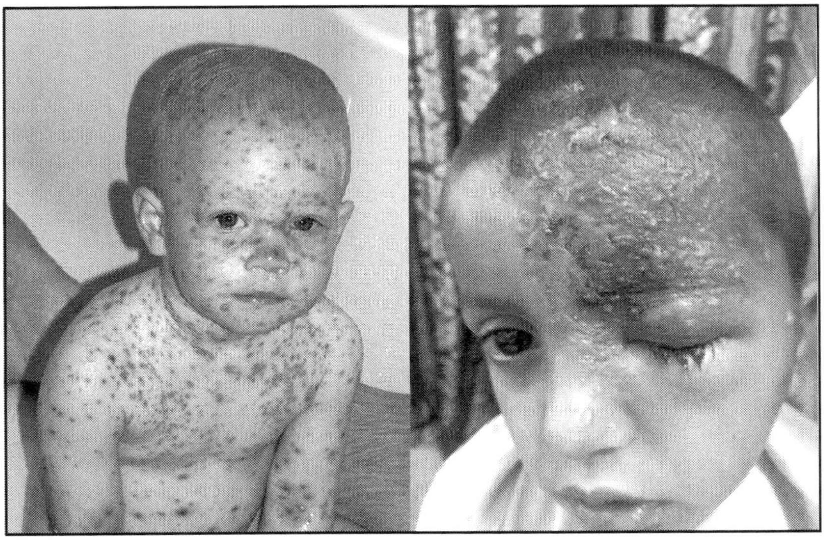

Chickenpox[177] and shingles,[178] both of which can be prevented by a vaccine. Image source: Wikimedia Commons, the free media repository

Outside of the UK, the idea that unvaccinated children should contract potentially deadly viruses to protect vulnerable adults was previously relegated to the fringes of the anti-vaccine movement. However, during the pandemic this ethos became mainstream and influenced governments around the world.

Doctors were integral to this effort. In February 2022, immediately after the Omicron variant hospitalized and killed a record number of children, Dr. Vinay Prasad and Allison Krug wrote glowingly of this philosophy in their essay, "Should We Let Children Catch Omicron?" saying:

> *Shielding kids from exposure only increases their future risk. This is partly why the UK does not vaccinate against chickenpox. Serious complications from the disease are rare among children, and the circulating virus allows adults to be naturally boosted against reactivation-driven shingles. By rebuilding population immunity among the least at-risk, moreover, we help buffer risk for those most vulnerable.*[13]

This is using infected children as human shields for vulnerable adults, at a time when the youngest children – those most at risk from COVID – were all unvaccinated against it.

Dr. John Ioannidis also wrote about the societal benefits of sick, unvaccinated children in an article titled "COVID-19 in Children and University Students." After presenting an argument for vaccinating young people based on "indirect benefits to other age groups and society at large,"[14] he invented an imagined world where children are vaccinated but not adults, and said:

> *However, the opposite arguments also exist, e.g. vaccinating the youngest age strata may shift infection to higher ages with high fatality especially as many elderly people in many countries are still not vaccinated and some vaccinated elderly have insufficient immune responses. Vaccinated people may still transmit the virus; given that vaccinations make infections milder/asymptomatic and people markedly increase exposures after vaccination (a risk compensatory behavior), vulnerable people may be exposed more frequently to vaccinated infected youth who are unaware of their infection.*

Via this strange reasoning, the fact that "vaccinations make infections milder/asymptomatic" is a strike *against* them. It's not enough for children to merely contract SARS-CoV-2, in order to protect elderly people, children must also feel really sick.

The notion that sick children should serve as human shields was also popular overseas. Some members of the UK's Joint Committee on Vaccination and Immunisation (JCVI) felt "that natural infection in children could have substantial long-term benefits on COVID-19 in the UK."[15] According to minutes from their meeting:

> *There is an argument for allowing the virus to circulate amongst children which could provide broader immunity to the children and boost immunity in adults...Members considered that in the absence of vaccination, future generations would be exposed to COVID-19 in childhood, with a relatively mild disease. This early infection would then provide protection against severe disease throughout life. Circulation of COVID-19 in childhood could therefore periodically boost immunity in adults through exposure.*

A sociologist who advised the JCVI, Robert Dingwall, previously voiced this opinion writing that school closures may, "have an immediate cost in terms of depriving children of the opportunity to acquire immunity to the infection."[16] He also said that "given the low risk of COVID for most teenagers, it is not immoral to think that they may be better protected by natural immunity generated through infection than by asking them to take the possible risk of a vaccine."[17]

At least Mr. Dingwall can't be accused of believing COVID is an "opportunity" only for children. He also felt death from COVID might be an unexpected gift for elderly people. He said:

> *There is, though, a first question: who says it is desirable to prevent every death regardless of the cost? My impression is that the loudest voices are coming from young or middle-aged people who have yet to accept that death is a normal part of life. It comes to all of us in good time. A wise person would, of course, prefer to die later rather than sooner, but they might also consider that some deaths are easier to bear than others. It is not for nothing that pneumonia was described as 'the old man's friend' in the days before antibiotics. Contrary to some media*

> *coverage, no-one is advocating that any old person is abandoned to die without professional nursing care. However, we should acknowledge that many frail old people might see COVID-19 infection as a relatively peaceful end compared with, say, several years of dementia or some cancers.*[18]

We'll see if Mr. Dingall chooses to contract COVID to ease his own passing when the time comes.

Dr. Francois Balloux, the chair of computational biology at the University College London, even said parents "have to" expose their youngest children to the virus. He said:

> *I'm not sure how to convey this message in a half-acceptable way. But, if the objective were to send SARCoV2 into endemicity, then healthy kids have to be exposed to the virus, ideally earlier than later. This is not 'eugenism'; it is bog-standard infection disease epidemiology.*[19]

He would also add, "Vaccinating healthy ≤ 12 year olds makes hardly difference to them directly, however we look at it."[20]

The notion that society benefits from sick children even appeared in prestigious medical journals. An editorial in the *BMJ* said:

> *Should childhood infection (and re-exposures in adults) continue to be typically mild, childhood vaccination will not be necessary to halt the pandemic...Once most adults are vaccinated, circulation of SARS-CoV-2 may in fact be desirable, as it is likely to lead to primary infection early in life when disease is mild, followed by booster re-exposures throughout adulthood as transmission blocking immunity wanes but disease blocking immunity remains high. This would keep reinfections mild and immunity up to date.*[21]

The idea that unvaccinated children and young adults should get infected with and feel sick from a potentially deadly virus to theoretically protect vulnerable adults became mainstream during the pandemic.

"The time to smoke is when you are a teen." ~ Mr. Jeffrey Tucker

No movement did more to encourage the mass infection of unvaccinated children and young adults than the Great Barrington Declaration (GBD), which was so named because its sponsor, a libertarian think tank called the American Institute for Economic Research (AIER), is headquartered in Great Barrington, Massachusetts.

The three signers of the GBD were: Dr. Sunetra Gupta, a professor of theoretical epidemiology at Oxford; Dr. Jay Bhattacharya, a medical school graduate turned health economist at Stanford; and Dr. Martin Kulldorff, a Swedish biostatistician who, at the time, was a professor of medicine at Harvard. Dr. Stefan Baral, a physician epidemiologist at Johns Hopkins, participated remotely in a 2-hour discussion on October 3, 2020, that led to the GBD.[22] Though Dr. Baral said "I did understand and agree with its start points," he ultimately did not sign the GBD, saying he had "differing perspectives on what to do."[23]

Three journalists – John Tamny, Jeanne Lenzer, and David Zweig – and a camera crew were also present at the initial meeting. This doesn't normally happen when epidemiologists get together to talk shop. The whole thing was a polished, choreographed spectacle, and their initial discussion has been viewed 162,000 times on *YouTube*.[22]

The symbiosis between medical professionals and other interests was an inauspicious start to a document that would come to influence much of our pandemic response. In an article titled "COVID-19 and the New Merchants of Doubt," Drs. Gavin Yamey and David Gorski wrote:

> *This declaration arose out of a conference hosted by the American Institute for Economic Research (AIER), and has been heavily promoted by the AIER, a libertarian, climate-denialist, free market think tank that receives "a large bulk of its funding from its own investment activities, not least in fossil fuels, energy*

> *utilities, tobacco, technology and consumer goods." The AIER's American Investment Services Inc. runs a private fund that is valued at $284,492,000, with holdings in a wide range of fossil fuel companies (e.g. Chevron, ExxonMobil) and in the tobacco giant Philip Morris International. The AIER has also received funding from the Charles Koch Foundation, which was founded and is chaired by the right-wing billionaire industrialist known for promoting climate change denial and opposing regulations on business. Koch linked organisations have also opposed public health measures to curb the spread of COVID-19.*[24]

The former editorial director of the AIER and one of the chief organizers of the GBD is a Mr. Jeffrey Tucker. Mr. Tucker did more than assemble the epidemiologists, journalists, and camera crew. He said he was "there while it was being drafted" and "I made a couple of suggestions here and there."[25] I am confident the final draft of the GBD aligned with Mr. Tucker's worldview.

According to his *Wikipedia* entry, Mr. Tucker:

> *Is an American libertarian writer, publisher, entrepreneur and advocate of anarcho-capitalism and Bitcoin. For many years he worked for Ron Paul, the Mises Institute, and Lew Rockwell. With the American Institute for Economic Research (AIER) he organized efforts against COVID-19 restrictions starting in 2020, and he founded the Brownstone Institute think tank in 2021 to continue such efforts.*[26]

His *Wikipedia* page also contains some troubling information. It says:

> *According to a 2000 report by the Southern Poverty Law Center (SPLC), Tucker wrote for publications of the League of the South, a group the SPLC considers neo-Confederate and white supremacist.*

Most people would also find Mr. Tucker's attitude towards

children disturbing. In 2016, he wrote an essay titled "Let the Kids Work," in which he said:

> *The Washington Post ran a beautiful photo montage of children at work from 100 years ago. I get it. It's not supposed to be beautiful. It's supposed to be horrifying. I'm looking at these kids. They are scruffy, dirty, and tired. No question.*
>
> *But I also think about their inner lives. They are working in the adult world, surrounded by cool bustling things and new technology. They are on the streets, in the factories, in the mines, with adults and with peers, learning and doing. They are being valued for what they do, which is to say being valued as people. They are earning money.*
>
> *Whatever else you want to say about this, it's an exciting life. You can talk about the dangers of coal mining or selling newspapers on the street. But let's not pretend that danger is something that every young teen wants to avoid...*
>
> *And I compare it to any scene you can observe today at the local public school, with 30 kids sitting in desks bored out of their minds, creativity and imagination beaten out of their brains, forbidden from earning money and providing value to others, learning no skills, and knowing full well that they are supposed to do this until they are 22 years old if they have the slightest chance of being a success in life: desk after desk, class after class, lecture after lecture, test after test, a confined world without end...*
>
> *If kids were allowed to work and compulsory school attendance was abolished, the jobs of choice would be at Chick-Fil-A and WalMart. And they would be fantastic jobs too, instilling in young people a work ethic, which is the inner drive to succeed, and an*

> *awareness of attitudes that make enterprise work for all. It would give them skills and discipline that build character, and help them become part of a professional network.*[27]

In another article, Mr. Tucker discussed why teenagers should be encouraged to smoke. He wrote:

> *The time to smoke is when you are a teen. It's when your lungs are strong, and your body is prepared to fight back the ill effects. It's also when you can gain the maximum advantage of the fact that smoking is very cool and enjoyable. I see no reason why parents shouldn't encourage it, while warning that they will probably have to stop after graduating college.*
>
> *And of course this is opposite of what the government says! The anti-smoking campaigns for young people are based on its supposed addictive quality. The fear is that once you start as a teen, you will never stop. But I've never understood what is meant by addictive. It's not like cigarettes take away your free will.*[28]

Mr. Tucker, who wants my daughter to drop out of school so she can smoke after her shift at Chick-Fil-A, greatly influenced America's COVID response, especially with regards to children. He "made a couple of suggestions here and there."[25]

"The most compassionate approach that balances the risks and benefits of reaching herd immunity, is to allow those who are at minimal risk of death to live their lives normally to build up immunity to the virus through natural infection, while better protecting those who are at highest risk."

~The Great Barrington Declaration

The GBD was published on October 4, 2020. The entirety of the GBD says:

As infectious disease epidemiologists and public health scientists we have grave concerns about the damaging physical and mental health impacts of the prevailing COVID-19 policies, and recommend an approach we call Focused Protection.

Coming from both the left and right, and around the world, we have devoted our careers to protecting people. Current lockdown policies are producing devastating effects on short and long-term public health. The results (to name a few) include lower childhood vaccination rates, worsening cardiovascular disease outcomes, fewer cancer screenings and deteriorating mental health – leading to greater excess mortality in years to come, with the working class and younger members of society carrying the heaviest burden. Keeping students out of school is a grave injustice.

Keeping these measures in place until a vaccine is available will cause irreparable damage, with the underprivileged disproportionately harmed.

Fortunately, our understanding of the virus is growing. We know that vulnerability to death from COVID-19 is more than a thousand-fold higher in the old and infirm than the young. Indeed, for children, COVID-19 is less dangerous than many other harms, including influenza.

As immunity builds in the population, the risk of infection to all – including the vulnerable – falls. We know that all populations will eventually reach herd immunity – i.e. the point at which the rate of new infections is stable – and that this can be assisted by (but is not dependent upon) a vaccine. Our goal should therefore be to minimize mortality and social harm until we reach herd immunity.

> *The most compassionate approach that balances the risks and benefits of reaching herd immunity, is to allow those who are at minimal risk of death to live their lives normally to build up immunity to the virus through natural infection, while better protecting those who are at highest risk. We call this Focused Protection.*
>
> *Adopting measures to protect the vulnerable should be the central aim of public health responses to COVID-19. By way of example, nursing homes should use staff with acquired immunity and perform frequent testing of other staff and all visitors. Staff rotation should be minimized. Retired people living at home should have groceries and other essentials delivered to their home. When possible, they should meet family members outside rather than inside. A comprehensive and detailed list of measures, including approaches to multi-generational households, can be implemented, and is well within the scope and capability of public health professionals.*
>
> *Those who are not vulnerable should immediately be allowed to resume life as normal. Simple hygiene measures, such as hand washing and staying home when sick should be practiced by everyone to reduce the herd immunity threshold. Schools and universities should be open for in-person teaching. Extracurricular activities, such as sports, should be resumed. Young low-risk adults should work normally, rather than from home. Restaurants and other businesses should open. Arts, music, sport and other cultural activities should resume. People who are more at risk may participate if they wish, while society as a whole enjoys the protection conferred upon the vulnerable by those who have built up herd immunity.*[29]

The GBD was based on the fact that COVID is much less fatal

for younger people than for older people. As they put it, "for people under the age of 70, the infection survival rate is 99.95%",[30] though 5 out of a thousand people dying is not a low death rate. Its core premise was called "focused protection," which meant protecting the vulnerable while encouraging everyone else to live as if there were no pandemic. They said:

> *For older people, COVID-19 is a deadly disease that should be met with overwhelming resources aimed at protecting them wherever they are, whether in nursing homes, at their own home, in the workplace, or in multi-generational homes. For the non-vulnerable, who face far greater harm from the lockdowns than they do from COVID-19 infection risk, the lockdowns should be lifted and – for those who so decide – normal life resumed.*

The authors of the GBD abhorred lockdowns, which they said, "shift infection risk from the professional class to the working class."[31] Instead, they claimed it wouldn't be hard to "shift infection risk from high-risk older adults to low-risk younger adults." They claimed that if hundreds of millions of non-vulnerable Americans got COVID at the same time, herd immunity would arrive, and the pandemic would end in a matter of *months* with minimal loss of life, so long as the vulnerable were protected. They wrote:

> *When herd immunity is reached, they can live normally again with minimal risks. How long that takes depends on the strategy used. If age-wide lockdown measures are used to try and suppress the disease, it could take a year or two or three, making it very difficult for older people to protect themselves for that long. If focused protection is used, it will likely only take 3 to 6 months.*

This notion that the pandemic could end this quickly was an incredibly optimistic message, and the authors of the GBD were eager to share it widely. For example, on December 24, 2020, just after vaccinations began, Dr. Kulldorff tweeted:

> *If the young live normal lives, some will be infected, but their risk is less than from lockdown collateral damage. Pandemic will then be naturally over in 3-6 months.*[32]

Although the non-pharmaceutical interventions they opposed were widely used to control many previous outbreaks, including the 1918 flu pandemic, the authors of the GBD repeatedly claimed their Declaration followed the "basic principles of public health."[33] In reality, no one had ever tried to stop a virus by spreading that virus, and humanity had never before achieved herd immunity through the mass infection of unvaccinated, young people.

Newspaper headlines show the widespread use of non-pharmaceutical interventions during the 1918 Flu Epidemic.[179] *Image source: Wikimedia Commons, the free media repository*

The authors of the GBD acknowledged that a vaccine was potentially just around the corner, writing that a vaccine "will arrive somewhere between 2 months from now and never."[31] However, they felt that "current lockdown policies are producing devastating effects on short and long-term public health"[29] and "keeping these measures in place until a vaccine is available will cause irreparable damage." Though Dr. Kulldorff tweeted in August 2020 that "the best way to get herd immunity is through a vaccine,"[34] the GBD itself said an eventual vaccine would be useful only for "older high-risk people as well as their care givers, such as hospital and nursing home staff."[31] Consistent with their belief that natural immunity led to permanent immunity, they said "those who have already had COVID-19 do not need to be vaccinated."

Though the GBD discouraged people from actively seeking out the virus, they felt not vulnerable people had a moral duty to live normally, ensuring they would soon contract COVID. In July 2020, Dr. Gupta said "We have to share the guilt. We have to share the responsibility. And we have to take on board certain risks ourselves in order to fulfill our obligations and to uphold the social contract."[35]

Dr. Kulldorff said young people should think of themselves as soldiers, writing in August 2020:

> *Is it age discrimination when young people take the small risks needed to protect the older more vulnerable members of society? Yes, for sure, but prior generations took much larger risks. As a society we should appreciate young adults who help generate herd immunity by living normal lives and keeping society afloat. Thank you, thank you, thank you. When people throw misguided complaints at you, falsely claiming that you are endangering others, remember that the opposite is true. Also, think of your grandfather. While risking his life fighting in World War II, he had much worse things thrown at him...That weakness is the near inability of the virus to kill younger people. Hence, it is the young adults among us that must stand in the front line as we fight this enemy. If not, we will have many more casualties than necessary...*
>
> *COVID-19 is a formidable enemy, and in any war, one must take advantage of the opponent's weaknesses. That weakness is the near inability of the virus to kill younger people. Hence, it is the young adults among us that must stand in the front line as we fight this enemy.*[36]

According to the authors of the GBD, it wasn't just acceptable for young, unvaccinated people to risk death to protect their grandparents, it was their moral obligation. They were soldiers on a mission to spread SARS-CoV-2 – a sort of Team COVID Army – and their duty required them to forgo vaccination for the sake of "natural immunity." Young, healthy people who stayed home weren't just selfish. They were to blame for prolonging the pandemic and causing "many more casualties than necessary."

Thousands of scientists would eventually sign the GBD, though the signatory list included many fake signatures, such as "Dr. Johnny Bananas", "Dr. Person Fakename", and "Professor Cominic Dummings."[37] One real signature was from Dr. Cody Meissner, a professor of pediatrics at Tufts Medical Center, who said in an interview on October 20, 2020:

> *We're beginning to think more about the consequences of that fairly dramatic step. Science needs to have a dialogue, have a discussion about the pros and cons of opening our society. And the longer we delay that conversation, the more harm that we're causing.*[38]

The article in which that quote appeared ended by saying:

> *The Institute for Health Metrics and Evaluation at the University of Washington estimates that if 40 percent of Americans were to get infected, about 800,000 people would die.*

Indeed, 800,000 Americans have died of COVID since that prediction was made.[39]

"If it's true that the novel coronavirus would kill millions without shelter-in-place orders and quarantines, then the extraordinary measures being carried out in cities and states around the country are surely justified."

~ Dr. Jay Bhattacharya

Though he did not sign the GBD, saying that he did not believe in science by petition, nearly all of its main themes can be found in Dr.

Ioannidis' comments from the spring of 2020. In an interview from April 2020, he minimized the virus's risk to young people saying, "For someone who is less than 65 and has no underlying diseases, the risk is completely negligible…it seems that these deaths are extremely exceptional."[40]

In his *STAT* article from March 2020 he warned of "draconian countermeasures" and warned they could lead to "financial crisis, unrest, civil strife, war, and a meltdown of the social fabric."[41] He speculated that "the majority of the extra deaths may not be due to coronavirus but to other common diseases and conditions such as heart attacks, strokes, trauma, bleeding, and the like that are not adequately treated." He likened lockdowns to "an elephant being attacked by a house cat. Frustrated and trying to avoid the cat, the elephant accidentally jumps off a cliff and dies." He thought that comparisons to the 1918 pandemic were overwrought. He wrote that measures to control the virus may "backfire" and lamented that "school closures may also diminish the chances of developing herd immunity in an age group that is spared serious disease."

Like Dr. Ioannidis, all three authors of the GBD greatly underestimated the virus in 2020. In September 2020, in response to the question "*Is there anybody that thinks COVID-19 represents a significant threat in terms of overwhelming hospitals in the United States*?" Dr. Kulldorff responded with a simple "No."[42] No one was vaccinated at that time, and hospitals were overwhelmed multiple times after this. 900,000 Americans have since died of COVID.[39]

After receiving almost £90,000 from a conservative donor, Dr. Gupta led a modeling study and claimed in March 2020 that between 36%-68% of the UK had been already contracted COVID.[43] In May 2020 she gave an interview titled "Sunetra Gupta: COVID-19 is On the Way Out," in which she said:

> *In almost every context we've seen the epidemic grow, turn around and die away — almost like clockwork…I think that the epidemic has largely come and is on its way out in this country so I think it (infection fatality rate) would be definitely less than 1 in 1000 and probably closer to 1 in 10,000.*[44]

This is another example of a doctor whose calculations require more people to have contracted COVID in a given area than actually exist in that area. As journalist Tom Chivers pointed out, Dr. Gupta's calculations were literally impossible. He wrote:

> *Professor Sunetra Gupta, the Oxford epidemiologist, said in May 2020 that the coronavirus might kill one person in every 10,000 it infected. Since 36,000 people had died in the UK when she made that claim, that would have implied that 360 million British people — five times as many as exist — had had the disease.*[45]

Like Dr. Ioannidis, Dr. Gupta was convinced the pandemic was close to over in the summer of 2020. In an interview from July that year titled "We May Already Have Herd Immunity – An Interview With Professor Sunetra Gupta," she said:

> *Having those ideas in mind, when the COVID-19 virus started to spread, I was pretty certain it wouldn't have a huge, devastating impact in terms of mortality, because we had all these other coronaviruses circulating...The epidemic appears to be over in the north east (USA).*[35]

Dr. Bhattacharya wrote an article in the *Wall Street Journal* in March 2020 titled "Is the Coronavirus as Deadly as They Say?" in which he said that "current estimates about the COVID-19 fatality rate may be too high by orders of magnitude."[46] He continued:

> *If it's true that the novel coronavirus would kill millions without shelter-in-place orders and quarantines, then the extraordinary measures being carried out in cities and states around the country are surely justified. But there's little evidence to confirm that premise—and projections of the death toll could plausibly be orders of magnitude too high.*
>
> *Fear of COVID-19 is based on its high estimated case fatality rate — 2% to 4% of people with confirmed*

> *COVID-19 have died, according to the World Health Organization and others. So if 100 million Americans ultimately get the disease, 2 million to 4 million could die. We believe that estimate is deeply flawed...*
>
> *If our surmise of six million cases is accurate, that's a mortality rate of 0.01%, assuming a two week lag between infection and death. This is one-tenth of the flu mortality rate of 0.1%. Such a low death rate would be cause for optimism.*

He wrote that "a 20,000- or 40,000-death epidemic is a far less severe problem than one that kills two million." His article concluded:

> *If we're right about the limited scale of the epidemic, then measures focused on older populations and hospitals are sensible... A universal quarantine may not be worth the costs it imposes on the economy, community and individual mental and physical health. We should undertake immediate steps to evaluate the empirical basis of the current lockdowns.*

Though Dr. Bhattacharya would later say "I never called it the flu,"[47] he was right in March 2020 that it would be a "cause for optimism" if COVID had "one-tenth of the flu mortality rate of 0.1%."[46] He was also correct that a 20,000- or 40,000-death epidemic would have been a far less severe problem than one that killed two million. Unfortunately, the U.S. would surpass 40,000 COVID deaths less than a month after Dr. Bhattacharya's optimistic editorial.[39]

In a podcast from March 2020, called "Questioning Conventional Wisdom in the COVID-19 Crisis," Dr. Bhattacharya spoke about the virus like it was a faucet that could easily be adjusted saying:

> *It doesn't have to be the case that our healthcare workers are overwhelmed, they could just be worked to the, they could just be whelmed if you will, like push to the point they can deal with it.*[48]

No doctor who worked with COVID patients would ever say anything this absurd. We knew the virus was unpredictable and could easily explode out of control.

Although all three authors of the GBD drastically underestimated COVID, their rhetoric about it hasn't changed one bit. As variants emerged and the bodies piled up, these three doctors doubled down on their initial pandemic pronouncements. What they said at the start of the pandemic is exactly what they say today – *COVID is only dangerous for older people and it's all going away.*

"An infection is a severe problem for older populations, . . . For younger populations under 70, it's much milder"

~ Dr. Jay Bhattacharya

The appeal of the GBD was obvious. So long as the non-vulnerable separated from the vulnerable, they could live as if there were no pandemic. A handful of young people might spend a day at home with the sniffles, herd immunity would arrive in 3- to 6-months, the vulnerable could then emerge unscathed, and life could return to normal. The loss of life would be minimal, the economy would be saved, and the entire pandemic would be a mere blip in history books. They made it all sound so incredibly easy.

While the GBD sounded great in theory, in reality some obvious problems emerged. First of all, who decides who is vulnerable and who is not? On October 30, 2020, Dr. Bhattacharya offered this guidance:

> *An infection is a severe problem for older populations, and also for people who have certain chronic conditions. For younger populations under 70, it's much milder.*[49]

The GBD itself said that "people in their 60s are at somewhat high risk"[31] and that "people with comorbidity risk factors should take the same precautions as somewhat older people without those risk factors." However, "comorbidity risk factors" exist on a spectrum, while the GBD was premised on a binary world where people were either "vulnerable" or "not vulnerable".

Clearly, an 80-year-old with diabetes and heart disease would be "vulnerable" and a healthy 10-year-old "not vulnerable" – though some healthy children this age have died of COVID[50] – but there's a large group of people in between these extremes. What exactly counts as a "comorbidity risk factor"? What about a 45-year-old with asthma, a 40-year-old smoker, a 35-year-old pregnant woman, a mildly overweight 50-year-old? Are these people "vulnerable" or "not vulnerable"?

Moreover, over 40% of Americans are obese, which is a significant risk factor for worse COVID outcomes.[51] How should they be protected? Many of my patients with multiple sclerosis are immunosuppressed and dependent on others for their needs. How could their young caregivers avoid the virus? COVID also turned out to be nasty for pregnant women, killing several hundred and causing miscarriages. How could a pregnant mother of three be isolated from her children for the duration of her pregnancy?

Although the entire premise of the GBD hinged on the idea that tens of millions of "vulnerable" people could be walled-off from "not vulnerable" people instantly and for up to 6-months, the GBD was silent on these crucial issues. The GBD gave no guidance beyond saying healthy people younger than 60 had no real risk.

Of course, COVID is not mild for everyone younger than 60, even if they are healthy. If you heard about a healthy 55-year-old dying of COVID, would that shock you? Of course not, especially if they weren't vaccinated. In fact, an analysis by the Kaiser Family Foundation (KFF) reported that COVID was the first or second leading cause of death for adults aged 35-54 in January 2021, just months after the GBD was published, and again from August 2021 to January 2022 when the Delta and Omicron variants arrived.[52] Many more young adults would have died without vaccines.

Death is not the only bad outcome from COVID, though it is the only one recognized by the GBD. The fact that "non-vulnerable" people could survive COVID, but still be gravely injured by it, did not factor into their Declaration.

"I wouldn't do it, and I don't think most people my age would."

~ Noah Louis-Ferdinand

A lot of "not vulnerable" people knew the risks, however, and didn't want to be cannon fodder on behalf of a virus in the GBD's war. From the pandemic's first days, it was obvious COVID could hurt some young people. Chinese ophthalmologist Dr. Li Wenliang was internationally famous when he died at age 33. One article in his honor said:

> *Dr. Li was admitted to the hospital at the end of January 2020. Once a nucleic acid-based diagnostic test became available for SARS-CoV2, he tested positive for this novel coronavirus. Unfortunately, his clinical condition deteriorated and in early February he was admitted to the intensive care unit, intubated and ventilated, and later started on extracorporeal membrane oxygenation (ECMO) for refractory hypoxia. His final hours were followed virtually by tens of millions of people. When he died on February 7, 2020, at the age of 33, he left behind a pregnant wife and a young son. One of his final online posts before becoming ill was a complaint about the high cost of prenatal vitamins.*[53]

It was clear before COVID arrived in the U.S. that COVID did not always spare young people. Once it arrived, news organizations began to report catastrophic outcomes in young people. One headline from *The Washington Post* in April 2020 declared "Young and Middle-Aged People, Barely Sick With COVID-19, Are Dying of Strokes."[54]

Anyone who worked on a COVID unit saw some young, healthy people be severely affected by the virus. The 23-year-old I saw die didn't make the news, but similar tragedies did. Nick Cordero was a 41-year-old Broadway star who died of COVID in July 2020.[55] Like my patient, he had his leg amputated before he died. All of this was well-publicized. His friend, Zach Braff, who became famous playing a doctor on the TV series *Scrubs*, wisely said, "Don't believe that COVID only claims the elderly and infirm."[56] While many people believed that COVID only claimed the elderly and infirm, most others knew to trust the guy who played a doctor on TV, rather than the actual doctors on TV. They didn't want to get COVID, especially before they were vaccinated.

The GBD assumed that most people changed their lives in 2020 only because of government restrictions. They were wrong. As vaccine-advocate Noah Louis-Ferdinand wrote:

> *Mobility data—combining Google's archive of location histories and GPS data from millions of cell phones—suggests not much. An analysis from June of 2020 immediately looking back shows that mobility decreased massively before the lockdowns even started. There was no sharp decline once they set in, mobility increased throughout the lockdown, and it did not increase sharply once they were lifted. Similar graphs show a sharp mobility decline (albeit less steep) in Stockholm, Sweden right around the same time. Sweden never locked down.*[57]

In order for the GBD to work, hundreds of millions of young, unvaccinated adults had to be willing to resume normal life, ensuring they would get COVID. That didn't happen. In reality, few if any young people rushed to resume normal life on October 4, 2020, when the GBD was published. They knew they had some risk from the virus, and they could pass it on to others. Everyone knew that if we were lucky, vaccines were just months away. Most young people wisely chose on their own volition to postpone their bout with COVID until they were vaccinated. The GBD didn't persuade them to change their behavior. They refused to be drafted into the GBD's Team COVID Army.

The GBD's overt calls for individual self-sacrifice to benefit the collective would appeal to conservatives at the *Wall Street Journal*, libertarians at the Cato Institute and *Reason Magazine*, as well as Ayn Rand acolytes at The Atlas Society, all of which promoted the GBD's ideas. Notably, there was never any evidence they were willing to join the herd before they were vaccinated. No one posted selfies at that time showing themselves in a crowded bar because they'd read the GBD and wanted to contribute to herd immunity. The GBD's supporters knew not to take that part of it seriously. They didn't want to be part of the herd. They wanted the herd to be there for them.

Even though he was in his early 50s when the pandemic started, Dr. Bhattacharya wisely avoided the virus until August 2021, after he had been fully vaccinated.[58] That many millions of "not vulnerable" people refused to "stand in the front line" before they were vaccinated was more than just a hypothetical flaw in the GBD's plan; it was a real-world failure. We don't have to ask the question "Could the GBD have worked?" In the real world, it failed.

In an alternate universe, where young people were initially willing to get COVID in large numbers, Mr. Louis-Ferdinand realized they would soon change their mind. He said:

> *They may change course as the virus spikes, hospitalizing 1-2 of their friends, classmates, or coworkers, and leaving others disabled potentially for months. Repeat waves which seriously hurt even a small minority of those we care about would be hard to just accept when the risk is modifiable. I wouldn't do it, and I don't think most people my age would.*[59]

Indeed, Mr. Louis-Ferdinand *didn't* do it, and neither did most people his age.

"Their plan is incongruent with my existence." ~ Abby Mahler

Many vulnerable people also rejected the GBD. Some vulnerable people thought the virus posed little threat to them, while others wanted to avoid it but still have some semblance of a normal life. Both groups posed a challenge for the GBD, which required that tens of millions of vulnerable people willingly submit to a punishing lockdown for months on end. In the GBD's vision, anytime "vulnerable" people entered the world of the "not vulnerable" they'd be immersed in the virus. They would have been in grave danger whenever they went into any building that wasn't their house, or when anyone from the outside came inside theirs.

In the real world, many vulnerable people rebelled against measures to control the virus. There are many pictures of older and overweight Americans protesting COVID restrictions in the pandemic's first months. These people rejected the GBD's plan to turn them into shut-ins, and they would have been at crowded bars and churches if they had the opportunity. The GBD didn't consider that large numbers of vulnerable people wouldn't play their assigned role. It would have been a disaster had they all contracted COVID along with hundreds of millions of "not vulnerable" people in October 2020. These people would have swamped hospitals had they all gotten COVID at the same time.

Obviously, the pandemic curtailed everyone's life drastically. However, in the real world, when communities made good faith efforts to control the virus, many vulnerable people were able to go shopping, see their doctor, and even protest COVID restrictions without a certainty they'd be exposed to the virus at every step along their journey. As a result, at least some vulnerable people, who initially denied COVID's threat, had an opportunity to wake up to the danger and get vaccinated. A survey by KFF from September 2021 found that grim realities on the ground moved the needle for some people. It found:

> *Adults who got vaccinated since June 1 cite as major reasons the increase in COVID cases due to the Delta variant (39%), reports of local hospitals filling up (38%), and knowing someone who became seriously ill or died (36%).*[60]

Drew Altman, the president and CEO of the KFF said:

> *Nothing motivates people to get vaccinated quite like the impact of seeing a family member, friend or neighbor die or become seriously ill with COVID-19, or to worry that your hospital might not be able to save your life if you need it. When a theoretical threat becomes a clear and present danger, people are more likely to act to protect themselves and their loved ones.*

The GBD would have provided no opportunity for misinformed, vulnerable people to recognize COVID's risk and get vaccinated instead of infected.

In contrast, when the virus was spreading out of control,

vulnerable people who wanted to avoid COVID felt like prisoners in their own home. Abby Mahler, a young woman with lupus who corrects misinformation about hydroxychloroquine, told me:

> *It has been a nightmare. My entire life has changed; I had to find new employment – leaving behind networks hard built – as well as forgo decades old family traditions, friendships, & medical maintenance for my existing chronic illnesses. Their plan is incongruent with my existence.*

The GBD never did any polling of people like Ms. Mahler to see if she was on board with their plan to completely shut down her life with no backup plan if herd immunity never arrived. The authors of the GBD wanted to impose their will on tens of millions of vulnerable Americans, and they just assumed they'd all be fine with it.

"With the focused protection measures outlined above, it will prove no more difficult to shift infection risk away from high-risk older people."
~ Drs. Martin Kulldorff, Sunetra Gupta, & Jay Bhattachary

Even if everyone came with labels stating whether they were "vulnerable" or not and everyone was willing to be foot soldiers for Team COVID Army, the GBD's plan still faced daunting obstacles.

15% of Americans are over 65 years of age.[61] Even if we pretend that no one else falls into the "vulnerable" category, that is still a lot of people. How could 55 million Americans be instantly and completely walled off from the other 280 million for 3-6 months, especially considering many "vulnerable" people depend on "not vulnerable" people for their basic needs? How could all 32,000 nursing homes in the U.S. – many of them greatly under-resourced – be hermetically sealed off from the rest of the world while COVID ran rampant outside?[62]

Even if nursing homes could be completely protected, 80% of COVID deaths occurred outside nursing homes. There's an obvious reason for this, and it poses a serious challenge to the

GBD. Vulnerable people are *everywhere*. "Vulnerable" and "not vulnerable" people interact all the time. As an immunocompromised disability-advocate Beatrice Adler-Bolton told me:

> *Their plan immediately tells me that they don't know a lot of vulnerable people, and they (incorrectly) assume all vulnerable people somehow live out of society and do not work or go to school, or share households with people who work or go to school. The non-workability of a plan like "focused protection" is immediately obvious to people who are vulnerable. We do not all live on a little island together, we do not all live in nursing homes, long term care facilities, and hospitals.*
>
> *We are all over the place and the GBD's plan not only clearly was ignorant of this: if it wasn't then it expects the vulnerable constantly disclose their vulnerability and that broad *collective* interventions like universal masking and vaccination be implemented in every single community that the vulnerable live in to accommodate their status...and spoiler alert that means every community when COVID is circulating in the air we all share.*

She's right and separating "vulnerable" people from "not vulnerable" people while they all contracted COVID in October 2020 would have been a Herculean challenge with innumerable opportunities for things to go drastically wrong. Dr. Kit Yates, a mathematical biologist who modeled whether the GBD proposal could have worked, said:

> *Shielding in real populations would have been imperfect, infections in the lower-risk population would have leaked through to vulnerable people who were shielding.*[63]

Indeed, a CDC report published just two days before the GBD unsurprisingly found that infections in young people soon spilled over to older people. It said:

> *Younger adults likely contribute to community transmission of COVID-19. Across the southern United States in June 2020, increases in percentage of positive SARS-CoV-2 test results among adults aged 20–39 years preceded increases among those aged ≥60 years by 4–15 days.*[64]

Though the GBD claimed that "in many publications and at the Great Barrington Declaration site itself, we have delineated many practical policies"[30] to protect the vulnerable, the GBD provided no meaningful guidance for how to actually do this. The "many publications" referenced articles in *Newsweek* and *The Spectator* titled "We Should Focus on Protecting the Vulnerable from COVID Infection",[65] "It's Time for an Alternative to Lockdown",[66] and "Lockdown Isn't Working."[67] These were brief opinion pieces that likely took an hour to write, not serious policy proposals.

For example, in response to the question, "*How can we better protect older people living at home?*" they wrote the following three sentences:

> *During times when transmission is high, older people should be offered home delivery of groceries and other essentials. At those times, it is best to meet family and friends outdoors. We should make rapid testing available for visiting relatives. Free N95 masks and instructions on their appropriate use should be provided when potential exposure cannot be avoided.*[65]

The article concluded that focused protection wouldn't be that hard. It said:

> *With the focused protection measures outlined above, it will prove no more difficult to shift infection risk away from high-risk older people.*

The authors of the GBD always made it sound like protecting

the vulnerable was trivial, even though they never specified exactly how this could be done. Beyond opening up everything, they only provided the roughest of outlines of what to actually do next. A public health official who wished to implement their "plan" to protect the vulnerable wouldn't actually know what her next step should be.

This is because the GBD didn't have a plan for her; it had many impossible demands of her. Once the GBD said "during high transmission times, older people should be offered home delivery of groceries and other essentials,"[31] their job was done. It was the responsibility of our poor public health official to figure out how to actually get groceries and other essentials to seniors for the duration of the pandemic. When she inevitably failed to meet their many demands, the authors of the GBD blamed her. Their "plan" was unimpeachable.

The "Frequently Asked Questions" section of the GBD laid out the harms of lockdowns and other measures to control the virus. It called for them to end immediately. This was the only part of the GBD that anyone took seriously, including its authors. This section of GBD also spread misinformation about COVID's risk to children. For example, it falsely claimed that "For children, the COVID-19 mortality risk is less than for the annual influenza." In reality, COVID had killed at least 112 children when the GBD was published,[68] while the flu killed a single child during the entire 2020-2021 flu season.[69]

The "Frequently Asked Questions" section of the GBD devoted less than 800 words to how to actually protect the "vulnerable". Their "plan" could easily have been written in an hour and it takes just a couple of minutes to read. By way of comparison, the protocol for one of the pediatric vaccine trials was 460 pages of detailed policies and procedures.[70] This is the kind of serious document that serious scientists produce when they actually intend for their plan to be implemented in the real world.

In contrast, the GBD's "plan" basically said a whole bunch of really complicated things should suddenly just happen everywhere at once. Most of their suggestions were common sense things that sound simple. For example, in response to the question *"How do we protect the elderly in nursing homes and other care settings?"* they suggested "frequent testing of nursing home staff members", "testing of visitors", "less staff rotation", and "COVID-19 infected individuals should not be sent to nursing homes."[31]

However, while it was easy for the authors of the GBD to type those words, I suspect that actually limiting staff rotations in nursing homes was a challenge. Staff shortages in these facilities were a chronic problem during the pandemic, especially when the virus surged. At the height of the Omicron wave in January 2022, 34% of nursing facilities reported a shortage.[71] Many nursing home workers were vulnerable themselves, and nearly 3,000 of them have died of COVID so far.[72] This is how the GBD made hard things sound easy. Moreover, the first home test to detect SARS-CoV-2 wasn't even authorized until 6 weeks after the GBD was written.[73] Frequent testing of nursing home staff members wasn't possible in October 2020. This is how the GBD made impossible things sound easy.

Even if all their measures to protect nursing homes were possible, they weren't foolproof. Once the virus was allowed to spread freely amongst "not vulnerable" citizens, it would easily find its way into "protected" places. This all happened in the real world. Though the GBD pretended otherwise, most of their suggestions reflected CDC guidance from the pandemic's first months. As Gideon Meyerowitz-Katz wrote:

> *Of the 19 policies proposed on the GBD website itself, 13 were commonplace, boring recommendations that virtually every developed country in the world implemented in March/April 2020. These are the sort of bland and obvious stuff that public health departments tried to promote at the very start, like "test people who are at high risk" or "meet outside to lower your risk of infection". That they form the vast majority of suggestions that made up Focused Protection gives us some insight into how useless the policy was and still is.*[74]

Despite these reasonable suggestions, COVID continued to ravish in nursing homes. We don't have to ask the question "Could the GBD have worked?" In the real world, it failed.

The rest of the GBD's "plan" was just wishful thinking and more impossible demands of public health workers. For example, they demanded:

> *Free home delivery of groceries for the home-bound vulnerable, providing disability job accommodations for older vulnerable workers, and temporary accommodations for older people living in multi-generational homes.*[30]

Again, "free home delivery of groceries for the home-bound vulnerable" sounds nice, but it's not a plan. Creating a program overnight to deliver fresh food to tens of millions of seniors for months on end throughout the entire country is not an easy task. Who would identify the home-bound vulnerable? How would they create their shopping lists? What if they weren't internet savvy? How would the funding structure be arranged? What if the people who were supposed to be delivering food were themselves bedbound with COVID or caring for a sick relative? What if they turned out to be scammers who left seniors hungry? What if seniors refused the service and went to crowded grocery stores anyway?

In an interview from October 2021, Dr. Bhattacharya answered these questions by saying:

> *We could have offered free DoorDash to older people. I mean, yeah, it would depend on the community and the living circumstances... It would be a local thing, right?*[58]

This was obviously something Dr. Bhattacharya just thought of off the top of his head. The idea of millions of homebound seniors surviving off of DoorDash for 6-months is not a plan. This shows little thought the authors of the GBD put into their plan. They did not take their own Declaration seriously, and in fact, worked to sabotage key parts of it.

The GBD also suggested that the government pay older workers who couldn't work from home "to take a 3- to 6-month sabbatical."[31] What about workers with underlying health conditions? They wrote that "disability laws should require employers to provide reasonable accommodations to protect high COVID19 risk workers without losing their jobs." The GBD gave lawmakers no guidance on what they thought these new laws should be or how they might be enforced.

The GBD recognized that protecting older people in multigenerational homes was "the toughest challenge" and that "family specific solutions must be found." The GBD's "solution" consisted of just three sentences. They said:

> *If the working-age household members can work from home, they can isolate together. If that is not possible, the older family member might temporarily be able to live with an older friend or sibling, with whom they can self-isolate together during the height of community transmission. As a last resort, empty hotel rooms could be used for temporary housing.*

Suggesting that a bunch of 90-year-olds suddenly become roommates for six months while a virus rages around them is not a serious plan. Additionally, there are nearly 60 million Americans who live in multigenerational housing[75] and only 5.3 million hotel rooms in the US.[76] Who would care for millions of seniors who suddenly found themselves living at a Holiday Inn for 6-months? The GBD avoided the problem of elderly people living with children by claiming they had "no further excess risk if also living with children."[31] If they were wrong about this, which they were, their plan would crumble.

In response to the question "How do we protect older people living at home?" they said:

> *During high transmission times, older people should be offered home delivery of groceries and other essentials. When seeing friends and relatives, it is best to do it outdoors. Testing should be available for relatives and friends who want to visit. Free N95 masks should be provided for when they cannot avoid potential exposure.*

That's it! Their whole plan for isolating millions of vulnerable people who live at home for 3-6 months was four sentences. It was as if a coach's entire game day plan was nothing more than "score more points than the other team." It's not the wrong plan, but it's not a good plan, and his team will lose.

"Since when is it ethical to burden children for the benefit of adults?"
~ Dr. Jay Bhattacharya

Predictably, the authors of the GBD never advocated for free N95 masks and testing kits. This half of their "plan" was just empty window dressing used to provide cover for removing all measures to limit the virus. In fact, though masks and tests were a vital part of their "plan" to protect older people at home, the authors of the GBD worked ceaselessly to destroy people's confidence in these simple measures.

Though the GBD itself endorsed N95 masks, Dr. Kulldorff said "children should not wear face masks. They don't need it for their own protection and they don't need it for protecting other people either."[77] Dr. Bhattacharya also said "I think the masks have not only not been ineffective but harmful."[78] He felt that masks "may be partially effective in shielding adults from COVID,"[79] but asked "since when is it ethical to burden children for the benefit of adults?" Of course, the entire GBD was premised on the idea that unvaccinated children should get COVID to benefit adults.

Though the GBD itself endorsed testing "for relatives and friends who want to visit,"[31] Drs. Bhattacharya and Kulldorff sought to undermine confidence in this suggestion as well, writing an article in the *Wall Street Journal* titled "The Case Against COVID Tests for the Young and Healthy." While this editorial was mostly about schools, it said that "hunting for asymptomatic cases encourages pointless shutdowns."[80]

This is how the authors of the GBD sabotaged their own Declaration. Serious scientists would have launched a public relations campaign to rally citizens behind their proposals. They would have lobbied politicians for free N95 masks and testing kits for the elderly. Instead, the authors of the GBD successfully poisoned key elements of their own "plan" in the public's mind. With their encouragement, masks became a tribal, political symbol, and millions of vulnerable Americans refused to wear one.

In response to the question "*How can older people know when to be extra careful?*", the GBD made yet more difficult demands of public health officials. In addition to feeding vulnerable people at home, sending them N95 masks, and setting up COVID hotels, the GBD also tasked them with tracking COVID metrics and communicating this information in a pitch-perfect way. The GBD said:

> *This information should be conveyed to the population in a nuanced way that does not induce panic but instead provides the basis for an accurate assessment of each person's risk based on their age and comorbid conditions. The goal should be that vulnerable people do not underestimate their risk from COVID-19 infection, and less vulnerable people do not overestimate their risk. Concrete recommendations should accompany the information – including perhaps recommendations to avoid crowds, hand washing, social distancing, and masks when their application to the situation is backed by sound science – that different people might take to reduce their infection risk.*[31]

Of course, the authors of the GBD encouraged many vulnerable people to underestimate their risk of COVID. For example, Dr. Bhattacharya said, "For younger populations under 70, it's much milder."[49] They also savaged public health officials who took measures they suggested, such as telling vulnerable people to avoid crowds, social distance, and wear masks. They sabotaged their own "plan".

Notably, the GBD and its authors always suggested hand washing to prevent COVID, which is like using a seat belt to prevent HIV.

"The Great Barrington Declaration was a one page document. It wasn't aimed at producing a comprehensive strategy for—a detailed tactical strategy for how to do focused protection in every single setting.

~ Dr. Jay Bhattacharya

Though the GBD claimed that "a comprehensive and detailed list of measures, including approaches to multi-generational households, can be implemented, and is well within the scope and capability of public health professionals,"[29] they failed to provide a comprehensive and detailed list of anything. They admitted this when pressed. According to one court filing from October 2021:

> *Dr. Bhattacharya noted that it would be for government to determine how to best implement the principles of the declaration as it was not his role to do so.*[81]

In another interview from November 2022, Dr. Bhattacharya expanded on the hollowness of the GBD by saying:

> *We wrote it, the vaccines were still not there. Right? I think that was probably the most legitimate criticism of the, of the Great Barrington Declaration is how do you do focused protection? Now, the Great Barrington Declaration was a one page document. It wasn't aimed at producing a comprehensive strategy for—a detailed tactical strategy for how to do focused protection in every single setting. What it was, was, was a change in principles, how we are managing the pandemic and an invitation to discussion and thinking and creative thinking by local public health. Right? So we gave some suggestions for how this might be accomplished in some settings, right? So for instance, in dense urban settings with lots of multigenerational homes, it might have involved making hotel rooms available for older people who live in multigenerational homes.*
>
> *So they've, if someone is exposed in the house, they can call local public health. Local public health, then offers them hotel room for a few days until they get cleared. Or organizing home deliveries. It would've been difficult no matter what, especially in very, very crowded places, very, very poor places, without the vaccine. But it would, I think it would've been possible, certainly, if we'd had that as a part*

> *of, as the main part of our strategy, we would never have sent COVID-infected patients back to nursing homes. Right? That came about because we were thinking about protection of hospital systems rather than protection of people. But I made a claim that I think it's been validated. I think the validation comes in countries that followed a focused vaccination strategy for older people. Right? So I'll just give the example of Sweden, but you could also point to the UK and other places.*[82]

In the real world, the examples of Sweden, the UK, and New Zealand, point to the dismal failure of a focused protection strategy.

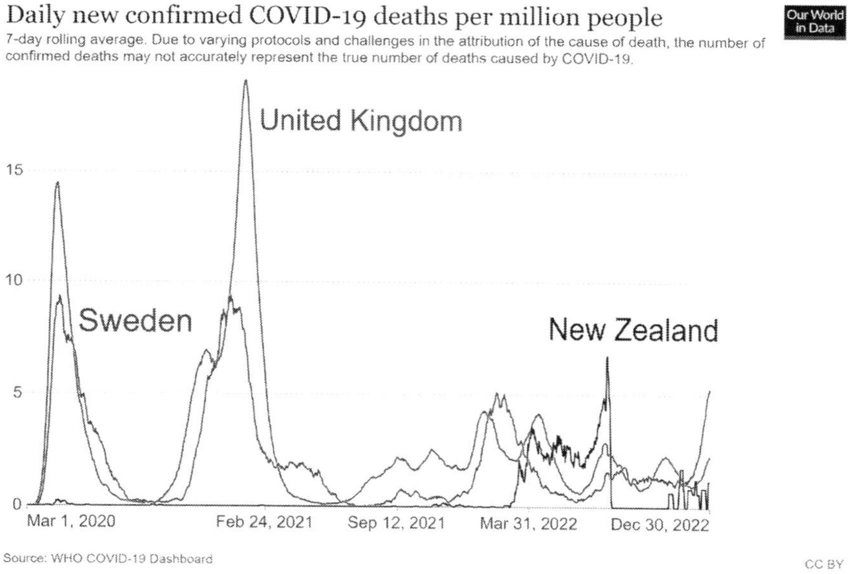
Daily new confirmed COVID-19 deaths per million people
7-day rolling average. Due to varying protocols and challenges in the attribution of the cause of death, the number of confirmed deaths may not accurately represent the true number of deaths caused by COVID-19.
Our World in Data
United Kingdom
Sweden
New Zealand
15
10
5
0
Mar 1, 2020
Feb 24, 2021
Sep 12, 2021
Mar 31, 2022
Dec 30, 2022
Source: WHO COVID-19 Dashboard
CC BY

COVID deaths in the United Kingdom, Sweden, and New Zealand[39]

Though they were calling for one of the greatest logistical challenges in the history of humanity in the middle of a pandemic, the attitude of the GBD authors was basically *someone else should figure out how to actually do this*. That someone else was always "public health officials". The GBD demanded that they accomplish miracles, while telling the general public that these miracles were "well within the scope and capability of public health professionals."[29]

In the real world, governments hadn't been showering public

health departments with money prior to 2020, preparing them for this exact moment. In fact, the opposite was true. Researchers who thought about this stuff seriously wrote reports titled "The Impact of Chronic Underfunding on America's Public Health System: Trends, Risks, and Recommendations, 2022." It said:

> *Lack of funding in core public health programs slowed the response to the COVID-19 pandemic and exacerbated its impact, particularly in low-income communities, communities of color, and for older Americans – populations that experience higher rates of chronic disease and have fewer resources to recover from an emergency.*[83]

Public health officials never had the "overwhelming resources" necessary to carry out the GBD's plan, and the authors of the GBD took no steps to rectify this situation. We don't have to ask the question "Could the GBD have worked?" In the real world, it never stood a chance.

"It's a complicated question." ~ Dr. Jay Bhattacharya

The GBD's proposals to abruptly and massively expand the welfare and regulatory state appealed to conservatives at the *Wall Street Journal*, libertarians at the Cato Institute and *Reason Magazine* as well as Ayn Rand acolytes at The Atlas Society. However, they knew that the GBD's "plan" to protect the vulnerable was empty pablum not to be taken seriously. Everyone was in on the joke.

The authors of the GBD never lobbied governments to actually create food delivery programs or make payments to allow older workers to stay home. They never called for public health officials to receive billions of dollars so they could enact their "plan". I've not seen them lament that more laws weren't passed to protect high risk workers. Everyone knew none of their "focused protection" measures were actually going to actually happen, especially at a national scale, in a few weeks' time. It would be like trying to build NASA from scratch in two weeks.

However, actually keeping vulnerable people protected never really seemed to be the goal. After the GBD was published, its authors only mentioned their "plan" to protect the vulnerable as an afterthought. Dr. Bhattacharya even defended Governor DeSantis' decision to deprioritize prisoners when vaccines first became available. Dr. Bhattacharya argued that most prisoners had been infected already and they don't interact with the general public anyways. "It's a complicated question,"[84] he said. In the real world, research from August 2020 unsurprisingly showed that COVID outbreaks in prisons spread to the surrounding community,[85] and of course, many prisoners were vulnerable themselves.

To this day, the authors of the GBD talk about little else beyond the evils of lockdowns and other measures to control the virus, all of which ended long ago. They don't write articles titled "10 Ways You Can Protect the Vulnerable." They never did. Though the GBD called for "overwhelming resources" to protect the vulnerable, all they really wanted was for unvaccinated, young people to contract COVID.

This may explain why the GBD didn't mention that, in the real world, large sums of money had already been spent on several of their proposals months before it was written. Though the GBD made it seem as if they had come up with entirely new ideas, by the end of March 2020, Congress had allocated $720 million for congregate and home-delivered nutrition.[86] In fact, over 2.2 *trillion* dollars had already been allocated to fight COVID and support the economy as part of the Coronavirus Aid, Relief, and Economic Security Act (CARES Act), which was signed into law in March 2020.[87] This legislation, which was meant to be taken seriously and acted upon, was 247 pages of dense text. Reading the CARES Act and GBD is a *very different* experience. Other federal legislation, such as the Families First Coronavirus Response Act,[88] which was an additional 44 pages long, gave 14-day paid leave for American workers affected by the pandemic and increased funding for food stamps. Later, in January 2022, President Biden made N95 masks and testing kits available to all Americans, which also paralleled suggestions of the GBD.

Maybe these laws could have been bigger and better, but the GBD contained no brilliant, original insights to improve them, and suggesting "free DoorDash to older people"[58] didn't add anything meaningful to the conversation. However, these asinine comments served a valuable purpose. They convinced many people that public health officials hadn't made any effort to protect the vulnerable, though doing so would have been easy if only they cared enough to try.

In reality, protecting the vulnerable was harder than just writing a few sentences in a Declaration. By March 2022 Congress had allocated 5 trillion dollars as part of pandemic stimulus packages, the largest infusion of money ever into the U.S. economy.[89] Much of the money was wasted. Scammers got their hands on large chunks of it. According to the U.S. Secret Service, $100 billion in pandemic relief funds had been stolen by December 2021.[90] One group in Minnesota called Feeding Our Future stole $250 million in pandemic funding meant to feed children.[91] The GBD would have created enormous opportunities for such scammers. What was their plan for dealing with this?

Additionally, in the real world, laws meant to protect the vulnerable were often ignored. One disgraceful headline read, "Tyson Managers Suspended After Allegedly Betting If Workers Would Contract COVID." According to the article:

> *The suspensions come one day after the family of a deceased employee filed a lawsuit claiming "fraudulent misrepresentations, gross negligence, and incorrigible, willful and wanton disregard for worker safety at its pork processing facility in Waterloo, Iowa."*[92]

What was the GBD's plan for dealing with this?

There's no question that things would have been much worse without these efforts, which gave us vaccines, but it wasn't enough to control the virus. However, if cash and laws alone could have protected the vulnerable, the U.S. would have had the best pandemic response in the world.

In reality, no amount of money or piece of brilliantly crafted legislation could protect the "vulnerable" so long as the virus was encouraged to spread freely amongst millions of "not vulnerable" citizens. What good are free tests and masks if no one uses them? Despite our government's largess and its legislative blitz, 1.1 million Americans are now dead of COVID,[39] including over 200,000 nursing home residents and staff.[93] Again, we don't have to ask the question "Could the GBD have worked?" In the real world, it failed.

Perhaps the authors of the GBD had brilliantly crafted laws that could have protected vulnerable people while everyone else was at crowded restaurants. If so, they kept them hidden. However, even if the GBD provided a perfect roadmap for public health officials, there would still be significant barriers to actually implementing their policies. Public health officials can't create, staff, and manage DoorDash food delivery programs out of thin air. They can't commandeer hotel rooms and force seniors to move in. They need approval, funding, and buy-in from the general public.

Enacting the GBD would require citizens everywhere and government officials of all political persuasions at all levels to be completely on board with the whole thing. A governor who didn't want hotels in her state to be turned into COVID housing could ruin everything. So could a governor who didn't want the virus to run wildly in his state. So could citizens who rejected the role the GBD assigned to them.

All of this happened in the real world. Politicians and their constituents were presented with the GBD and most of them rejected it. They didn't want to be like Florida during the Delta wave. They are not to blame for rejecting the GBD. The GBD is at fault for not convincing them.

Many defenders of the GBD say we never "really tried the GBD" without acknowledging this presupposes a world where everyone shares their pandemic philosophy. Hundreds of millions of "not vulnerable" Americans had to be willing to get COVID before they were vaccinated, tens of millions of "vulnerable" people had to be willing to be placed under house arrest, and public health departments, supported by politicians everywhere, had to be able to perfectly protect the "vulnerable" during this time. This is a fantasy world, and anyone could hammer out a "plan" to control COVID if they assumed that the entire country would march in lockstep in accordance with their wishes.

That many people rejected the GBD in the real world does not mean it wasn't enormously influential. Half of it was. It gave cover to anyone who wanted to abandon efforts to control the virus. The GBD and its supporters are part of the reason why even the *slightest* efforts to control the virus are met with fierce resistance and mockery today, including from supposedly liberal publications such as the *New*

York Times and the *New Yorker*. Even Dr. Bhattacharya recognized his influence, saying in August 2022 that, by abandoning measures to control COVID, the CDC "finally adopted focused protection as its COVID strategy."[176] He added, "It's crucial for people at the local level to insist that futile/harmful COVID suppression policies be ended. Speak up at school board meetings against vax discrimination & asymptomatic testing."

However, not even Florida "really tried the GBD." Though its authors never complained about it, Governor DeSantis rejected their proposals to shield vulnerable people. He just let the virus spread uncontrollably, with tragic consequences for tens of thousands of people, both "vulnerable" and "not".

"The reaction of… many people in the public health community was to just to throw up their hands and say, 'We can't do it.'"

~ Dr. Jay Bhattacharya

Not only did the GBD fail in the real world, but its authors also worked hard to ensure this outcome. Although the GBD requires political unanimity and cooperation to work, its authors became pandemic brawlers, and they relished the fight. They cultivated reputations as "brave heterodox thinkers", fighting against dastardly public health officials who wanted to indefinitely lockdown humanity for fun and profit. In a typically pugnacious Tweet, Dr. Martin Kulldorff wrote:

> *Faucism and Fascism are not the same, but there are some similarities*
> *- Blind belief in an all-knowing leader*
> *- Government-corporate partnership*
> *- Censoring and blacklisting opponents*
> *- Disregarding scientific principles and knowledge*
> *- Harming workers and the poor*
> *- Scapegoating*[94]

They made nasty, juvenile comments like this all the time, especially towards the very public health officials they needed to enact their plan. Dr. Bhattacharya even called Dr. Anthony Fauci

America's "'number one anti-vaxxer'"[95] after Dr. Fauci advised vaccinated people to not let their guard down in the spring of 2021. They never criticized him for not delivering food to homebound seniors or not giving them free N95 masks.

The authors of the GBD didn't see people who disagreed with them as honest brokers to be won over with science and evidence. Rather, they treated anyone who objected to the mass infection of unvaccinated youth as villainous opponents who deserved to be shamed, exposed, and punished. They fought fiercely for their ideas – at least those that spread SARS-CoV-2 – but rarely with an eye to persuade people and build a consensus. They never seemed bothered by the enmity they engendered, even though this doomed any chance their "plan" had of succeeding. They were purposefully divisive and, again, sabotaged their own Declaration.

However, the fact that the GBD was destined to be a failure was very valuable to its authors. It allowed them to blame public health workers for not figuring out how to enact their "plan". For example, Dr. Bhattacharya said in October 2021 that the inability of anywhere in the world to fully implement the GBD "was a failure of imagination on the part of public health."[58] He said:

> *The public health community that I know has all kinds of creative ideas of how to help people in a population be protected against disease. They're very creative generally in thinking of ways to do focus protection for many, many diseases and conditions. The reaction of... many people in the public health community was to just to throw up their hands and say, "We can't do it."*

That's like our coach, the one whose entire plan was "score more points than the other team," putting all the blame on his players after his team's inevitable loss. "I told them *exactly* what to do. They just didn't listen to me," he might say.

The GBD's inevitable failure also allowed its authors to say to maintain the fantasy that everything would have been just fine if only public health workers had listened to them. As Dr. Kulldorff said in December 2021:

If we had done focused protection, as outlined in the Great Barrington Declaration, the pandemic would have been over now with fewer COVID deaths and less collateral public health damage.[96]

Immediately after this, the Omicron variant spread widely in unvaccinated children, exactly as the GBD intended. Though they should have celebrated these sick children as the culmination of their vision, I suspect headlines such as "A Fifth of All US Child COVID Deaths Occurred During Omicron Surge"[97] dissuaded them from taking a well-deserved public victory lap. Of course, even this mass infection of children did not bring herd immunity. Again, we don't have to ask the question "Could the GBD have worked?" In the real world, it failed.

Unfortunately, the myth that under-resourced public health departments could have easily used "focused protection" to tame the pandemic contributed to a pattern of abuse and threats towards the people who worked there. One article, titled "The Pandemic Has Devastated the Mental Health of Public Health Workers," described the problem. It said:

Even as frontline health workers have been celebrated during the COVID-19 pandemic, many others working to track the virus, stem its spread and help Americans avoid infection have found themselves under siege.

Those public health workers have been vilified by a portion of the public and attacked by some political leaders and media figures. They have been fired or forced from office. They have been subjected to protests—some on their own front lawns—as well as curses, threats and even, on at least one occasion, racist taunts.

All that while working endless hours, sometimes in unfamiliar roles, to save as many people as possible from a virus that has so far killed more than 614,000 Americans.[98]

Matthew Brignall, a pro-vaccine naturopath, who volunteered for the Medical Reserve Corps tracking outbreaks, giving vaccines, and doing community education, told me:

> *It is incredibly disheartening to have spent three years servicing my community in the COVID-19 response only to be threatened with Nuremberg-style trials and execution weekly whenever I write anything about the experience. Yet the same people who have mobilized and monetized this anger whine about being silenced and marginalized.*

This was the inevitable consequence of highly credentialed doctors repeatedly telling angry people that "the pandemic would have been over now with fewer COVID deaths and less collateral public health damage" if only incompetent public health officials had listened to the GBD.

"You don't roll out disease – you roll out vaccination."
~ Dr. Rochelle Walensky

The GBD advocated Zero COVID for 55 million Americans and Pure COVID for the other 280 million with no contingency plan if herd immunity failed to arrive in under 6 months. There were many opportunities for things to go wrong, and serious people recognized this right away.

In an email from October 8, 2020, Dr. Francis Collins, the head of the National Institutes of Health, wrote that the authors of the GBD were "fringe epidemiologists" and suggested "there needs to be a quick and devastating published take down of its premises."[99] When this email was revealed a year later, it became a touchstone moment for the authors of the GBD, the same way seeing a healthy 23-year-old die during the first wave was the pandemic's defining moment for me. The mere idea that Dr. Collins even *considered* writing a "devastating" refutation of the "premises" of the GBD led to Dr. Bhattacharya to say:

> *So now I know what it feels like to be the subject of a propaganda attack by my own government.*

> *Discussion and engagement would have been a better path.*[100]

The editorial page of the Wall Street Journal agreed and wrote an article titled "How Fauci and Collins Shut Down COVID Debate." They felt that three credentialed, but essentially random epidemiologists, who merely hammered out a short Declaration filmed under the watchful eye of Mr. Jeffrey Tucker, were owed an audience with top government scientists, as well as publicity from them and only praise for their premises.101

However, Dr. Collins was just one of many people to spot the obvious flaws with the GBD. Soon after it was published, many devastating takedowns of its premises were published. Articles appeared titled "A Viral Theory Cited by Health Officials Draws Fire From Scientists"[102] and "Researchers Blast 'Dangerous' COVID-19 Herd Immunity Strategy."[103] Dr Rupert Beale, a cell biologist, said:

> *It is not possible to fully identify vulnerable individuals, and it is not possible to fully isolate them. Furthermore, we know that immunity to coronaviruses wanes over time, and re-infection is possible – so lasting protection of vulnerable individuals by establishing 'herd immunity' is very unlikely to be achieved in the absence of a vaccine.*[104]

Dr. Rochelle Walensky said:

> *I think it's wrong, I think it's unsafe, I think it invites people to act in ways that have the potential to do an enormous amount of harm. You don't roll out disease – you roll out vaccination.*[103]

Dr. William Hanage, an epidemiologist at Harvard, wrote an article titled "I'm an Epidemiologist. When I Heard About Britain's 'Herd Immunity' Coronavirus Plan, I Thought it Was Satire" in which he said:

> *This is an actual pandemic that will make a very large number of people sick, and some of them will*

die. Even though the mortality rate is likely quite low, a small fraction of a very large number is still a large number...However, arguments about the case fatality rate, the transmission parameters and presymptomatic transmission all miss the point. This virus is capable of shutting down countries. You should not want to be the next after Wuhan, Iran, Italy or Spain.[105]

Dr. Gregg Gonsalves, an epidemiologist at Yale, was unsparing in his criticism, saying:

The idea that you can keep outbreaks among the young away from the elderly is ridiculous. They can spin it however they like, but they don't really have a plan—it's grotesque, and it borders on eugenics.[106]

In a *Twitte*r thread called "Taking the Great Barrington Declaration seriously," Neil O'Brien, a Member of Parliament in England, did something the GBD authors never bothered to do: he took the GBD seriously and ran the numbers to get a sense of how it might actually work. It's worth quoting him length, as it shows how impossible their strategy actually was.

First, how many people would need to totally isolate as the virus accelerates through the rest of the population? There were 12,374,440 people aged 65+ in the UK in 2019. But there are 14,843,119 people who lived in a household with someone aged 65+. Additionally (in England alone) there were 2,240,850 patients on the Shielded List – though some of these over 65, so there's some overlap).

Trying to isolate and supply food to all these 15-16m people while the virus spiked would be a monumental undertaking, & much like a hard (6 month at least) lockdown for a large part of the population. It's not clear how we'd safely supply them with food as the virus spiked.
Second, how many people would likely die? If we

look at English mortality rates from this Nature article and apply them to the UK population, we can get a range of answers. Everyone accepts that the isolation of old and ill people couldn't be 100% complete: some will choose not to isolate, some will have to go to hospital or see carers, or live in care homes, or the young people living with them will not fully isolate and they'll get it.

About 8% of people have had the virus (call it 10% to be generous). Let's say we need to get to 60% for herd immunity. So we'd need a bit over 50% of the younger population to get it (and somehow avoid overshooting, which seems unlikely, but let's assume we could do that for a mo).

Using data from England suggests that if only half of the younger population got it and (miraculously) only 5% of pensioners (because isolation is near complete), that would mean 90,000 deaths. If 10% pensioners get it, that would be 130,000. If 15% then about 175,000. ...That's a lot of deaths. But that's still assuming that healthcare is not overwhelmed, and so all those who need treatment for COVID are still getting it. It's also assuming there are no non-COVID deaths caused by the NHS being overwhelmed. Both assumptions are very unlikely.

If we again assume 50% of younger people get the virus and 5% to 15% of pensioners that means between 860,000 and around 1.1m hospitalisations. Given the geometric way the virus grows without interventions, they would likely come at roughly the same time in a pronounced spike. In England there are 4,123 adult critical care beds (up from 3,593 in 2010). Not everyone in hospital would need critical care, but even a small % of hundreds of thousands of people into 4,000 beds doesn't go. Liverpool is already at 95% capacity.

So the likely spike in admissions would likely wash over the NHS like a tidal wave over a tiny sandcastle. So we should add to the directly-caused deaths two additional large numbers. First, the COVID patients who would die because they won't be able to get treatment, and second, the patients with other diseases who would die because the health service is knocked out. It's likely to add up to hundreds of thousands dead.

There is then a further cost in terms of people who get the disease, don't die but will have long term health problems. We don't know how large this would be. The KCL study suggests 60,000 have been seriously ill for over three months. Scale that up and it is a large number.[107]

Mr. O'Brien was right and it's worthwhile to think about what actually would have happened if the U.S. had "really tried" the GBD. What if 73 million children and another 175 million "not vulnerable" younger adults all resumed normal life and contracted COVID at the same time in October 2020? Could the "vulnerable" really have been protected under these circumstances? Of course not. It would have been a disaster of epic proportions. However, the fact that this didn't happen then, now allows the authors of the GBD to pretend everything would have been just fine.

"To allow large numbers of people today to die of COVID, in wealthy countries, is akin to charging the hill and taking casualties two days before the end of World War I."

~ Tyler Cowen

Mr. O'Brien concluded his Twitter thread by saying:

To go with the GBD, you'd have to be 100% certain than NONE of the three permanent solutions will arrive: no vaccines, no mass rapid testing & no medical improvements such that ppl get the virus but don't die. It seems pretty likely that several of these will arrive next year.[107]

Again, Mr. O'Brien was right. As lockdowns had ended in most of the country, never to return, much of the GBD was a relic when it was first published. Even New York City began to reopen indoor dining the week before the GBD was published. However, even if one engages with the fantasy that the GBD could have worked flawlessly, two things happened – one good, one bad – that rendered it utterly obsolete within months.

Vaccines were the good thing. The GBD's most optimistic time frame for vaccines proved correct. Two months after the GBD was signed, on December 8, 2020, 90-year-old Margaret Keenan stepped into history as the first person to receive a COVID vaccine outside of a clinical trial,[108] and over the next several months hundreds of millions of people were vaccinated in the fortunate parts of the world. The vaccines have since proven extremely effective at keeping people alive and out of the hospital. A CDC report found:

Receiving 2 or 3 doses of an mRNA COVID-19 vaccine was associated with a 90% reduction in risk for COVID-19–associated invasive mechanical ventilation or death. Protection of 3 mRNA vaccine doses during the period of Omicron predominance was 94%.[109]

Though the GBD recognized that vaccines could plausibly be available as soon as December 2020, they decided October 2020 was the time to let the virus run rampant in unvaccinated young people. As economist Tyler Cowen wrote at the time, "To allow large numbers of people today to die of COVID, in wealthy countries, is akin to charging the hill and taking casualties two days before the end of World War I."[110] Unbelievably, nearly 3,000 soldiers died on the last day of World War I, the last with 1 minute left to go. We were much worse. The virus killed 2,000-3,000 Americans every day in the winter of 2020-2021, just as vaccination campaigns were ramping up.[111]

"We have seen only a handful of reinfections." ~ The Great Barrington Declaration

Variants were the bad thing. The GBD was a version of letting kids get chickenpox to protect grandma. Except this time, it wasn't loony anti-vaxxers and UK vaccine regulators saying this. It was highly credentialed doctors and scientists from prestigious universities saying it about a much more dangerous virus.

Of course, SARS-CoV-2 was more than a dangerous virus, it was also a new virus. It was just an article of faith that a single COVID infection provided robust, durable immunity for years to come. Indeed, the GBD was entirely premised on the fiction that "natural immunity" meant permanent immunity. They wrote:

> *We have seen only a handful of reinfections. If the virus is like other corona viruses in its immune response, recovery from infection will provide lasting protection against reinfection, either complete immunity or protection that makes a severe reinfection less likely.*[31]

They also spread this optimistic message to the public. During a roundtable with Governor DeSantis in September 2020 Dr. Bhattacharya said:

> *We've only seen 2 reinfections out of millions of cases worldwide, so it's very clear that there's some long-lasting immune protection.*[41]

If vaccines knocked the GBD's relevance to the floor, highly contagious variants with immune-escape rung the death knell for its fantasy of herd immunity through mass infection, though even before the GBD had been written, cases of reinfections were being reported on social media and in the medical literature.[112]

Reinfections meant that vulnerable people would never be able to reenter society in a world with herd immunity to SARS-CoV-2, no matter how many young, unvaccinated people got COVID. We're in a much better place than we were when the pandemic started – at the cost of a million lives – but hundreds of Americans, mostly older, vulnerable adults are still dying of COVID every day. Herd immunity remains as elusive as a unicorn, even though lockdowns ended long ago and nearly all young people have contracted COVID.

Dr. Gupta would later claim that she always knew immunity to COVID was going to be transient, stating:

> *One thing we have always known, because there are other coronaviruses circulating, is that we lose our immunity against the infection very rapidly, whether the virus changes or not.*[113]

Of course, she did not feel this was a problem, saying that "waning immunity should not alarm us . . . the vulnerable have been protected against severe disease."[114]

Additionally, the GBD depended entirely on the premise that children don't spread the virus to adults. The GBD said that older adults who lived with children had "no further excess risk",[31] and the authors of the GBD spread this idea widely in 2020. In September 2020, Drs. Bhattacharya and Kulldorff wrote in the *Wall Street Journal*:

> *There is little purpose in using tests to check asymptomatic children to see if it is safe for them to come to school. When children are infected, most are asymptomatic, and the mortality risk is lower than for the flu. While adult-to-adult and adult-to-child transmission is common, child-to-adult transmission isn't. Children thus pose minimal risk to their teachers. If a child has a cough, a runny nose or other respiratory symptoms, he should stay home. You don't need a test for that.*[80]

Dr. Bhattacharya reiterated this belief during a September 2020 roundtable with Governor DeSantis. Dr. Bhattacharya said:

> *Children seem to pass the virus on to adults at lower rates than you would expect from your experience with other respiratory viruses. That's really good news, right? Kids, in some sense, pose less risk to the*

> *teachers in the classroom than the teachers pose to each other in the staff room.*[42]

Even if we imagine that children were poor spreaders of the initial SARS-CoV-2 virus, this wasn't the case for subsequent variants.[115] Younger children in particular spread the virus quite well, and no reasonable person today claims otherwise. Much of the GBD was premised on this not happening. Again, we don't have to ask the question "Could the GBD have worked?" In the real world, it failed.

"The idea that everyone must be vaccinated against COVID-19 is as misguided as the anti-vax idea that no one should. The former is more dangerous for public health."

~ Drs. Martin Kulldorff & Jay Bhattacharya

With the arrival of vaccines and variants, the authors of the GBD were forced to choose between acknowledging uncomfortable but obvious truths about the irrelevance of their Declaration or maintaining allegiance to it. They chose allegiance to their Declaration and continue to trash vaccines, testing, masks, lockdowns, and anything except hand washing, that prevents unvaccinated, young people from contracting COVID.

All three authors continue to deny the virus can impact young people and are now overtly anti-vaccine for this population. Even after the successful pediatric randomized-controlled trials and evidence from over 20 studies showing the vaccine keeps children safe and out of the hospital, the authors of the GBD still want unvaccinated children to get COVID. In fact, their plan depends on it. Nearly 4 million babies are born annually in the U.S., none with natural immunity. Even though babies and toddlers have the highest risk of all children – 650 have died so far in the U.S.[116] – the GBD requires that they get infected sooner rather than later. A large reservoir of children without natural immunity would ruin their fantasy of herd immunity.

To that end, Drs. Bhattacharya and Kulldorff authored an article titled "The Ill-Advised Push to Vaccinate the Young," in which they said it would be better if no one was vaccinated than if everyone was vaccinated. They wrote:

> *The idea that everyone must be vaccinated against COVID-19 is as misguided as the anti-vax idea that no one should. The former is more dangerous for public health.*[117]

They said those who want to vaccinate children are "more dangerous to public health" than anti-vaxxers who don't want anyone to be vaccinated. To them, I am more dangerous than Dr. Kelly Brogan. Dr. Bhattacharya even said that vaccine mandates lead to "more COVID spread b/c vax does not stop infection."[118] In reality, one study of California prison found the vaccine limits the spread of COVID by 20-40%, even with the Omicron variant.[119] That's not great, but it's not nothing either.

Dr. Gupta authored an article titled "A Focused Protection Vaccination Strategy: Why We Should Not Target Children With COVID-19 Vaccination Policies," which argued that "vaccinating children pose risks on them without any substantial direct benefit."[120] In January 2022, she wrote an article titled "Why It's Time to End COVID Self-Isolation" in which she said, "By interfering with the maintenance of herd immunity, measures such as self-isolation actually increase the risk to the vulnerable."[121] She said:

> *In order to move fully into "living with the virus", it is essential to recognise that trying to limit its spread is not only extremely difficult but also undesirable if we are aiming for the sort of relationship we have established with other endemic coronaviruses.*

During the height of the Omicron wave, when pediatric hospitals were deluged with sick children, Dr. Gupta still felt the real problem was that too few unvaccinated children were getting COVID.

"Biggest public health mistake we've ever made…The harm to people is catastrophic."
~ Dr. Jay Bhattacharya

Since lockdowns interfered with their plan to infect unvaccinated young people, the authors of the GBD blame them for all manners of maladies. They anointed themselves as spokesmen for "the working class" and use histrionic language to claim they continue to be harmed by lockdowns of varying stringency, that lasted several months, and ended years ago. Dr. Bhattacharya said lockdowns were the "biggest public health mistake we've ever made…The harm to people is catastrophic."[122] Dr. Kulldorff wrote about the "devastating lockdown carnage on children, workers and the poor"[123] and said lockdowns were "the worst assault on the working class since segregation and the Vietnam War".[124]

No one claims lockdowns were harmless. Many people lost their social connections and income in an instant. It was a brutal solution to a terrible problem, and I recognize I was sheltered from its worst consequences. I was never lonely, and I never missed a paycheck. However, in the real world, many workers and their families found it "catastrophic" that they were left defenseless against the virus. According to one news article on poultry workers:

> *Annie Grant, 55, had been feverish for two nights. Worried about the coronavirus outbreak, her adult children had begged her to stay home rather than return to the frigid poultry plant in Georgia where she had been on the packing line for nearly 15 years.*
>
> *But on the third day she was ill, they got a text from their mother. "They told me I had to come back to work," it said.*
>
> *Ms. Grant ended up returning home, and died in a hospital on Thursday morning after fighting for her life on a ventilator for more than a week. Two other workers at the Tyson Foods poultry plant where she worked in Camilla, Ga., have also died in recent days.*
>
> *"My mom said the guy at the plant said they had to work to feed America. But my mom was sick," said one of Ms. Grant's sons, Willie Martin, 34, a teacher in South Carolina. He said he watched on his phone as his mother took her last breath.*[125]

"We are crying out for help but no one is listening. Our work conditions are out of control. We literally work shoulder to shoulder daily" said one poultry worker. The authors of the GBD have nothing to say about these people, and I could not find any news account where such workers complained their company leadership took excessive measures to protect them against COVID.

Dr. Kulldorff also blamed lockdowns for variants, tweeting that they "generate more contagious variants, increasing herd immunity threshold needed for endemic stage, so more people infected."[126] This is obviously preposterous, especially considering that in the same tweet he lamented that lockdowns "postpone infections", and new infections are the key driver of new variants.[127]

Notably, the authors of the GBD don't object to lockdowns because they failed to slow the virus. Rather, they object to lockdowns precisely *because* they succeeded in this regard, ruining their dream of herd immunity through mass infection. They readily admit that lockdowns allowed countless millions of people to avoid the virus until after they were vaccinated. For example, Dr. Kulldorff wrote in January 2022 that many people had been able to avoid the virus for nearly two years, writing "the laptop class is now getting infected with COVID."[128]

This reveals a key complaint of the GBD, namely that lockdowns protected only the "laptop class", which is their derogatory term for people – like them – who could safely isolate themselves. As Dr. Kulldorff put it:

> *In the US, we locked down the laptop class. The people, the professionals, the lawyers, the bankers, the generalists, the scientists and so on, who can work from home.*[129]

It's obviously true that people who couldn't stay home, like frontline healthcare workers, contracted COVID at a much higher rate than people who could isolate themselves. However, we wouldn't have been better off had bankers contracted COVID during the first wave. It's not just about us, of course. Bus drivers wouldn't have been better off if only more hedge fund managers contracted COVID in April 2020.

Had the laptop class been infected all at the same time then, the catastrophe that befell us in New York City and elsewhere would have been much worse. Hospitals were deluged as it was and no one working in one bemoaned the fact that lockdowns protected the laptop class. We wanted everyone to be safe and would have been furious had we learned of young lawyers partying inside while mass death surrounded us. Even if they all turned out fine, we knew their infections would spill over into vulnerable people.

Dr. Bhattacharya feels we were selfish and unethical for this reason. He said:

> *If you think about medicine as a vocation, you're supposed to devote your well-being to the life a patient that you are caring for...lockdowns actually reversed that and said look, '**you the population should suffer so that my job in medicine can be easier**', so a reversal of the norms of medicine where medicine serves people, not people serve medicine. The fact that medicine, especially the leaders of medicine were so strongly in favor of the lockdowns is a violation of the ethics of the medical profession. It essentially transforms the doctor-patient relationship to one where the patient serves the doctor rather than the other way around.*[130]

Dr. Bhattacharya feels we should have looked at overflowing morgues and honored the ethics of their profession by declaring: *We need more people to get COVID.*

Another key complaint of the GBD is that lockdowns merely "postponed the inevitable." Of course, postponing the inevitable is a core goal of medicine, and it's unambiguously good that countless millions of people avoided the virus until after they were vaccinated and medical care improved.[131] A fully vaccinated and boosted person who contracts COVID today has *much better* odds of a good outcome than someone who contracted it in April of 2020 when hospitals were overflowing and we had no idea how to treat it. This is true even for "not vulnerable" people.

Dr. Kulldorff recognized this in September 2020, writing:

> *Countries like S Korea and NZ have mainly kept number low through lockdowns, including nation-*

> *wide isolation, which can postpone outbreaks until we have a vaccine 3 month to never from now.*[132]

He was right then about the value of postponing outbreaks. One study estimated that COVID vaccines prevented 3.2 million deaths and 18 million hospitalizations in the U.S. in less than two years.[133] Yet, the authors of the GBD still regret that 250 million Americans didn't suddenly resume normal life on October 4, 2020, two months before vaccinations began.

Sadly, countless thousands of people failed to take advantage of the fact that the inevitable had been postponed for them. They believed doctors who told them they were "not vulnerable" and that getting vaccinated was therefore "ill-advised." Many of them turned out to be vulnerable after all, and they expressed regret about not getting vaccinated just before COVID killed them.

Lydia and Lawrence Rodriguez were both in their 40s when they died of COVID. They had four children and Lydia's last words to her sister were "please make sure my kids get vaccinated."[134] Another typical news report said:

> *Christian Cabrera, 40, a father of a 3-year-old, sent a text to his brother, Jino Cabrera, the night before he died. The message read "I can't breathe again. I really regret not getting my vaccine. If I can do it all over again I would do it in a heartbeat to save my life. I'm fighting for my life here and I wish I would have gotten vaccinated.*[135]

Such tragedies became commonplace. One newspaper ran a story titled "21 Heartbreaking Stories of People Who Regret Not Getting a COVID-19 Vaccine."[136] Doctors who didn't work in hospitals could insulate themselves from such tragedies. In contrast, Dr. Ryan Dare, a physician in Arkansas, said:

> *It is heart-wrenching to see unvaccinated individuals come into the hospital with regret. . . . if they could do it all over again, would have had the vaccine in a second.*[137]

The authors of the GBD didn't experience any of this.

"Study after study have shown that natural immunity after COVID infection is superior to vaccine immunity" ~ Dr. Martin Kulldorff

While the authors of the GBD lambast measures to limit COVID, they continue to fetishize the virus, speaking about it in glowing terms. They essentially function as lawyers for the Team COVID Army, defending SARS-CoV-2 against allegations that it is dangerous or something to be avoided.

In March 2021, during a roundtable with Governor DeSantis, Dr. Bhattacharya said something no doctor who treated COVID patients would say. He said:

> *Although people think about the disease as mainly just this deadly viral pneumonia that results in hospitalization and death. In fact, the vast majority of cases are relatively mild, asymptomatic, or with mild symptoms.*[83]

530,000 Americans had already died of COVID when he said that. Another 570,000 have died since.[39]

COVID remains the third leading cause of death in the US,[138] and no reasonable person would speak in this soothing fashion about other top killers. Imagine an epidemiologist saying:

> *Although people think about trauma as mainly just these deadly accidents that result in hospitalization and death. In fact, the vast majority of injuries are relatively mild, asymptomatic, or with mild symptoms.*

Yet, this is exactly how the authors of the GBD, and many other doctors, spoke about COVID.

During this roundtable Dr. Bhattacharya spoke with great confidence about a new, mutating virus, which had existed for barely over a year. He said:

> *There's a vast array of evidence in the scientific literature that shows definitively that if you've had COVID and recovered, the vast, vast majority of*

people have a durable immunity that it's very unlikely that you'll be reinfected and you'll be protected from, from reinfection. Even if you do get reinfected at some later time, it's very likely to be less severe than the first time.[83]

The Delta variant arrived soon thereafter, and Dr. Bhattacharya responded by saying "I don't think the delta variant changes the calculus or the evidence in any fundamental way."[139] Although the Delta variant *did* change the calculus in a fundamental way, Dr. Bhattacharya repeated himself when the Omicron variant emerged. In a segment called "No One Should Panic About the Omicron Variant" Dr. Bhattacharya continued to defend the virus. He said:

So I think now we can look and then do empirical studies to see if it is more severe and if it does evade, I don't, it seems really unlikely, just from a first principles point of view that because it's still the same virus with a few mutations. The other variants have not escaped natural immunity, have not escaped vaccine immunity, in terms of protection against severe disease, and that's something we should tell the public. I mean this is not something to panic about. We have many tools to address this and we are in the process of developing new ones.[140]

In reality, more children were hospitalized and died during the Omicron wave than ever before.[96] Adults didn't fare well either. According to an article in the New York Times titled "During the Omicron Wave, Death Rates Soared for Older People":

Almost as many Americans 65 and older died in four months of the Omicron surge as did in six months of the Delta wave, even though the Delta variant, for any one person, tended to cause more severe illness.[141]

Dr. Gupta similarly said in September 2020 that children "would benefit from being exposed to this and other seasonal coronaviruses."[142] She has since suggested vaccines for "everyone over 65+ and pregnant women,"[112] but even after admitting acquired immunity fades, she continued to be a cheerleader for the virus, saying:

> *The main reason that it (the pandemic) is going to end is that many of us have been naturally infected and have natural immunity, which gets topped up again.*

Dr. Kulldorff said that "the pandemic ends when enough people have natural immunity after COVID recovery. With herd immunity, we then enter the endemic stage."[143] He said, "the denial of natural immunity after COVID disease is the worst unscientific folly in the past 75 years."[144] I am confident that medical historians will not view the "denial of natural immunity" as the worst unscientific folly in the past 75 years.

He said "Study after study have shown that natural immunity after COVID infection is superior to vaccine immunity"[145] though of course "natural immunity" killed over a million Americans. In a pro-virus essay titled "The Triumph of Natural Immunity," he wrote:

> *A new CDC study shows that around 75% of American children have already had COVID. That means that they have strong natural immunity that protects them from COVID infections as they get older. Despite this, the CDC, the FDA and other government agencies are pushing all of them to get vaccinated.*[146]

This is exactly how anti-vaxxers talk about viruses and vaccines. For example, Dr. Kelly Brogan said, "HPV infectious exposures *actually protect* against the progression of HPV linked cervical changes to cancer."[147] The idea that the best way to protect yourself from a virus is to get the virus is like using pregnancy as a form of contraception, and it was previously promoted only by anti-vaccine cranks.

"Compared to no reinfection, reinfection contributed additional risks of death and sequelae including pulmonary, cardiovascular, hematological, diabetes, gastrointestinal, kidney, mental health, musculoskeletal and neurological disorders."

Like Dr. Brogan, the authors of the GBD are wrong about the "triumph of natural immunity." Though Dr. Kulldorff said the pandemic will end "when enough people have natural immunity,"[143] we have a ton of natural immunity and not so much herd immunity. Moreover, there's no evidence that natural immunity protects children from "COVID infections as they get older."[146] There's not a "vast array of evidence in the scientific literature" that a baby who had COVID in March 2020 will be protected from reinfections well into adulthood, and we don't know what variants will be circulating in a few years' time.

This is a totally new virus, and it has already thrown us a lot of curveballs. Yet, doctors who underestimated the virus at every turn, continue to speak as if they know exactly how it's going to behave many years into the future. For example, Dr. Kulldorff said infected children "have strong natural immunity that protects them from COVID infections as they get older." How does he know this? The only predictable thing about future variants is that the authors of the GBD will tell us they are nothing to worry about and that we have many tools to address them.

No one says natural immunity is useless, but it shouldn't be sanctified either. Stories of people getting COVID multiple times are commonplace, and while reinfections are usually less severe, one reason why is because dead people can only be infected once. COVID has already killed the most vulnerable amongst us. Moreover, repeated COVID infections are not necessarily benign. One study using a U.S. Department of Veterans Affairs' national healthcare database found:

> *Compared to no reinfection, reinfection contributed additional risks of death and sequelae including pulmonary, cardiovascular, hematological, diabetes, gastrointestinal, kidney, mental health,*

musculoskeletal and neurological disorders. The risks were evident regardless of vaccination status. The risks were most pronounced in the acute phase but persisted in the postacute phase at 6 months. Compared to noninfected controls, cumulative risks and burdens of repeat infection increased according to the number of infections.[148]

Study author Ziyad Al-Aly said, "Reinfection with COVID-19 increases the risk of both acute outcomes and long COVID, This was evident in unvaccinated, vaccinated and boosted people."[149] It's easy to imagine children born during the pandemic will get COVID multiple times in their life. What will be the consequences of this?

Meanwhile, multiple studies have shown that vaccination is beneficial even in those with natural immunity. There's evidence that even "a single dose of vaccine after infection reinforced protection against reinfection."[150]

"We cannot afford to allow scientific misinformation and conspiracy theories to run rampant either on social media or in-person interactions."
~ Congressman Raja Krishnamoorth

While the authors of the GBD were able to convince some politicians to take the side of the virus, not all were fooled. During a hearing of the House Select Subcommittee on the Coronavirus Crisis titled "Combating Coronavirus Cons And The Monetization of Misinformation," Congressman Raja Krishnamoorthi said:

It is unfortunate and ironic that my Republican colleagues selected Dr. Bhattacharya as a witness for our COVID-19 misinformation hearing when he himself is a purveyor of COVID-19 misinformation. As Dr. Bhattacharya acknowledged in questioning, he has drawn criticism from multiple judges for misrepresenting scientific studies and the consensus of medical professionals, while even testifying as an expert on matters on which he admitted he was not qualified. The presence of Dr. Bhattacharya as

> *a witness today is a stark example of the challenges of combating pandemic misinformation. During a pandemic that has taken the lives of over 765,000 Americans, we cannot afford to allow scientific misinformation and conspiracy theories to run rampant either on social media or in-person interactions.*[151]

In a ruling about mask mandates where Dr. Bhattacharya was a witness, U.S. District Judge Waverly D. Crenshaw said Bhattacharya's testimony was "troubling and problematic for several reasons."[152] An article about his ruling said:

> *The doctor oversimplified conclusions of at least one study he cited, Crenshaw wrote, "suggesting he may have been apt to do so with other studies upon which he relied."*
>
> *"He offered opinions regarding the pediatric effects of masks on children, a discipline on which he admitted he was not qualified to speak," Crenshaw said. "His demeanor and tone while testifying suggest that he is advancing a personal agenda. At this stage of the proceedings, the Court is simply unwilling to trust Dr. Bhattacharya."*

The winning lawyer, who represented two families of children with disabilities, said "The court shredded the Governor's anti-mask 'expert' as lacking in credibility, and being 'replete with contradictions'."

After Dr. Bhattacharya pushed to send unvaccinated children and teachers back to school in Florida in 2020, another judge noted that Dr. Bhattacharya "admitted Stanford University will not be holding in-person classes in the fall. Classes there will be taught remotely because of the pandemic."[153]

As their reputation amongst reputable scientists and doctors with real world responsibility plummeted, the authors of the GBD further aligned themselves with members of the anti-vaccine fringe. Drs. Bhattacharya and Kulldorff have been favorably profiled by *The*

Defender, the anti-vaccine page run by Robert F. Kennedy, Jr., and have associated themselves with outright anti-vaccine disinformation agents. At one public meeting, they listened politely as businessman Steve Kirsch spreads blatant disinformation, claiming COVID vaccines killed over 500,000 people while saving less than 25,000.

Both Drs. Bhattacharya and Kulldorff tweeted their support to right-wing, anti-vaccine Canadian truckers who occupied Ottawa in the winter of 2022, some waving swastika and Confederate flags. 13 families with children battling cancer had their treatment delayed or rescheduled due to the trucker' actions.[154] Nonetheless, Dr. Kulldorff said "thank you, #TruckerConvoy,"[155] while Dr. Bhattacharya said:

> *A day is coming when Canada's biomedical security state recedes and the strong democracy that Canada enjoyed before COVID returns. #HonkHonk*[156]

Dr. Bhattacharya appeared on a podcast called "COVID Vaccine Breakdown" with Dr. Simone Gold, who founded the anti-vaccine group America's Frontline Doctors and served six months in prison for her role in the January 6th insurrection.[157] He also asked "Did lockdowns cause the Ukraine war?"[158] and has suggested that quack cures have been suppressed, saying:

> *There is not a definitive study that's been done on it. That is a scandal: the idea that ivermectin might work was known in 2020.*[159]

Dr. Kulldorff compared masking children to the Taliban's treatment of women, and as frontline healthcare workers quit due to threats and violent patients, Dr. Kulldorff poured gasoline on that fire, tweeting about "carnage" and the "people responsible", along with a picture of a guillotine.

Along with other anti-vaccine doctors (Drs. Joseph Ladapo, Tracy Høeg, and Joseph Fraiman) Drs. Bhattacharya and Kulldorff are also part of a new Public Health Integrity Committee formed by Governor DeSantis. According to Governor DeSantis:

> *Florida will hold the medical establishment accountable by:*

- *Creating a grand jury to investigate mRNA shots & Big Pharma*
- *Investigating cardiac-related deaths tied to the mRNA vaccine*
- *Forming a Public Health Integrity Committee to oversee the medical establishment* [160]

In December 2022, The Florida Supreme Court allowed Governor DeSantis to impanel a grand jury to investigate COVID vaccines and consider bringing charges against pharmaceutical companies and vaccine-advocates. According to court filings:

> *There are good and sufficient reasons to deem it to be in the public interest to impanel a statewide grand jury to investigate criminal or wrongful activity in Florida relating to the development, promotion, and distribution of vaccines purported to prevent COVID-19 infection, symptoms, and transmission... The pharmaceutical industry has a notorious history of misleading the public for financial gain. Questions have been raised regarding the veracity of the representations made by the pharmaceutical manufacturers of COVID-19 vaccines, particularly with respect to transmission, prevention, efficacy, and safety. An investigation is warranted to determine whether the pharmaceutical industry has engaged in fraudulent practices.*[161]

This "investigation" is designed to bolster the political prospects of Governor DeSantis, and there's no question what it will find. Dr. Ladapo, the state's anti-vaccine Surgeon General, had previously shared "research" claiming the vaccine was riskier than the virus for young men. However, a report from the University of Florida found this was "seriously flawed,"[162] and that Dr. Ladapo engaged in "careless, irregular, or contentious research practices."

With doctors leading the way and providing cover, the state of Florida is now officially anti-vaccine, and predictably, misinformation about the COVID vaccine is now seeping into routine vaccinations.[163] One headline from December 2022 read,

"Non-COVID Vaccine Rates For Florida School Children Are Lowest in More Than 10 Years."

"It was a murderous calamity" ~ Jeffrey Tucker

After the signing of the GBD, Jeffrey Tucker founded a right-wing think tank called the Brownstone Institute,[164] which describes itself as the "spiritual child" of the GBD. Many doctors mentioned in this book have had their work featured there. Dr. Kulldroff even left Harvard and is now a "senior scholar" at the Brownstone Institute where he continues to rail against measures to control the virus.

Mr. Tucker and the Brownstone Institute have become major spreaders of COVID conspiracies and anti-vaccine balderdash. For example, in an essay titled "The 70 Seconds that Shook the World," Mr. Tucker analyzed 70 seconds of a press conference and became convinced that Drs. Deborah Birx and Anthony Fauci hoodwinked President Trump into approving lockdowns at the pandemic's start.[165] He also tweeted that "Fauci pushed lockdowns to cover up a lab leak for which he was personally responsible."[166]

There's a dark side to this ridiculousness. Mr. Tucker also promoted the myth that doctors killed patients with ventilators, calling it a "murderous calamity" and falsely claimed that "88% of those forced on ventilators died."[167] He published an article titled "More Questions about Spring 2020 COVID in New York City Hospitals," which claimed that "NYC Emergency Departments weren't overrun by people with COVID-19" and that "NYC Emergency Room respiratory visit spike may have been panic-driven."[168] The article concluded that doctors were more dangerous than the virus. It said:

> *It was misuse of ventilators, protocol-induced staffing shortages, isolation, failure to treat, similar factors that resulted in thousands of Spring 2020 iatrogenic deaths in New York City and elsewhere.*

He even exported his anti-vaccine beliefs, telling Ugandans in an online forum that COVID vaccines were "a technology that's not been proven as safe and effective."[169]

"Zero COVID Has Cost New Zealand Dearly" ~ Dr. Jay Bhattacharya

We can now return to the discussion of New Zealand. Dr. Bhattacharya unsurprisingly disagreed with New Zealand's pandemic approach. In August 2022, he authored a piece titled "Zero COVID Has Cost New Zealand Dearly" in which he said that "Jacinda Ardern was never the pandemic heroine she was made out to be."[170]

Because Dr. Bhattacharya wanted unvaccinated young people to contract COVID, New Zealand's success in protecting all of its citizens represented the antithesis of his pro-virus stance. Nonetheless, Dr. Bhattacharya was forced to concede the obvious, writing:

> *New Zealand's strategy delayed the inevitable spread of COVID throughout the population to a time after the development, testing and deployment of a vaccine capable of reducing the burden of severe COVID disease....New Zealand has a tiny proportion of the US's COVID-attributable deaths per capita.*

Dr. Bhattacharya was also forced to concede another uncomfortable point, writing that "All-cause excess deaths – below baseline levels in 2020 – shot up in 2021 and in 2022." The link in his article led to a graph from *Our World in Data* showing that countries that let the virus run rampant had much greater excess mortality than New Zealand for nearly all of the pandemic.[171] New Zealand's largest increase in mortality occurred only after they abandoned their Zero COVID strategy, but because most of their population was vaccinated by then, they fared much better than the U.S. and UK.

Despite this, Dr. Bhattacharya did not feel that this mattered compared to the economy. He didn't tell his readers that 800,000 Americans would be alive today if the U.S. had New Zealand's COVID death rate. Instead, he presented detailed statistics about New Zealand's economy. He wrote:

> *There was economic damage as well during the Zero COVID period. New Zealand's typically robust tourist industry collapsed as overseas visitors stopped coming. The New Zealand economy shrank by two per cent in 2020 despite Zero COVID, recovered to grow by 5.6 per cent in 2021, but shrank again in the first quarter of 2022 as Omicron cases spread throughout the nation. In July 2022, inflation reached 7.3 per cent, sharply reducing the purchasing power of New Zealanders.*[170]

Of course, it's farcical to claim that New Zealand's tourist industry would have run normally had they made no efforts to contain the virus. Countries that let the virus run rampant didn't exactly have booming economies either. Millions of Americans lost their jobs[172] and the whole world suffered from inflation.[173] It's not good for offices, restaurants, and theaters when so many corpses accumulate that morgue workers have to use forklifts to move them into giant refrigerated trucks, as happened here in New York City.[174] Life would not have continued as normal but for lockdowns. It's also not good for business when workers get sick. One study from August 2022 estimated that 4 million Americans are out of work due to long COVID.[175]

However, even if all of New Zealand's economic woes were from their "Zero COVID period," it's not obvious this financial price was not counterbalanced by their citizens not dying.

Dr. Bhattacharya concluded:

> *Finally, New Zealand's strategy relied entirely on the development and testing of a vaccine outside of its borders. Indeed, the vaccines could never have been tested in 2020 and 2021 within New Zealand because there were insufficient COVID cases to run a meaningful randomised trial. In effect, New Zealand relied on the fact that other countries did not adopt a Zero COVID policy to create conditions that permitted New Zealand to escape from the Zero COVID trap it embraced until spring 2022.*

Ultimately, New Zealand's Zero COVID strategy was immoral, incoherent and a grand failure.[170]

In essence, Dr. Bhattacharya felt that, since the rest of the world suffered from COVID, New Zealand had no right to skip the party. He feels New Zealand was "immoral" for not letting more of its citizens get COVID before they were vaccinated, even as he concedes that "New Zealand has a tiny proportion of the US's COVID-attributable deaths per capita."

I wonder how many New Zealanders feel their country's COVID approach was "immoral, incoherent and a grand failure." I wonder how Americans, especially those who lost a loved one, feel their country's approach was "immoral, incoherent and a grand failure."

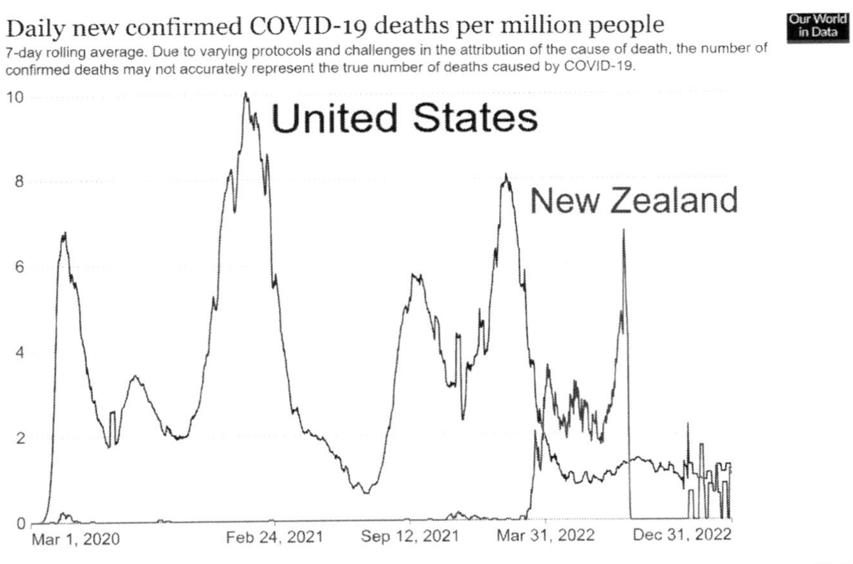
Daily new confirmed COVID-19 deaths per million people
Our World in Data
7-day rolling average. Due to varying protocols and challenges in the attribution of the cause of death, the number of confirmed deaths may not accurately represent the true number of deaths caused by COVID-19.
10
8
6
4
2
0
United States
New Zealand
Mar 1, 2020
Feb 24, 2021
Sep 12, 2021
Mar 31, 2022
Dec 31, 2022
Source: WHO COVID-19 Dashboard
CC BY

COVID deaths in the United States and New Zealand[39]

Chapter 6: "Infants, kids, teens, young people, young adults, middle aged with no conditions etc. have zero to little risk.... so we use them to develop herd...we want them infected...."

"I think our ideas have inflitrated *[sic]* the White House regardless."

~ Dr. John Ioannidis

The Great Barrington Declaration (GBD) was premised on the fantastical notion that herd immunity would have arrived in a few months had we only let 250 million unvaccinated, "not vulnerable" Americans contract COVID in October 2020 and turned everyone else into shut-ins. It was not a thoughtful policy proposal or an actionable plan to protect the vulnerable. Rather, the GBD was drafted to provide intellectual cover for those who opposed all measures to limit the spread of SARS-CoV-2. It was a political document masquerading as a scientific one.

It was also a rallying cry, and its authors were not silent academics, ensconced in an ivory tower. Though they purport to be "censored" and "muzzled" whenever they are merely criticized, the authors and supporters of the GBD were ubiquitous media presences during the pandemic. They've been on Fox News dozens of times[1] and written multiple editorials in the *Wall Street Journal* and other international publications. They write for right-wing think tanks and publications like the Brownstone Institute and *The Epoch Times*. They testified before Congress and in courtrooms. They have big social media presences. They've been on many podcasts and have made many *YouTube* videos. One video titled; "Dissenting Scientists Issue COVID-19 Herd Immunity Declaration" has been viewed over a million times.[2] They have legions of adoring fans. Elon Musk has tweeted his support. The authors of the GBD weren't silent or censored. They were loud and they were everywhere. They've become mini celebrities of sorts.

They were also very influential. The authors and backers of the GBD had access to powerful politicians around the world. Though few frontline doctors took the GBD seriously – we knew what the virus could do to "not vulnerable" people – some politicians were enamored by its false promises. The GBD told them they could have their cake and eat it too. Not only were politicians told that it was acceptable to ask nothing of their citizens aside from being careful around grandpa, but they were also told this would end the entire pandemic in just 3 to 6 months with minimal loss of life or economic disruption.

Those who felt measures to control the virus would do more harm than the virus itself immediately reached out to politicians to share this message. They felt they knew a lot about this brand-new virus, namely that it wasn't that dangerous. They also felt they could easily predict its behavior and never considered the possibility of new variants. Though the GBD was months away from being written, Dr. John Ioannidis was clearly sympathetic to its ideas and worked to get its message to the White House at the pandemic's start. According to the reporting of Stephanie Lee:

> *In late March, as COVID-19 cases overran hospitals overseas, Ioannidis tried to organize a meeting at the White House where he and a small band of colleagues would caution the president against "shutting down the country for [a] very long time and jeopardizing so many lives in doing this," according to a statement Ioannidis submitted on the group's behalf. Their goal, the statement said, was "to both save more lives and avoid serious damage to the US economy using the most reliable data."*
>
> *Although the meeting did not happen, Ioannidis believed their message had reached the right people. Within a day of him sending it to the White House, Trump announced that he wanted the country reopened by Easter. "I think our ideas have inflitrated* [sic] *the White House regardless," Ioannidis told his collaborators on March 28.*[3]

Dr. Ioannidis was right about this at least. Dr. Paul Alexander, an official in the U.S. Department of Health and Human Services during the Trump Administration, would push the premises of the GBD months before the official document had been written. In a series of emails in the summer of 2020 to FDA Commissioner Dr. Stephen Hahn and CDC Director Dr. Robert Redfield, he said things such as:

> *There is no other way, we need to establish herd, and it only comes about allowing the non-high risk groups expose themselves to the virus. PERIOD.*
>
> *Infants, kids, teens, young people, young adults, middle aged with no conditions etc. have zero to little risk....so we use them to develop herd...we want them infected...*
>
> [I]*t may be that it will be best if we open up and flood the zone and let the kids and young folk get infected* [in order to get] *natural immunity...natural exposure.*
>
> [W]*e essentially took off the battlefield the most potent weapon we had...younger healthy people, children, teens, young people who we needed to fastly* [sic] *infect themselves, spread it around, develop immunity, and help stop the spread.*
>
> *"If it is causing more cases in young, my word is who cares...as long as we make sensible decisions, and protect the elderely* [sic] *and nursing homes, we must go on with life....who cares if we test more and get more positive tests."*[4]

At least Dr. Alexander didn't beat around the bush with euphemisms that young people should "resume normal life." In private, he was willing to admit that the goal was always to infect "infants, kids, teens, young people, young adults, middle aged with no conditions" with a new virus that would kill and disable some of them.

Today, Dr. Alexander is a writer for The Brownstone Institute and has called for the lynching of people who interfered with this plan. In an article titled "The Greatest Crime in GLOBAL History, GREATEST, Without Exception, Is The Fraud COVID Pandemic, Lockdowns & The Vaccine; All Of It Was A Pure Lie, All Of It; TRUMP Was Devastatingly MISLED! You Were!" he ranted:

> *We never stop, we become the COVIDian hunters, like Nazi hunters, we be relentless, we get these people into courtrooms and many more of these people, I did not list all, and you investigate and if shown they caused lives to be lost, we take all their money, and jail them, jail each and anyone of them, and if a judge says we can hang them, we hang them too! High! Publicly. No one is to be spared, no matter you connections. No one. You must hang if you killed people by your actions. It is that simple.*[5]

Drs. Joseph Ladapo, Scott Atlas, Martin Kulldorff, Cody Meissner, and Jay Bhattacharya meet with President Trump in the Oval Office in August 2020 (Image Credit: Official White House Photographers)[18]

Other leading proponents of infecting unvaccinated young people, namely Drs. Joseph Ladapo, Scott Atlas, Martin Kulldorff, Cody Meissner, and Jay Bhattacharya, met with President Trump in August 2020. He would soon promote their talking points verbatim. For example, at the Republican National Convention later that month President Trump said, "We are aggressively sheltering those at highest risk, especially the elderly, while allowing lower-risk Americans to safely return to work and to school."[6]

According to the House Select Subcommittee on the Coronavirus Crisis, the authors and supporters of the GBD were invited there by Dr. Scott Atlas, a neuroradiologist and Senior Fellow in health care policy at the Hoover Institution, a conservative think tank at Stanford University. The report stated:

> *According to Director Redfield, Dr. Atlas brought these individuals to the White House specifically "to convince people that herd immunity was going to save us, and this thing was going to go bye-bye."*[7]

Indeed, no one translated the GBD's fantasy of herd immunity through mass infection of unvaccinated youth into policy more effectively than Dr. Scott Atlas. Like them, he thought COVID's threat was overblown. At the start of the pandemic, he parroted the talking points of Dr. Ioannidis.[8] In an email to Centers for Medicare and Medicaid Services Administrator Seema Verma, Dr. Atlas said the "virus would cause about 10,000 deaths." He claimed this number "would be unnoticed" in a normal flu season.

Given this, Dr. Atlas was more fearful of measures to contain the virus than the virus itself. Though the GBD was months away from being published, Dr. Atlas outlined its core points in an essay from April 20, 2020, titled "The Data Is In – Stop the Panic and End the Total Isolation." It was based on 5 central "facts":

- *Fact 1: The overwhelming majority of people do not have any significant risk of dying from COVID-19.*
- *Fact 2: Protecting older, at-risk people eliminates hospital overcrowding*
- *Fact 3: Vital population immunity is prevented by total isolation policies, prolonging the problem.*
- *Fact 4: People are dying because other medical care is not getting done due to hypothetical projections.*
- *Fact 5: We have a clearly defined population at risk who can be protected with targeted measures.*[9]

It's remarkable to think that with everything that has happened since April 2020, Dr. Atlas hasn't changed his opinion about these "facts" one bit. Though he thought only 10,000 Americans would die of COVID, a million dead Americans later Dr. Atlas feels these initial pandemic pronouncements have been vindicated.

Like many such doctors, Dr. Atlas could be found on TV at the pandemic's start, not in a hospital. Indeed, this is how he came to President Trump's attention in the first place. In an interview with Tucker Carlson from June 29, 2020, Dr. Atlas spread misinformation about pediatric COVID and celebrated spread of the virus, saying:

> *We expected more cases with more social mingling... But the fact is the overwhelming majority of these cases are in younger healthier people. These people do not have a significant problem. They do not have the serious complications. They do not die. And so it's fantastic news that we have a lot of cases, but we don't see deaths going up, and what that means is A: we're are doing a better job of protecting the vulnerable, B: We're in good shape here.*
>
> *We like the fact that there's a lot of cases in low-risk populations, because that's exactly how we're going to get herd immunity, population immunity, when low-risk people, with no significant problem handling this virus, which is basically 99% of people get this, they become immunity and they block the pathway of connectivity of contagiousness for older sicker people...Children have virtually zero risk of getting a serious complication, virtually a zero risk of dying...Children only rarely if ever transmit the disease.*[10]

"When you isolate everyone, including all the healthy people, you're prolonging the problem because you're preventing population immunity,"[11] Dr. Atlas told Fox News host Brian Kilmeade in July 2020. "Low-risk groups getting the infection is not a problem. In fact, it's a positive." Dr. Atlas praised President Trump's approach in an interview with Laura Ingraham on Fox News saying:

> *The strategy here that has been outlined by the briefings this week is very clear. We know that more relaxation is going to get more cases. By the way, you don't eradicate a virus by locking down. That's just a complete misconception. We know that with socializing, we are going to get more cases. We need to protect the vulnerable, double down on that. We need to make sure that hospitals are not overextended, and, in fact, most hospitals are not.*[12]

Though he'd been an informal White House advisor for some time, on August 10, 2020, Dr. Atlas – who said it was "fantastic news that we have a lot of cases"[10] – became President Trump's COVID advisor. From then on, the virus had an ally in a very powerful place. Indeed, on October 5, 2020, just one day after the GBD was signed, Dr. Atlas invited its three authors – Drs. Jay Bhattacharya, Martin Kulldorff, and Sunetra Gupta – to meet with Alex Azar, an "attorney, businessman, lobbyist, and former pharmaceutical executive"[13] who served as the U.S. Secretary of Health and Human Services.

There is no evidence they discussed the free home delivery of groceries for the home-bound seniors, disability job accommodations for vulnerable workers, or temporary accommodations for older people living in multi-generational homes, even though these measures were theoretically the core premise of the GBD. Politicians who met with the authors of the GBD never promoted these policies, and the authors of the GBD never seemed perturbed that their "plan" to protect the vulnerable was completely ignored.

"Herd immunity was going to save us, and this thing was going to go bye-bye."
~ The Atlas Dogma

This all had a significant amount of real-world influence. Eight days after Drs. Bhattacharya, Kulldorff, and Gupta met with Secretary Azar, a headline in the New York Times declared, "White House Embraces a Declaration from Scientists That Opposes Lockdowns and Relies on 'Herd Immunity.'" According to this article:

> *On a call convened Monday by the White House,*

two senior administration officials, both speaking anonymously because they were not authorized to give their names, cited an October 4 petition titled The Great Barrington Declaration, which argues against lockdowns and calls for a reopening of businesses and schools.[14]

The GBD's influence in the White House has been thoroughly documented by The House Select Subcommittee on the Coronavirus Crisis United States, which is a House of Representatives select subcommittee that has been reporting on the Trump administration's handling of the pandemic. Because I cannot improve on it, I will share relevant sections from their report, "The Atlas Dogma: The Trump Administration's Embrace of a Dangerous and Discredited Herd Immunity Via Mass Infection Strategy."[7]

The Trump White House Recruited an Outspoken Proponent of a Dangerous and Discredited Herd Immunity Strategy

As early as March 2020—the same month that President Donald Trump first declared the coronavirus a national emergency amid thousands of Americans contracting a novel virus for which there were no known treatments or vaccines – Dr. Scott Atlas was downplaying the risk posed by the coronavirus and advocating against the federal government taking meaningful action to mitigate its spread. A Senior Fellow at the conservative think tank the Hoover Institution and former adviser to Rudy Giuliani's presidential campaign, Dr. Atlas was one of the earliest and most vocal opponents of public health measures designed to mitigate the spread of the virus and prevent the collapse of the nation's hospital systems. Although he was a radiologist by training and did not have a background in infectious diseases, Dr. Atlas appeared on Fox News, One America News Network, and other conservative media platforms in the spring of 2020 to attack mainstream public health measures and call for a vastly different approach to the pandemic. In an April 22 op-ed published in The Hill, Dr. Atlas argued that "[t]he overwhelming majority of people do not have any significant risk of dying from COVID19" and that "[v]ital population immunity is prevented by total isolation policies, prolonging the problem."

On March 21, 2020, Dr. Atlas sent an email to CMS Administrator Seema Verma to advocate against "the need for lockdown and even the frantic need for urgent testing," calling the federal government's approach to combating the virus "a massive overreaction" that was "inciting irrational fear" in Americans. Dr. Atlas stated that the early data showed the "virus would cause about 10,000 deaths" – a number that he claimed "would be unnoticed" in a normal flu season – and argued that "[t]he panic needs to be stopped." In the months that followed, Dr. Atlas and other proponents of his fringe views on the coronavirus became increasingly influential in shaping government policy. Despite lacking expertise in infectious diseases, Dr. Atlas would go on to informally advise Florida Governor Ron DeSantis on the coronavirus – eventually leading to a job advising President Donald Trump and formulating pandemic-related policies in the Trump White House.

The herd immunity strategy pushed by Dr. Atlas was premised on the theory that the best response to the pandemic was to expose enough people to the virus – without any vaccines and few effective treatments – so that a large enough portion of the population would become immune and stop the virus from spreading widely. A central element of the strategy was so-called "focused protection," which assumed that "high risk" individuals – such as the elderly and individuals with underlying medical conditions like obesity, diabetes, or heart disease – could be easily identified and effectively isolated while the rest of society resumed pre-pandemic life and were even encouraged to become infected. Then, when enough of the "low risk" individuals had been infected and developed immunity (a threshold that was unknown and, as it turned out given waning immunity and the emergence of new variants capable of evading prior immunity, likely unattainable), the "focused protection" could end and everyone could resume their normal lives with the protection of herd immunity.

Leading public health experts recognized that this approach was not implementable in practice. Even if it had been possible to accurately designate every American as high or low risk, experts warned that it would not have been possible to fully isolate all high-risk individuals from any possible exposure to the coronavirus, particularly in areas with high community spread. This view was held by White House Coronavirus Response Coordinator Dr. Deborah Birx, who told the Select Subcommittee in a transcribed interview that "the majority of Americans that were over 70 and most vulnerable" were "often in the community with multigenerational households of essential workers or other workers" and that "there was no way to isolate the vulnerable family member from the other family members."

Even before Dr. Atlas's hiring, at least one Trump Administration official was aggressively advocating for a herd immunity strategy. Throughout the early months of the pandemic – as Dr. Atlas appeared on television claiming it was "a good thing" that "younger, healthier people get infected... because that's exactly the way that population immunity develops" – an HHS political appointee, Dr. Paul Alexander, was pushing Trump Administration officials to adopt this strategy. For example, on July 4, 2020, Dr. Alexander wrote to senior HHS officials urging: "There is no other way, we need to establish herd, and it only comes about allowing the non-high risk groups expose themselves to the virus. PERIOD." In a follow-up message, Dr. Alexander elaborated:

"Infants, kids, teens, young people, young adults, middle aged with no conditions etc. have zero to little risk....so we use them to develop herd...we want them infected....

Despite the widespread rejection of a disease-acquired herd immunity strategy by the mainstream scientific community, this strategy caught the attention of the Trump White House as it searched for a way to deflect from the President's disastrous coronavirus response in the lead-up to the 2020 presidential election. During a transcribed interview, Dr. Birx told the Select Subcommittee that senior leaders in the White House appeared to be influenced by Dr. Atlas's fringe theories as early as late March 2020, speculating that Dr. Atlas may have been providing them with "biased antibody data out of California that the virus was much more widespread" and "the disease was no worse than flu."

In mid-July 2020, John McEntee, the Director of the White House Presidential Personnel Office, invited Dr. Atlas to come to the White House to meet with senior Trump Administration officials. During a series of one-on-one meetings with Vice President Mike Pence, White House Chief of Staff Mark Meadows, White House Senior Adviser Stephen Miller, White House Press Secretary Kayleigh McEnany, and other officials, Dr. Atlas discussed his perception that the coronavirus posed a low risk to the vast majority of Americans and that mitigation measures should be eliminated. Dr. Atlas also met with President Trump in the Oval Office, along with White House Senior Adviser Jared Kushner. During a transcribed interview, Dr. Atlas informed the Select Subcommittee that President Trump asked about his views on a variety of subjects related to the coronavirus during this meeting, including his opinion on "lockdowns," Sweden's approach to the pandemic, and the drug hydroxychloroquine – even though FDA had revoked its authorization as a coronavirus treatment the prior month…

President Trump publicly announced that Dr. Atlas had been hired as a White House adviser on the pandemic during a press briefing on August 12, 2020. Following that announcement, Dr. Atlas would take on a more prominent role within the Trump Administration in directing pandemic policy and communicating those policies to the public. With Dr. Atlas firmly entrenched, Dr. Birx noted that "inside the White House is a person that is basically wanting community spread to increase."

Dr. Atlas Received Wide Access Inside the Trump White House and Became an Influential Voice Pushing for Herd Immunity Policies

Dr. Atlas was given an office at the White House and was granted extensive access to the highest levels of the federal government's pandemic response. For instance, Dr. Atlas was added as a member of the White House Coronavirus Task Force in mid-August 2020, which allowed him to participate directly in Task Force meetings led by Vice President Pence and attended by Cabinet members and other senior officials. In this role, Dr. Atlas was able to influence the Administration's pandemic response policies in critical ways, including orchestrating significant changes to public health guidance. The

Select Subcommittee's investigation found that Dr. Atlas participated in a series of meetings that the Trump White House referred to internally as "China Virus Huddles." Separate from the White House Coronavirus Task Force, these meetings were run by Mr. Kushner and attended by an exclusive group of senior Trump Administration officials, including Dr. Birx, Senior Counselor to the President Kellyanne Conway, Assistant to the President Hope Hicks, and HHS Deputy Chief of Staff for Policy Paul Mango. Dr. Atlas informed the Select Subcommittee that these meetings were held three times a week and were used to hone the Trump White House's messaging on the pandemic. Dr. Birx said these meetings were also used to address key "operational aspects" of the federal government's coronavirus response.

Dr. Atlas received direct access to President Trump and, according to CDC Director Dr. Robert Redfield, "had the ear" of the president when it came to advising on pandemic policy. During a transcribed interview with the Select Subcommittee, Dr. Atlas recounted that he attended at least a half dozen "pre-briefings" with the president in the Oval Office, which occurred before President Trump held press conferences on the coronavirus response. In these briefings, Dr. Atlas conveyed to President Trump strategies and recommendations that were consistent with his herd immunity theory. Dr. Atlas also reviewed and provided edits on President Trump's public remarks, which incorporated aspects of Dr. Atlas's theories. The Trump White House also authorized Dr. Atlas to publish at least two op-eds in his formal capacity as a Special Advisor to President Trump and member of the White House Coronavirus Task Force, both of which advanced elements of his herd immunity theory. Dr. Birx told the Select Subcommittee that "parallel data streams" flowed into the Oval Office during Dr. Atlas's White House tenure and influenced

President Trump to downplay the severity of the virus and reject many science-backed mitigation measures.

At Dr. Atlas's Urging, Trump Administration Officials Promoted a Herd Immunity Strategy, with Deadly Consequences

After joining the White House, Dr. Atlas sought to build support for his herd immunity strategy inside the Trump Administration and redirect the federal government's pandemic response away from proven public health measures. The Select Subcommittee's investigation uncovered documents prepared by Dr. Atlas and new details of key meetings coordinated by Dr. Atlas with senior officials to push the Administration to jettison mitigation measures and reduce testing in an effort to hasten reaching disease-acquired herd immunity while vaccines were still in development.

During his first days in the White House, Dr. Atlas drafted memoranda outlining his views on the need to lift public health measures for the vast majority of Americans and reduce broad surveillance testing…

Dr. Atlas Recruited Proponents of a Herd Immunity Strategy to Advocate for Its Adoption by the Trump Administration

Within weeks of arriving in the White House, Dr. Atlas set out to arrange a roundtable event in the Oval Office to build support among senior Trump Administration officials for his herd immunity strategy. In August 2020, Dr. Atlas invited Dr. Jay Bhattacharya, Dr. Martin Kulldorff, Dr. Joseph Ladapo, and Dr. Cody Meissner – all of whom supported this approach – "to speak with the President and the Vice President" and other Administration officials about the pandemic response…

Dr. Birx told the Select Subcommittee that she believed these meetings were "dangerous" and feared that "any credibility given to these individuals in this moment while we were headed into the fall would be dangerous for our overall response and ability to contain the virus." According to Director Redfield, Dr. Atlas brought these individuals to the White House specifically "to convince people that herd immunity was going to save us, and this thing was going to go bye-bye."

As previously reported, Dr. Atlas arranged another meeting between senior Trump Administration officials and herd immunity proponents—this time bringing them to HHS's headquarters in Washington, D.C. Working with Mr. Mango, Dr. Atlas arranged for Dr. Bhattacharya, Dr. Kulldorff, and Dr. Sunetra Gupta to meet with HHS Secretary Alex Azar in early October 2020. The day before this meeting took place, the three individuals scheduled to meet with Secretary Azar released the "Great Barrington Declaration," which advocated for the herd immunity strategy that Dr. Atlas was actively promoting inside the White House...

Secretary Azar met with Dr. Atlas and the three authors of the Great Barrington Declaration for approximately 30 minutes on October 5, 2020, during which they discussed a range of topics on which Dr. Atlas's herd immunity strategy centered.

Later that day, Secretary Azar issued a tweet recognizing that the approach articulated by the Great Barrington Declaration authors during the meeting was a "strong reinforcement" of the Trump Administration's ongoing response strategy, stating:

In the conversation with Martin Kulldorff, PhD (Harvard), Jay Bhattacharya, MD, PhD (Stanford), and Sunetra Gupta, PhD (Oxford), we heard strong reinforcement of the Trump Administration's strategy of aggressively protecting the vulnerable while opening schools and the workplace.

Echoing this tweet, Dr. Atlas issued a statement to The Hill confirming that the Great Barrington Declaration authors' "targeted protection of the vulnerable and opening schools and society policy matches the policy of the President and what I have advised."

Dr. Atlas Successfully Pressed the Trump Administration to Change CDC's Guidance to Curtail the Amount of Testing Conducted in the Country, Without Any Alternate Mitigation Measures

New evidence obtained by the Select Subcommittee shows that Dr. Atlas set in motion significant changes to CDC's testing guidance within days of arriving in the White House that minimized the need for testing of close contacts of infected individuals, while a proposed addition to the guidance recommending that close contacts isolate was not included in the published version.

Dr. Atlas Undermined and Politicized the Widespread Use of Mask Wearing as a Mitigation Tool

As part of Dr. Atlas's efforts to cease mitigation measures – a key prong of his herd immunity strategy – he took steps to dissuade the Trump Administration from embracing the widespread use of masks as a mitigation tool.

Support for Dr. Atlas's Herd Immunity Strategy Grew Inside the Trump Administration

Shortly after Secretary Azar met with the authors of the Great Barrington Declaration and announced on Twitter that they had offered "strong reinforcement" of the Trump Administration's ongoing response strategy at that time, two Trump Administration officials held a background call with members of the press on October 12, 2020 – speaking on condition of anonymity – to discuss the Great Barrington Declaration and the Administration's pandemic strategy. On the call, the officials cited President Trump's refrain that "the cure cannot be worse than the problem itself" and urged for ending many coronavirus mitigation measures, which they claimed were "destroying people." While mitigation measures undoubtedly came at a cost, their cost paled in comparison to the cost of lives lost and illness suffered, in some cases with certain symptoms lingering indefinitely, as a result of the Trump Administration's refusal to pursue such measures during this stage of the pandemic –a refusal that was closely linked to officials' increasing openness to the herd immunity strategy.

According to Dr. Birx, the herd immunity approach championed by Dr. Atlas gained steam inside the White House around this time, despite warnings from her and other leading doctors. Dr. Birx told the Select Subcommittee: "I was constantly raising the alert in the doctors' meetings of the depth of my concern about Dr. Atlas' position, Dr. Atlas' access, Dr. Atlas' theories and hypothesis" on the coronavirus. She said that she had "numerous" conversations regarding Dr. Atlas's dangerous views with Mr. Meadows, Mr. Kushner, and Mr. Short – raising her concerns to senior White House officials at least once a week. Dr. Birx stated that Vice President Pence, who led the White House Coronavirus Task Force, was also "well aware" of her concerns about Dr. Atlas's presence. Commissioner Hahn told the Select Subcommittee that he was similarly compelled to intervene with Mr. Short regarding Dr. Atlas, out of concern that the approach urged by Dr. Atlas would be particularly lethal for those who are immunocompromised.

Despite internal warnings, multiple senior Trump Administration officials ultimately embraced the core tenets of the herd immunity strategy advocated by Dr. Atlas. According to Dr. Atlas, Mr. Meadows, Ms. Hicks, Mr. Short, and Mr. Mango, among others, came to support at least some of the pandemic strategies he was urging the Administration to adopt. Dr. Atlas also inferred that President Trump "was in agreement" with Dr. Atlas's views on the pandemic, given President Trump's "own words." For example, after Dr. Atlas joined the White House, President Trump made explicit reference to "herd" immunity in an August 31, 2020, interview with Fox News host Laura Ingraham, stating: "Well, once you get to a certain number – we use the word 'herd,' right – once you get to a certain number it's going to go away." Weeks later, President Trump once again affirmatively raised a herd immunity strategy, stating during a September 15 townhall event, "you'll develop herd – like a herd mentality," and predicting, "it's going to be herd-developed, and that's going to happen."

Director Redfield also acknowledged that Dr. "Atlas had successfully got a lot of people within the Task Force and the White House to believe that all we had to do was get to herd immunity" in order to contain the virus...
As the country was entering into the deadly fall and winter 2020 surge, Dr. Atlas continued to advocate against proven mitigation measures under the misguided premise that most regions of the country had already achieved sufficient disease-acquired herd immunity to prevent future surges. Despite an attempted intervention by multiple doctors on the

White House Coronavirus Task Force with Vice President Pence's office in November or December 2020 to warn about the deadly consequences if the Trump Administration did not take meaningful action to mitigate the virus's spread, it appears that White House officials – after months of absorbing the "Atlas Dogma" – were largely unresponsive to these concerns. During the period from November 2020 through February 2021 – as the deadly fall and winter surge swept across the country while the Trump Administration did little to curb its impact – the United States saw the most coronavirus deaths recorded in any four-month period throughout the entirety of the pandemic.

The Trump Administration's flagrant disregard for proven mitigation measures in those months resulted in a federal response that differed little from the implementation of a deliberate herd immunity strategy. Administration officials used the "Atlas Dogma" to justify their downplaying of the virus before the November presidential election and their continued deprioritization of the crisis as they worked to overturn the election results. The Administration's embrace of this ill-advised approach not only impaired the nation's ability to respond effectively to the pandemic at a critical juncture before the deployment of vaccines and widespread availability of effective treatments – it also helped to lay the foundation for a wide swath of the public to persistently reject other vital tools to combat the virus, including coronavirus vaccines.

Throughout the series of interviews conducted by the Select Subcommittee over the past year, senior officials who worked closely on the coronavirus response emphasized that Dr. Atlas's presence in the White House undermined the work of the White House Coronavirus Task Force and impaired the effectiveness of the overall pandemic response effort. By Dr. Birx's estimate, more than 130,000 American lives could have been saved after the first wave of the pandemic if President Trump and his Administration had implemented proven mitigation measures. Multiple studies have likewise indicated that the widespread adoption of masks and other non-pharmaceutical mitigation measures could have prevented numerous lives lost during the fall and winter 2020-2021.

On November 30, 2020, Dr. Atlas submitted his resignation letter,[15] having successfully convinced many politicians "that herd immunity was going to save us, and this thing was going to go bye-bye."[7] In October that year, the White House's Office of Science and Technology Policy ranked "ending the COVID-19 pandemic" as one of President Trump's top accomplishments and a press release from that same office credited his administration for its "decisive actions to engage scientists and health professionals in academia, industry, and government to understand, treat, and defeat the disease."[16]

Unfortunately, the virus wasn't so easily persuaded. Immediately after his departure, 2,000-3,000 Americans would die daily of COVID.[17] Many thousands would have been saved had they avoided the virus just a few more months until after they were vaccinated.

Dr. Atlas would later write that he spoke with Drs. Ioannidis and Bhattacharya several times per week during his time in the Trump administration. "They never let me give up, they never stopped encouraging me,"[18] he said. He would again cite their influence in an article ironically titled "When Will Academia Account for Its COVID Failures?" Dr. Atlas wrote:

Virtually every scientific point I made exactly matched those of Jay Bhattacharya and John Ioannidis, both Stanford professors of medicine, including the risk for children, spread from children, focused protection, postinfection immunity, masks, and the harm from school closures and lockdowns.[19]

Both Drs. Bhattacharya and Ioannidis felt that less than 40,000 people would die of COVID at the pandemic's start. Yet, Dr. Atlas wanted to emphasize that virtually every scientific point he made exactly matched these poor prognosticators.

Even after his predictions of herd immunity failed to materialize, Dr. Atlas continued to publicly underestimate the virus. In the introduction to his 2021 book, *A Plague Upon Our House: My Fight at the Trump White House to Stop COVID from Destroying America*, Dr. Atlas asked:

> *If the US tallies 50,000 deaths from COVID next year, will we accept that with the relaxed attitude we have about the flu? ...Are we a nation of science or science-deniers?*[18]

791,126 Americans had died of COVID when his book was published, and 300,000 more died of COVID in the following year.[17]

The GBD's political influence was not limited to the U.S. According to news reports from December 2020, Boris Johnson's was also influenced by "herd immunity" proponents. It was reported that the decision:

> *Not to impose a circuit-breaker lockdown was influenced by a meeting involving the prime minister, the chancellor and three proponents of a "herd immunity" approach to managing the virus: Prof Sunetra Gupta and Prof Carl Heneghan of the University of Oxford and Prof Anders Tegnell, the Swedish epidemiologist who has masterminded Sweden's catastrophic COVID control policy (in the last month, Sweden has reported 1,400 COVID deaths, while neighbours Norway and Finland, both of which have roughly half its population, reported 100 and 80 respectively). The delay in imposing national restrictions resulted in an estimated 1.3 million extra COVID infections.*[20]

And this is how doctors and scientists – who knew they would never care for a COVID patient themselves – set policy for wealthy countries, which ended up having some of the worst pandemic responses in the world.

"Many elderly people were administered morphine instead of oxygen despite available supplies, effectively ending their lives."
~ Brusselaers et al.

Could the GBD have worked is not a question that needs asking. It didn't work. Young people avoided the virus until they were vaccinated and politicians refused to marshal "overwhelming resources" to protect the vulnerable. No country or state used "focused protection" to achieve herd immunity in 3-6 months. Even though the CDC reported that 75% of American children had contracted COVID by February 2022,[21] the oft-promised herd immunity has yet to arrive. Similarly, the only "substantial long-term benefits" the UK got for their high rates of pediatric "natural immunity" were headlines that read "Children Drive Britain's Longest-Running COVID Surge",[22] "COVID Absences in Schools in England Triple in Two Weeks",[23] and "Twice as Many People Died With COVID in UK This Summer Compared With 2021."[24] As I write this in December 2022, the National Health Service seems to have collapsed in parts of the UK.

Sweden, which aimed for herd immunity through mass infection, had a much higher death rate than its Nordic neighbors. According to a report in *Science*:

> *The virus took a shocking toll on the most vulnerable. It had free rein in nursing homes, where nearly 1000 people died in a matter of weeks. Stockholm's nursing homes ended up losing 7% of their 14,000 residents to the virus. The vast majority were not taken to hospitals.*[25]

An interim report from the Swedish government said that uncontrolled spread of the virus was the "single most important factor behind the major outbreaks and the high number of deaths in residential care."[26] The report, which was published in *Humanities and Social Sciences Communications*, included one damning investigation that found "the Swedish people were kept in ignorance of basic facts such as the airborne SARS-CoV-2 transmission, that asymptomatic individuals can be contagious." Horrifyingly, it found that:

Many elderly people were administered morphine instead of oxygen despite available supplies, effectively ending their lives.

Children weren't necessarily spared. Dr. Jonas Ludvigsson, a Swedish pediatrician and epidemiologist who was an original signer of the GBD, claimed that there were "no major school outbreaks in Sweden,"[27] even though such outbreaks had been reported in Swedish media. He also published a letter in *The New England Journal of Medicine* that claimed there had been no excess mortality in Swedish children in 2020 compared to 2019.[28] However, in emails to Swedish chief epidemiologist Anders Tegnell from July 2020, Dr. Ludvigsson wrote "unfortunately we see a clear indication of excess mortality among children ages 7-16 old, the ages where 'kids went to school.'"[29]

Despite rumors to the contrary, Sweden had to close high schools[30] and reduce public gatherings from 50 to eight people[31] to deal with uncontrolled viral spread. Even though schools for younger children were officially "open", many went to remote learning when cases spiked. David Steadson, a public health researcher who co-authored the investigation referenced above, told me:

Contrary to popular myth, Sweden ***did*** *close schools. In early March 2020, the Government amended the school regulations to allow all schools from preschool and up, to move to remote or hybrid learning in the event of outbreaks of staff issues. On March 27, 2020, on the recommendation of the Swedish Public Health Agency, all high schools (Grade 10 and up) and Universities and adult education moved to remote learning, with 3 months summer holidays beginning a few weeks later.*

Following the 2020 summer break, many schools, predominantly middle school and up (from grade 7) - elected to continue with hybrid and remote classes, however, no statistics on school closures were kept.

Mr. Steadson also lives in Sweden and told me about his

experience with his own children. He said:

> *I had kids in grades 4, 7, and 8 when the pandemic broke out. The latter two were remote for a year and then hybrid for another 6 months or so.*

Looking back on Sweden's response, King Carl XVI Gustaf said, "I think we have failed. We have a large number who have died and that is terrible."[32] Prime Minister Stefan Lofven agreed, saying "Of course the fact that so many have died can't be considered as anything other than a failure."

"One place where we had some success was Florida." ~ Dr. Martin Kulldorff

Perhaps nowhere proved the folly of the GBD more than Florida where Governor Ron DeSantis based his policies on the advice of its three authors as well as Dr. Atlas and Dr. Michael Levitt, a professor of structural biology at Stanford and Nobel Prize winner who also underestimated the virus, saying on July 25, 2020, "US COVID19 will be done in 4 weeks with a total reported death below 170,000."[33]

During a discussion in September 2020, before anyone was vaccinated, these doctors told Governor DeSantis what he wanted to hear: the virus was harmful only to older people and that measures to limit infections in young people only prolonged the pandemic.[34] A few quotes from that meeting are:

> ***Dr. Levitt:*** *Everything we've heard here, for example, in treating age groups differently, makes complete sense. The need to let young people interact with each other, both for social reasons and for herd immunity, makes perfectly good common sense. I think there should have been more of that.*

> ***Dr. Martin Kulldorff:*** *What helps the elderly is if the young take this very minimal risk and live normal life until there's herd immunity, and then, when we have herd immunity, then the older people can also live more normal lives.*

> ***Dr. Bhattacharya (disparaging masks and testing):*** *Checking asymptomatic kids, the main purpose of it is essentially to close the school, to create a panic and close the school down I think.*

These themes were reiterated during a roundtable discussion from March 2021, along with copious misinformation about COVID's risk to young people, the durability of "natural immunity", and the risks of masks.[35] Some representative quotes are:

Dr. Martin Kulldorff:

> *So for old people have to be very careful because this is more dangerous than the annual influenza. But for children, this is less dangerous than the influenza. So we should have utilized that feature of COVID to protect the old with focus protection while letting a younger people live normal life to avoid all the collateral public health damage from lockdown, which are enormous.*
>
> *It's not dangerous for children to be in school and it's not dangerous for teachers either. The only exception is that if you're a teacher and you're above 60, maybe you should be allowed to do online teaching until you have the vaccine. But other than that, there's no reason to do that...*
>
> *Children should not wear face masks. No. They don't need it for their own protection and they don't need it for protecting other people either...*
>
> *Yeah. So we know, I mean, there'd be very few reinfection, so we know that there's good immunity from national infection for at least a year now will that last five years, or 10 years, or 20 years, we obviously do not know that, but also for vaccines, we have good immunity, but it's not quite as good because we've seen numbers of 95% and we know that still after a number of months. So at this point,*

it's very clear that naturally infection, there's much more evidence that naturally infection provide immunity than it is from vaccines.

Dr. Scott Atlas:

The reality is that the kids have extremely low risk from COVID-19...It happens to be icing on the cake, as we say, that children are not significant spreaders to adults. But that's really just icing on the cake...

It's bad to wear a mask during exercise, yet where I'm from in California, the gyms that are open, they require you to wear a mask during exercise. It's not just unnecessary, it's harmful. And people have not really been explained this kind of negative harms...

There's zero reason to prioritize or insist the teachers get to the front of the line for vaccination...

The overwhelming majority of people do not have a problem with this virus. And so this idea, this panic driven fear of getting this infection if you're under 70, your infection fatality rate is very low...There's a moral, ethical question here if you're going to start saying that young children should be vaccinated for an infection that they have essentially no problem with.

Dr. Jay Bhattacharya:

We should instead have adopted a policy, and most places, should have adopted a policy that got rid of lockdowns and instead focused on people we knew to be truly vulnerable to disease, older populations, people with certain chronic diseases, adopted policies, actually much more similar to what Florida has done, rather than the state where I live, California, which has relied on lockdowns to a disastrous effect...

> *I think masks, in fact, in some ways they've been harmful because people believe that masks protect them, vulnerable people, and they end up taking more risks than they ought because they feel like they're protected by something that actually does not protect them. So I think on net, I think the masks not only have not been effective, but have been harmful...*
>
> *There's a vast array of evidence in the scientific literature that shows definitively that if you've had COVID and recovered, the vast, vast majority of people have a durable immunity that it's very unlikely that you'll be reinfected and you'll be protected from, from reinfection...I think a very large fraction of the population is already been infected and are immune the evidence from the trials don't demonstrate any efficacy of vaccinating that population.*
>
> *In fact, the vast majority of cases are relatively mild, asymptomatic, or with mild symptoms.*

It was in this context that Dr. Bhattacharya falsely told the citizens of Florida in July 2021 that the Delta variant changed nothing and the vulnerable had been protected.[36] Dr. Jason Salemi, a University of South Florida epidemiologist, would later provide a reality check by saying:

> *The fact we had record numbers of hospitalizations, record numbers of deaths, even in younger populations -- that was just so astonishing to me, it showed you just how bad the Delta wave was.*[37]

Despite this, the authors of the GBD remain unapologetic about their influence in Florida. Even after the Delta wave killed thousands of Floridians, Dr. Kulldorff bragged about his impact there, saying "one place where we had some success was Florida."[39] Dr. Bhattacharya tried to excuse their failure by blaming the state's demographics. He said one reason so many Floridians died during the Delta wave was "simply because there's more old people."[40]

Given that the entire premise behind the GBD was to protect these old people, Dr. Bhattacharya's comment was a clear, though unintended, admission of abject failure. As vaccine-advocate Noah Louis-Ferdinand wrote:

> *[Their] defense was that you needed to adjust for age and Florida looked as good as other states, which in plain language means: "Well we had more vulnerable people, so of course we had more deaths." It's a statement he is correct in making—and I wouldn't blame him—but only insofar as he is willing to admit that focused protection doesn't work.*[41]

It bears repeating, actually protecting the vulnerable was infinitely harder than sheltered doctors made it out to be in their podcasts, editorials, and Declarations.

However, not even headlines of dead children nor giant trucks overflowing with corpses were powerful enough to make the GBD supporters lose faith in their holy grail of herd immunity through the mass infection of unvaccinated youth. Even today, they still claim that herd immunity is only months away, if we only allow more unvaccinated children and young adults to contract COVID.

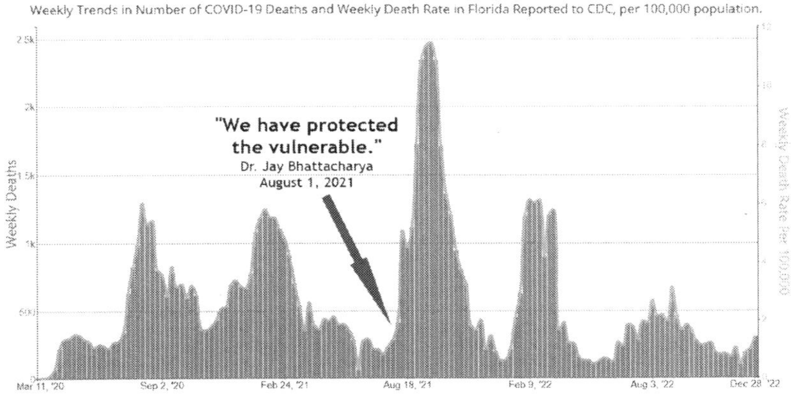

COVID deaths in Florida[42]

Chapter 7: "We'll Have Herd Immunity by April."

"A correspondent suggested I should have known that the pandemic was over months ago. That's obviously a myth. But where did that idea come from?"
~ Dr. Harriet Hall

On June 29, 2021, Dr. Harriet Hall penned an essay on the website *Science Based Medicine* titled "A New COVID-19 Myth?" in which she wrote:

> *A correspondent suggested I should have known that the pandemic was over months ago. That's obviously a myth. But where did that idea come from?*[1]

I knew the answer. Even before the first wave peaked, doctors suggested the worst was over and that measures to control the virus were more dangerous than the virus itself. This message was repeated regularly throughout the pandemic.

On March 17, 2020, Dr. Zubin Damania – a physician, comedian, and internet personality known as ZDoggMD to his fans in the "ZPAC Supporter Tribe"[2] – recorded a podcast titled "COVID-19: Is Our Cure Worse Than the Disease?"[3] He made four similar podcasts with Dr. Monica Gandhi. In October 2020 they recorded "How to Stop Living in Fear of COVID"[4] where listeners heard Dr. Gandhi say that "you can still see your friends and family while keeping yourself safe, and you're not gonna die of this." In February 2021 they recorded "The End of the Pandemic"[5] where listeners heard that "a UCSF infectious disease doctor is convinced this pandemic is ending, and sooner than you think." Drs. Gandhi and Damania shared a belly laugh then, mocking variants by saying "variants shmariants." The Delta and Omicron variants would both arrive several months later, and Dr. Gandhi would admit to regretting this comment.[6]

This didn't stop her from making a nearly identical podcast in May 2022 titled "Living with COVID,"[7] which declared "we now have all the necessary tools to end the COVID 'emergency phase'. Here's how (and why) we can live with this coronavirus." They recorded another podcast in December 2022 titled "A Better Pandemic Playbook", where Dr. Gandhi again made her case for "COVID optimism" and spoke of "how little severe disease there is."[8] She said that, due to high rates of immunity, "since March of 2022 we've seen very little severe disease in the hospital." In reality, 160,000 Americans died of COVID from March to December 2022, and COVID was the third leading cause of death for the third year in a row.[9]

Early in the pandemic Dr. Gandhi believed that if COVID killed over 100 Americans daily, citizens would band together and prevent this at all costs.[10] Sadly, she was wrong about this too. Despite her near-perfect record of poor predictions – which included her predicting she would stop making predictions on *The Mehdi Hasan Show*[6] – San Mateo County celebrated their re-opening with Dr. Monica Gandhi Day on June 15, 2021. Although 596,374 Americans had died of COVID by then, Dr. Gandhi cut a ribbon of masks as part of the celebration. The Delta variant arrived immediately after, and 500,000 more Americans would die of COVID before the end of 2022.

Many times, doctors' sarcastic admonition to "wait two more weeks" turned out to be extremely reliable indicators of when cases would spike again. In a since-deleted tweet, Dr. Ramin Farzaneh-Far said this in November 2020, right before the deadliest wave of the pandemic. In June 2021, Dr. Anish Koka mocked those who were concerned about the Delta variant, saying "we'll know in 2 weeks,"[11] along with an eye roll emoji. A month later, the headlines would read "Pediatric Hospitals in U.S. in Peril as Delta Hits Children."[12] Economist Dr. Andreas Backhaus quipped about the Great Barrington Declaration and one of its authors, Dr. Sunetra Gupta, by saying:

> *I thought about writing a paper that estimates how long it takes for a country or region to suffer from a severe COVID19 outbreak after the GBD crew said that it had already reached herd immunity. One might call this new relationship the "Gupta predictor".*[13]

Dr. Gupta was not the only author of the GBD to repeatedly claim the virus has been tamed. Dr. Jay Bhattacharya said COVID had been "defanged" on: April 14, 2021[14]; May 3, 2021[15]; July 21, 2021[16]; July 28, 2021[17]; and January 6, 2022.[18]

I too was overly optimistic, writing on July 25, 2021:

> *We will almost certainly never have months in a row where over 1,000 Americans die daily. Again with the caveat that a nasty variant could change everything, I am confident the worst is over for the US as a whole, at least for vaccinated people.*[19]

Sadly, those new variants appeared, and the worst had yet to arrive in much of the country.

Notably, nearly every doctor who declared the pandemic over continues to discuss COVID constantly, undermining their admonitions that everyone else should treat COVID like any other disease.

San Mateo County celebrates California's re-opening by designating June 15, 2021, as Monica Gandhi Day

"We'll Have Herd Immunity by April."
~ Dr. Marty Makary

It's clear many doctors believe the pandemic ended long ago, and they spread this belief to millions of Americans. So, to answer Dr. Hall's question, here's where the idea that the worst of the pandemic was behind us came from, presented along with the cumulative number of Americans who had died of COVID by that date according to *Our World in Data*.[20]

- **Dr. John Ioannidis - March 19, 2020 - *266 deaths***: If only part of resources mobilized to implement extreme measures for COVID-19 had been invested towards enhancing influenza vaccination uptake, tens of thousands of influenza deaths might have been averted.[21]

- **Dr. John Ioannidis - April 17, 2020 - *39,591 deaths***: Acknowledging for the fact that the epidemic is still evolving, and we cannot be sure whether we will hit even higher peaks in the future, although this doesn't seem to be the case, at least for the European countries, and it seems to be that even in the US, in most states we're very close to the peak, if not past the peak, the risk is something that should be manageable as opposed to the panic and horror stories that are circulating about.[22]

- **Dr. John Mandrola - May 1, 2020 - *68,515 deaths***: I recoil against the idea that moderation of distancing measures in places in the US and Sweden is akin to human sacrifice. That sort of hyperbole and fear-mongering in medicine always leads to bad decisions. Also, no US hospital is now unprepared. It's May, not March 9.[23]

- **Dr. John Mandrola - May 4, 2020 - *72,831 deaths***: 1) US Hospitals not close to being over-run. It's the opposite in most places 2) Everyplace I know of is opening up for more regular healthcare. Good. 3) We have learned how to limit nosocomial spread. It's May not March.[24]

- **Dr. John Mandrola - May 5, 2020 - *75,010 deaths***: US hospitals are now prepared and in little danger of being over-whelmed. In fact, many hospitals are so dormant they are nearing financial ruin.[25]

- **Dr. John Mandrola - May 7, 2020 - *79,237 deaths***: May is different from March. People are not stupid. Public health surveillance is better. Hospitals are ready. NYC-like situations are unlikely now in the US.[26]

- **Dr. Scott Atlas - June 29, 2020 - *126,869 deaths***: We expected more cases with more social mingling…But the fact is the overwhelming majority of these cases are in younger healthier people. These people do not have a significant problem. They do not have the serious complications. They do not die. And so it's fantastic news that we have a lot of cases, but we don't see deaths going up, and what that means is A: we're are doing a better job of protecting the vulnerable, B: we're in good shape here.[27]

- **Dr. Scott Atlas - July 23, 2020 - *145,106 deaths***: I'm cautiously optimistic because we actually know a lot now. We know the fatality rate is much lower, and we know who to protect. We are doubling down on the high-risk group. We are doing better with patients in the hospitals. I think we have to tell the American people, this is not out of control here.[28]

- **Dr. Michael Levitt - July 25, 2020 - *147,164 deaths***: US COVID19 will be done in 4 weeks with a total reported death below 170,000. How will we know it is over? Like for Europe, when all cause excess deaths are at normal level for week. Reported COVID19 deaths may continue after 25 Aug. & reported cases will, but it will be over.[29]

- **Dr. Monica Gandhi - August 8, 2020 - *162,312 deaths***: A high rate of asymptomatic infection is a good thing. It's a good thing for the individual and a good thing for society. It is an intriguing hypothesis that asymptomatic infection triggering immunity may lead us to get more population-level immunity. That itself will limit spread.[30]

- **Dr. John Ioannidis - August 25, 2020 - *177,693 deaths***: Very few hospitals were eventually stressed and only for a couple of weeks. Most hospitals maintained largely empty wards, expecting tsunamis that never came… Tragically, many health systems faced major adverse consequences, not by COVID-19 cases overload, but for very different reasons.[31]

- **Florida Governor Ron DeSantis, Drs. Martin Kulldorff, Jay Bhattacharya, and Michael Levitt - September 24, 2020 - *201,821 deaths***:[32]

 Governor Ron DeSantis: Is there anybody that thinks COVID-19 represents a significant threat in terms of overwhelming hospitals in the United States?

 Dr. Kulldorff: No.

 Dr. Bhattacharya: It's the opposite, Governor. I think a lot of hospitals around the country have faced financial difficulties because they've been empty. At this point, certainly not.

 Dr. Levitt: I certainly would agree, but I think that we're in the minority, worldwide. People are still locking down and engaging in behavior which is likely to be detrimental in the long run.

- **Dr. John Mandrola - December 15, 2020 - *307,343 deaths***: Barring something (very) unforeseen the #COVID19 pandemic is over soon. Such good news![33]

- **Dr. Marty Makary - December 22, 2020 - *326,966 deaths***: There's a false construct out there. There's a recommendation that we need to get every American immunized in order to get a handle on the pandemic. The reality is that about 25-50% of Americans have already had the infection and have some natural immunity…So we may only need to get an additional 20% of the population immunized by say February or March to really hit those 70% herd immunity levels.[34]

- **Dr. Martin Kulldorff - December 24, 2020 - *333,135 deaths***: If the young live normal lives, some will be infected, but their risk is less than from lockdown collateral damage. Pandemic will then be naturally over in 3-6 months.[35]

- **Dr. John Ioannidis - December 28, 2020 - *339,875 deaths***: Several countries like India had 60% seroprevalence already by November, which means that they have pretty much reached herd immunity already. The same may be true for some hard-hit locations even in the USA and Europe (e.g. locations in Northern Greece) where, sadly, the virus has already spread very widely.[36]

- **Dr. Marty Makary - January 1, 2021 - *352,760 deaths***: To hit herd immunity this spring, we may only need 20-30% of people not previously infected to get the vaccine. By March, up to 50% of US will have natural immunity from prior infection.[37]

- **Dr. Vinay Prasad - January 13, 2021 - *389,829 deaths***: Let me be perfectly clear: children DO NOT NEED a sars-cov-2 vaccine before they are permitted to return to normal activities, such as school and visiting loved ones. … If the epidemic is abating, how can you justify giving 100 kids those AEs (adverse events).[38]

- **Dr. Marty Makary - January 17, 2021 - *402,953 deaths***: I believe herd immunity is closer than people think. I predict April. The old guard medical establishment has been dismissive (inappropriately) of the data on natural immunity from prior infection & its prevalence.[39]

- **Dr. Marty Makary - January 22, 2021 - *419,206 deaths***: COVID daily cases are DOWN 27% in the last 13 days! Natural Immunity is slowing the spread We will see a rapid case decel in Feb & March.[40]

- **Dr. Marty Makary - January 24, 2021 - *424,555 deaths***: We may be starting to see the early signs of herd immunity. There has been a 32% decrease in daily cases over the last 15 days.[41]

- **Dr. Monica Gandhi - January 29, 2021 - *441,750 deaths***: You only have to live like this until summer. Please listen to all of the optimism and try to phase out the doom.[42]

- **Dr. Monica Gandhi - January 31, 2021 - *446,538 deaths***: What will happen with vaccines is that - when we see the hospitalizations go away (100% effective for this dire outcome so far, still marveling)- all arguments on messaging and who can be the most doom-filled will go away.[43]

- **Drs. Stefan Baral and Monica Gandhi – February 8, 2021 – *468,902 deaths***:

  Dr. Stefan Baral: I don't think variants are going to cause a third wave of #COVID19 in the coming weeks or months across Northern Europe or North America.[183]

  Dr. Monica Gandhi: completely agree[184]

- **Dr. John Mandrola – February 13, 2021 – *483,543 deaths***:

  Twitter Comment: Reasons to be cheerful. The R rate is definitely below 1 for the first time since July, infection rates falling faster than anticipated, cases down 26% on week before, deaths down 27%...

  Dr. Mandrola: The good news on #COVID19 continues.[185]

- **Dr. John Mandrola - February 14, 2021 - *484,694 deaths***: Good news on #COVID19 is getting to be a routine now.[186]

- **Dr. Marty Makary - February 18, 2021 - *492,250 deaths***: We'll have herd immunity by April. COVID cases have dropped 77% in six weeks. Experts should level with the public about the good news. There is reason to think the country is racing toward an extremely low level of infection. As more people have been infected, most of whom have mild or no symptoms, there are fewer Americans left to be infected. At the current trajectory, I expect COVID will be mostly gone by April, allowing Americans to resume normal life.[44]

- **Dr. Vinay Prasad - February 18, 2021 - *492,250 deaths***: This NYTimes story on Jan 24th "Vaccines alone won't end the pandemic" Did not age well (as of Feb 18) It was completely off, and just another squeeze of fear Enough with these models They have often been erroneous[187]

- **Dr. Monica Gandhi - February 22, 2021 - *499,101 deaths***: We are just facing like complete dawn of hope and light and love. Like it's gonna be so great. It is getting so great. So what happened, right? Like March 11th was the day that the WHO declared this a worldwide pandemic. November 9, we got the first press release from the first vaccine. Phase three clinical trial, that fast. And then we've had seven phase three clinical trials. So we have seven vaccines in circulation around the globe that work. And they work exactly using the same protein in different ways using that protein, and they work beautifully, and they all work beautifully against preventing what even made us notice on January 31, 2019, or December 31, 2019, that something terrible was happening, which is severe disease. They all work almost 100% to prevent… 100% for hospitalizations. And then like in the 90s to prevent you not even feeling well at home. So they're amazing… I started in April 2020 and I hope I can stop it in April 2021. I think that may be a little soon, but we will get to herd immunity and it will all fall away. It will all fall away. All this anguish, all this yelling at each other, all this politicization, all this depression, it will fall away…So we're fully vaccinated. We cannot get sick and we should be close. Vaccinated people should be close and they should spend time together.[5]

- **Dr. Zubin Damania - February 22, 2021 - *499,101 deaths***: So we have tons of PhD epidemiologists who are painting gloom and doom pictures everywhere. Well, you know, first it was this. And then, you know, okay, now we have a vaccine but you know what, the variants are coming. So we're probably gonna have to wear seven masks and stay shut down. And by the way, don't even think about opening schools. Why are you thinking about opening schools? Oh, by the way it's your bad behavior that caused all this death, and so we're gonna shame you. And on top of that, it's never gonna get better…Before we were like, God, the amount of fear that's being generated is out of proportion to the actual response to the threat. And actually, our response may be damaging. But now, the vibe is, oh my God, the end is here.[5]

- **Dr. Monica Gandhi - February 23, 2021 - *501,359 deaths***: Doom & gloom seems to be part of the narrative from many in the scientific community because they got politicized in the last administration and they are sticking to it. But it is okay; all of this will fall away when we watch what happens (like is happening elsewhere) w/mass vax.[45]

- **Dr. Monica Gandhi - February 23, 2021 - *501,359 deaths***:

  Dr. Gandhi: All the vaccines down the line will offer 100% protection against hospitalization from COVID-19. I've been surprised by all the doom and gloom messaging about the variants and the vaccines, and I'm concerned it will lead to vaccine hesitancy. We should be pushing more optimism about the vaccines.

  Interviewer question: Do you believe we're truly near the end?

  Dr. Gandhi: Yes. I truly believe we're panicking way too much about the variants. It's quite common for any RNA virus to mutate at high rate. I'm extremely optimistic that all of the vaccines will prevent severe illness — even against variants.[46]

- **Dr. Lucy McBride - March 2, 2021 - *514,948 deaths***: COVID-19 cases are dropping, but anxiety is everywhere.[47]

-

- **Drs. Vinay Prasad and Monica Gandhi - March 2, 2021 - *514,948 deaths***: *audio podcast discussing "the end of the pandemic" and the need to reopen schools.*[188]

- **Dr. Monica Gandhi - March 4, 2021 - *519,394 deaths***: I genuinely with all my heart apologize for anyone who continues to try to scare you about variants; we have been through so much already. This is not like coming down from another surge; this time we have the increasing protection from vaccines as cases/ hospitalizations drop. Honestly, it makes me so sad. Like the public has not been terrorized already by the reality of this virus. The decreasing cases and hospitalizations in places where vaccination is occurring quickly (variants notwithstanding) is the only reality we need to understand now.[48]

- **Dr. Lucy McBride - March 9, 2021 - *525,809 deaths***: I've been yearning for an end to the pandemic. Now that it's here, I'm a little afraid...The pandemic will end. With dropping case rates and three incredible vaccines robustly protecting us from COVID-19, soon we'll be able to relax the restrictions of pandemic life.[49]

- **Dr. John Mandrola - March 10, 2021 - *527,345 deaths***: The pandemic is essentially done. Human life has to be more than avoiding one pathogen.[50]

- **Dr. John Mandrola - March 10, 2021 - *527,345 deaths***: Ky has vaccinated about 1 in 3 older people. CT has done even better. The vaccine squelches severe cases Millions have natural immunity. Young have almost no risk. The pandemic (of bad disease) is nearly over. And this is a really worthy cause of celebration!!!!!![51]

- **Dr. John Mandrola - March 11, 2021 - *528,887 deaths***: I wish I had wrote "almost done here in the US." Frustration with fear-mongering got the best of me.[52]

- **Dr. Marty Makary - March 11, 2021 - *528,887 deaths***: Natural immunity + vax immun = herd immun soon.[53]

- **Dr. Lucy McBride - March 23, 2021 - *540,572 deaths***: It's what some medical professionals, including myself, are calling "post-pandemic stress."[54]

- **Dr. Monica Gandhi - March 24, 2021 - *542,034 deaths***: Natural immunity after COVID-19 infection is likely lifelong, extrapolating from data on other coronaviruses that cause severe illness, SARS and MERS.[55]

- **Dr. Marty Makary - March 24, 2021 - *542,034 deaths***: Anthony Fauci has been saying that the country needs to vaccinate 70% to 85% of the population to reach herd immunity from COVID-19. But he inexplicably ignores natural immunity. If you account for previous infections, herd immunity is likely close at hand.[55]

- **Dr. Jay Bhattacharya - March 25, 2021 - *543,379 deaths***: The virus is seasonal and late fall/winter is its season. It is very unlikely, given that this is the case, that the virus will spread very widely during the summer months...We should not be particularly concerned about the variants that have arisen to date. First, prior infection with the wild type virus and vaccination provide protection against severe outcomes arising from reinfection with the mutated virus. Second, though the mutants have taken over the few remaining cases, their rise has coincided with a sharp drop in cases and deaths, even in countries where they have come to dominate.[56]

- **Dr. Vinay Prasad - March 30, 2021 - *547,309 deaths***: Perhaps COVID-19 is winding down...This summer, when cases fall, when vaccination grows, put down your iPads and phones, and meet real people in real life.[57]

- **Dr. Monica Gandhi - April 1, 2021 - *549,480 deaths***: I have a new saying. Even the most doom-filled, pessimistic, variant-steeped expert is no match for the vaccines![58]

- **Dr. Tracy Høeg - April 2, 2021 - *587,372 deaths***: The same trend continues in Israel. As of yesterday, just over 60% of the population has received the first dose of the vaccine and there appears to be no need to vaccinate children to reach herd immunity (as anticipated).[59]

- **Dr. Lucy McBride - April 3, 2021 - *551,128 deaths***: The first steps toward post-pandemic health are seemingly simple yet vexingly hard for most of us...We have every reason to be hopeful. COVID-related deaths and hospitalizations are falling fast.[60]

- **Dr. Lucy McBride - April 3, 2021 - *551,128 deaths***: But as you know, once you've been vaccinated, your risk of death & severe disease essentially goes away. The risk is of getting milder illness. And even that risk goes down as herd immunity takes hold.[61]

- **Dr. Marty Makary - April 3, 2021 - *551,128 deaths***: Alaska had zero COVID deaths in the last 10 days. They are #2 in the nation in their vax rate. More states will hit herd immunity this month, others will get there in May, depending on several factors. Cases in unvaccinated young people (most ASx or mild) will linger.[62]

- **Dr. Marty Makary - April 3, 2021 - *551,128 deaths:*** Herd immunity has many definitions, but that looks like herd immunity to me.[189]
- **Dr. Lucy McBride - April 5, 2021 - *551,907 deaths***: Preparing for post-pandemic life: a doctor's guide. Hope is alive. COVID-19 case rates and hospitalizations are falling fast.[63]

- **Dr. Lucy McBride - April 6, 2021 - *552,739 deaths***: After a year under duress, many of us will have a hard time with re-entry. Some degree of #anxiety is expected. So I coined the term "FONO" or Fear Of Normal[64]

- **Dr. Lucy McBride - April 6, 2021 - *552,739 deaths***: The risks of getting #COVID19 and transmitting #SARSCoV2 both drop significantly after #vaccination. Neither risk is zero (zero isn't even on the menu). As we approach herd immunity, these risks will get even smaller than they already are.[65]

- **Dr. Lucy McBride - April 13, 2021 - *559,625 deaths***: The benefits of patient-doctor rapport & the human connection, especially as we address the enormous post-pandemic health toll on our physical & #mentalhealth? HUGE.[66]

- **Dr. Jay Bhattacharya -April 14, 2021 - *560,562 deaths***: We should no longer look at cases as a marker of doom to come. Right? Because the vaccine is incredibly effective. There's just good news about the, I mean we can talk about the Johnson Johnson bit in a bit but like on the whole, the vaccine, or just it's an incredible achievement. And in many ways has defanged the epidemic, it's taken away the specter of death and hospitalization that comes with the disease for the older population to the extent that the older population is vaccinated. And so the, the worry that we have, over running hospital systems, large numbers of people dying from getting COVID. We should stop thinking that way when we see cases.[14]

- **Drs. Jay Bhattacharya and Zubin Damania April 14, 2021 - *560,562 deaths***:

  Dr. Damania: Do you think the danger is gone? Where are we in that?

  Dr. Bhattacharya: I mean, I think we're close. I think we're very, very close to that. I think that it, I mean, and in many places, it is gone, just be paid at a high cost of course, but it's, but it's very close to that.[14]

- **Dr. Lucy McBride - April 19, 2021 - *563,894 deaths***: I've been using the "off-ramp" analogy with patients — both for how restrictions should END & how we can expect our brains to adjust post-pandemic.[67]

- **Dr. Monica Gandhi - April 20, 2021 - *564,731 deaths***: It's simple math. We don't need to vaccinate those under 11 to get to herd immunity.[68]

- **Dr. Monica Gandhi - April 21, 2021 - *565,629 deaths***: Think we are getting closer and closer to that inflection point when things turn around in these regions of the US. So, this is important- we are not in a 4th surge overall.[69]

- **Dr. Monica Gandhi - April 21, 2021 - *565,629 deaths***: Israel has population-level immunity. We'll get there. But it will take a good part of the next three months to get to or exceed where Israel is right now. The difference is we have 330 million people and they have 9 million. If I thought herd immunity had to happen at 90%, which we were thinking four months or even a week ago, I'd be more worried. But now that we see it's not going to be that high, I'm not as worried.[70]

- **Dr. Lucy McBride - April 21, 2021 - *565,629 deaths***: Vaccines aren't 100% effective (though these are close!), but we don't need them to be 100% to gradually resume regular life as we head toward herd immunity.[71]

- **Dr. Lucy McBride - April 22, 2021 - *566,570 deaths***: My (humble) impression is this: nothing in life is risk-free. Certainly the risk of COVID transmission is higher w/ the circulating variants, but as we edge toward herd immunity, outdoor masking is less important (if at all) unless in a crowded space like a rally w/ shouting etc.[72]

- **Dr. Monica Gandhi - April 25, 2021 - *568,392 deaths***: We certainly seemed to have reached inflection point in US with ~32,000 cases today (lowest since June); see inflection on CDC graph. This is at 42.2% 1st dose as of today. My data analyst had predicted this by end week so seems (like Israel), once it starts, cases go down fast.[73]

- **Dr. Monica Gandhi - April 29, 2021 - *571,407 deaths***: SF [San Francisco] may be at herd immunity now.[74]

- **Dr. Jay Bhattacharya - May 3, 2021 - *573,769 deaths***: So we've done a very good job protecting the vulnerable with this Vaccine. But there's a thousand fold difference in the risk of death between young and old. And you take away the old from the population that could be – could die from the virus vaccine, you've defanged it. So there's a lot of good news to tell here.[15]

- **Dr. Lucy McBride - May 4, 2021 - *574,644 deaths***: I wrote an article for *The Huffington Post* about what I call "coronaphobia," and I also wrote a piece for *The Washington Post* about what I call "fear of normal," or FONO. What I'm seeing is an epidemic of unbridled fear that is basically the reverberations of the anxiety that we all experienced when the pandemic was happening in full force. As the pandemic comes under much better control, we need to shift our thinking and then our behaviors to reflect reality.[75]

- **Dr. Marty Makary - May 4, 2021 - *574,644 deaths***: In February, I projected that "based on the current trajectory" we'd see significant population immunity take hold in April from the combination of vaccinated and natural immunity. While most states are now witnessing the strong suppression of the epidemic today, other states will get there in May. But herd immunity is not a finish line. In that article, I maintained that "coronavirus will be here for decades to come." The question is, at what point is it no longer a major public-health threat? For most states, it's now.[76]

- **Dr. Vinay Prasad - May 4, 2021 - *574,644 deaths***: I have been out and about in the USA lately. At least here, COVID is ending. It's visible.[77]

- **Dr. Monica Gandhi - May 5, 2021 - *575,458 deaths***: June 15 is when we're (California) going to be done…get to herd immunity. He's (Governor Newsome) going to have to open up more without masks. All of that will show us as we mingle, the cases aren't going up….that we have enough of the population being immune.[78]

- **Dr. Vinay Prasad - May 8, 2021 - *577,651 deaths***: Vast majority of kids recover quickly from SARS cov 2. And after all adults are vaccinated their risk of COVID will decline precipitously. It's ok to awknowledge [*sic*] that COVID19 is not an emergency for kids.[79]

- **Dr. Monica Gandhi - May 10, 2021 - *578,316 deaths:*** What I have seen in this pandemic is that experts start saying same thing: we need boosters; immunity won't be long lived; can't reach herd immunity; schools sources of spread; Americans won't get to 70% vax; demand slowing; variants will escape immune system; then becomes truth.[80]

- **Dr. Marty Makary - May 15, 2021 - *581,664 deaths*:**

  Dr. Eric Topol: The 1st time without a red state in the US pandemic

  Dr. Makary: Nice herd immunity, Eric[190]

- **Dr. Marty Makary - May 21, 2021 - *585,056 deaths***: COVID cases are collapsing in front of our eyes. Daily cases are now one-tenth the number of daily flu cases in the middle of a mild flu season, with a now-identical case fatality rate. Projections for the coming weeks and months are even more favorable. That's because roughly 80% to 85% of adults are now immune — more than 6 in 10 adults are now vaccinated and more than half of unvaccinated adults have natural immunity from prior infection. In public health, when a virus has trouble jumping around because more than 8 in 10 adults in a community are blocking its transmission, we call that herd immunity. Yet some people want the pandemic to stretch out longer.[81]

- **Dr. Monica Gandhi - May 24, 2021 - *586,190 deaths***: 7 Reasons Why We Should Not Need Boosters for COVID-19. Coronaviruses are RNA viruses, like influenza and HIV (which is actually a retrovirus), but do not mutate as quickly as either one… However, the COVID-19 virus will not be mutating like this when we tamp down transmission with mass vaccination. In conclusion, I and many of my infectious disease colleagues expect the immunity from natural infection or vaccination to COVID-19 to be durable.[82]

- **Dr. Monica Gandhi - May 25, 2021 - *586,829 deaths***: I wanted to explain what it feels like to be an ID doctor in the US with measles. Once we get to control of COVID (which we are or already have) which is similar to the concept of herd immunity, COVID is no longer the public's problem but an ID doctor's problem. For instance, I have seen measles in my career, but it has been rare and has occurred due to someone unvaccinated here traveling back from a place with more vaccine hesitancy in Europe or place with more measles circulating or a community declining vax here. RARE, no longer public's problem.[83]

- **Dr. Monica Gandhi - May 25, 2021 - *586,829 deaths:*** Disagree with conclusion we can't get to herd immunity without kids being vaccinated. In past 4 weeks, with adult vax, COVID incidence has decreased by 50% among kids.[84]

- **Dr. Monica Gandhi - May 26, 2021 - *587,814 deaths***: California really has the lowest in-person learning in entire US (although we have likely reached herd immunity by now).[85]

- **Dr. Lucy McBride - May 26, 2021 - *587,814 deaths***: Parents need to role model confidence and optimism about the end of the pandemic.[86]

- **Allison Krug, Drs. Tracy Høeg, Lucy McBride, and Monica Gandhi - May 26, 2021 - *587,814 deaths***: Children should return to their normal lives this summer and in the upcoming school year, without masks and regardless of their vaccination status. Overall, the risk to children is too low to justify the remaining restrictions they face…This low risk for children nearly vanishes as cases plummet. As we saw in Israel and Britain, vaccinating adults indirectly protects children. The same trend is evident here in the United States: Adult vaccination has lowered COVID-19 incidence among children by 50 percent in the past four weeks.[87]

- **Dr. Marty Makary - May 27, 2021 - *589,164 deaths***: They are moving the goal posts. Now that 80-85% of the adult U.S. population is immune (vax + natural immunity), they suddenly stop talking about herd immunity and suggest it will never happen.[88]

- **Dr. Monica Gandhi - June 4, 2021 - *592,707 deaths***: With the vaccines+ natural immunity getting us to population immunity (herd immunity), it is so easy now to message on #COVID19 because it will end (not eradicate, but like measles, not bother the public, just ID doctors).[89]

- **Dr. Marty Makary - June 8, 2021 - *594,078 deaths***: With more than 8 in 10 adults protected from either contracting or transmitting the virus, it can't readily propagate by jumping around in the population. In public health, we call that herd immunity, defined broadly on the Johns Hopkins COVID information webpage as "when most of a population is immune." It's not eradication, but it's powerful.[90]

- **Dr. Marty Makary - June 8, 2021 - *594,078 deaths***: There's a lot of good news out there, and I think that people need to hear that good news right now. People have an entirely distorted perception of risk. (People) need to be careful if they're unvaccinated and not had the infection, but we need to move on at some point.[90]

- **Dr. Monica Gandhi - June 8, 2021 - *594,078 deaths***: San Francisco on track to be 1st CA metro city to reach full herd immunity.[91]

- **Dr. Monica Gandhi - June 8, 2021 - *594,078 deaths***: You don't need to vaccinate the whole population to get to herd immunity.[92]

- **Dr. John Mandrola - June 11, 2021 - *595,482 deaths***: It appears to me that we have crushed COVID by simply vaccinating susceptible adults. Why not wait for more data before extending these novel therapies to young people?[93]

- **Dr. Monica Gandhi - June 21, 2021 - *598,165 deaths***: San Francisco nears herd immunity- I and others on CGTN. When you get to herd immunity, those unvaccinated protected by others' immunity.[94]

- **Dr. Monica Gandhi - June 22, 2021 - *598,509 deaths***: And cases continue to go lower despite 20% being delta, so it is okay to want to motivate vaccination, but please don't continue the doom/gloom messaging, please[95]

- **Dr. Monica Gandhi - June 23, 2021 - *598,895 deaths*:** Know we are all delta variant right now but look- plummeting cases since April 14 when we passed 40% 1st dose, cases continue to go down, deaths reached <300, this is the impact of vaccines on the US epidemic. Instead of doom, celebration that we have means to end epidemic in US.[96]

- **Dr. Vinay Prasad - June 23, 2021 - *598,895 deaths*:** First, let us all remember cases are FALLING PRECIPITOUSLY…The raw number of adolescent cases is the point THAT IS FALLING… The actual numbers show both COVID and MIS-C is plummeting with adult vaccination.[97]

- **Dr. Monica Gandhi - June 24, 2021 - *599,236 deaths*:** Children are not more susceptible to the delta variant, they're threefold less likely to get any infection with any variant with any ancestral strain, and they're half as likely to spread it. And they can mask on the plane, as they should. You yourself are completely protected against the delta variant, and you should go and enjoy your summer. It's been a hard time, and people should have their summer. Delta variant, delta shmariant.[98]

- **Drs. Martin Kulldorff and Jay Bhattacharya - June 27, 2021 - *600,000 deaths:*** The pandemic is on its way out.[99]

- **Dr. Monica Gandhi - June 29, 2021 - *600,488 deaths*:** I feel really protected against all these variants by my vaccine, and I also feel that I can't spread it to others. . . these vaccines are effective against variants, they make it so that you can't transmit. . . Nothing has changed with the Delta variant.[100]

- **Drs. Vinay Prasad and Mary Makary- June 30, 2021 - *600,788 deaths*:**

    Dr. Prasad: What is the term used in ID epi for Rt dropping to less than 1 due to natural immunity & vaccination? cc @MartyMakary[191]

    Dr. Makary: The term is herd immunity ☺ But that was

before the human immune became politicized. We now say high population immunity to avoid arguing with people moving the goalposts.

- **Dr. Monica Gandhi - July 15, 2021 - *604,568 deaths***: The reassuring data on the Delta variant. There's no sign of a surge in hospitalization or severe illness, and the vaccines remain extremely effective. As the virus that causes COVID-19 evolves and mutates, the same concerns pop up about whether the variant evades vaccines, makes people sicker than the old versions, and increases transmissibility. What we know about the Delta variant is reassuring.[101]

- **Dr. Monica Gandhi - July 15, 2021 - *604,568 deaths***: 1st step is to show hospitalizations not increasing in kids with delta.[102]

- **Dr. Jay Bhattacharya - July 21, 2021 - *606,039 death*s**: The disease has been defanged. We actually should be declaring victory. We have done a fantastic job. We have developed a vaccine that has essentially turned this pandemic into something much milder.[16]

- **Dr. Jay Bhattacharya - July 26, 2021 - *607,367 deaths***: We have protected the vulnerable—by vaccinating the older population, we have provided them with enormous protection against severe disease and death. That's why you see, even as the cases have risen in Sweden in the past wave, or in the UK in this past wave, and in Florida in this past wave, the number of deaths have not risen proportionally. Why? Because we protected the vulnerable. The key thing to me is hospitalizations and deaths from COVID. While we've done an incredible job at decoupling the cases from the deaths, the public focus on cases at this point, I think, only serves to panic people without actually serving any other public health purpose… I don't think the delta variant changes the calculus or the evidence in any fundamental way… In Florida in this past wave, the number of deaths have not risen proportionally. Why? Because we protected the vulnerable.[103]

- **Dr. Jay Bhattacharya - July 28, 2021 - *608,208 deaths***: It is striking that COVID mortality is at such low levels despite the fact that we are seeing an increase in cases of late. By immunizing the elderly and many other vulnerable people, we have provided them with excellent protection against severe disease in case they get infected. Also contributing is widespread natural immunity from recovered COVID patients. Though cases may rise, deaths will no longer follow in proportion. We have effectively defanged the disease with our successful vaccination rollout. We should be declaring a great and resounding success. The COVID emergency is over. We still need to take COVID seriously, and there are still vulnerable people here and abroad left to vaccinate. But we can start to treat it as one disease among many that afflict people rather than an all-consuming threat.[17]

- **Dr. John Mandrola - July 29, 2021 - *608,526 deaths***: If you were vaccinated and had mild to moderate URI symptoms, why on earth would you get a COVID test? Have the vaccines not transformed SARSCOV2 into just another regular respiratory virus?[104]

- **Dr. Michael Levitt - August 1, 2021 - *609,820 deaths***: With no move in added reported COVID19 deaths & Delta Variant CFR from UK of 0.14%, it seems that FL (Florida) is likely to be fine.[105]

- **Dr. Zubin Damania - August 17, 2021 - *620,152 deaths***: Now, the thing is it may take a little while. It may take multiple re-exposures, which is why a mix of boosters and natural infection, Delta may be a blessing to people who are vaccinated, because it's gonna quickly make this thing endemic. But to people who are unvaccinated, you are pretty much screwed. So just get vaccinated, all right?[106]

- **Dr. Jay Bhattacharya - August 26, 2021 - *631,948 deaths***: With the vulnerable elderly and others with certain co-morbid conditions now protected by the vaccine, high community prevalence of COVID no longer poses the risk of mortality it did in 2020...The virus now joins 200 other pathogens (give or take) in regular circulation in human societies. The war on COVID should be over.[107]

- **Dr. Monica Gandhi - September 4, 2021 - *645,470 deaths***: I truly, truly think we are in the endgame. The cases will start plummeting in mid- to late September and by mid-October, we will be in a manageable place, where the virus is a concern for health professionals, but not really for the general public.[10]

- **Dr. Jay Bhattacharya - September 4, 2021 - *645,470 deaths***: The emergency phase of the disease is over. Now, we need to work very hard to undo the sense of emergency. We should be treating COVID as one of 200 diseases that affect people.[10]

- **Dr. Jay Bhattacharya - September 8, 2021 - *650,921 deaths***: Now that we have (mostly) vaccinated the vulnerable, the pandemic will end when the people say it is over. At that point, no amount of panic mongering will work.[108]

- **Dr. Monica Gandhi - September 21, 2021 - *676,768 deaths***: We won't eradicate COVID. The pandemic will still end. In a matter of months, viral circulation in the United States could dwindle to levels so low we will no longer need to require masks, distancing, ventilation, asymptomatic testing or contact tracing.[109]

- **Dr. Monica Gandhi - September 30, 2021 - *696,943 deaths***: COVID will soon Be endemic, thank goodness. Widespread immunity, vaccinated and natural, will bring control and a full return to normal…With a highly transmissible variant driving up immunity in the unvaccinated and bolstering it in the vaccinated, COVID-19 will inevitably make the transition from epidemic to endemic.[110]

- **Dr. Monica Gandhi - October 6, 2021 - *706,953 deaths***: But [even] if we don't get our vaccination rates up, I think by the end of this year we will have enough immunity in our population, either through vaccination and natural infection. I think delta will be the variant to end them all.[111]

- **Dr. Monica Gandhi - October 25, 2021 - *737,054 deaths***: NYC's high rates of vax, some prior infection and precautions keeping the worst outcomes of COVID-19 in check: "We're on our way to an endemic phase."[112]

- **Dr. Monica Gandhi - November 3, 2021 - *749,501 deaths***: It's time to contemplate the end of the crisis. Immunity is rising, and the approval of shots for young children is one of the last thresholds before a return to greater normalcy. Americans should be asking ourselves what else needs to happen before we can declare an end to the crisis phase of the pandemic. Although the coronavirus's course remains unpredictable—and bad surprises are still possible—the Delta-variant surge that started in early July ushered in what may have been the final major wave of disease in the United States. The U.S. still has more progress to make, but the reality is that the coronavirus is encountering fewer and fewer Americans who are defenseless against it.[113]

- **Dr. Jay Bhattacharya - November 15, 2021 - *763,391 deaths***: Vaccinating children is neither necessary nor sufficient to end the pandemic.[114]

- **Dr. Jay Bhattacharya - December 1, 2021 - *781,573 deaths***: So I think now we can look and then do empirical studies to see if it is more severe and if (the Omicron variant) it does evade, I don't, it seems really unlikely, just from a first principles point of view that because it's still the same virus with a few mutations. The other variants have not escaped natural immunity, have not escaped vaccine immunity, in terms of protection against severe disease, and that's something we should tell the public. I mean this is not something to panic about. We have many tools to address this and we are in the process of developing new ones.[115]

- **Dr. Marty Makary - December 16, 2021 - *803,665 deaths***: Now I call it omi-cold. If you look at the epidemiological data, the epicenter is now way down from omicron. The hospitals had some hospitalizations, not much. They were short. They averaged two and a half days instead of eight days. But a study just came out of the University of Hong Kong telling us that omicron does not invade the lung tissue that's deep in the respiratory tract. It stays superficial in the nose and bronchus. So that's why we're seeing a common cold-like illness. This new scientific data from the lab explains the epidemiological data and the bedside observation of doctors that this is far more mild... and that's why I call it omi-cold.[116]

- **Dr. Jay Bhattacharya - December 16, 2021 - *803,665 deaths***: Focused protection by mass vaccinating the vulnerable (without coercion!) will end the pandemic if we can muster the political will to accept the good news.[117]

- **Dr. Jay Bhattacharya - December 18, 2021 - *806,208 deaths***: With the new and effective technologies available and the focused protection ideas outlined in the GBD, we can end the pandemic if only we can muster the courage and political will to do so. As normal society resumes, the vast majority will find that living with the virus is not so hard after all.[118]

- **Dr. Marty Makary - January 2, 2022 - *826,421 deaths***: So we got a lot of good news this week. .. So for much of the world that will not have access to a vaccine, Omicron will be nature's vaccine. We can recognize that there is an end in sight to this particular variant as Omicron sweeps across many countries.. Probably in the next few weeks we will see Omicron peak, and it is spreading so quickly that may even be accelerated further. Think of it as a bad flu season when about half of everybody you know will probably get this infection. It will confer immunity to Delta, that evidence is in.[119]

- **Dr. Zubin Damania - January 5, 2022 - *832,888 deaths***: So there's a lot of existing immunity. All right? So that's very good news if it pans out further. Because it says we have a less deadly virus, that's more in the kin of a seasonal flu, or a bad cold...You now have effectively an endemic virus that's with us every year, like the other four coronaviruses there. It's the fifth coronavirus. It causes Omi-cold, and we generate immunity from being infected by it.[120]

- **Dr. Jay Bhattacharya - January 6, 2022 - *834,983 deaths***: The disease now is defanged...Governments should be telling people about tools to get back to normal life.[18]

- **Dr. Lucy McBride - January 11, 2022 - *843,487 deaths***: More ppl are becoming immune to COVID, but *no one* is immune to the stress of the pandemic.[121]

- **Dr. John Ioannidis - January 17, 2022 - *854,498 deaths***: Omicron has the characteristics of an endemic wave...seasonal appearance, high rates of transmission, disproportionately low death burden in a setting where there is very high background immunity due to prior infection and/or vaccination.[122]

- **Drs. Jay Bhattacharya, Harvey Risch, & Paul Alexander - January 23, 2022 - *868,806 deaths***: The time has come to terminate the pandemic state of emergency. It is time to end the controls, the closures, the restrictions, the plexiglass, the stickers, the exhortations, the panic-mongering, the distancing announcements, the ubiquitous commercials, the forced masking, the vaccine mandates. Omicron is mild enough that most people, even many high-risk people, can adequately cope with the infection. Omicron infection is no more severe than seasonal flu, and generally less so.... Given that omicron, with its mild infection, is running its course to the end, there is no justification for maintaining emergency status....Omicron is circulating but it is not an emergency. The emergency is over. The current emergency declaration must be canceled. It is time.[123]

- **Dr. Jay Bhattacharya - January 29, 2022 - *885,931 deaths***: To me the term pandemic no longer has any epidemiological definition. It is a political term to designate whatever it is we just went through the last two years. So the end of the pandemic is a political decision, not an epidemiological one.[124]

- **Dr. Jay Bhattacharya - January 31, 2022 - *889,023 deaths***: If Democrats are pivoting away from lockdowns, the end of the pandemic may be nigh.[125]

- **Dr. Zubin Damania - February 13, 2022 - *920,546 deaths***: Cases are plummeting, as we sort of predicted they would in December…We need to stop every single pandemic restriction, including vaccine mandates including mask mandates, including kids wearing masks, including thinking about it, including hearing about it on the news. All of it, I want it gone.[126]

- **Dr. Jay Bhattacharya - March 12, 2022 - *967,132 deaths***: It is far past time to end the state of emergency in California, end the rule of the technocrats, and restore normal order.[127]

- **Dr. Jay Bhattacharya - March 20, 2022 - *974,254 deaths***: The pandemic, however, is drawing to a close as government after government has accepted the fact that the virus is here to stay forever, joining the 200 or so other pathogens that cause diseases in humans and the other circulating human coronaviruses.[128]

- **Dr. John Ioannidis - March 28, 2022 - *980,671 deaths***: Public health officials need to declare the end of the pandemic… With increasingly ageing global population and massive testing, 'normal' may still correspond to higher death counts than pre-COVID-19 influenza-related illnesses. This should not be mistaken as a continued pandemic phase…Pandemic preparedness should be carefully thought and pre-organized, but should not disrupt life.[129]

- **Dr. Marty Makary - May 2, 2022 - *996,661 deaths***: Hospitals are virtually empty of COVID-ill patients, yet the pandemic of fear continues.[130]

- **Dr. Monica Gandhi - May 15, 2022 - *1,001,833 deaths***: TOOLS TO KEEP COVID ENDEMIC NOW HERE: Long thread to explain that we now have all the tools necessary in the US to keep COVID in the endemic & out of the emergency phase. At this point in the pandemic (May '22), world & US seeing its lowest number of COVID deaths since March 2020.[131]

- **Dr. Jay Bhattacharya - May 26, 2022 - *1,006,355 deaths***: It's far past time for the COVID state of emergency to end. No more biomedical security state.[132]

- **Dr. Vinay Prasad - June 2, 2022 - *1,008,356 deaths***: COVID-19 is really over when the New York Times health section returns to hard-hitting coverage such as: How many blueberries should you eat? How dark should your chocolate be? Is tea better than coffee? Can saunas prevent Alzheimer's[133]

- **Dr. Vinay Prasad - June 29, 2022 - *1,017,930 deaths***: We should treat COVID-19 exactly like flu 2018.[134]

- **Dr. Jay Bhattacharya - July 12, 2022 - *1,022,237 deaths***: The virus is endemic and will circulate forever. Most of the population has been infected and recovered and is protected vs. future severe reinfection. The decision to end the pandemic emergency is a political one, not epidemiological.[135]

- **Dr. John Mandrola - July 27, 2022 - *1,029,290 deaths***: We now have a diff disease: many if not most COVID+ pts we consult on have + test but an adm Dx (admitting diagnosis) for something else The pneumonias of 2020-2021 are thankfully rare.[136]

- **Dr. Jay Bhattacharya - August 16, 2022 - *1,038,301 deaths***: It's far past time for the US COVID state of emergency declaration to end. Many states have already ended theirs. When the state of emergency ends, the oversized COVID industrial complex will end with it…[137]

- **Dr. Jay Bhattacharya - August 22, 2022 - *1,041,192 deaths***: We've created an interest group to keep the pandemic going. Their argument is 'we're keeping people safe when in fact we're just keeping the anxiety going.[138]

- **Dr. Monica Gandhi - September 10, 2022 - *1,050,543 deaths***: POPULATION IMMUNITY IN 2022. Very different than COVID prior to immunity; we have widespread vaccines & 60-75% of planet having been infected with Omicron. Good to provide the good news of COVID immunity in 2022.[139]

- **Dr. Vinay Prasad - September 11, 2022 - *1,050,564 deaths*:** The new variant is less lethal. When you combine this with high rates of natural immunity, and vaccination, the net result is simple: the IFR (infection fatality rate) for COVID19 is now far less than flu. That's what many Americans intuitively get, which is why they have returned to normal. It also means policy needs to readjust. The emergency is over.[140]

- **Dr. Monica Gandhi - September 16, 2022 - *1,053,621 deaths*:** We have all been questioning, 'When does COVID look like influenza?' And, I would say, 'Yes, we are there.'[141]

- **Dr. Vinay Prasad - September 18, 2022 - *1,053,677 deaths*:** The emergency or pandemic phase is over. COVID will be around for tens of thousands of years. Time to stop using EUA at FDA and time to actively advise people to throw away their n95s and get back to living. Getting COVID is inevitable.[142]

- **Dr. Jay Bhattacharya - September 19, 2022 - *1,054,075 deaths:*** Pres. Biden is right. The pandemic emergency is over.[143]

- **Dr. Monica Gandhi - December 13, 2022 - *1,085,224 deaths*:** There are many reasons to be optimistic. A combination of factors—a high level of population immunity, Omicron family antigenic drift, convergence of mutations that seem to have hit an evolutionary ceiling, almost nonexistent severe COVID illness in the hospital, and viral interference from RSV and Influenza surges—means we are in a surprisingly good place with COVID-19 in winter 2022-23.[144]

Hopefully, Dr. Gandhi is right, and we are in a surprisingly good place with COVID. But I've heard that before, often right before some new variant ruins everything.

There will never be an official declaration that the pandemic is over. However, I will consider it over when these doctors stop telling us it is over, when they discuss COVID as often as they discuss outbreaks that have ended, such as the New York City's measles outbreak in 2019. These doctors have been saying in essence: *You should stop talking about COVID, but I should continue to tell you why you should stop.* However, I feel they should model the behavior they expect from others.

"Majority Indians have natural immunity. Vaccinating entire population can cause great harm."
~Dr. Jay Bhattacharya

Declarations the pandemic was over were not limited to the U.S. Dr. Jay Bhattacharya co-wrote an article titled "Majority Indians Have Natural Immunity. Vaccinating Entire Population Can Cause Great Harm"[145] in January 2021 and the next month Dr. Monica Gandhi tweeted that "India was 'wide open' now as herd immunity. Schools just opening now".[146] Several months later the headlines would read "India's Holiest River is Swollen with Bodies",[147] and Dr. Gandhi would also express regret for this error.[148]

On April 3, 2021, Dr. Marty Makary wrote:

> *U.K. has now vaccinated 60% of adults with 1 dose by delaying 2nd doses a few months--a winning strategy the U.S. debated but Fauci & FDA sternly and repeatedly rejected. Well the U.K. won. Today, they are on the brink of herd immunity.*

Similarly, Dr. Martin Kulldorff tweeted in April 2020:

> *Extremely surprising if past infection does not give some immunity. Around 1/3 of ppl in Stockholm has now had COVID-19, and it is likely to be the first place to reach herd immunity. Those are important things to communicate about.*[192]

He repeated this in May 2020 saying, "With age-specific counter measures rather than universal lockdown, Sweden is as close to herd immunity with fewer deaths, saving lives"[149] and, in August 2021, he tweeted "Essentially #ZeroCOVID deaths in Sweden for a month now."[150] On July 13, 2021, he said:

> *With vaccine generated #FocusedProtection of the*

> *old, UK #COVID case are mostly among young people with miniscule risk of death. That is why COVID mortality is now so low compared to cases.*[151]

Dr. Levitt said in March 2020, "I will be surprised if the number of deaths in Israel surpasses 10"[152] and tweeted in April 2020 that it "looks like Sweden has done the right thing after all. Herd immunity, intact economy, little social hardship."[153] In July 2020, he estimated that in Israel "the epidemic will naturally fade away when 5 to 15 percent of the population is infected."[154] In fact, more than 10 Israelis died, Sweden did not reach herd immunity, and the epidemic did not naturally fade away.

Dr. Marty Makary also told citizens of the UK the pandemic was over in their country. On April 3, 2021, he said:

> *U.K. has now vaccinated 60% of adults with 1 dose by delaying 2nd doses a few months--a winning strategy the U.S. debated but Fauci & FDA sternly and repeatedly rejected. Well the U.K. won. Today, they are on the brink of herd immunity-deaths there ↓↓ 97%* [193]

By May 2021 Delta would have a firm grip on the UK and the death rate would begin to climb.[194]

"Health must be viewed holistically— yet school policymakers have narrowly defined 'safety' as the mere absence of COVID"

~ Urgency of Normal

Many doctors who declared the pandemic over in the spring of 2021 banded together in January 2022 to claim they had been correct. Their collective commitment to the end of the pandemic was formalized via a group called the Urgency of Normal, which included Allison Krug, Drs. Lucy McBride, Vinay Prasad, and Tracy Høeg, amongst others. Their mission statement sounds reasonable:

> *We are a group of scientists and pediatric, infectious*

disease, emergency, mental health, and ICU doctors concerned that COVID-19 mitigation measures for children are doing more harm than good. Health must be viewed holistically— yet school policymakers have narrowly defined "safety" as the mere absence of COVID, putting children into a loop of mitigation measures that are uncoupled from actual risk. After two years of living with one disruption after another, the toll on children's mental and physical health is increasingly evident and alarming. To protect them, an urgent return to fully normal life and schooling is needed.[155]

Like the authors of the Great Barrington Declaration, the Urgency of Normal doctors did not want their ideas relegated to academic journals. They were ubiquitous media presences and even created a "toolkit"[156] parents could use to advocate against COVID mitigation policies at their child's school.

However, their efforts to convince parents that everything was normal included dubious claims and blatantly false statistics. It told parents that "long COVID is not a major risk to children" and embraced principles of the Great Barrington Declaration, such as "focused protection for the vulnerable." It said that "COVID is a flu-like risk" for unvaccinated children, even though when it was published, the flu had killed six children,[157] while COVID had killed over 1,200.[158] Some Urgency of Normal doctors told parents that schools were magically immune to the spread of COVID. For example, in March 2021, Dr. Tracy Høeg wrote:

Children have not been found to be superspreaders and since there is high over dispersion of this disease schools have not been found to be centers for super spreading events or large amounts of disease spread.[159]

Of course, research revealed the unsurprising news that the virus spreads quite well schools, especially those without any mitigation measures.[160]

Despite their purported commitment to opening schools, the

Urgency of Normal team opposed all measures – such as masks, testing, and vaccine requirements – that might have helped schools to safely open. Dr. Prasad wrote an article titled "The Downsides of Masking Young Students Are Real" in which he said:

> *The potential educational harms of mandatory-masking policies are much more firmly established, at least at this point, than their possible benefits in stopping the spread of COVID-19 in schools.*[161]

He presented no evidence that masks actually harm children because no such evidence exists. In contrast, several studies show masks help keep COVID cases down in schools.[162]

The Urgency of Normal doctors were lukewarm on vaccines, and many of its leaders spread blatant misinformation about the pediatric vaccine throughout the pandemic. They acknowledged that "vaccinated children have almost no risk of severe disease,"[156] but never suggested that parents actually vaccinate their children. Instead, they lamented that "vaccine recommendations continue to be made for populations in which there is no evidence of benefit."[163] The Urgency of Normal doctors were not concerned by the prospect of an unvaccinated child getting COVID. They were instead concerned that a child who contracted COVID might get vaccinated. One of these things is dangerous, while the other is likely beneficial.

In addition to spreading false statistics, the Urgency of Normal doctors specialized in omitting vital information to mislead their audience. While it's true that millions of children had remote schooling due to difficult decisions made by adults, in the real world, schools were also closed by overwhelming COVID outbreaks. This didn't just happen in Democratic states. One typical headline from Texas from September 2021 read, "At Least 45 Districts Shut Down In-Person Classes Due to COVID-19 Cases, Affecting More Than 40,000 Students."[164] Another headline from that time declared "4 Georgia Districts Stop In-Person Classes Due to COVID".[165] Similar headlines appeared throughout the country whenever cases soared, and it's still happening in December 2022.

Even when schools were "open", students were often absent in large numbers. Either they were sick, or their caregivers didn't want them bringing the virus home to a vulnerable relative. The Urgency of Normal doctors never seemed to consider that some caregivers didn't feel comfortable sending their child to school when COVID was spreading out of control. Beyond minimizing COVID's risk for children, they put no effort into making these parents feel safe. For these reasons, students were often absent. A headline from January 2022, when the Omicron variant was spreading widely, read "A Record Number of NYC Kids Have Missed the Last Two Weeks of School."[166]

Teachers were affected too. In New York City alone, 30 teachers and 44 other Department of Education employees died in the first wave.[167] All but four of them worked in schools. Hundreds of teachers died over the course of the pandemic,[168] and sick teachers couldn't teach. Some states used the National Guard to act as substitute "teachers" during the Omicron wave, and at least one school in New York City had their kids sit in an auditorium all day. There weren't enough teachers.

This was all bad for children, and the Urgency of Normal doctors responded to it by pretending it never happened. Unwanted facts were unmentionable facts, and politicians and teachers were always to blame, never SARS-CoV-2. As with protecting nursing homes, doctors who had no real-world responsibility for opening schools spent much of the pandemic portraying this as a trivial task, one that wasn't done to perfection because those with real world responsibility were incompetent or indifferent. In reality, keeping students and teachers in classrooms was infinitely harder than saying "open schools" in podcasts, editorials, and tweets.

The Urgency of Normal doctors, few of whom were overly concerned about teenage suicide before the pandemic, also made false claims about children's mental health, saying "child deaths from suicide vastly outnumber deaths from COVID and are increasing."[169] While some states (Georgia, Indiana, Oklahoma) saw an increase in adolescent suicide in 2020, others (California, Colorado) did not, and Montana saw a decrease.[170] Suicides increased in 2021 compared to 2020 for males age 15–24, even though schools were open more in 2021.[171] A paper from December 2022 even found remote schooling led to a decrease in suicides.[172] It reported that:

> *Teen suicides plummeted in March 2020, when the COVID-19 pandemic began in the U.S. and remained*

> *low throughout the summer before rising in Fall 2020 when many K-12 schools returned to in-person instruction.*

Dr. Tyler Black, a child and adolescent psychiatrist who corrected the Urgency of Normal's misinformation on this point, said, "I consider it ghoulish to wield child suicide statistics inaccurately to make advocacy points".[173]

The Urgency of Normal team attributed all childhood mental health issues to remote schooling, without considering that children were profoundly affected by their bout with COVID or from losing a loved one to it.[174] Despite early pandemic musings that children could not spread the virus, there's no question that children can bring the virus home and spread it to more vulnerable relatives.[175] By the spring of 2022, over 200,000 American children had lost a parent or caregiver to the virus.[176] In New York City alone, 8,600 children – 1 in 200 children – have lost a parent or caregiver.[177] Around the world, an estimated 10.5 million children have lost parents or caregivers to COVID, and 7.5 million were orphaned.[178]

This can be a disaster for children. As Tim Requarth wrote in an article on COVID orphans:

> *Losing a parent may be one of the most destabilizing events of the human experience. Orphans are at increased risk of substance abuse, dropping out of school, and poverty. They are almost twice as likely as non-orphans to die by suicide, and they remain more susceptible to almost every major cause of death for the rest of their life.*[179]

He's right. After the death of her father, 15-year-old Elizabeth George said, "I didn't want to go to school. I just wanted to stay at home."[174] Charles Nelson, a professor of pediatrics and psychology at Harvard University who has studied separation from caregivers said, "Honestly, it makes me sick to my stomach to think of the hurt so many kids are experiencing. We could have done better to protect these kids." The Urgency of Normal doctors never mentioned COVID orphans. They pretended these children didn't exist.

"Hope is accurate. It's not like we're slinging a lie."
~ Dr. Zubin Damania

I'll end with one final exchange between Drs. Damania and Makary, which comes from a podcast titled *Least Wrong About COVID?* from May 24, 2021.[180]

> ***Dr. Damania****: Then you (Dr. Marty Makary) say things like, for example, just now, "Hey, we're going to have herd immunity by the end of April", "and by the way, this pandemic's going to be over", "because the vaccines are great, and by the way", "natural immunity is a thing." And guess what? You were pretty much right about everything, 'cause cases have plummeted, natural immunity does contribute, and probably the left was like, "Oh, who is this fascist going on Fox News, saying that this thing's over?"*
>
> ***Dr. Makary****: Well, it's amazing. Ignoring natural immunity, which, oddly, our public health officials have done, and I think it's more a function of the old school nature of those officials. "We don't have data on natural immunity." It's like open your eyes. No one is getting reinfected at any appreciable degree–...*
>
> ***Dr. Makary****: So why are public health officials dangling variant fear so much, at a time when, honestly, people need hope.*
>
> ***Dr. Damania****: They not only need... Hope is accurate. It's not like we're slinging a lie.*

I'm not a mind reader so I can't say whether or not these doctors were slinging a lie. However, they certainly weren't slinging the truth. Over 500,000 Americans have died of COVID since that podcast aired.[20]

Yet, Drs. Damania and Makary applauded themselves for being "right about everything," and mercilessly mocked those who doubted the arrival of herd immunity. Contrarian doctors engaged in similar spasms of mutual self-congratulations and recriminations against "the left" and "public health officials" whenever there was a temporary dip in cases. They never paused to reflect on the dismal failure of their past projections or grapple with potential consequences of their poor prognostications.

However, their preposterous predictions didn't occur in a vacuum. Many people were listening. Contrarian doctors gained significant media attention along with a large, loyal following on social media by telling people what they wanted to hear. One typical *Twitter* commentator said to Dr. Gandhi in March 2021:

> *Thank you for the positivity, I see so many other people cheering on a 4th surge like it was a sports team. It is all so puzzling. Have some people gotten so comfortable staying at home that they are praying for the COVID crisis? I really appreciate your positive insight.*[181]

While contrarian doctors often acted as if their false forecasts were just idle chatter, I can't help but wonder about their real-world impact. Did a young person with a cough visit their grandma because they were told vaccines "transformed SARSCOV2 into just another regular respiratory virus"?[104] Did an immunocompromised person stop wearing a mask because she heard the virus was now "nature's vaccine"[119] or "omi-cold"?[116] Did a vulnerable person not bother getting vaccinated because he believed we'd "have herd immunity by April"?[44] We'll never know.

One question has an answer, however. How many children contracted COVID after Dr. Prasad said "*cases are FALLING PRECIPITOUSLY*" in June 2021?[97] Dr. Prasad answered that question himself. In an article written one year later, Dr. Prasad used the mass infection of children as his top reason why they should not get vaccinated. He wrote:

> *Most kids already had COVID-19. CDC estimates 75% as of February, but this number is an underestimate, as millions have been infected since.*[182]

He wasn't wrong about that. However, he didn't mention that

COVID killed 1,000 children[158] from when he said, "cases are FALLING PRECIPITOUSLY"[97] to when he said "most kids already had COVID-19,"[182] though he used both as reasons why children should remain unvaccinated.

Chapter 8: "The fear that's driving this pandemic has been heartbreaking to see."

"Infectious diseases fall into this emotional fear-based primal mental algorithm."
~ Roman Bystrianyk

Anti-vaxxers have long said that those who wish to avoid vaccine-preventable diseases are driven by irrational fear, which is both shameful and worse than any virus. Prior to the pandemic, anti-vaccine doctors spoke about the "panic" regarding measles outbreaks. For example, Dr. Bob Sears said in 2014:

> *Why is it that every time there are a few cases of measles, everyone panics? I just don't get it.*[1]

This idea was flushed out in an article titled "Measles: The New Red Scare" on the anti-vaccine site *GreenMedInfo*, which claimed that "irrational measles fear is being used as a pretext for infringing on individual rights."[2] The article, by anti-vaccine activist Roman Bystrianyk, said:

> *Fear. It's a natural and primal human emotion. While human instinct is exceptional in evaluating and reacting to a natural personal risk, as in facing a predator, humans are terrible at assessing modern risks. According to Psychology Today this is because our ancestors were programmed to quickly react and respond to a situation before it is even consciously perceived. Our reactions aren't based in logic and statistics, but in lightning fast primitive responses...*
>
> *Infectious diseases fall into this emotional fear-based primal mental algorithm. This reaction is completely understandable with mankind's horrifying historical experience with deadly microbes. ..So with the recent spate of measles cases in the United States, the enormous amount of fear and anger comes as no surprise.*

Mr. Bystrianyk asked readers to "take a deep breath and a moment to step back from the hysteria and look at some information that is never part of the discussion involving infectious diseases." He made the case that the danger of measles is overblown, saying:

> *In 1962, measles was sixth from the bottom for causes of death. You can look through the list of causes of death and find almost everything from "Birth Injuries" at 28,199 to "Ulcers" at 12,228 to "Asthma" at 4,896 were far higher than the 408 deaths attributed to "Measles" that year.*

This is all nonsense. It doesn't matter where measles ranked in pediatric deaths in 1962. 408 children is a very large number of dead children and zero children should suffer from measles today.

Beyond that, the article was unctuously condescending towards people who wanted to protect their children against measles. Though Mr. Bystrianyk claims a fear of deadly viruses is "completely understandable," he clearly disdains people who want to protect their children against them. Mr. Bystrianyk feels their "reactions aren't based in logic and statistics, but in lightning fast primitive responses." They are fearful and angry, operating on an "emotional fear-based primal mental algorithm." Mr. Bystrianyk basically feels parents who vaccinate their children are cowardly, angry Neanderthals.

Of course, people should be angry when unvaccinated children suffer from measles. In the fall of 2022, a measles outbreak struck Ohio. According to a news report:

> *Of the 73 confirmed cases, four of them are partially vaccinated children who have received one dose of the MMR vaccine. Two people who have a confirmed case are listed as having an unknown vaccinated status while the other 67 cases are in unvaccinated children. 70% of the cases are in children 5 years old or younger.*[3]

26 children have been hospitalized for measles so far. This all could have been easily avoided. Anger is the only appropriate response to

this. Apathy is not a moral virtue when unvaccinated children suffer from measles or any other vaccine-preventable disease.

During the pandemic, anti-vaxxers continued to speak this way, lamenting fear of COVID, not the disease itself. At the pandemic's start, right-wing rocker Ted Nugent shared a provocative message on *Facebook*. It said:

> *Why do I have to stay home just because are scared? How about stay home.... stay in house indefinitely, wear a mask, socially distance yourself from me, avoid restaurants, avoid baseball games, stay off the roads, avoid malls and beaches and parks, believe the made up death numbers, believe the media hype, Get your toxic vaccine while avoiding vitamin C, sunshine and the things God gave us to actually heal,*
>
> *I'm done playing dumb game. We are not "all in this together." I'm not wearing dumb tin foil hat anymore. I'm no longer going to be a prisoner of your fear. I'm no longer staying in my house or catering to because are scared. I'm not wearing a mask and I'm not staying 6 feet away from you anymore because I'm not afraid of you. You are not my enemy and if I get sick, it's not because of , it's because of me and my system, which not only have I been addressing for quite some time, but I also know how to treat if I get sick.*
>
> *This virus (or whatever it is) is already circulating. Millions of people have already encountered it, as it's been circulating around the world probably since last September. You WILL have to confront this thing, if you haven't already. There is no way around it, unless you lock yourself up in your house and it somehow doesn't manage to hop on some mail or some groceries that you ordered online.*
>
> *Fear is not an excuse to destroy America. fear is not my fear and your fear does not have the right*

> *to interfere with my life, my job, my income or my future as a free American citizen. So if you're scared, you can just put your tin foil hat on, or even wrap foil all around your whole body – or around your whole house if you wish – but please keep your fear contained to your little corner of the world and don't contaminate me or my family or my Country.*[4]

I'll discuss Mr. Nugent again at the end of this chapter, but he was not alone. This sort of narrative was very popular with anti-vaxxers at the pandemic's start. Sayer Ji, founder of the anti-vaccine site *GreenMedInfo*, was on a podcast in March 2020 where he talked "first and foremost about the coronavirus and the multiple fear narratives surrounding it."[5] Dr. Kelly Brogan similarly spoke about fear as the main problem at the pandemic's start. In a video described by Matthew Remski:

> *Brogan's core theme was that the rise in COVID-19 deaths are "likely being accelerated by the fear" of the virus. That fear, she said, was being stoked by a "mainstream media" intent on the "curation of reality" to make people distrustful of each other.*[6]

These people all agreed that anyone who wanted to avoid COVID was using an "emotional fear-based primal mental algorithm."[2]

As the pandemic progressed, anti-vaxxers continued to minimize new variants. Dr. Joseph Mercola, who has long been one of America's most prominent anti-vaccine doctors, wrote an article on Robert F. Kennedy, Jr.'s anti-vaccine website in which he said:

> *The risk-benefit ratio of the COVID shot is becoming even more inverted with the emergence of Omicron, as this variant produces far milder illness than previous variants, putting children at even lower risk of hospitalization or death from infection than they were before, and their risk was already negligible.*[7]

In reality, the Omicron variant killed and hospitalized more children than ever before.

"I think that there is no reason to fear."
~ Dr. John Ioannidis

The notion that fear *of* the virus was worse than the virus itself would also prove popular amongst contrarian doctors. Many doctors found themselves *very concerned* that strangers might be trying too hard to avoid COVID. A corollary to their idea that the pandemic had ended was that anyone who still treated the virus as a threat was "living in fear" and letting life "pass them by." Contrarian doctors routinely mocked and shamed people who tried to avoid the virus, some even suggesting that they suffered from a mental disorder. Yet, in the same way that sarcastic requests to "wait two weeks" turned out to be reliable indicators of when cases would spike, anyone contrarian doctors accused of "fear mongering" turned out to be reliable and accurate.

This notion that fear was worse than the virus started in the pandemic's first months. On April 17, 2020, Dr. John Ioannidis said:

> *It's very, very difficult to fathom the consequences of what is going on and what we are doing, but I really worry that unless we manage to have a viable plan to exit from lockdown and shelter in place and reopen our world, the consequences will be far worse than coronavirus. Our data suggests that COVID-19 has an infection fatality rate that is in the same ballpark as seasonal influenza. It suggests that even though this is a very serious problem, we should not fear. It suggests that we have solid ground to have optimism about the possibility of eventually reopening our society and gaining back our lives...We have data now that the infection fatality rate is much, much lower, compared to our original expectations and fears. I think that there is no reason to fear.*[8]

He thought that hospitals were being overrun with worried but well people. He said:

> *I think that in many of these places, unfortunately, we saw many people going to the hospital probably*

under a sense of fear and threat and panic, and we had the environment heavily contaminated, generating hospital chains of infection and therefore infecting lots of people who were very susceptible, and who would do very poorly if, on top of whatever they had, they also got COVID-19 infection.

No doctor who worked in a COVID hot spot at that time would have said anything this absurd. In reality, many healthcare workers used war analogies to describe their experience at the time. A doctor at Elmhurst Hospital in Queens, New York said:

If you watch a war movie to see people shooting from all over, that's what this almost felt like. One thing after the next after next, you can't even catch up with what has to happen.[9]

Frontline healthcare workers knew that fear was a justified and appropriate response to COVID.

In an interview with the *Wall Street Journal* in April 2020, Dr. Ioannidis lamented that "bad news, negative news, are more attractive than positive news."[10] "We have generated a very heavily panic-driven, horror-driven, death-reality-show type of situation," he said. "We will see many young people committing suicide . . . just because we are spreading horror stories with COVID-19," he added. Dr. Ioannidis felt those who disagreed with him were incapable of independent thought, saying:

There's some sort of mob mentality here operating that they just insist that this has to be the end of the world, and it has to be that the sky is falling.

Like Mr. Bystrianyk, Dr. Ioannidis felt that those who wanted to avoid COVID were using an "emotional fear-based primal mental algorithm."[2]

"Creating excess fear can be dangerous. Fear destroys rational decision-making."

~ Dr. John Mandrola

Dr. Ioannidis was hardly alone in telling Americans fear was an inappropriate response to the virus. Many doctors felt that anyone who wanted to avoid SARS-CoV-2 was using an "emotional fear-based primal mental algorithm." They repeated this message regularly throughout the pandemic, well after it was clear what the virus could do.

As early as March 5, 2020, Dr. John Mandrola praised the "strikingly calm words"[11] of a politician who said, "Fear can do more harm than the virus itself." In September 2020, when COVID death toll was 188,000 people,[12] Dr. Mandrola tweeted "I am seeing lots of fear-mongering in #COVID19 Let's be clear: the virus deserves respect…But … creating excess fear can be dangerous. Fear destroys rational decision-making."[13]

In December that year he wrote an article titled "No, Young Adults Should Not Live in Fear from Coronavirus," in which he said that "the young have many reasons – ethical and moral – to adhere to social distancing during the pandemic. Fear of death is not one of them."[14] In reality, 40,000 young adults died of COVID in the pandemic's first 2.5 years, and during many months, COVID was the number 1 or 2 leading cause of death amongst young adults. Even after the deadly winter wave of 2020-2021, Dr. Mandrola's main "frustration"[15] remained with those who still warned of the virus and their "fear-mongering." Of course, Dr. Mandrola leveled this accusation against anyone who disagreed with him that the pandemic was over.

"I want to write a children's book about a bear who didn't want to leave home till it was perfectly safe. He never left and life passed him by."

~ Dr. Vinay Prasad

At the literal peak of death for the entire pandemic, during the winter wave of 2021 and on a day when 3,523 Americans died and the U.S. cumulative death toll reached 422,729 deaths,[11] Dr. Prasad sarcastically tweeted:

> *I want to write a children's book about a bear who didn't want to leave home till it was perfectly safe. He never left and life passed him by. In the sequel,*

> *he stands at the window shouting at anyone outside that they are killing fellow bears and spreading disinformation.*[16]

Most Americans were unvaccinated at that time, and over 650,000 Americans have died since.[12]

In an article titled "Legitimizing Irrational Anxiety is Bad Medicine," Dr. Prasad would say that "Fear of long COVID is irrational. In so far as it exists, you have to accept it"[17] and that:

> *It's time for medical professionals to advise young, middle age, healthy people to throw away your n95, leave your C02 monitor at home and get back to life. These are not proportionate responses. You are not acting reasonably. Someone needs to tell you.*

He expanded on this theme in an essay titled "When Scientists' Anxiety Disorder Interferes With Other People's Lives," in which he said:

> *What word do we use to describe doctors, scientists and policy makers whose personal mental health issues affect their policy recommendations? The lives of others?..It is pathologic for anxiety to harm your own life, but I believe we enter the realm of catastrophe when personal mental health issues affect sweeping policy matters.*[18]

He went on to shame and pathologize "vocal policy analysts (doctors, scientists, professors) who's comments might be concerning."

As the pandemic progressed, Dr. Prasad continued to say that people who were trying too hard to avoid the virus were mentally unstable. In November 2022 he wrote:

> *Some adults who have had multiple boosters wear masks to concerts. Why? You will get COVID anyway later. One in 4 won't eat at a restaurant. I am deeply concerned these people need counseling.*[19]

He said such people were "demented" and "betray a deep ignorance about COVID19, and more generally show that they are incapable of judging risk." Of course, masks are completely normal in countries like Japan, which suffered a fraction of our COVID loss.

While RSV, flu, and COVID were overwhelming pediatric hospitals, Dr. Prasad said parents who wanted to limit playdates were "cruel and stupid." He implied that only people who were willing to repeatedly expose themselves to SARS-CoV-2 were properly living. He wrote:

> *Despite millions of news stories on COVID19, no one asked the obvious question. Respiratory viruses exist because human beings have to be close to each other. We are a social animal. We have to breathe each others air, and everything wonderful in life happens in proximity.*[20]

Dr. Brogan said the same thing at the pandemic's start. She said:

> *Am I convinced that this is true, that there are little invisible pathogens that randomly jump around from person to person and have the capacity to really harm, injure and even kill? That's a really hard way to live. At a time when we know that our biology knows that we need each other. We need touch, we need contact, we need togetherness.*[21]

"If you live life as if there are no respiratory viruses, you'll sometimes get sick, and you'll live your life."
~ Dr. Jay Bhattacharya

On May 12, 2021, after over 575,000 Americans had died,[12] Dr. Jay Bhattacharya told anti-vaccine Fox News star Tucker Carlson that public health officials were driven by an irrational fear of COVID. He said:

> *We've also created this fear. I think -- I think part of it, Tucker, to try to answer your question is that I think the people that sort of rule public health are actually scared of the disease outside the port of what actually*

> *the evidence shows in a way -- and they've decided that almost any action is necessary, okay, as long as it reduces the risk of the spread of the disease, even if it causes all kinds of other harms.*[22]

Mr. Carlson would agree, saying "I think people with obvious mental illness are in charge of making our policies, I mean, certainly neurotic." Over 500,000 more Americans have died since then.[12]

Dr. Bhattacharya, who had the wisdom to avoid COVID until he was vaccinated, would later say:

> *If you live life as if there are no respiratory viruses, you'll sometimes get sick, and you'll live your life. If you live your life to avoid all respiratory viruses, you'll sometimes get sick, and you'll have let your life pass unlived.*[23]

Obviously, countless thousands of people who lived their life like there are no respiratory viruses are no longer here to comment on the wisdom of their decision. In contrast, millions of people who have avoided the virus thus far are quite content with their lives, even if they aren't living like it's 2019.

"Don't Buy the Fearmongering: The COVID-19 Threat is Waning"
~ Dr. Marty Makary

Dr. Marty Makary wrote several articles in May 2021 claiming fear was a bigger threat than COVID. One was titled "Don't Buy the Fearmongering: The COVID-19 Threat is Waning," in which he said:

> *As the COVID pandemic wanes, Americans are being fed a distorted perception of the risks by the media and some experts. They continue to fuel fear by repeating speculation that variants will evade vaccines. Don't buy it.*[24]

Millions of Americans heeded this advice.

The other was titled "Risk of COVID is Now Very Low – It's Time to Stop Living in Fear," in which he said:

> *The fear-mongering will likely ramp up in the months ahead with warnings of new variants, and medical pundits fixated on "what ifs" over good news. They've already started. The CDC director, Rochelle Walensky, recently reported on the good news of rapidly declining case counts in the US. Then she added that variants "are a wild card that could reverse this progress we have made."*[25]

The Delta and Omicron variants arrived soon thereafter, and COVID would kill another 500,000 Americans over the next 18 months.[12]

On July 28, 2021, as the Delta variant loomed, Dr. Makary said, "You're going to see a lot of fear, you're going to see a lot of draconian policies come back in certain parts of the country."[26] Dr. Makary's fear of "draconian" policies was misplaced, but the Delta variant caused unprecedented illness and suffering in children and young adults immediately thereafter.

Dr. Makary continued to be afraid of fear as the Omicron variant appeared. Mocking those who were worried about Omicron, he said on December 16, 2021, "We're seeing this massive new wave of fear that is fueling our second pandemic after COVID-19, which is a pandemic of lunacy, which is Omicron."[27] Approximately 300,000 Americans have died of COVID[12] since Dr. Makary decided Omicron was "a pandemic of lunacy."

"There are people who are truly not actually living right now."

~ Dr. Monica Gandhi

In March 2020 Dr. Zubin Damania recorded a podcast called "Hacking Our Anxious Brain in Uncertain Times" that said "the COVID-19 pandemic has led to a secondary outbreak of fear, anxiety, and social contagion."[28] Listeners heard not how to avoid the virus, but rather "how we can fight anxiety and panic." They were advised to "Stop feeling 'covish' and start recognizing how our minds work when faced with uncertainty." He discussed "the nature of the psychological benefit of kindness and how the COVID-19 crisis may be a huge opportunity in disguise."

COVID did not turn out to be a huge opportunity in disguise.

Dr. Damania had recorded another podcast earlier that same month called "COVID-19: Is Our Cure Worse Than The Disease?" that asked, "As panic descends and aggressive lockdown measures start in the US, are we causing more harm on a population level than good?"[29] He further explored this theme in a podcast from June 2020 titled "COVID-19 Live Update: Should We Panic?"[30] After COVID ravished New York City, Dr. Damania asked, "This is a disaster, so what do you do? Do you panic? Do you shut down life as we know it? Do you continue to hide in your house?" However, Dr. Damania didn't think the pandemic was a disaster. He told his listeners:

> *This is nothing in the grand scheme of history. It's nothing, it's a rounding error on 1918 Spanish flu. It's a rounding error on the plague…Some people would rather die of COVID then suffer through what we've been through. And you know what, I get it, it sucks. It sucks, especially when we have a disease that maybe has a point 0.5% mortality. You know, so it's like your absolute risk of dying of it. This is for the people with panic disorder, with anxiety, with fear around this. Your absolute risk of dying of COVID is tiny. It's still really, really tiny. Even though COVID is rising internationally as the number one cause of death and all of this, that doesn't matter, it's still unlikely to die from it on average. So take a breath, we can put on our rational thinker because our fear-based elephant can calm down. Stop watching the news, stop losing yourself in these stories.*

In other words, ignore COVID.

Dr. Damania compared SAR-CoV-2, a virus with zero benefits and the potential for exponential growth, to the static, unavoidable risks we try very hard to mitigate, such as crossing the street. He warned that protecting children and their families from COVID would create a generation of weaklings. He said:

> *Is there risk, sure, there's risk crossing the street to take your kid to school, there's risk driving them to school, there's risk on the bus, we take those risks. We don't shut down the fabric of our society because of fear and a culture of safetyism. Safetyism says, we do everything possible to keep our children safe from anything, no matter what the cost, no matter creating a fragile generation of children that crumble at the slightest adversity, that look to their authority figures to keep them safe from words, from words that hurt them. I'm triggered, I need to save space, shut that comedian up. Don't let that person say that on Twitter. Do not let that speaker come to my campus and say something that frightens and offends me. My feelings are more important than any discourse.*
>
> *In this world, we have one way to deal with conflict. And that's talking about it. What happens when you take that one way away with a fragile generation that can't handle themselves? The only thing left is violent conflict. Is that what we want? We need to get back to discourse in this country, which means put the kids in school, let them hash stuff out.*

I disagree that trying to keep children and their families safe from COVID at the pandemic's start was an inevitable pathway to violent conflict.

It also turns out that Dr. Damania was extremely sympathetic to those who crumbled at slightest adversity, so long as that "adversity" required them to make the slightest effort to avoid COVID. To his credit, he said that he would wear a mask at the pandemic's start, and that protecting others was a core reason why. That's important. However, he provided ample reasons for his audience to not wear a mask and asked them to "stop shaming people who oppose this". He said:

> *And I'll tell you why, they have reasons to oppose this that aren't that they wanna kill your grandma. Many people are up your face with a mask. You're a young*

> *person, you can't flirt, you can't socialize, you can't read cues, you can't understand people. It's another thing you have to remember leaving the house. It feels constricting on how you're breathing....And listen, I'm talking to you, bro, 'cause you and I are on the same page, masks are dumb, they don't look cool, they're constricting. We shouldn't have to do it. I don't like people telling me what to do.*

Over 900 Americans were dying of COVID daily when this podcast aired, and three months later the headlines would read "200,000 People Have Died From COVID-19 in the US. That's More Than the US Battle Deaths From 5 Wars Combined."[31] Two years later, with vaccines and widespread natural immunity, COVID remains the 3rd leading cause of death in the U.S.[32] Dr. Damania did not consider adverse outcomes other than death.

In October 2020, just prior to COVID's deadliest wave, Dr. Damania recorded a podcast called "How to Stop Living in Fear of COVID" with Dr. Monica Gandhi in which he said, "the fear that's driving this pandemic has been heartbreaking to see."[33] He referred to a Dr. Michael Osterholm, an epidemiologist who accurately predicted 800,000 Americans would die over 18-months[34], as "the prophet of doom and fear."[33]

Dr. Gandhi said people who were trying too hard to avoid the virus needed to accept the inevitability of their death. She said:

> *What kind of life do you have where you don't see anyone, where you don't hug your children, where you have so much fear that you're not actually living, right? And there are people who are truly not actually living right now... And if you've come and it is spiritual to come to the fundamental understanding that you're gonna die. And if you've never come to that understanding that you're gonna die, your fear will rule everything.*

Even though everyone knew that vaccines were potentially months away, Dr. Gandhi said that people who tried to avoid the virus were "truly not actually living right now." In reality, many people who approached the pandemic with Dr. Gandhi's attitude are truly not actually living right now.

Dr. Damania agreed and spoke about fear as a fate worse than death. He described a conversation with his paid subscribers where he said:

> *We live in this now moment that is so colored by anxiety, "fear of mortality, fear of other, fear of everything." And that's all a coloration of what we actually are, "which is beyond death and life." And it has nothing to do with religion, this is purely an experience you can have through meditation. And once you have that experience, your fear of death, and in fact, in many ways, when you really have an experience like that, and you can have it through prayer, you can have it through meditation, you can have it looking at the stars as an atheist, the ego dies, transiently, you experience death. And what you're left with is this still, ever-present awareness. And you go, "Hey, that's not so bad."*

Healthcare workers who worked on COVID units felt that it was so bad. Recall the nurse, who served in Iraq and Afghanistan and after seeing 3,000 people die of COVID, said "war doesn't even compare to this. I would rather die, any other way of dying, than dying with coronavirus"?[35]

Dr. Gandhi said she didn't want to be around people who were fearful of COVID, saying:

> *I have a friend whose husband is very anxious and it makes me sad that he feels so sad. And it has led to tension between the friend and me. And we have come to a resolution now. I have other friends that their level of fear has made it difficult for me to interact with them and now we won't interact for the time being.*[33]

She would later add:

> *Well, people are fearful, they're actually truly fearful of their own mortality. And now I have a new theory that I can only hang out with people that don't have profound fear about COVID.*

However, Dr. Gandhi felt that way because she didn't feel anyone was going to die of COVID. She said:

> *You can keep yourself safe from this particular virus, SARS-CoV-2, you can. You can still see your friends and family while keeping yourself safe, and you're not gonna die of this. And we have to keep everyone safe so they won't die of it. And I'm sorry that people are so fearful because I think it feels terrible.*

Over 800,000 Americans died of COVID[12] since Dr. Gandhi said, "you're not gonna die of this."[33]

In another podcast with Dr. Gandhi from February 2021 called "The End of the Pandemic", Dr. Damania again warned of a "contagion of panic and fear."[36] After the Delta variant ravaged India,[37] he said that "everybody's wetting their pants about it".[38] He later belittled young couple he saw on a plane for "wearing two masks, a full goggles, like they're flying a plane." He said this cautious behavior was a "pet peeve" of his and that young, healthy people "need to be out doing their thing. Instead, they're hiding behind two face shields." He had previously mocked these strangers on a podcast from April 2021, saying they were "wearing like hazmat suits on a plane…What are you doing? I mean, it looks cool, but not really."[39] This is the same doctor who previously advised his audience to stop shaming people who refuse to wear masks.

Dr. Damania's guest on that podcast, Dr. Bhattacharya, said "I think that the central problem right now I think is the fear that people still feel about COVID." In reality, the central problem in the spring of 2021 was rolling out vaccines and the possibility of variants. No medical historian will conclude that the central problem at that time was the fear some people still felt about COVID.

In fact, Dr. Bhattacharya, who felt estimates of mass death were "deeply flawed"[40] at the pandemic's start, said that learning how to manage fear was one of the pandemic's lessons. He said:

> *So I think there are lessons to be learned from this about pandemic management and the failures of pandemic management, when we know there's gonna be fear in the population. So how do you create a situation, a process of good developing, good pandemic responses in the atmosphere of fear?*[39]

Drs. Damania, Makary, and Prasad would make a podcast in December 2021 about the "Omicron panic,"[41] where they laughed at people who wanted to get a booster and bragged that they were "Unmasked, unboosted and unrepentant."

"'Coronaphobia'" can be defined as an exaggerated fear of COVID-19."
~ Dr. Lucy McBride

Dr. Lucy McBride coined several new medical diagnoses to pathologize those she thought were too fearful COVID. In her article, "I'm A Doctor Seeing Patients with Coronaphobia. Here's What You Need to Know" from March 2, 2021, she wrote:

> *"Coronaphobia" can be defined as an exaggerated fear of COVID-19 that is rooted in rational anxiety about the very real threat of COVID-19.*[42]

A week later, Dr. McBride wrote an article titled "I've Been Yearning for an End to the Pandemic. Now That it's Here, I'm a Little Afraid," in which she coined the term "Fear of Normal"[43] (FONO) to describe people who didn't agree the pandemic was over. 600,000 Americans have since died of COVID.[12] How many Americans have died of coronaphobia, I wonder?

In the middle of the Delta wave, Dr. McBride authored an article titled "Fear of COVID-19 in Kids is Getting Ahead of the Data."[44] Pediatricians with real world responsibility for treating sick children weren't so blasé. "This is different,"[45] one said. "What we're seeing now is previously healthy kids coming in with symptomatic infection." Another said that "we're not only seeing more children now with acute SARS-CoV2 in the hospital, we're starting also to see an uptick of MISC – or Multisystem Inflammatory Syndrome in

Children." By the time it was all over, the Delta variant would cause a 5-fold increase in pediatric hospitalizations.[46] Dr. McBride got her data, though it was too late for many children. They were the data.

Having used "coronaphobia" and "Fear of Normal" in 2021, Dr. McBride used a new term to pathologize people the exact same way in March 2022. In an article titled "Dealing With 'Post-Pandemic Stress': A Doctor's Guide", she said:

> *It's what some medical professionals, including myself, are calling "post-pandemic stress" which is not an official diagnosis (nor does it mean that COVID is gone!) but is characterized by anxiety, mood instability, and mental exhaustion that is interfering with quality of life.*[47]

Fortunately, Dr. McBride knew the cure for "post-pandemic stress." In May 2022, she said, "I'm finding that the 'cure' for some of my patients' outsize fear of COVID is … COVID."[48]

"The devastation (of lockdowns) can be extreme, and it can be far worse than anything that coronavirus can do."

~ Dr. John Ioannidis

While contrarian doctors said those who sought to avoid COVID were irrationally fearful, they spoke in starkly different terms about measures to contain the virus. With these interventions, people were told to be afraid, very afraid.

At the start of the pandemic, Dr. Ioannidis said, "draconian countermeasures have been adopted in many countries,"[49] and he was right. While America's lockdowns were much less stringent than some other countries, drastic measures were needed to prevent the whole country from turning into New York City.

However, long after the lockdowns ended contrarian doctors described *any* measures to control the virus as "draconian." Dr. McBride said, "I honestly cannot figure out for the life of me how these colleges can justify the draconian measures,"[50] while Dr. Makary said "this is harm from a political CDC that still, today, actively demands that kids submit to draconian restrictions instead of living & playing as they should."[51] Dr. Martin Kulldorff tweeted about "a local medical officer [who] was heavily criticized for resisting Canada's draconian pandemic policies,"[52] while Dr. Prasad said, "COVID19 & how societies have chosen to respond to it, mostly w draconian restrictions."[53] Dr. Bhattacharya tweeted "The public sacrificed itself to comply with the draconian orders that never had a chance of succeeding, but with devastating collateral harms that will play out over decades."[54] He also spoke of "Canada's biomedical security state"[55] and referred to all measures to control the virus as "lockdown by stealth."[56] This included minor interventions such as testing asymptomatic people, vaccine requirements, masks, as well as "panic-mongering on twitter."

Unsurprisingly, contrarian doctors portrayed these "draconian" restrictions as far more dangerous than the virus. In April 2020, Dr. Ioannidis feared "the devastation (of lockdowns) can be extreme, and it can be far worse than anything that coronavirus can do."[8] He worried attempts to control the virus could lead to "financial crisis, unrest, civil strife, war, and a meltdown of the social fabric."

Dr. Damania similarly asked in March 2020, "Are we doing more harm than good with our current draconian approach to COVID-19 mitigation?"[57] He also worried about measures to control the virus, warning in June 2020 of a:

> *Toxic stew of economic collapse, social and cultural destruction, which is what we're seeing, instability in the very fabric of society, along with massive economic disaster hurting regressively poor people and minorities more. So then what do you have? You have unemployed young people out in the world that it's gonna create an absolute chaos.*[30]

Dr. Damania told his audience that pediatricians who wanted to protect children from COVID were ignorant. He said:

> *We need to get back to discourse in this country, which means put the kids in school, let them hash stuff out. The pediatricians don't know. There's this multi system inflammatory syndrome of children. It's so rare as to be a rounding error on the dangers*

> *that face children. But you know what's not rare? Domestic abuse, poor education, huge socioeconomic variations and outcomes for children, and yet we're making that worse.*

In reality, over 9,100 children have suffered from Multisystem Inflammatory Syndrome in Children (MIS-C), and more than 70 children have died from it.[58]

The same doctors who spent the entire pandemic telling us that fear of COVID was dangerous and irrational were also the same doctors who expressed fear that measures to control the virus could lead to "financial crisis, unrest, civil strife, war, and a meltdown of the social fabric," as Dr. Ioannidis put it in March 2020. Unfortunately, their fear mongering was not limited to "draconian pandemic policies." The last section of this book will discuss how many of these doctors, who incessantly told us not to fear the virus, instead, incessantly told us *to* fear the vaccine.

"I don't think they overtly do this, but I think this is an unconscious way to control people that frighten them."

~ Dr. Zubin Damania

Given their fear over "draconian" measures to control COVID, contrarian doctors were eager to cast aspersions on those who didn't want it spread widely. Their ideological opponents weren't people who wanted to save lives and prevent suffering. According to contrarian doctors they wanted attention or even to control people.

Dr. Mandrola suggested that those who warned of the virus did so for social media clout. In October 2020, prior to the deadly winter wave, Dr. Mandrola tweeted, "Way to gain followers during the pandemic: bash the US. Promote fear. Consider every #COVID19 case as a stab in the heart."[59] In February 2021 he tweeted, "More good news to report on #COVID19: poorly thought out virtual-signaling Tweets seem to be getting less attention. #progress."[60] Dr. Mandrola thought doctors who warned of COVID were just virtue-signaling. Nearly 600,000 Americans have since died of COVID.[12]

Dr. Gandhi, a ubiquitous media presence herself, similarly suggested that those who disagreed with her that the pandemic was over had ulterior motives. She said:

> *I think it's an addition to fear, an addition to doom, and perhaps an addiction to being on TV or in the paper.*[61]

Though she would eventually write a strong defense of pediatric vaccination, Dr. Gandhi also implied that anyone who wanted to vaccinate children was motivated by nefarious financial ties. She wrote:

> *To be honest, I am wonder if those pushing that children younger than 12 will need to be immunized to have school/full life have any connections with vaccine companies.*[62]

Dr. Damania went down an even darker road. In his October 2020 podcast "How to Stop Living in Fear of COVID," Dr. Damania suggested that those who accurately warned of the virus had nefarious ulterior motives. He said:

> *Being doom and gloom is gonna get us nowhere, it is a terrible thing to say. It's like saying that humans are lab rats and that we have to control them. They can't be controlled, they have to work. They have to work, they have to make money for their families to actually have food so that you can have nutrition to fight off illness so that you're not malnourished and you don't get COVID. I mean, really, that's an isolated way of thinking, It doesn't make sense in the context of the real world.*[33]

Over 800,000 Americans have since died of COVID.[12]

In this podcast, Dr. Damania said that measures to contain the virus were actually an unconscious way for the elites to control poor people. He stated:

> *It seems like every conversation I have nowadays with very smart people leads to the same exact conclusion*

> *that this is almost a suburban zoomocracy elite that is saying to poor people, "Shh, stay home. "No, you can't have school, which is also childcare for you, "which is also food for you, which is also a future for you, "which is also breaking the cycle of poverty. "You can't have that because we, in the zoomocracy, "in this elite class that can live like this "are afraid for the safety "of whoever, whoever and whatever." And in a way, I don't think they overtly do this, but I think this is an unconscious way to control people that frighten them.*[33]

Dr. Kelly Brogan said the same thing at the pandemic's start, writing that measures to control the virus represented "the stripping of liberties and ever-expanding surveillance and control of the people for our 'safety'."[63]

"COVID19 policy shows a (potential) path to the end of America."

~ Dr. Vinay Prasad

Dr. Prasad called for the dismantling of institutions that tried to stop the spread of COVID. He wrote an article titled "We Need to Strip CDC and Public Health of Powers," which was scarcely different from Dr. Brogan's 2014 article titled "CDC: You're Fired. Autism Cover-up Exposed." Dr. Prasad also called for the American Academy of Pediatrics (AAP) to be disbanded, making a YouTube video and writing an article titled "The AAP is Broken, Failed Organization: Kids Need a New Advocate Who Puts Kids First." He wrote:

> *The American Academy of Pediatrics (AAP) is a failed organization. For years, they have made mistakes, but the pandemic elevated their failings to catastrophic errors.*[64]

Dr. Prasad wanted to put kids first by sending 60 million of them back to school before any were vaccinated.

Dr. Prasad so feared these organizations, he felt the next Hitler could emerge from measures to control a virus. He authored an article, titled "How Democracy Ends: COVID19 Policy Shows a (Potential) Path to the End of America,"[65] in which he said:

> *COVID19 policy shows a (potential) path to the end of America. The pandemic events of 2020-2021 outline a potential pathway for a future democratically elected President of the United States to systematically end democracy. The course of events leading to this outcome need not be a repeat of the direct assault on the Capitol, but a distortion of risk of illness as a justification for military force and suspension of democratic norms...*
>
> *When democratically elected systems transform into totalitarian regimes, the transition is subtle, stepwise, and involves a combination of pre-planned as well as serendipitous events. Indeed, this was the case with Germany in the years 1929-1939, where Hitler was given a chance at governing, the president subsequently died, a key general resigned after a scandal and the pathway to the Fuhrer was inevitable.*

Dr. Brogan said a similar thing at the pandemic's start, claiming that the government was planning to "link our passports with our vaccination records" in order to achieve "totalitarian governmental control not unlike the divide-and-conquer dehumanization agendas that preceded the Holocaust."[21]

This appalling and historically inaccurate drivel is nothing new. Anti-vaxxers have long equated vaccine-advocates with Nazis and their barbaric torture of humans in medical experiments. In 2015, the anti-vaccine site Age of Autism featured an essay titled "First They Came for the Anti-Vaxxers"[66] and some anti-vaxxers wore yellow Stars of David to protest their perceived persecution, a despicable behavior that continued during the pandemic.[67]

Prior to the pandemic, anti-vaxxers also threatened vaccine-advocates and called for them to face Nuremberg-style trials. Dr. Richard Pan, a pediatrician and California lawmaker, was assaulted on the street[68] and had blood in a menstrual cup hurled at him[69] to protest his efforts to prevent measles outbreaks by passing legislation that eliminated nonmedical exemptions to school vaccine mandates. Leading anti-vaxxer, TV producer Del Bigtree made even more ominous threats at the time. He said:

> *Do you think it's a good idea to let the government own your baby's body and right behind it your body? That is the end for me. Anyone who believes in the right to bear arms. To stand up against your government. I don't know what you were saving that gun for then. I don't know when you planned on using it if they were going to take control of your own body away. It's now. Now's the time.*[70]

A man holds a yellow Star of David to protest his COVID mitigation measures. Photo used via Creative Commons license courtesy Paxson Woelber, The Alaska Landmine[123]

"There seems to have been a large uptick in antivaccine rhetoric centered around portraying COVID-19 vaccines as a new Holocaust and the concomitant desire for Nuremberg-style trials."
~ Dr. David Gorski

Anti-vaxxers' delusions of persecution, aided by mainstream doctors telling them they were victims of would-be Nazis, worsened during the pandemic. Dr. David Gorski, who has been chronicling violence and threats in the anti-vaccine movement for many years, wrote in September 2022:

> *There seems to have been a large uptick in antivaccine rhetoric centered around portraying COVID-19 vaccines as a new Holocaust and the concomitant desire for Nuremberg-style trials—complete with hashtags on Twitter like #Nuremberg2, #NurembergTribunal, the ominous-sounding #Nuremberg2TickTock, and related hashtags targeting Anthony Fauci, Bill Gates, and other perceived "enemies"—for public health officials, with punishment meted out afterwards for their "crimes."*[68]

This is all scary stuff. It is not just isolated chatter. Most people think it's both necessary and heroic to resist Nazis. The caricature of public health officials and frontline healthcare workers as torturers had consequences in the real world. This is how exhausted frontline workers went from being healthcare heroes to literal punching bags around the globe.[71] Here are a few examples of what this rhetoric has led to:

- Hundreds of public health officials have resigned or retired rather than face abuse and threats. According to news reports, "some have become the target of far-right activists, conservative groups and anti-vaccination extremists who have coalesced around common goals: fighting mask orders, quarantines and contact tracing with protests, threats and personal attacks."[72] According to a survey from *The New York Times*, "public health agencies have seen a staggering exodus of personnel, many exhausted and demoralized, in part because of abuse and threats."[73] They report "more than 500 top health officials who left their jobs in the past 19 months."

- A *Nature* survey of 321 scientists found that "more than two-thirds of researchers reported negative experiences as a result of their media appearances or their social media comments, and 22% had received threats of physical or sexual violence. Some scientists said that their employer had received complaints about them or that their home address had been revealed online. Six scientists said they were physically attacked."[74] Dr. Steven Novella discussed both the survey and the abuse in an article published October 2021.[75]

- Dr. Anthony Fauci needed "personal security from law enforcement at all times, including at his home."[76] According to news reports, "he and his family have required continued security in the face of harassment and death threats from people angry over his guidance on the coronavirus pandemic."[77]

- Vaccine-advocate Dr. Peter Hotez has been doxed and subject to coordinated campaigns of harassment for his vaccine advocacy.[78] According to Dr. Hotez, the hate mail he received "was filled with all sorts of Nazi imagery, Nuremberg hangings and terrible, terrible stuff. It was pretty upsetting."[79] Prior to the pandemic, Dr. Richard Pan was assaulted in the street for advocating for vaccines.[80] Dr. David Gorski has been the victim of harassment campaigns.[81]

- Anti-vaxxers have protested outside hospitals in Canada and elsewhere. According to news reports, "A crowd rallying against vaccination for COVID-19 clogged the streets outside a Vancouver hospital this week, haranguing and, in one case, assaulting health care workers, slowing ambulances, delaying patients entering for treatment, and disturbing those recovering inside."[82]

- Pro-fascist groups opposed to vaccines have staged violent rallies in Italy.[83] This included storming an emergency room and attacking nurses and police officers.

- In France, "demonstrators carried signs evoking the Auschwitz death camp or South Africa's apartheid regime."[84] In Russia, an actor wore a yellow star at an awards ceremony and spoke of "waking up in a world where [COVID-19 vaccination] became an identification mark." Across the world, Jewish stars are used as a symbol of anti-vaxxer "persecution."

- In Australia, "Anti-vaccine and extreme right-wing groups have led violent rallies" while "prominent fascists were among the crowd."[85] In Germany, an "anti-lockdown, anti-vaccine movement with links to the far right has recruited hundreds of children into a private online group."[86] Anti-vaccine protesters in Berlin yelled "Hands off our children."[87]

- Anti-vaccine rallies turned violent in Los Angeles[88] and anti-vaxxers disrupted vaccination sites there.[89] They did the same thing in Georgia.[90] In New York City, they attacked a COVID-19 testing station.[91]

- A man in Maryland killed his brother, who was a pharmacist, as well as his sister-in-law because they were "killing people with the COVID shot."[92]

- A principal in Arizona was confronted by men carrying zip ties and was threatened with a "citizen's arrest" after the child of one of the men was told to quarantine because of a possible exposure to the virus.[93] The principal also received threats such as, "Next time it will be a barrel pointed at your Nazi face."[94]

- According to news reports, "a parent in Northern California barged into his daughter's elementary school and punched a teacher in the face over mask rules. At a school in Texas, a parent ripped a mask off a teacher's face during a 'Meet the Teacher' event."[95]

- In Georgia, "a customer who argued about wearing a face mask at a Georgia supermarket shot and killed a cashier on Monday and wounded a sheriff's deputy who was providing security at the store."[96] This is an extreme example of a sadly common occurrence.[94]

- A pharmacist in Wisconsin destroyed COVID-19 vaccines as he believed that the "COVID-19 vaccine was not safe for people and could harm them and change their DNA."[97]

- Doctors in Idaho "have been accused of killing patients by grieving family members who don't believe COVID-19 is real."[98] A hospital spokesperson said, "Our health care workers are almost feeling like Vietnam veterans, scared to go into the community after a shift." Hospitals are installing extra "panic buttons" to protect their workers from assaults.[99]

- According to news reports, "the Hawaii lieutenant governor watched in horror as protesters showed up outside his condo, yelled at him through bullhorns and beamed strobe lights into the building to harass him over vaccine requirements."[95]

- In Canada, a man "...punched a nurse in the face multiple times, knocking her to the ground after she administered a COVID-19 vaccine to his wife without his permission."[100] Nurses have also been attacked in Guatemala by anti-vaccine residents of a village.[101]

- Anti-vaxxers have harassed children and their parents. In the UK, one yelled at a mother, "She'll have immunity, you shouldn't be getting the vaccine since you have natural immunity. You shouldn't be using her as a lab rat."[102] In California, an anti-vaxxer yelled at children walking to school, "They're trying to rape our children with this poison. They're going to rape their lives away,"[103] while another compared masking to "child abuse."

- Rep. Marjorie Taylor Greene (Georgia) suggested that citizens use their "Second Amendment rights" to greet community members knocking on doors to encourage vaccination.[104] Rep. Madison Cawthorn (North Carolina) suggested that such vaccination campaigns could be a pretense to "take" people's guns and Bibles.[105]

- Tucker Carlson said the Pentagon's vaccine mandate was an attempt to weed out "men with high testosterone," that it was "anti-Christian," and that the military is "doing PR for Satanists."[106] He also said that "Buying a fake vaccination card is an act of desperation by decent, law-abiding Americans who have been forced into a corner by tyrants."[107]

- Some people apparently believe that "COVID-19 vaccines are called Luciferase, have the patent number 060606, and come from a digital program called Inferno."[108] Republican officials in Florida[109] and New Hampshire[110] have likened the vaccine to Satanism as have several religious leaders in the US[111] and Bolivia.[112] The imagined connection between vaccines and Satan is also not new.

- According to news reports, "anti-vaccine demonstrations across Ohio in recent weeks are drawing extremists that include conspiracy theorists, white supremacists and people who misappropriate the Holocaust."[113]

- In Washington "anti-mask protesters that included the Proud Boys attempted to gain entry" to three schools, forcing them to lockdown.[114]

- After anti-vaxxers showed up at health officials' homes in Los Angeles, "city leaders approved an ordinance Tuesday that would bar protests within 300 feet of the residence belonging to the person being targeted, a move that came following months of demonstrations outside the homes of public and elected officials."[115]

- In Texas, "a man has been charged after allegedly

threatening to gun down a Maryland doctor who urged the public to take the coronavirus vaccine."[116]

- Countless school board meetings have been disrupted by anti-vaxxers, often linked with the Proud Boys and other right-wing extremist groups. According to news reports, "drawing false equivalence between COVID regulations and Nazi fascism is popular among anti-vax, anti-mask groups, including some local teachers and school board members."[117]

- In California, "a breast cancer patient says she was sprayed with bear mace, physically assaulted, and verbally abused outside a cancer treatment center in West Hollywood, Los Angeles by far-right activists who were angry over the clinic's mandatory mask policy."[118]

Think about why these public health officials were threatened and attacked. Think about what they were actually trying to do. They made mistakes and are not immune from criticism. Beaches and outdoor playgrounds never needed to be closed. Dr. Anthony Fauci admits he goofed when he said on March 8, 2020:

> *Right now, people should not be walking — there's no reason to be walking around with a mask.*[119]

But fundamentally, public health officials were trying to stop hundreds of thousands, if not millions, of Americans from dying of COVID. SARS-CoV-2 was a brand-new virus, and public health officials were learning about it in real time just like everyone else. We should judge the wisdom of their decisions by what we knew about the virus in March 2020, not what we know about it now. They were overwhelmed and under-resourced. They were certainly under-appreciated. We'll never know how many lives they saved or how much suffering they prevented. Right now, someone who threatened these officials is alive because of their actions, though he'll never know it.

Dr. Prasad was not wrong to worry about political violence and authoritarianism. No society is immune to those evil twins. However, when they came to America, they weren't brought here by people trying to stop a virus. In the real world, white supremacists bearing Nazi flags turned up at protests *against* COVID-mitigation measures.[120] This came as no surprise to anyone who paid attention to the anti-vaccine movement prior to the pandemic.

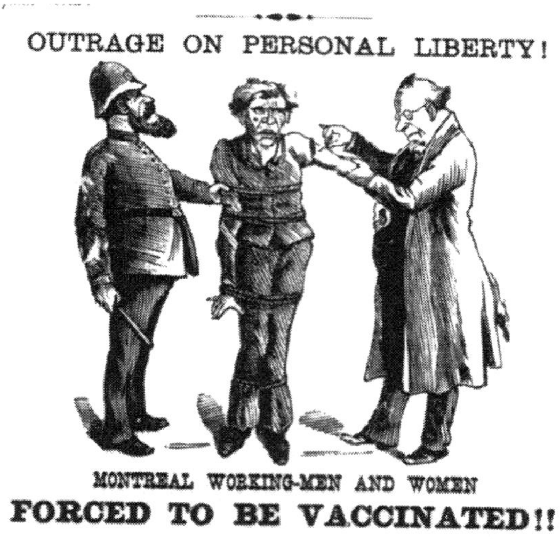

An old anti-vaccine image. Image courtesy of HathiTrust.org

"The best way to reduce fear is by reducing danger."
~ Loretta Torrago

Fear is horrible. I saw it everywhere at the start of the pandemic. I felt it myself the first few times a COVID patient coughed all over me.

Fear is also necessary. You exist because your ancestors – all of them – had enough fear to survive until they were old enough to have children. Graveyards are full of fearless young people, and I've seen many patients over the years whose lives would have been much better had they been a bit more afraid in one way or another.

Though Dr. McBride lamented that "Fear of COVID-19 in Kids is Getting Ahead of the Data,"[44] it's not always bad when this happens. For the Delta variant, that "data" was suffering children. Underreacting to a deadly threat might be a once-in-lifetime mistake, and children intubated in the ICU should make people fearful.

Many children were spared this fate because their fearful parents vaccinated them.

It's true that a handful of doctors gained large social media followings by posting a daily RED ALERT WARNING!!! for every SARS-CoV-2 mutation. Such scaremongering numbs people to more realistic threats, and I won't defend it. However, doctors who systematically led people to overestimate their COVID risk did much less damage than those who did the opposite.

Let's pretend that Drs. Ioannidis and Bhattacharya were correct in March 2020 that COVID would kill less than 40,000 people. Let's say we shut everything down, and COVID turned out to be a dud. What would have happened? We'll never know for sure, but I imagine that we all would have figured it out pretty quickly, and everything would have opened up again. False alarms are never a good thing, but 20 years from now, I think it would be viewed as more of a historical curiosity than a catastrophe of epic proportions. In contrast, had nothing been done to control COVID, the whole country would have been like New York City at our peak. The harms of underreacting versus overreacting to a potentially deadly virus are not symmetrical, and looking back, there haven't been too many times where our biggest problem was that too many people were trying too hard to avoid SARS-CoV-2.

You wouldn't know this from reading the work of contrarian doctors. Their message was consistent and clear: The virus isn't the problem, and those who make no effort to avoid it deserve sympathy and grace. The problem is that too many people are trying to avoid COVID, and these people are shameful, mentally unwell objects of ridicule.

I am sure there are still a handful of healthy, vaccinated, young people who are so afraid of COVID that they still wash their mail and refuse to see their friends, even outside. These people need sympathy and support, not to be mocked or told the cure for their anxiety is to get COVID. They certainly don't need to have contrarian doctors taking turns, writing the exact same article, bemoaning their fate. These articles did nothing to help the overly anxious, and instead served as signifiers that, except for grandma, *anyone* who tried to avoid the virus was similarly neurotic.

In one sense, contrarian doctors. were right that many of their followers – the young, healthy, and wealthy – had relatively little to fear from COVID. It's doubtful that their core audience is derived from nursing home residents, impoverished citizens in Appalachia, or immigrants living in multi-generational homes. The vast majority of people who heard Dr. Gandhi say, "*you're not gonna die of this*" are probably still alive. Yet, contrarian doctors only rarely entertained the possibility that healthy young people weren't trying to just protect themselves, but also to protect their community. We'll never know how many vulnerable people were vaccinated instead of infected because a young person they never met avoided COVID – not because he feared it, but because he had empathy.

Doctors have an obligation to keep people safe from a dangerous virus while at the same time helping them cope with serious mental health consequences that may result. It's not an easy balance, especially when we're trying to navigate this in our own lives. I don't have all the answers. Many people are less cautious than I, and I don't shame them. It's normal to want to eat in restaurants and go to parties. We can't expect people to give this up forever.

Many people are more cautious than I, and I don't shame them either. It is not irrational to want to avoid repeated bouts of COVID. As such, I've yet to diagnose anyone with "coronaphobia". I've not told anyone they need therapy if they wear a mask at the gym. I've never said "you're not truly living" to someone who doesn't feel comfortable going to a packed bar. I certainly wouldn't say these things to strangers when I know nothing about their life. These are reasonable adults making decisions in accordance with their risk tolerance and desire to protect those around them. I know many people who have not resumed all their pre-pandemic activities, but this does not mean their lives are empty, devoid of meaning and value.

Contrarian doctors felt otherwise. It was never clear exactly why they were so irate that strangers didn't want to eat in a restaurant or attend a concert without a mask. How did this affect them? They never showed an interest in anxiety disorders before, and today are bothered by only "coronaphobia" and nothing else. Yet when COVID was killing hundreds or even thousands of people every day, they treated it as a catastrophe whenever someone wanted to avoid it. Perhaps every cautious person was a reminder that the pandemic didn't end in the spring of 2021, as they claimed it would.

Again, I wonder about the real-world consequences of this. Did a vulnerable person stop wearing a mask because she didn't want to be accused of "post-pandemic stress"? Did a young person eat in a crowded restaurant before seeing her grandma because she was told "life was passing her by"? We'll never know.

Vaccine-advocate Loretta Torrago said, "the best way to reduce fear is by reducing danger."[121] She's right. Maybe we all could have lived with a bit less fear and fewer "draconian" restrictions if influential doctors hadn't convinced so many people the worst was over, when in fact, the worst was yet to come.

After his bout with the virus, Ted Nugent would come to understand real fear. He said, "I literally couldn't function for about 20 hours, and then they came and they rescued me... I've never been so scared in all my life."[122] Fortunately, he survived. Thousands of other Americans who also decided not to live in fear aren't here to share their experience.

Chapter 9: "Any strong advocate for kid COVID vaccination is off their rocker"

"Although it is true that most children experience asymptomatic or mild disease, some will get quite sick, and a small number will die."
~ Drs. Jeffrey Gerber and Paul Offit

The only good thing about COVID is that the vast majority of children with it will be just fine. All the children in my life had it at some point. They had the mildest of symptoms, thankfully. I was never particularly worried about them, even the ones who hadn't been vaccinated yet.

While serious illness is rare in children – 86% of children had SARS-CoV-2 antibodies as of August 2022[1] – rare events multiplied tens of millions of times add up. There's a world of difference between "no risk" and "miniscule risk" for a virus that's infected tens of millions of children. A small percentage of a big number can be a big number, especially when we are talking about sick and injured children. However, no myth was more enduring or widespread than the idea that children are invulnerable to COVID and don't require even the most basic protection against it, not even a simple vaccine.

The rest of this book can be summarized this way. We would not tolerate unvaccinated children suffering or dying of measles, polio, or diphtheria, and we should not tolerate it with COVID.

There is some uncertainty about the exact number of pediatric fatalities. While death certificates for adults have been reliable, this may not be as true for children. A CDC analysis of 182 pediatric death certificates found that 35% were unlikely to be due to COVID and the CDC once had to revise its pediatric death tally downwards due to an error.[2]

While flawed death certificates would inflate the pediatric death tally, there is no guarantee that every pediatric COVID death is properly recognized and reported to the CDC. With the flu, for example, the CDC states:

> *Even though each flu death in a child is supposed to be reported to CDC, it is likely that not all flu-related*

> *deaths in children are captured and that the actual number of deaths is higher. CDC has developed statistical models that account for the underreporting of flu-related deaths in children to estimate the actual number of deaths.*[3]

The CDC's estimates of pediatric flu deaths can be more than double their official tally to account for underreporting.

As I write this, at the end of December 2022, the CDC's COVID Data Tracker reports that 1,975 children aged 0-17 years have died of COVID.[4] This is based on 937,000 total deaths, or 85% of the total deaths. A separate tally, maintained by the National Center for Health Statistics, reports 1,593 deaths in children aged 0-18 years,[5] which is the number I will use.

However, while accurate numbers are important, no argument I make about vaccinating children hinges on the precise number of pediatric fatalities. My arguments would be no different if the exact number were 2,000 or "only" 1,000 fatalities. I think zero children should suffer or die for lack of a vaccine, and prior to the pandemic this belief was not controversial amongst doctors.

Whatever the exact number, COVID has killed a tragically large number of children, and it's important to remember they were more than just statistics on a government spreadsheet. Each deceased child was robbed of their entire life and leaves behind a broken, grieving family. The sister of Jorja Halliday, a teenager from the UK who died from COVID the day she was supposed to be vaccinated, "cries herself to sleep every night, as she described the shock of losing her older sibling."[6]

By way of comparison, about 300 American children die annually from all other vaccine-preventable diseases combined,[7] and COVID's pediatric death toll exceeds that of multiple other vaccine-preventable diseases before vaccines were available. As Drs. Jeffrey Gerber and Paul Offit said:

> *Although it is true that most children experience asymptomatic or mild disease, some will get quite sick, and a small number will die. It's why children are vaccinated against influenza, meningitis, chickenpox, and hepatitis – none of which, even before vaccines were available, killed as many as*

SARS-CoV-2 per year.[8]

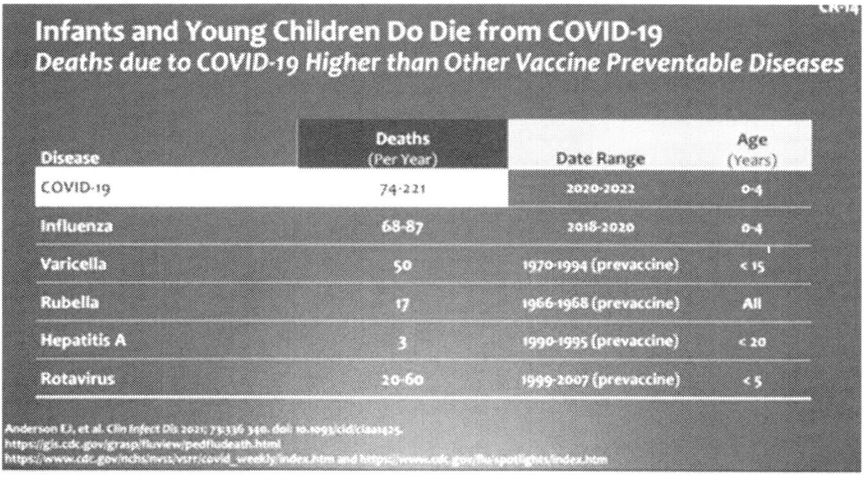

Infants and Young Children Do Die from COVID-19
Deaths due to COVID-19 Higher than Other Vaccine Preventable Diseases

Disease	Deaths (Per Year)	Date Range	Age (Years)
COVID-19	74-221	2020-2022	0-4
Influenza	68-87	2018-2020	0-4
Varicella	50	1970-1994 (prevaccine)	< 15
Rubella	17	1966-1968 (prevaccine)	All
Hepatitis A	3	1990-1995 (prevaccine)	< 20
Rotavirus	20-60	1999-2007 (prevaccine)	< 5

Anderson EJ, et al. Clin Infect Dis 2021; 73:336 340. doi: 10.1093/cid/ciaa1425.
https://gis.cdc.gov/grasp/fluview/pedfludeath.html
https://www.cdc.gov/nchs/nvss/vsrr/covid_weekly/index.htm and https://www.cdc.gov/flu/spotlights/index.htm

Data regarding the number of pediatric deaths from COVID and other vaccine-preventable diseases.[469]

Not all children have the same risk of dying. Babies have by far the highest risk, while elementary school children have the lowest. Children with underlying conditions, such as obesity, asthma, and neurological ailments, are also much more vulnerable, though COVID has almost certainly killed several hundred healthy children.

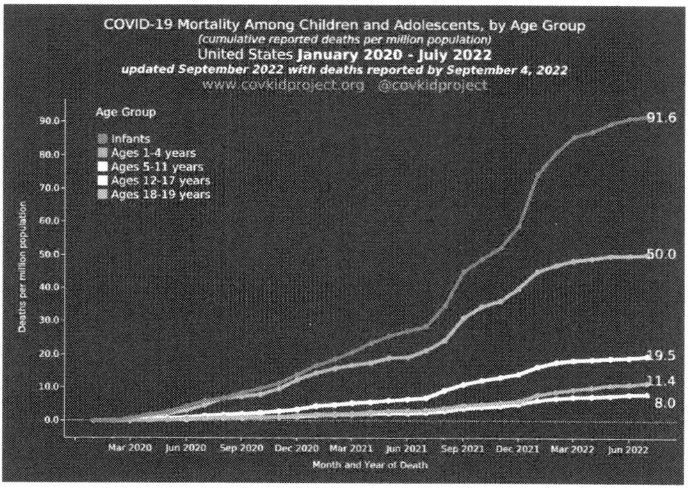

Pediatric COVID mortality by age. Source: https://www.covkidproject.org/

Black and Hispanic children die at a much higher rate than White children. Black children die at more than double the rate of White children.

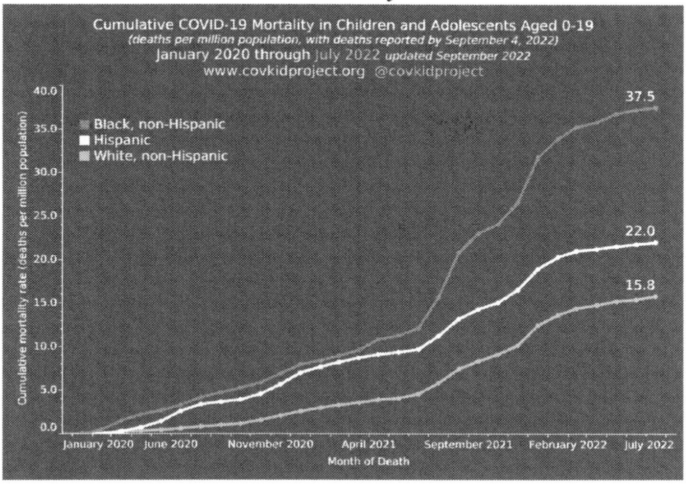

Pediatric COVID mortality by race. Source: https://www.covkidproject.org/

Children who lived in the Southwest died at double the rate of children in the Rocky Mountain states.

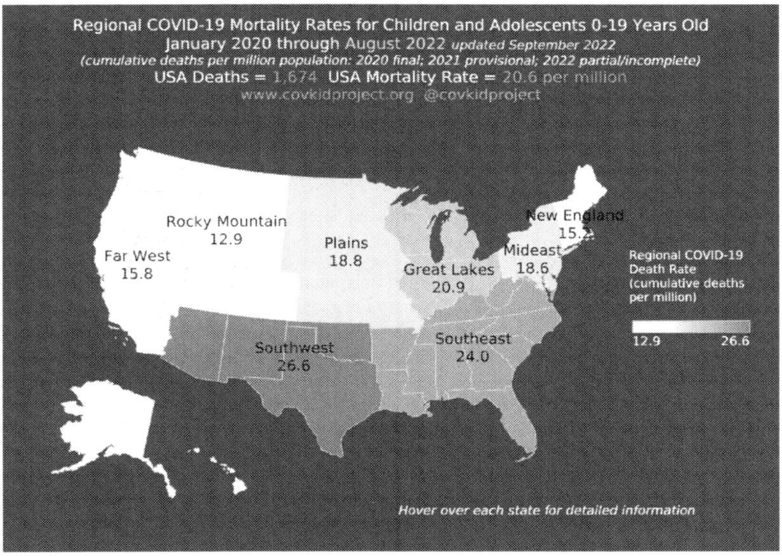

Pediatric COVID mortality by location. Source: https://www.covkidproject.org/

While death is the worst outcome from COVID, it is not the only bad one. According to the CDC's COVID Data Tracker, over 174,000 children have been hospitalized thus far,[9] though this is a very imprecise number. Again, whatever the exact number, a large number of children have been hospitalized with COVID, and some of these children can be very sick. Depending on the variant, 20-

30% of children needed treatment in the ICU, and 2-6% needed mechanical ventilation.[10] This can be terrifying for small children. One news report from when the Omicron variant was dominant said:

> *"I sorry, Mommy. Mommy hugs, I scared. I don't like it. Mommy!" Those were the last words 3-year-old Justin Lee Francis spoke to his mother, Yvonne, before he was sedated and put on a ventilator at Primary Children's Hospital last week, when he was diagnosed with COVID-19, asthma, pneumonia and other illnesses.*[11]

While most children recover well, not all do. One study of over 15,000 hospitalized children found that 7% suffered a neurological disorder such as seizures or encephalopathy.[12] Rarely, children have had strokes, severe brain inflammation (encephalitis), or needed amputations. They survived, but their lives will never be the same.

Though it has happily vanished with current variants, thousands of children have been affected by Multisystem Inflammatory Syndrome in Children (MIS-C), a post-infectious inflammatory condition that affects the heart, lungs, kidneys, brain, skin, eyes, and gastrointestinal organs.[13] MIS-C most commonly occurs in healthy children ages 6-12 years and most children are sick enough to need ICU-level care. In one study of 191 children with MIS-C, 80% were admitted to the ICU and 2 died.[14]

With earlier SARS-CoV-2 variants, about 1 in 3,000-4,000 children developed MIS-C,[465] and over 9,100 cases of MIS-C have been reported to the CDC,[15] though this may be a substantial undercount.[16] When the entire state of Texas reported fewer than 100 cases of MIS-C to the CDC, Dr. Lara Shekerdemian, the chief of critical care at Texas Children's Hospital said, "If our hospital has seen well over 150, then clearly that number is not accurate." At least 74 children have died from MIS-C.[15]

Additionally, millions of children have just felt miserable from their bout with COVID and not all of them make a full or rapid recovery. Though the prevalence ranges greatly from one study to another, some children have been severely affected by Long-COVID, which manifests as fatigue, poor concentration, mood lability, and other symptoms.[17] It's common enough that several hospitals have established pediatric Long-COVID clinics.[18]

We also have to be humble about the possibility of long-term consequences we cannot currently appreciate. Some teenagers report persistent "brain fog" after their illness, and there's evidence that COVID increases the risk of diabetes,[19] though the overall risk remains low. Slightly more than 1% of children have seizures after COVID, and the risk was highest in children who had not been hospitalized.[20] Another study found "persistent pulmonary dysfunction in both children and adolescents recovered from COVID and with long COVID", indicating long-term damage to the lungs.[21] As Dr. Scott Gottlieb said:

> *COVID is a novel and pathogenic virus. Most kids will have a mild course and recover fine from acute illness. But we should show humility that we don't know its long term implications. Letting an entire generation of kids get infected, with no baseline immunity, may be imprudent.*[22]

We'll be learning about COVID for decades, especially the consequences of repeated infections. After all, it wasn't until 2019 that researchers discovered that measles weakens the immune system's ability to fight multiple other pathogens.[23] Children with COVID and other infections, such as the flu or respiratory syncytial virus, had worse outcomes compared to children infected with just one virus.[466] What surprises does SARS-CoV-2 have in store for us?

COVID's risk to children varied widely over the course of the pandemic. Fewer than 500 children died during the first year of the pandemic. It wasn't until the Delta wave in the summer of 2021 that pediatric hospitals were first overwhelmed. By this time, adolescents were eligible to be vaccinated and some unvaccinated teenagers died preventable deaths.

While the Omicron variant was milder than the Delta variant, it was much more contagious and therefore hospitalized 5-times more children.[24] Over 900 children per day were hospitalized during its peak in January 2022 and pediatric hospitals were again overwhelmed,[25] schools closed due to sick staff,[26] and about 20% of pediatric deaths occurred during the Omicron wave.[27] 181 children died in January 2022 alone.[5] Many of them were old enough to have been vaccinated.

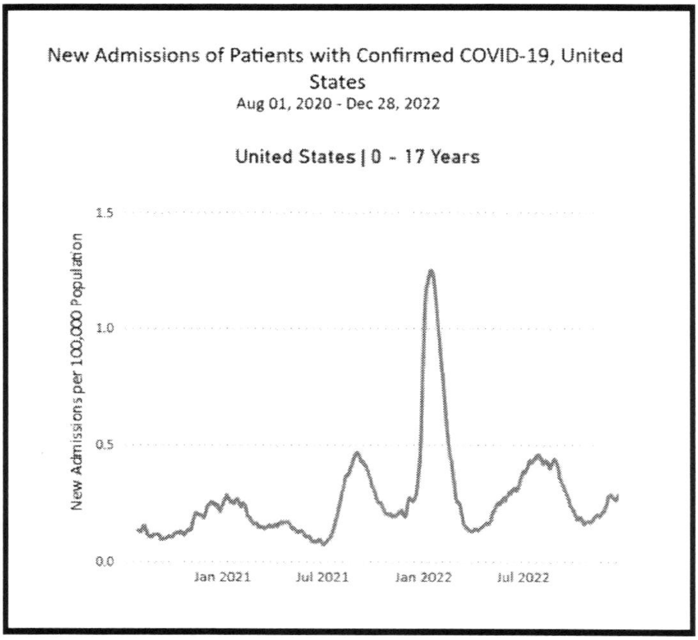

Hospital admission rates for children over the course of the pandemic

Though COVID's risk to any individual child is very small, by any measure, COVID's overall effect on children has not been benign, and it would have been substantially worse had the virus been allowed to rip through all 73 million unvaccinated children at the pandemic's start. It's only because we didn't allow this to happen that contrarian doctors can now pretend everything would have been just fine if we had.

"All 7 deaths occurred in patients who were unvaccinated"

Even before the results of the pediatric randomized-controlled trials (RCTs) were announced, there was every reason to believe the vaccine would protect children. The pediatric RCTs didn't start off with a 50% chance the vaccine would work, and there was every expectation they would be generally safe. The vaccines had proven their value in tens of millions of young adults by then, and adolescents are not an entirely different species.

The pediatric RCTs and eventual vaccine authorizations were carefully planned to keep children safe, with adolescents going first, then elementary school children, and finally babies and toddlers. The Johnson & Johnson vaccine never made it to children because rare but severe clots had formed in adults. Many parents and pediatricians feel pediatric vaccines were rolled out much too slowly. There was a steep price to be paid for being "cautious."

Pfizer and Moderna each performed separate RCTs of pediatric vaccines for adolescents,[28,29] elementary school children,[30,31] and babies and toddlers.[32,33] Nearly 25,000 children were involved in these trials, five of which have been published in *The New England Journal of Medicine*. Depending on which trial, the vaccine generated a robust immune response and/or protected children against symptomatic COVID. No serious safety signals emerged in these trials.

See Table 1: Pediatric randomized controlled trials (BNT162b2/ Pfizer & mRNA-1273/Moderna) on page 424.

The RCTs were not large enough to show the vaccine prevented hospitalizations and deaths, as these outcomes are rare in children. However, over 20 observational studies have since shown that the vaccine does just that. These studies all report things like:

- "All 7 deaths occurred in patients who were unvaccinated."[34]
- "Among critically ill MIS-C case-patients requiring life support, all were unvaccinated."[35]
- "All 29 critically ill case-patients, and both deaths occurred among unvaccinated case-patients."[36]
- "Of the 155 vaccine-eligible patients with neurologic involvement and confirmed vaccination status, 147 (95%) were unvaccinated, including 15 of 16 patients (94%) with life-threatening neurologic conditions."[37]
- "Fifty-one deaths related to COVID-19 were notified among cases, of which seven occurred in the delta period (all in unvaccinated participants)."[38]

- "Hospitalization rates were 10 times higher among unvaccinated than among fully vaccinated adolescents."[39]

Another study found that unvaccinated children were at higher risk for Long COVID.[40] Every single observational study shows that the vaccine can make a *huge difference* for some children.

Though vaccine-efficacy waned for children with the Omicron variant, just as it did with adults, the vaccine still protects children from COVID's most severe harms. Even if a new variant renders our current vaccines useless, they have already prevented a great deal of suffering.

The COVID vaccines aren't perfect, but they are still much safer than the virus, even for children without underlying conditions.

See Table 2: Observational trials on the COVID vaccine for children on page 426.

The American Academy of Pediatrics and American Medical Association strongly endorse pediatric vaccination, and members of the Advisory Committee on Immunization Practices (ACIP) voted unanimously to approve them. As Dr. Monica Gandhi said in an essay titled "The Childhood Vaccine Debate Ignores a Crucial Point: Kids Aren't Supposed to Die":

> *We should not be discussing the necessity of vaccinating children against COVID; instead we should be determining the best way to do it.*[57]

She's right. Unfortunately, the notion that kids aren't supposed to die became a surprising source of controversy amongst doctors during the pandemic.

"Any strong advocate for kid COVID vaccination is off their rocker"

~ Dr. Vinay Prasad

Consider this passage from an article titled "NY Times Deceives about the Odds of Dying from Measles in the US," which was published on Robert F. Kennedy, Jr.'s anti-vaccine website:

> *During the pre-vaccine era in the US, measles was seen as a mostly benign illness that, yes, could and did sometimes cause death, but which most children's immune systems handled just fine on their own, resulting in the development of a robust lifelong immunity...During the pre-vaccine era in the US, according to the CDC's own data, there were about 500 deaths annually out of an estimated 3 – 4 million cases. That's not 10 to 30 but 1 to 2 deaths for every 10,000 cases...Of the estimated 3 – 4 million cases, most were mild infections that did not lead to hospitalization or complications.*[58]

This reflects a central tenet of the anti-vaccine movement: Measles won't kill that many children, so it isn't worth preventing. It's just a couple hundred children anyways.

All anti-vaxxers minimize the harms caused by viruses this way, and this naturally continued during the pandemic. Dr. Simone Gold, who founded the anti-vaccine group America's Frontline Doctors, provided a typical example. In an article titled "Physicians Group Files Motion to Halt Use of COVID Vaccines in Children," she said:

> *We will not be silent while Americans are used as guinea pigs for a virus with survivability of 99.8% globally and 99.97% under age 70. Under age 20 it is 99.997% – 'statistical zero. There are 104 children age 0-17 who died from COVID-19 and 287 from COVID + Influenza – out of ~72 million. This equals zero risk. And we doctors won't stand for children being offered something they do not need and of whom some unknown percentage will suffer.*[59]

There it is again. COVID won't kill that many children, so it isn't worth preventing. It's just a couple hundred children anyways.

Dr. Gold was not the only doctor to minimize pediatric COVID in this manner. Influential doctors waged a systematic, multifaceted campaign to ensure children contracted COVID instead of being vaccinated against it. To achieve this goal, they repeatedly minimized pediatric COVID, spread blatantly false statistics, and made illogical arguments against vaccines. Their belief that the virus was safer than the vaccine for children was widely spread in newspapers, podcasts, television, social media, and even prestigious medical journals such as the *BMJ*.[60]

In the same way that anti-vaccine doctors started formulating a plan to attack COVID vaccines at the pandemic's start, the campaign against the pediatric COVID vaccine began months before any child had even been vaccinated and before any information even existed about the pediatric vaccine. One of the earliest opponents of pediatric vaccination was Dr. Vinay Prasad, an adult oncologist who had no obvious interest or expertise in pediatrics, infectious diseases, or vaccines before the pandemic. In fact, prior to the pandemic, Dr. Prasad told vaccine-advocates they were wasting their time, likening their efforts to dunking on a 7-foot basketball hoop.[61]

However, during the pandemic, Dr. Prasad became a vocal opponent of pediatric COVID vaccination. He expressed these views widely on social media, podcasts, mainstream publications, and medical journals.

On January 13, 2021, Dr. Prasad devoted a long *Twitter* thread as to why children need not be vaccinated. He said:

> *Let me be perfectly clear: children DO NOT NEED a sars-cov-2 vaccine before they are permitted to return to normal activities, such as school and visiting loved ones..The virus meanwhile is *thank god* not that bad for most healthy kids, on par with seasonal influenza. Even the rate of multi-inflammatory syndrome is vanishingly low.-- although you wouldn't know that from the breathless news coverage and tweets. Third, who even says the vaccine will offer a favorable risk benefit profile in kids?..*
>
> *If the epidemic is abating, how can you justify giving 100 kids those AEs (adverse events) so that perhaps 1 or 2 or even 3 will be spared a case of COVID that might be as mild as the AEs themselves?...One has to think of the cumulative days a kid is resting in bed, vaccination might outweigh the benefits in low age.*[62]

Sadly, the pandemic wasn't abating, and neither was Dr. Prasad. His *Twitter* thread ended with:

> *Putting it all together, it is unlikely kids will have a vaccine with a proven benefit/harm profile in the near future, if at all. Once adults, particularly older adults are vaccinated, and if *god willing* there is not vaccine escape, COVID19 is over. We are going back to normal.*

Dr. Prasad put these thoughts in an article titled "Kids Don't Need COVID-19 Vaccines to Return to School," which was published on *STAT* on February 3, 2021. He gave "five reasons why schools can and should open at 100% capacity before a vaccine for those under age 16 is available."[63] He wrote:

> *Kids are less likely to acquire SARS-CoV-2, the virus that causes COVID-19, than adults ... In addition, the risk of death or other bad outcomes is low for children. Between March and October of 2020, among those between the ages of five and 14, the risk of dying of COVID-19 in the United States was 1 in 1,000,000. To put that in perspective, in that same age group during non-COVID times, the risk of suicide is 10 times higher. For young adults ages 15 to 24, the risk of dying from COVID19 was 9.9 in 1,000,000, and they are also generally 10 times more likely to commit suicide....The vaccine might save one life for every 1 million kids who get it... For them it is a respiratory pathogen with a rate of harm that is comparable to other, annual respiratory pathogens like influenza.*

There it is again. COVID won't kill that many children, so it isn't worth preventing. It's just a couple hundred children anyways.

Moreover, much of this was untrue. Kids easily acquire SARS-CoV-2, it kills more than one in a million children, and COVID has killed and injured many more children than the flu, a disease for which we vaccinate children. All of this was known by February

2021. Though Dr. Prasad did not inform his readers of this, by that point in the pandemic, over 200 American children had died of COVID,[5] while one child had died of the flu.[64] Tens of thousands more children had been hospitalized with COVID,[65] and several thousand children had MIS-C.[15] Tens of millions of children were still vulnerable, and Dr Prasad felt they should remain this way.

While Dr. Prasad felt children had little to fear from the virus, he thought the vaccine posed a risk. He wrote:

> *45,000 kids will develop severe headaches requiring analgesics and interfering with daily living, 14,000 will have a fever higher than 104 degrees F for less than a day, and 880 will have this fever last for more than a day.*[63]

In a podcast titled *Should We Vaccinate Kids for COVID*? from February 4, 2021, Dr. Prasad again minimized the pediatric death rate, and continued to preemptively scare parents about the vaccine saying:

> *We're talking about grade three fevers, which is like, I think, 104 degrees for less than 24 hours, and grade four, which is 104 degrees for two days, for more than 24 hours. We're talking about of a million kids, you might take that risk of death from one, and let's say you drop it to zero, because there's a 95% reduction in COVID, and there appears to be almost a full protection against severe COVID. So let's say to save that one life, you gotta inoculate a million kids with vaccination to save one life. And you're talking about maybe 14,000 kids suffering grade three fevers, and maybe 880 suffering grade four fevers, which is more than one day. And I guess when you add in the myalgia, when you add in the arthralgia, when you add in the sort of headache, the fogginess, all these things, I mean, I think you have a tough sell.*[66]

The adolescent vaccine randomized-controlled trial was

published 5-months later. Yes, the vaccine made kids tired and gave them a headache. Out of 1,131 children who received the vaccine, one had a fever with a temperature higher than 40°C (104°F). However, all 16 COVID cases occurred among placebo recipients.[28] Once that result was known, it was *very reasonable* to assume that the vaccine would prevent rare, but grave harms in some children, which is exactly what happened, of course.

Yet, on May 7, 2021, three days before vaccines were authorized for adolescents, Dr. Prasad published his article entitled "COVID Vaccines for Children Should Not Get Emergency Use Authorization" in the *BMJ*. It said, "For adults, the benefits of COVID-19 vaccination are enormous, while for children they are relatively minor."[67]

If regulators had heeded this advice, zero healthy children under age 12-years would be vaccinated today. The vaccine is not fully licensed for them presently. The vaccine wasn't fully licensed for children ages 12-15 years until July 2022. Tens of millions of unvaccinated children would have contracted COVID had vaccines not been made available to them via the emergency use authorization. There would have been many more sick and injured children.

Fortunately, regulators made an obvious decision and tens of millions of children around the world were safely vaccinated against COVID. There are now over 50 studies on the safety and efficacy of the vaccine, none of which conclude it is more dangerous than the virus. We know a lot more about the pediatric vaccine than we did in the winter of 2021 when we knew nothing at all. Moreover, two new variants arrived – Delta and Omicron – each causing substantially more suffering in children than the variants that were circulating at that time. We are in a very different place than when Dr. Prasad made his initial comments on vaccinating children.

Despite this, Dr. Prasad and like-minded doctors continue to recycle the exact same talking points they formulated before a single child had been vaccinated and before worse variants arrived, when they thought the pandemic was "abating." If anything, Dr. Prasad has become more entrenched in his belief that children should remain unvaccinated against COVID. In a podcast from October 2022, he said it would be a "catastrophic error" if the COVID vaccine was made a part of the routine vaccination schedule for children.[468] He even implied vaccine-advocates are mentally ill, saying "Any strong advocate for kid COVID vaccination is off their rocker."[68]

It's clear that some doctors were *always* against vaccinating children and no data was going to sway them. Though they claim to "follow the evidence," their minds were made up many months before any evidence about the vaccine existed.

However, before I discuss the specific flaws in the myriad of arguments contrarian doctors used against the COVID vaccine, it's important to get a general sense of how these doctors – none of whom cared for a sick child – relentlessly minimized the dangers of the virus for young people.

Dr. John Ioannidis:

- ***March 17, 2020***: School closures may also diminish the chances of developing herd immunity in an age group that is spared serious disease.[69]

- ***April 17, 2020***: People who are less than 65 and have no underlying conditions (the risk of dying) is extremely extremely tiny…For someone who is less than 65 and has no underlying diseases, the risk is completely negligible…it seems that these deaths are extremely exceptional.[70]

- ***June 27, 2020***: For people younger than 45, the infection fatality rate is almost 0%.[71]

Dr. Sunetra Gupta

- ***December 12, 2021***: There is no reason to believe that children are more at risk. They never have been…Also, resources are limited. If all the money is spent on the coronavirus vaccine, we are going to allow a lot of children to miss out on vaccines that protect them from diseases like measles, which do kill.[72]

Dr. Scott Atlas

- ***April 22, 2020***: We can allow a lot of people to get infected. Those who are not at risk to die or have a serious hospital-requiring illness, we should be fine with letting them get infected, generating immunity on their own, and the more immunity in the community, the better we can eradicate the threat of the virus.[73]

- ***June 23, 2020***: There is virtually zero risks of death and virtually zero risks of a serious illness in children. This is the fact. This is inarguable. This is proven not only every country outside the United States but by our own data in the CDC itself. Of the first hundred-plus-thousand deaths analyzed, 99.98 deaths were not in children. I'm talking about percent, 99.9% of deaths are in people over 24.[74]

Allison Krug, Drs. Tracy Høeg, Lucy McBride, and Monica Gandhi

- ***May 26, 2021***: This low risk for children nearly vanishes as cases plummet. As we saw in Israel and Britain, vaccinating adults indirectly protects children. The same trend is evident here in the United States: Adult vaccination has lowered COVID-19 incidence among children by 50 percent in the past four weeks.[75]

Dr. John Mandrola

- ***December 29, 2020***: Young Adults Should Not Live in Fear from #COVID19[76]

- ***March 10, 2021***: Young have almost no risk.[77]

- ***April 23, 2021***: Children incur almost no risk from virus.[78]

- ***April 23, 2021***: I love this vaccine, but before we give an intervention to a kid who has almost no risk, I think we should use the precautionary principle.[79]

Dr. Zubin Damania

- ***April 14, 2021***: A fear. And they're saying, well, but now younger kids with these new variants, we don't know it's a little more infectious now, school age kids. What if they get really sick? And, you know, even though this thing has killed less than you know, or, or about as many as flu would kill in a normal year in kids, I say hardly any.[80]

Dr. Marty Makary

- ***May 24, 2021***: Let's say they're healthy. People might appropriately say, "Hey, the risk of death is infinitesimally small. Do I really need to do this?" Legitimate question. It's not necessarily to save their life with a vaccine.[81]

Dr. Vinay Prasad and Allison Krug

- ***February 2, 2022***: While the death of any child is a tragedy, COVID-19 is less deadly to children than many other risks we accept as a matter of course, including drowning, vehicle accidents, and even cardiovascular disease.[82]

Dr. Jay Bhattacharya

- ***May 10, 2021***: No, I don't think if there's any good reason to vaccinate kids that young did for kids, they face a vanishingly small risk from COVID itself, near zero from mortality from COVID. At the same time, they haven't really tested the vaccine on enough children to know that with any confidence with the adverse – serious adverse event rate is anything more than zero. And you say you wouldn't the balanced this doesn't work. Why would I vaccinate my kid against something but disease for whom but it's not actually all that deadly? Where there's might be some serious adverse events, I think that it is a mistake to think about this, as good for kids. It's not good for kids.[83]

Dr. Martin Kulldorff

- ***March 8, 2022***: For older people who have not yet had

COVID it makes sense to get vaccinated. While there may be unknown low-risk adverse reactions, the large reduction in mortality risk far outweighs any such risks. For children, the mortality risk is very small and the known and any still unknown risks from adverse reactions may outweigh the benefits at reducing hospitalizations and death from COVID, which are unfortunately still unknown.[84]

Dr. Joseph A. Ladapo

- ***March 8, 2022***: As Surgeon General, I cannot recommend that healthy children receive the COVID-19 vaccine. When their overall risk is low, & there is a higher than anticipated rate of serious adverse events in clinical trials, it is unclear if benefits outweigh the risks. Especially when the COVID-19 vaccine shows rapid decline in efficacy among children, and many already have natural immunity after two years.[85]

- ***October 29, 2022***: Parents, don't hold your breath… CDC & FDA abandoned their posts. Keep sticking with your intuition and keep those COVID jabs away from your kids.[86]

Dr. Vinay Prasad

- ***May 8, 2021***: Vast majority of kids recover quickly from SARS cov 2. And after all adults are vaccinated their risk of COVID will decline precipitously. It's ok to awknowledge [sic] that COVID19 is not an emergency for kids.[87]

- ***July 21, 2022***: Any strong advocate for kid COVID vaccination is off their rocker. It really doesn't matter. The risks are super low.[88]

I could fill many pages with quotes like these. Parents were inundated with this message. I've never seen such a sustained effort to minimize a virus or attack a vaccine in my decade observing the anti-vaccine movement.

Whether they were saying children shouldn't be vaccinated because COVID was going away or because they've all already had COVID, contrarian doctors grasped at any and all reasons to dissuade parents against vaccinating their children. Eventually some doctors' vaccine "skepticism" bled into adult vaccination as well.

Unfortunately, these doctors had a great deal of success. I've also never seen such a successful attack on a vaccine in my decade observing the anti-vaccine movement. Powerful politicians disparaged pediatric vaccination and parents were convinced it wasn't necessary. As a result, pediatric vaccination rates are abysmally low, children keep getting infected, a small percentage get hospitalized, and COVID's death tally edges slowly upwards.

The following sections focus on 27 arguments contrarian doctors made against vaccinating children and how they recycled arguments anti-vaxxers have made for years about other vaccines. It was all very familiar to anyone who bothered to pay attention to the anti-vaccine movement. What was new was who was making these arguments and how influential they were.

Reasons not to vaccinate children: COVID is harmless or even beneficial for children.

#1 ~ "For children, getting sick and recovering is part of a natural and healthy life."

The idea that as long as something is natural it must also be healthy appeals to many people, as does the idea that vaccine-preventable diseases are "natural and healthy" for children. Dr. Jennifer Margulis, an anti-vaccine activist who describes herself by saying "I am not anti-vaccine, I am pro-questions,"[89] asked a question in a 2010 documentary called *The Vaccine War*. She asked:

> *Why are we giving children so many vaccines? They get four times the number of vaccines than I got when I was child growing up in the '70s. As a parent, I would rather see my child get a natural illness and contract that the way that illnesses have been contracted for at least 200,000 years that homo sapiens has been around. I'm not afraid of my children getting chicken pox. There are reasons that children get sick. Getting sick is not a bad thing.*[90]

In reality, getting sick is a bad thing.

Anti-vaccine sites feature articles such as "The Unreported Health Benefits of Measles," which appeared on *GreenMedInfo*. "Measles and other childhood infections may actually protect against life-threatening conditions like cancer and heart disease,"[91] it said. There's even a children's book, called *Melanie's Marvelous Measles*, that celebrates children getting sick. The blurb on the back says:

> *Melanie's Marvelous Measles was written to educate children on the benefits of having measles and how you can heal from them naturally and successfully. Often today, we are being bombarded with messages from vested interests to fear all diseases in order for someone to sell some potion or vaccine, when, in fact, history shows that in industrialised countries, these diseases are quite benign and, according to natural health sources, beneficial to the body.*[92]

Before the pandemic, anti-vaccine doctors spread the myth that vaccine-preventable diseases are beneficial for children. In his book *Vaccines, Autoimmunity, and the Changing Nature of Childhood Illness*, Dr. Thomas Cowan, who blamed 5G for COVID,[93] said:

> *We (modern doctors) have forgotten (or never learned) that acute disease – disease that is typically self-limiting and usually accompanied by fever, rash, and pus – is the primary way the body rids itself of unwanted toxins or other substances.*[94]

Dr. Suzanne Humphries, a nephrologist turned anti-vaccine homeopath,[95] wrote an article titled "The Benefits of Having a Natural Measles Infection," which claimed that measles treats kidney disease and cancer. She wrote:

> *Today, half a century after measles vaccines have become commonplace, and two to three generations beyond the expectation of contracting measles during childhood as a regular event, measles is now thought*

> *of as a potentially deadly disease with no redeeming qualities. However, a look into the medical literature of the past shows us that wild measles may indeed have afforded immunologic advantages to those infected.*[96]

"Why not just let wild measles circulate and do the job nature intended at the time of life it was intended, which leads to 65 years of immunity and no need for life-span vaccination?" she asked.

Anti-vaccine doctors also claimed it's beneficial when children feel sick. In her article "Vaccination: Your Body. Your Baby. Their Flu," Dr. Kelly Brogan claimed that sickness should be embraced. She wrote:

> *This better way embraces periodic sickness as part of comprehensive wellness. The only way to truly protect ourselves and our infants is through natural immunity bolstered by wild-type exposure in the community. Once you have a particular flu strain, when it comes around again, you will be uniquely protected, and you will pass on this protection to your newborn. There is no replacement for this.*[97]

Parents who have been misled by such pro-virus rhetoric occasionally seek out diseases for their children. A report on a measles outbreak in 2019 was titled "Low Vaccination Rates and 'Measles Parties' Fueled 2019 Measles Outbreak in NYC."[98] According to a news report from 2019:

> *Gov. Matt Bevin of Kentucky said this week that he and his wife made sure all nine of their children got chickenpox. "Every single one of my kids had the chickenpox," Mr. Bevin said in an interview on Tuesday with a radio station in Bowling Green, Ky. "They got the chickenpox on purpose because we found a neighbor that had it and I went and made sure every one of my kids was exposed to it, and they got it. They had it as children. They were miserable for a few days, and they all turned out fine."*[99]

Nothing catastrophic happened, fortunately, but there was a small chance of a disastrous outcome. Moreover, these children didn't have to be miserable even for a few days. They could have been protected from shingles as well. Instead, their misinformed father *purposefully sought out* this suffering for them, thinking he was acting in their best interest. If a parent threw a caustic substance on their child's body that made them "miserable for a few days", that child would need to be taken into protective custody, even if they "turned out fine".

While most doctors used to discourage parents from exposing children to viruses that can cause suffering and death, this idea gained mainstream acceptance during the pandemic. On February 2, 2022, Dr. Vinay Prasad and Allison Krug penned an article titled "Should We Let Children Catch Omicron?" They wrote that measures to protect children "are premised on the idea that America's children must be shielded from exposure to COVID-19."[82] They felt this was misguided. They wrote:

> *What kids really need, however, is a return to normal. And when it comes to infectious disease, normality means a world where they are routinely exposed to, and overcome, viral illness. For children, getting sick and recovering is part of a natural and healthy life...*
>
> *Parents must consider that exposures are how we best protect our children against the variants of the future. In fact, it is reckless to let children age into a more serious encounter with a disease best dealt with while younger.*

Even though their article appeared before the youngest, most vulnerable children were eligible to be vaccinated, Dr. Prasad and Krug favorably quoted Dr. Francois Balloux, who said "if the objective were to send SARCoV2 into endemicity, then healthy kids have to be exposed to the virus, ideally earlier than later."[100] Dr. Prasad and Krug wrote that "this idea is not as frightening as it may sound. We know that even unvaccinated children generally do well after COVID-19 infection."[82] Obviously, parents do not have to expose their unvaccinated babies to SARS-CoV-2 in a misguided attempt to send SARCoV2 into endemicity.

Dr. Prasad and Krug further wrote that "immunity is built through illness," though immunity is also built through vaccines, of course. While they acknowledged that vaccines reduce severe COVID outcomes in children, they did not advocate for vaccination, nor did they explain how getting sick with COVID was "healthy" for a child, especially considering their article was published immediately after the Omicron variant hospitalized and killed the highest number of children of the entire pandemic.[5] Instead of informing their readers of this sad fact, Dr. Prasad and Krug played word-games by writing that the "Omicron variant resulted in 66% fewer hospitalisations than [Delta] in a study of children younger than 5 years."[82]

Dr. Prasad later elaborated on this belief that "getting sick and recovering is part of a natural and healthy life" for children. In a passage that could have been written by Dr. Margulis. He said:

> *Why do humans get respiratory viruses? Despite millions of news stories on COVID19, no one asked the obvious question...Children have gotten and will get respiratory viruses for as long as we exist. Our knowledge of the immune system is so primitive it would be a mistake to conclude: it would be better to avoid such viruses. The truth is we do not know. It might actually be bad. And yet, here we are with arrogant pundits confident in the unyielding power of humankind to bend the natural world to our will. Arrogant but not wise. Clueless that we don't even know what is best.*[101]

In an article titled "I Am Going to Mask Because I Want to Get Fewer Colds & Other Flawed Ideas," he sounded exactly like Drs. Humphries and Brogan. Dr. Prasad wrote:

> *There is the arrogance that avoiding colds and flu is good for us. Of course it is the case that getting sick is unpleasant, but our knowledge of immunology and the body is so primitive we should not conclude that avoiding it is 'good for us.' We have no idea if that is true in the long run. It is natural to be infected*

> *repeatedly with respiratory viruses— if we got fewer infections what would that mean for auto-immunity for cancer?*[102]

While no one claims it would be healthy for a child to grow up in a completely sterile environment, this does not mean that COVID, polio, HPV, measles, or any other vaccine-preventable disease is beneficial for children. Indeed, two months after Dr. Prasad wrote his article, news headlines would read "'Tripledemic' of Flu, RSV and COVID-19 Strains Hospitals, Worries Doctors as Cases Spike." The article explained that "at Mass General Hospital for Children, the pediatric ICU is at full capacity. Most patients there are on oxygen or ventilators."[103]

This is not "healthy" for children. There's no evidence they'll emerge from the ICU with a lower risk of autoimmune diseases and cancer. In fact, certain viruses are known to cause these conditions. For example, HPV infection can result in cervical, throat, penile, and other cancers,[104] and the Epstein-Barr virus (EBV) has been linked to various cancers as well as autoimmune disorders like multiple sclerosis.[105]

COVID was certainly not "healthy and natural" for 10-year-old Zyrin Foots. His mother, Amber McDaniel, tried to vaccinate him, but he was too young.[106] Zyrin had heart attacks after his bout with COVID, needing open heart surgery. He then developed MIS-C. According to news reports:

> *About ten days after Zyrin's hospitalization, doctors presented McDaniel with an excruciating choice: she could take her son off life support, allowing him to die, or she could give doctors permission to amputate his right arm and both of his legs. His left arm would be left intact but likely unusable because of multiple strokes he'd endured. After undergoing these procedures, McDaniel said, the doctors estimated the child would have a 25 percent chance of survival. Assuming he did make it through the surgeries, Zyrin wouldn't be able to wear prosthetic legs—the procedures would leave too little of his thighs intact. They gave her a couple of days to make her decision.*

Zyrin died several days later. "At that moment, I knew he was in too much pain to continue," his mother said.

Whether it's Dr. Brogan saying we should embrace 'periodic sickness as part of comprehensive wellness"[97] or Dr. Prasad and Krug saying, "for children, getting sick and recovering is part of a natural and healthy life,"[82] there's no evidence that it's healthy for children to get sick with a vaccine-preventable disease.

Just because something is natural, doesn't mean it's healthy, and prior to the pandemic, only quack doctors argued otherwise.

#2 ~ "I am not aware of a single healthy child in the US who has died of COVID-19 to date."

The notion that only children with underlying conditions suffer grave outcomes from vaccine-preventable diseases is an old anti-vaccine talking point. In an article from 2007 regarding children who were hospitalized with measles, Dr. Sherri Tenpenny, an anti-vaccine doctor who claimed that COVID vaccines magnetize people,[107] asked:

> *Did they have underlying conditions that made them more susceptible to a severe case of measles?*[108]

Dr. Kelly Brogan shared the essay "First They Came for the Anti-Vaxxers," which expressed a similar sentiment about measles. It said:

> *Not only is measles a relatively benign illness for healthy people living in developed countries, contracting and surviving the disease confers benefits to the immune system – as well as strengthening herd immunity – in ways that vaccines cannot.*[109]

Likewise, Dr. Bob Sears said about measles:

> *Deadly? Not in the US or any other developed country with a well-nourished population. The risk of fatality here isn't zero, but it's as close to zero as you can get without actually being zero.*[110]

The myth that healthy children are invulnerable to COVID continued to resonate with anti-vaxxers during the pandemic. The anti-vaccine website, *Autism Action Network*, gave the following reasons "to reject the Pfizer and Moderna applications to inject mRNA into little kids":

> ***There is no COVID emergency for children under five years old.***
>
> - *Children have a 99.997% recovery rate and a body of medical literature indicates that almost zero healthy children under five years old have died from COVID.*
> - *A large study conducted in Germany showed zero deaths for children under 5 and a case fatality rate of three out of a million in children without comorbidities.*
> - *A Johns Hopkins study monitoring 48,000 children diagnosed with COVID showed a zero mortality rate in children under 18 without comorbidities.*
> - *A study in Nature demonstrated that children under 18 with no comorbidities have virtually no risk of death.* [111]

Contrarian doctors also spread the myth that healthy children don't die from COVID, none more so than Dr. Marty Makary, the chair of Virginia Governor Glenn Youngkin's COVID team and the author of the "Johns Hopkins study" referenced by *Autism Action Network.*

On June 10, 2021, Dr. Makary published an article on *MedPage Today* titled "Think Twice Before Giving the COVID Vax to Healthy Kids." It contained the following sentence:

> *In reviewing the medical literature and news reports, and in talking to pediatricians across the country, I am not aware of a single healthy child in the U.S.*

who has died of COVID-19 to date.[112]

As evidence for his extraordinary claim, Dr. Makary referenced a paper of his titled "Risk Factors for COVID-19 Mortality among Privately Insured Patients." This was a "white paper" published by FAIR Health,[113] not a medical journal. However, Dr. Makary claimed this was a study of "pediatric COVID-19 deaths" and that it found "100% of pediatric COVID-19 deaths were in children with a pre-existing condition."

In another editorial titled "The Flimsy Evidence Behind the CDC's Push to Vaccinate Children," which was published in the *Wall Street Journal*, he again touted his white paper, saying it examined "approximately 48,000 children under 18 diagnosed with COVID"[114] and that the "report found a mortality rate of zero among children without a pre-existing medical condition such as leukemia." "If that trend holds, it has significant implications for healthy kids and whether they need two vaccine doses," he continued. In yet a third editorial, he said "that children without chronic conditions had a COVID-19 mortality rate of zero",[115] and on Dr. Zubin Damania's podcast he said, "there's never been a documented case of an entirely healthy kid dying of COVID... we did an analysis with FAIR Health, and it turns out that in looking at half of the nation's health insurance state, there was not a single healthy kid who'd died."[81]

However, Dr. Makary's report was not a study of "pediatric COVID-19 deaths" as he claimed. The words "child," "children," and "pediatrics" do not appear in the paper,[113] though there is a discussion of Alzheimer's disease in relation to COVID. The paper reported on 2,753 people who died of COVID from April 1, 2020, through August 31, 2020. Of these, 0.11% of deaths occurred in children under 18-years. This means his supposed study of "pediatric COVID-19 deaths" reported on just three deceased children. It presented no data about the three children beyond noting they were under 18-years of age and had some underlying condition. Over 300 children had died of COVID by June 2021[5] when Dr. Makary promoted his study, meaning it reported on less than 1% of the pediatric deaths to that point.[116]

Despite this, Dr. Makary mentioned his paper in at least three editorials, which equals the number of deceased children it contained. Moreover, the study reported on a total of 31,000 children, not 48,000 as he claimed, which means 1 in 10,000 children in his "study" died of COVID, a very high death rate.[113] Dr. Makary did not mention this finding, though the true overall pediatric death rate is lower than this.[5]

Though Dr. Makary claimed to have reviewed "the medical literature and news reports" and was unable to find "a single healthy child in the U.S. who has died of COVID-19 to date,"[112] I was able to find many such tragedies at the time. My simple internet search returned an article titled "Parents Say 5-Year-Old Daughter Who Died From COVID-19 was 'Perfectly Healthy'"[117] and another titled "4-Year-Old CNY Boy Who Died of COVID Complications Had Been Healthy: 'I Lost My Miracle Baby.'"[118] An article from Minnesota was titled "Child Under 10 With No Underlying Conditions Dies From COVID,"[119] and another article reported on a 9-month-old who "did not have an underlying health condition"[120] who died in that state. One article reported on a child "with no underlying conditions"[121] who died in Tennessee and another discussed a 7-year-old from Georgia who "had no underlying health conditions."[122] A 9-year-old with "no underlying conditions" died in July 2020.[123] Skylar Herbert, a 5 year-old from Detroit also had "no underlying health conditions" when she died of COVID.[124] There was also Dykota Morgan, a 15-year-old girl from Illinois, "whose parents said she had no underlying medical conditions."[125] She was a basketball player who died just two days after contracting the virus.

A quick internet search yielded *triple* the number of data points as Dr. Makary's paper. However, the only conclusion that can be drawn from such a small sample size is that Dr. Makary was wrong – some healthy children have died of COVID.

More formal evidence was readily available. In September 2020, the CDC reported on 121 deaths of people younger than 21 years, half of whom were younger than 18 years. It found that "among the 121 decedents, 30 (25%) were previously healthy (no reported underlying medical condition)."[126] The most common underlying conditions in deceased young people were asthma (28%), obesity (27%), neurologic and developmental conditions (22%), and cardiovascular conditions (18%). Dr. Makary did not mention this study in his discussions of the topic.

There is no question that it's exceptionally rare for a healthy child to die of COVID. It is so rare that these tragedies can make the news. But there is *some* risk of a devastating outcome for healthy children, and these low-risk events multiplied many millions of times add up to non-trivial numbers. As around 25% of deaths are in healthy children, this means COVID has killed between 300-400 healthy children so far, including some who were eligible to be vaccinated.[5] Of course, death is not the only bad outcome from COVID and, during New York City's winter Omicron wave, 54% of hospitalized children had no underlying conditions.[127] Another study of hospitalized infants found 66% were previously healthy, and 13% received mechanical ventilation.[128]

Unfortunately, Dr. Makary thought through the implications of his claim that COVID doesn't kill healthy children and told parents on Dr. Zubin Damania's podcast:

> *Let's say they're healthy. People might appropriately say, "Hey, the risk of death is infinitesimally small. Do I really need to do this?" Legitimate question. It's not necessarily to save their life with a vaccine.*[81]

Even if we lived in a fantasy world where healthy children were completely immune to COVID, telling parents such children shouldn't be vaccinated inappropriately puts the onus on them to determine if their child is healthy or not. I suspect that many parents think their child is healthy, when in fact they are at risk. Many people believe that only kids already on their deathbed with cancer die from COVID.

Contrarian doctors stressed this point. Dr. Vinay Prasad wrote an entire article about a German study where "among kids who died of COVID19, 38% were already on palliative/hospice care."[129] He neglected to tell his readers this study concluded just before the arrival of the Delta variant. Dr. Makary similarly claimed that the only children who died of COVID had a "pre-existing medical condition such as leukemia."[114]

This was also false. The most common underlying conditions in deceased young people are extremely common conditions, like asthma and obesity, not leukemia.[126] 20% of American children are obese, and it's likely that many of their parents believe COVID poses no risk to their child, who doesn't have leukemia after all.

Though the diseases that predispose children to poor outcomes in pediatric COVID are common, they are not fatal for children. Most children with underlying conditions who died from COVID were robbed of many decades of life. Very few COVID deaths occurred in children with leukemia who were fated to die on a Saturday when they, instead, succumbed to the virus on a Friday. Even leukemia is no longer a death sentence for children. The 5-year survival rate is 60%-90%, depending on the type of leukemia.[130]

Unfortunately, contrarian doctors were not interested in raising awareness that common childhood conditions are a risk factor for severe COVID. They didn't launch a campaign to ensure obese children with asthma were vaccinated. This would have been a laudable goal. They also didn't launch a campaign to ensure children with leukemia were vaccinated. Instead, they wanted parents to think: *My child isn't at risk. She doesn't need the vaccine.*

Of course, the death of a vulnerable child is just as tragic as the death of a healthy child. As one mother asked on *Twitter*:

> *Can you please explain to me personally how my child's life, with a pre-existing condition, is less valuable and her death would be tolerable?*[131]

Children are not supposed to die.

Moreover, death is not the only bad outcome from COVID. After the Delta variant led to several children being intubated and needing extracorporeal membrane oxygenation (ECMO) at her hospital, Dr. Allison Eckard, a pediatric infectious disease specialist, said:

> *We are seeing more healthy children with no underlying condition with severe COVID, and that is different than the rest of the pandemic.; There has been a switch. ... We would really like to encourage families to understand that things have changed.*[132]

Even though Dr. Makary's myth could be refuted with a simple internet search, this didn't stop Drs. Monica Gandhi and Tracy Høeg from amplifying his message on Twitter.133 U.S. Senator Roger Marshall, a Republican from Kansas and obstetrician, said "probably zero"134 healthy children died of COVID during a Senate hearing with the CDC Director. Anti-vaccine propagandist Tucker Carlson repeated Dr. Makary's claim verbatim on his program saying:

> *So, researchers at Johns Hopkins led by Dr. Marty Makary looked closely at those numbers and what they actually meant and here's what they found, quote: "A mortality rate of zero among children without a preexisting medical condition such as leukemia."*[135]

Unfortunately, this myth had real world impact, especially in Florida, where the Surgeon General, Dr. Joseph Ladapo, led a successful campaign to ensure unvaccinated children contracted COVID. Despite Dr. Ladapo's stellar credentials – he trained at Harvard and New York University – Dr. Ladapo embraced all manner of quackery during the pandemic. According to his Wikipedia entry:

> *Around early 2020, Ladapo began to write op-eds for The Wall Street Journal on the emerging COVID-19 pandemic, gaining prominence as a skeptic against the mainstream consensus despite not having any specialization in infectious diseases. Across these columns, Ladapo promoted unproven treatments — hydroxychloroquine and ivermectin — questioned the safety of vaccines, opposed lockdown and mask mandates, and associated with America's Frontline Doctors. He courted particular controversy after arguing against lockdowns citing from his "experience in treating COVID-19 patients at UCLA" when their staff scheduling roster did not have him assigned to treat COVID-19 patients, and several of his colleagues rejected that Ladapo had treated any COVID-19 patient. Ladapo had also signed the Great Barrington Declaration.*[136]

This is the type of doctor who made pivotal decisions about vaccinating children. In explaining his decision not to vaccinate healthy children, Dr. Ladapo said, "Based on currently available data, the risks of administering COVID-19 vaccination among healthy children may outweigh the benefits."[137] However, the data

Dr. Ladapo presented and selectively quoted from scientific papers in a misleading way prompted one of the researchers they quoted to say, "You don't just pick one sentence from one paper that agrees with what you think you want to say."[138] However, they accurately quoted Dr. Joseph Fraiman, who inaccurately said:

> *If you have a healthy child, the chances of that child dying are incredibly low, essentially close to zero, if not actually zero. Then the next part of the analysis that you would have to think about are the side effects of the vaccine and the symptoms of COVID-19. The vaccine causes severe symptoms in children and adults."*[137]

When vaccines became available to the youngest children, those most at risk, Florida was the only state that refused to order vaccines from the federal government. "It is also no surprise we chose not to participate in distribution of the COVID-19 vaccine when the Department does not recommend it for all children,"[139] the Florida Department of Health said.

Vaccines weren't available when 9-year-old Kimora Lynum died of COVID in my hometown of Gainesville, Florida during the summer of 2020. Her mother, Mikasha Young-Holmes, who has no other children, said that "we were extremely close. It had just been me and her for a while."[123] After Kimora didn't awake from a nap, Ms. Young-Holmes described what happened next:

> *I was shaking her, yelling at her. I yelled at my mom and told her to come in here because Kim is not breathing. I was just trying to bring her back. I tried, I tried everything I could to bring her back. On the way, I was just hoping and praying that they could just get her back.*

Kimora's family said she was healthy when she died. Anyone could have discovered this with a simple Google search.

#3 ~ "COVID-19 is less deadly to children than many other risks we accept as a matter of course, including drowning, vehicle accidents, and even cardiovascular disease."

On December 1, 2020 the American Academy of Pediatrics tweeted the following warning:

> *Using the fireplace more as temperatures drop this winter? Here are tips on smoke detectors and how to prepare your family. Don't forget, fire safety at home is important all year round!*[140]

Around 500 children die from fires each year, and it would have been bizarre and inappropriate had anyone argued these deaths are not worth preventing because more children die of suicide or car accidents. Yet, anti-vaxxers have long diminished vaccine-preventable diseases by comparing them to other things that kill more children.

Consider the following paragraph, which comes from an article titled "Measles Scare Tactics Hurt Us All" that was published on the anti-vaccine website *GreenMedInfo*:

> *By the time the measles vaccine was patented in 1963 in the US, the mortality rate from measles was about 1 in 500,000. This is less than your risk of death from falling off furniture. Let's also consider that over 600,000 people annually die of heart disease in the US, over 500,000 people die from cancer in the US each year.*[141]

This reveals a very common anti-vaccine technique. Instead of simply telling people the basic facts about how measles hurt children, anti-vaxxers instead use irrelevant and often bogus statistics to trick people into thinking vaccine-preventable diseases are not worth preventing. They are essentially saying that *even if the measles vaccine saves children, we're only talking about 500 children here, so what's the point anyways.*

It's true that heart disease and cancer kill many more people than measles, but that's not a valid reason to let some unvaccinated children die from the measles. Moreover, the passage contained predictable falsehoods. Around 40 children are killed annually by furniture,[142] while measles killed around 500 children in the pre-vaccine era. Obviously, measles can damage children without killing them, and it's good that the MMR can prevent these injuries too.

During the pandemic, anti-vaxxers continued to argue that there was no point in using the vaccine to try to save children's lives, since not *that many* of them died of COVID. An article posted on Robert F. Kennedy, Jr.'s anti-vaccine site titled "Top Ten Reasons Not to Let Your Child Get a COVID Shot," gave the following reason not to vaccinate children:

> *As a cause of death for children aged 1-17, COVID-19 ranks behind injury, suicide, cancer, homicide, congenital anomalies, heart disease, influenza, chronic lower respiratory disease and cerebrovascular causes.*[143]

Again, the passage contained predictable falsehoods - since March 2020, COVID killed many more children than influenza and cerebrovascular diseases.[144] But even if all these conditions killed more children than COVID, this is not a good reason to let some unvaccinated children die from COVID or suffer from it.

Contrarian doctors made liberal use of this technique to minimize pediatric COVID. Consider this simple, and very good, paragraph by Drs. Jeffrey Gerber and Paul Offit in November 2021:

> *Make no mistake – COVID-19 is a childhood illness. When SARS-CoV-2 entered the United States early in 2020, children accounted for fewer than 3% of cases; today, they account for more than 25%. More than 6 million US children have been infected with SARS-CoV-2, including 2 million between the ages of 5 and 11. At the end of October 2021, about 100,000 children per week were infected. Of the tens of thousands of children who have been hospitalized, about one-third had no preexisting medical conditions, and many have required the intensive care unit. Almost 700 children have died*

> *from COVID-19, placing SARS-CoV-2 infection among the top 10 causes of death in US children. No children have died from vaccination.*[8]

If every article on pediatric COVID laid out the risks of pediatric COVID as clearly as this, more children would be alive today.

Though it's extremely easy to report such information, most contrarian doctors refused to do it. Though the paragraph above is really just an unremarkable tally of how COVID had affected children up to that time, you can read the entire canon of some prolific pontificators on pediatric COVID and not learn any of these essential facts. The dozens of studies showing the vaccine's benefits for children are similarly unmentionable. They simply do not exist in the world of anti-vaxxers or contrarian doctors, even in their articles meant for the general public.

A prototypical example is an article titled "Kids Don't Need COVID-19 Vaccines to Return to School," which was written by Dr. Vinay Prasad on February 3, 2021, before any children had been vaccinated. He wrote:

> *Between March and October of 2020, among those between the ages of five and 14, the risk of dying of COVID-19 in the United States was 1 in 1,000,000. To put that in perspective, in that same age group during non-COVID times, the risk of suicide is 10 times higher. For young adults ages 15 to 24, the risk of dying from COVID19 was 9.9 in 1,000,000, and they are also generally 10 times more likely to commit suicide...*
>
> *Contrast these outcomes with those of adults. For the sake of comparison, imagine 100,000 infected people at different ages, using data from a meta-analysis conducted by an international team: two of those age 10 might die compared to 1,400 adults aged 65 and 15,000 adults aged 85. In other words, the risk of an 85-year-old dying from COVID-19 is 7,500 times greater than that of a 10-year-old.*[63]

Such articles, essentially devoid of basic facts regarding pediatric COVID, were commonplace during the pandemic. Whether in medical journals, newspapers, or on social media, such omissions and spurious comparisons were the norm for contrarian doctors. Instead of simply telling their readers the number of children killed by or hospitalized with COVID, contrarian doctors danced around them with largely irrelevant factoids, all designed to minimize the virus, of course.

The one relevant statistic that Dr. Prasad shared was also framed in a misleading way. That only 1 in a million elementary school children died of COVID in the pandemic's first 7 months showed we did a decent job of protecting them at that time. This low death rate did not imply that children would not benefit from a vaccine. Dr. Prasad was able to report that more children died of suicide than COVID only because we vaccinated tens of millions of children instead of letting them all get infected simultaneously in the spring of 2020. COVID's impact would have been much more severe had we made no efforts to protect children at the start of the pandemic as many doctors suggested.

Moreover, when Dr. Prasad wrote his article, at least 227 children had died of COVID.[116] Most people think that's a lot of dead children. However, instead of providing this important number, he only stated that more children died of suicide and that COVID was much worse for older people.

These comparisons are not wrong, nor are they necessarily useless. We all need help contextualizing the myriad of numbers we encounter daily, and an essential feature of COVID is that elderly people are much more vulnerable to it, and it is not the top killer of children. However, the number of children killed or injured by COVID does not depend on how the disease affects adults or how many children commit suicide each year.

This way of framing data is no accident. Salesmen know that how we perceive a number depends on how it is framed (the anchoring effect). A savvy salesman whose true goal is to sell you a $40,000 car may first show you one that costs $80,000. He hopes that, by comparison, $40,000 won't sound like a lot of money. At least our imaginary salesman will tell you the price of the car. It's notable that contrarian doctors who seek to contextualize pediatric COVID this way always choose a number that is *larger* than the pediatric death toll. They'll never tell you that in the past year, COVID killed 10 times the number of children who die in bike accidents annually, for example.

Despite writing prolifically on the subject, I am not sure Dr. Prasad has ever simply stated the number of children killed by COVID, though his readers will know that the risk of a child dying of COVID is "lower than risks kids face in a typical year from automobile accidents or drowning."[145] He's made that point repeatedly even though around 1,000 children died in the past year from COVID[5] and drownings,[146] and in 2020, 607 children under age 12 died in car crashes.[147]

In arguing that children should be left vulnerable to COVID because more children died from other causes or because older people are more vulnerable, Dr. Prasad is committing what is known as the *fallacy of relative privation*, which states that problem X should be ignored because problem Y is bigger. This fallacy can be found on every anti-vaccine site, and its absurdity is obvious when applied to other killers of children. No doctor would write the paragraph below, for example:

> *There are 73 million children in the USA. According to the National Cancer Institute, only 0.0024% of them die of cancer each year. Adults are 100 times more likely to die from cancer than children, and children are a mere 0.3% of cancer deaths every year. To put things in perspective, more children will be born in the U.S. between the hours of 12:00 PM and 5:00PM today than will die of cancer this entire year. The risk of you getting struck by lightning in your life is three times higher than the risk of a child dying of cancer.*

Yet, this is how doctors routinely discussed pediatric COVID.

Although COVID was a leading killer of children at various points during the pandemic, the fact that it wasn't the number 1 top cause is not a valid reason to oppose pediatric vaccination. The case to vaccinate children is not strengthened by the fact that more die from COVID than from school shootings.[148] Similarly, it's asinine to argue that children should remain unvaccinated because COVID is much worse for elderly people. If COVID magically stopped killing adults, it wouldn't suddenly become worse for children.

The only thing that matters is whether the vaccine is safer than the virus for children, which it is, of course. The fact that the COVID vaccine won't save the lives of *that many* children is not a reasonable argument against it, even though this is the essence of every argument not to vaccine them.

Beyond this, there's another glaring flaw in comparing pediatric and geriatric COVID: Unlike 80-year-olds, children who die of COVID are robbed of their entire lives. As Dr. Ester Choo put it:

> *It's odd to see comparisons between children and older adults, as if the health indicators and expectations are the same. We have fundamentally different frames for children's health.*[149]

She's right, and Dr. Prasad recognized this prior to the pandemic, writing in 2016:

> *When it comes to determining the impact of death, we intuitively understand that a 95-year-old dying of a medical error, while regrettable, is not as tragic as a 17-year-old dying from one. The 95-year-old had lived a full life, while the teenager missed out on so much. Most analyses treat each error-related death as the same. A better statistic to use would be years of life lost. It corrects for the fact that some deaths are more untimely than others.*

We go to great lengths to prevent children from dying, and they are so normalized, we hardly notice them. For example, in an article titled "Should We Let Children Catch Omicron?", Dr. Prasad and Allison Krug wrote:

> *While the death of any child is a tragedy, COVID-19 is less deadly to children than many other risks we accept as a matter of course, including drowning, vehicle accidents, and even cardiovascular disease.*[82]

This is doubly false. The CDC's COVID data tracker added 1,000 deaths to its grim tally in the year before that article was published, which is about the same as the number of children who drown annually and larger than the number of children who die from cardiovascular disease.[144]

Moreover, we absolutely don't accept children dying from car accidents and drownings "as a matter of course." We normally do whatever we can to keep children safe and alive. Products that injure a handful of children are rightly removed from the market. Sadly, there is no vaccine against drowning and car accidents, and so we go to *much greater* lengths to keep children safe. There are crossing guards, seat belts, air bags, traffic laws, lifeguards, swim lessons, life preservers, and fences around pools. None of these are as simple as a vaccine, yet none are controversial. No reasonable person would reject an improved car seat that slashed car fatalities by arguing that we should just accept such deaths as a "matter of course." In fact, pediatric car deaths have been cut in half over the past 20 years because we didn't accept them as a "matter of course."

At least Dr. Prasad and Krug were right that the death of any child is a tragedy. 7-year-old Adalyn Graviss died of acute disseminated encephalomyelitis less than 72-hours after testing positive for COVID. Her mother said:

> *She loves Jesus music, she loved being around her family and friends, she loved basketball, she loved dance, she loved going to church, she loved to play dress-up. Every day she wore my high heels and she was dancing up and down the hallway.*[150]

According to news reports, Adalyn's parents "had been considering taking Adalyn to get her COVID-19 vaccine after she became eligible in November but held off."[151] Many doctors told Adalyn's parents that holding off was the right move.

1,593 children have died of COVID[5], no matter how many die from other causes, and it's only with COVID that doctors argue these deaths are acceptable because the virus is more dangerous for grandma.

#4 ~ "Children are less at risk from COVID-19 than from influenza."

Imagine you were told in March 2020 that over the next 2.5 years or so, Virus A would kill 1,593 children, while Virus B would kill 106 children. Which virus would you say is worse? This is not a trick question. The answer is obvious.

In the real world, during the first 2.5 years of the pandemic in the U.S. COVID killed 1,593 children, while the flu killed 106.[64] Which virus would you say is worse?

An article on Robert F. Kennedy, Jr's anti-vaccine website titled "Pfizer COVID Vaccine Fails Risk-Benefit Analysis in Children 5 to 11" argued that the virus that killed 1,593 children was less worrisome than the virus that killed 106. It said:

> *Depending on the study one looks at, COVID is slightly less dangerous or roughly equivalent to the flu in children.*[152]

Beyond the simple fact that 1,593 is a larger number than 106, it's worthwhile to explore why this sentence was wrong and why comparisons between pediatric flu and COVID were rarely made in good faith.

Hopefully, it is not controversial to say that normal life ended when the pandemic began. Everything but hospitals shut down, and we all started wearing masks. Further, it is not controversial to argue that human behavior affects the spread of viruses. A lone hermit in the woods will never contract or spread COVID, while fans of crowded, indoor karaoke bars have encountered the virus many times by now, and likely spread it to others as well. As such, the only apples to apples comparison between the flu and COVID is to examine their impact since the pandemic started.

Moreover, when discussing the threat posed by any particular virus, we must consider two factors; the danger the virus poses to an individual with it and the danger the virus poses to the community at large. These can be very different metrics. Think about Ebola versus COVID.

The danger the virus poses to an individual is the infection fatality rate (IFR), which are the chances of a person dying if they contract a virus. In February 2022, Dr. Vinay Prasad shared a graph made by data reporter John Burn-Murdoch, which showed that a child with the flu was slightly more likely to die than a child with

COVID.[153] Every news story of sars-cov-2 particularly around rushing kids vax 6 mo-4yo, vax & mask mandates in the young & stories about mailing out tests & n95s to people should include this figure," Dr. Prasad said.

If my child contracted a virus, its IFR would be the only thing I'd want to know. This is vital information, though it has shifted throughout the pandemic depending on which variant was dominant and how much immunity there was amongst children. Had this graph been made when the Delta variant was circulating, it would have looked different.

However, one cannot understand how these viruses impacted children overall by looking just at the graph Dr. Prasad shared. He omitted a crucial piece of information. To grasp how many children a virus might kill, we need to know not just its IFR, we also need to know how contagious it is, termed the R0.

While a child with COVID has the same very low risk of dying as a child with the flu, COVID is much more contagious, and so many more children were affected. Mr. Burn-Murdoch knew this when he made his graph. Though Dr. Prasad did not share it, Mr. Burn-Murdoch said:

> *We must also remember COVID is much more transmissible than flu, so even though its lethality per-infection has fallen, the number of infections in any given year is still far, far higher.*[154]

Indeed, in 2018-2019, the flu caused symptomatic illnesses in about 1 in 7 children.[155] In contrast, nearly 90% of children contracted COVID in the first 2.5 years of the pandemic.

The death tallies for the two viruses tell an unambiguous story. Mitigation measures that dented COVID obliterated the flu. During the 2020-2021 flu season, the flu killed just 1 child.[64] As things opened up, that number predictably rose, and according to the CDC's FluView, the pediatric flu death toll now stands at 106 over the past 3 flu seasons. During the same period, COVID has killed over 1,593 children.[4] In January 2022 – the pandemic's worst month for children – 181 children died, which is 75 more children than the flu killed in 2.5 years.[156] Even looking at pre-pandemic years, COVID still extracted a higher toll on children than nearly every flu season.[157]

Hospitalization numbers reinforce this point. The CDC reported that the flu hospitalized just 9 children ages 5-11 during the 2020/2021 flu season, while COVID hospitalized 8,300 children that age during this time.[158] Additionally, a study of 66 pediatric ICUs found:

> *The number of children admitted each quarter with a primary diagnosis of COVID-19 or MISC during the first 15 months of the pandemic was twice as high as that for influenza during the 2 years before the pandemic. Influenza outcomes were observed during a time with no unusual public health measures in place (2018 to early 2020), while those of SARS-CoV-2 occurred while masking, social distancing, and remote schooling occurred. Those measures were sufficient to markedly decrease critical illness from many respiratory viruses, including nearly eliminating influenza admissions to these PICUs. Without these measures in place for this largely unvaccinated population, SARS-CoV-2 would likely have led to a number of critically ill children several-fold higher than seen with prepandemic influenza as well as more deaths.*[159]

I think if I was told in January 2020 that virus A would kill 1,593 children, while virus B would kill 106 children, I would have said virus A was much worse for children than virus B. That's how I feel about COVID and the flu. While future flu seasons may be worse than COVID, especially now that nearly all children have contracted COVID and/or been vaccinated against it, there's no question that COVID hurt children more than the flu during the first 2.5 years of the pandemic.

Amazingly, my belief that 1,593 is larger than 106 proved extremely controversial. Prominent and influential doctors claimed the flu is equivalent to or even worse than COVID for children, and some of them used this belief to argue against pediatric vaccination.

- **Martin Kulldorff (August 8, 2020)**: Children are less at risk from COVID-19 than from influenza.[160]

- **Scott Atlas (August 15, 2020)**: We know that the risk of the disease is extremely low for children, even less than that of seasonal flu.[161]

- **John Mandrola (September 27, 2020)**: The risk to children is greater from influenza than #COVID19.[162]

- **Vinay Prasad (February 4, 2021)**: It is generally not controversial to argue that SARS-CoV-2 in kids is roughly, roughly the same as influenza, maybe even less severe than influenza, seasonal influenza in kids… it's far more deadly in older people than it is in younger people.[66]

- **Dr. Zubin Damania (April 14, 2021)**: Even though this thing has killed less than you know, or, or about as many as flu would kill in a normal year in kids, I say hardly any.[80]

- **Lucy McBride (May 4, 2021)**: The risk of COVID-19 is really, really small in kids. It's a smaller risk than the seasonal flu. We don't close schools and mask kids in flu season. We have somehow as a society, quote-unquote, "tolerated" the fact that hundreds of kids die from the flu every year.[163]

- **Vinay Prasad, Monica Gandhi, Tracy Høeg (May 12, 2021)**: For children, the risk of disease is not zero, but the mortality risk is comparable to that from seasonal influenza.[164]

- **Jay Bhattacharya (July 21, 2021)**: They are, as you say, Steve, at very low risk for bad outcomes from this virus. Very few healthy, young children died from this virus, more died from the flu last year.[165]
- **Scott Atlas (September 22, 2021)**: Children "die from the flu at a higher rate" than from COVID.[166]

- **Jay Bhattacharya & Martin Kulldorff (November 6, 2021)**: Schools are major transmission points for influenza, but not for COVID. While children do get infected, their risk for COVID death is minuscule, lower than their already low risk of dying from the flu.[167]

- **Martin Kulldorff (December 17, 2021)**: Their COVID mortality risk is miniscule and less than the already low risk from the annual influenza, so the vaccine benefit for healthy children is very small.[168]

- **Dr. Tracy Høeg, Dr. Vinay Prasad (February 8, 2022)**: First, children are at extremely low risk of severe COVID-19. Even before the emergence of omicron, which is considerably more mild than earlier strains, the virus was less deadly to children than flu and pneumonia, heart disease, car crashes or guns.[169]

- **John P.A. Ioannidis (March 28, 2022)**: COVID-19 probably caused substantially fewer deaths in children and adolescents <20 years old (~20,000) versus 3 seasons of typical influenza.[170]

For reference, 300 children had died of COVID[5] when Dr. Damania said "hardly any" had died. When Dr. Kulldorff made his comment in December 2021, over 1,000 children died of COVID,[5] while one child had died of the flu.[64] COVID has been killing many more children than the flu since the start of the pandemic, though these doctors claim the opposite is true.

Several organizations also endorsed the myth that flu and COVID present equivalent risks to children. The Great Barrington Declaration declared that "for children, COVID-19 is less dangerous than many other harms, including influenza"[171] and the Urgency of Normal said in one of their parent "toolkits" that "influenza has a higher fatality rate per infection than COVID in young children."[172] This is true of many viruses, and without a sense of how many children will be infected, this fact alone is useless to determine how many children might die from COVID overall. Rabies kills everyone who gets it, but it kills less than five Americans per year.

It's revealing that doctors who argued that COVID is equivalent to the flu for children never felt confident enough to actually share the raw numbers of children killed by each virus. None of them wrote an essay titled "COVID Killed 1,593 Kids, the Flu 106: Here's Why the Flu is Worse and Why Kids Shouldn't be Vaccinated Against COVID."

So why were contrarian doctors so intent on comparing the flu and COVID? I think it's because they know that most people don't think the flu is a big deal. We often say we have "the flu" whenever we get the sniffles, and we don't structure our lives around the flu. We think of the flu as a minor inconvenience, and that's how contrarian doctors wanted people to think about pediatric COVID. Dr. Prasad explicitly made that argument in February 2022, saying "of course for children COVID and flu have always been comparable. We never upended their life over flu."[173]

This is false. While the flu never infected as many children as SARS-CoV-2, the flu could also shut schools occasionally. A news article from 2019 reported:

> *The flu season is wreaking havoc nationwide, with schools are closing and hospitals restricting visitors to try to control the spread of illness. Schools in Alabama, Idaho, Oklahoma, Tennessee and Texas closed this week as students called in sick and officials struggled to find teachers healthy enough to work.*[174]

It was *normal* for Americans to go great lengths to keep children safe from dangerous viruses, especially when not much learning was going on in classrooms anyway. People hardly noticed.

Obviously, comparisons between the flu and COVID have zero relevance to vaccinating children. To argue that children shouldn't be vaccinated against virus A because virus B is worse is just another example of the fallacy of relative privation. Doctors shouldn't want *any* child to suffer or die for lack of a vaccine. As pediatric neurologist Dr. Daniel Freedman stated:

Those comparing COVID in children to flu in children really seem to forget that pediatricians were encouraging flu vaccines in kids for years before this pandemic. Protect eligible kids from both vaccine preventable diseases. Not complicated.[175]

He's right, and before the pandemic, no reasonable doctor would have opposed the measles vaccine because a child with diphtheria is much more likely to die. In fact, in 2017 Dr. Prasad correctly said a doctor who spread misinformation about the flu vaccine was a "quack".[176]

Despite this, no contrarian doctor equated the flu and COVID to encourage pediatric flu vaccination, even though the flu normally kills several hundred children annually, most of them unvaccinated.[177] Dr. McBride was right when she said, "We have somehow as a society, quote-unquote, 'tolerated' the fact that hundreds of kids die from the flu every year."[163] That's an awful indictment of how we casually let unvaccinated children die from the flu each year.

There were real world consequences to convincing parents that COVID was "just the flu." After seeing her 13-year-old child Alexx intubated due to COVID, his mother said:

> *I just want people to get their kids their shots. Everybody just needs to get the shot. It's a much better route than the one we're in. It's very hard to see him in this situation. It's very hard not knowing if he's really going to come home anymore or not. It's heartbreaking. I wish I would've made better choices.*[178]

Alexx survived, thankfully, but spent 37 days on a ventilator and four months in the hospital, learning how to walk, talk, and breathe again.[179] "I just had a false sense of security that it was just like the flu and it wasn't that serious. Obviously it is that serious and it was that serious. Now, I can see," his mother said. It wasn't her fault she had a false sense of security.

#5~*"You gotta inoculate a million kids with vaccination to save one life."*

Anti-vaxxers often have trouble with simple math. In an article on the anti-vaccine site *GreenMedInfo* titled "Measles Transmitted By The Vaccinated, Gov. Researchers Confirm," Sayer Ji thought he had scored a clever point against the measles vaccine by writing:

> *18% of the measles cases occurred in those who had been vaccinated against it – hardly the vaccine's two-dose claimed "97% effectiveness.*[180]

Let's run the numbers. Suppose 10,000 people were exposed to the measles and 95% of them were vaccinated. Let us further suppose that all unvaccinated people will get the disease, while only 1% of vaccinated people will contract measles. This means that 500 unvaccinated people will get sick, compared to 90 vaccinated people. This means that 18% of the people who contracted measles were vaccinated. Given that the population of vaccinated people is much larger than the population of unvaccinated people, this is to be expected, even with a vaccine that works 99% of the time. People who forget this are guilty of the base rate fallacy.

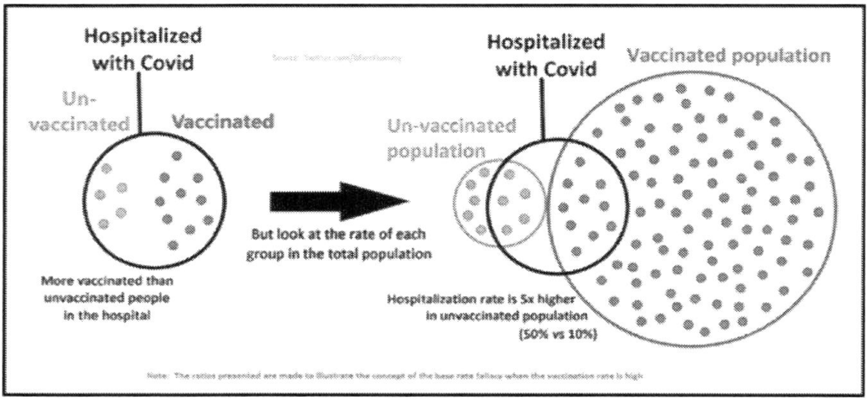

The Base Rate Fallacy

Anti-vaxxers' math skills didn't improve during the pandemic. On December 17, 2020, an article was published in *JAMA* titled "COVID-19 as the Leading Cause of Death in the United States." It reported that, as of October 2020, the COVID death rate for all children, whether they were infected or not, was 7.4 per million for children younger than 1 year, 1 per million for children ages 1-14 years, and 9.9 per million for those ages 15-24 years.[181] These numbers reflected a child's risk of dying of COVID only during the pandemic's first 10-months. Unless COVID vanished, this number would grow over time as more children were infected, which is exactly what happened.

Nonetheless, a new myth was born – COVID kills only 1 in a million children – and anti-vaxxers were eager to spread it. An article titled "FDA Used 'Critically Flawed' Risk-Benefit Analysis to 'Justify' COVID Vaccines for Children" on Robert F. Kennedy, Jr.'s anti-vaccine website said:

> *The FDA's risk-benefit analysis estimated that fully vaccinating 1 million children ages 5-11 would prevent one COVID-19 death.*[182]

Again, let's run the numbers. There are about 73 million children in the U.S. If only one in a million children died of COVID, then no more than 73 children could die in the entire country, assuming every child was infected with SARS-CoV-2. Even though it didn't collect data from all 50 states, the American Academy of Pediatrics (AAP) reported that 76 children had died of COVID by July 23, 2020.[116] Every death after this proved the pediatric infection fatality rate was higher than one in a million. As 1,593 American children have died of COVID,[5] a pediatric death rate of 1 in a million would require 1.59 billion infections, nearly 5 times the entire population of the US, including adults.

Although it only takes simple math and knowledge of basic pandemic facts to know that more than 1 in a million children will die of COVID, several contrarian doctors repeated these odds in podcasts and in the mainstream media. During a podcast with Dr. Zubin Damania from February 2021 called "Should We Vaccinate Kids for COVID?", Dr. Vinay Prasad said:

> *We're talking about of a million kids, you might take that risk of death from one, and let's say you drop it to zero, because there's a 95% reduction in COVID, and there appears to be almost a full protection against severe COVID. So let's say to save that one life, you gotta inoculate a million kids with vaccination to save one life.*[66]

As at least 227 children had died of COVID[116] when he said this. A death rate of 1 in a million would necessitate 227 million pediatric infections, more than triple the number of children in the U.S.

Dr. Monica Gandhi also reported this incorrect statistic in an interview on May 11, 2021, saying:

> *Children and young adults are very low risk for severe disease, about one in a million chance of death for a child under 19 from COVID.*[183]

At least 306 children had died of COVID[116] when she said this. A death rate of 1 in a million would necessitate 306 million pediatric infections, more than quadruple the number of children in the U.S.

Even as late as October 2022, Dr. John Ioannidis co-authored a paper that claimed that the infection fatality rate for children 19-years and younger was just 3 per million.[184] This was based on data from 38 countries before the arrival of the Delta and Omicron variants, and it included countries such as Afghanistan where the data is of dubious reliability. However, again, all it took was basic math and basic knowledge to know the pediatric death rate is higher than this. There are 82 million Americans aged 0-19 years. If the infection fatality rate were only 3 per million, then 246 children would die of COVID if all of them were infected. In fact, this many children had died of COVID by February 2021,[116] and around 2,200 people this age had already died[4] when Dr. Ioannidis published his article, 9-times higher than what he calculated, again assuming that every child had been infected.

Thus far, about 1 in 45,000 American children has died of COVID, though not all children have equal risk. Babies have the highest risk by far, while children ages 2-14 have the lowest risk. According to the COVKID Project, as of September 2022, 91.8 per million (1 in 11,000) infants under age 1 year have died of COVID, while 6.7 per million (1 in 139,000) 4-year-olds have died.[185] Teenagers have an intermediate risk, and 33.1 per million (1 in 30,000) 17-year-olds have died. These numbers would have been much higher had the virus been allowed to rip through the pediatric population before any child was vaccinated.

#6 ~ "This equates to a 0.0052% risk of dying from COVID19."

In 2019, the American Academy of Pediatrics (AAP) launched a campaign to prevent children from drowning. They said:

> *The AAP wants to raise awareness that drowning is the No. 1 cause of injury-related death among children ages 1-4, and a leading cause of death among teens. Drowning can happen to any family, and it's quick, and it's silent. Nearly 1,000 children*

> *and teens drown every year in the U.S.*[186]

It would have been odd if someone used the fact that 73 million children don't drown annually to oppose the AAP's attempt to stop 1,000 children from dying this way.

Yet, anti-vaxxers have long used this technique to minimize the tragedy of children who die from vaccine-preventable diseases. For example, an article from 2019 titled "Measles Scare Tactics Hurt Us All," published on the anti-vaccine website *GreenMedInfo,* asked readers to focus on the many children who didn't die of measles. It said:

> *By the time the measles vaccine was patented in 1963 in the US, the mortality rate from measles was about 1 in 500,000.*[141]

This technique was easily adapted to COVID. An article on Robert F. Kennedy, Jr.'s anti-vaccine website titled "Top Ten Reasons Not to Let Your Child Get a COVID Shot" said:

> *As of May 29, 2021, the and Prevention (CDC) attributed 366 deaths in children aged 0-18 to COVID out of a child population of 74 million—a mortality rate of 0.00049%.*[143]

Contrarian doctors used this same strategy to minimize COVID's impact on young people. A typical example can be found in an article titled "No, Young Adults Should Not Live in Fear from Coronavirus" by Drs. John Mandrola and Andrew Foy. They said a "fear of death" was not a valid reason for young adults to avoid the virus. Sure, "an excess of 12,000 deaths sounds bad" they wrote, but it's just a "tiny absolute increase in risk". They felt our focus should be on all the people who didn't die. They added:

> *Thus, the* ***individual*** *risk for a person this age is found by dividing 4,560 (the number dead from COVID19 in this study) by 88 million. This equates to a 0.0052% risk of dying from COVID19.*[187]

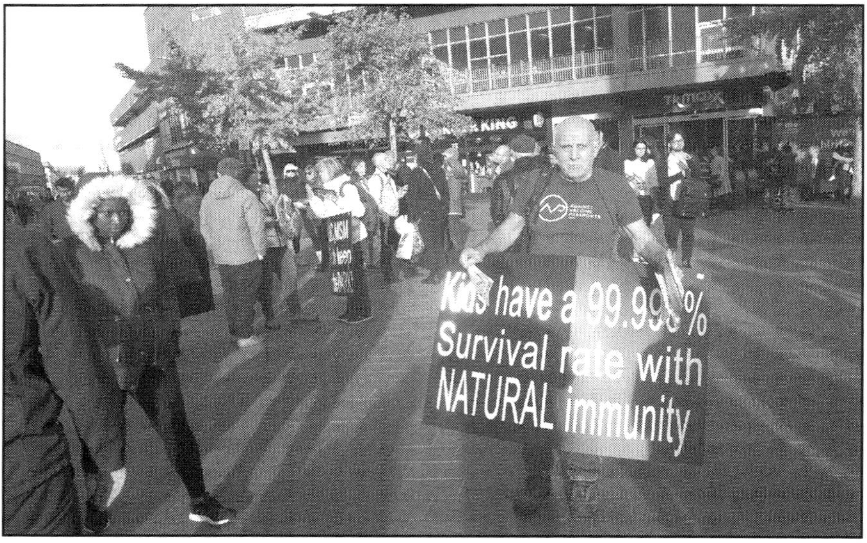

An anti-vaccine protester notes that most children don't die of COVID[470]
Wikimedia Commons, the free media repository

Anti-vaccine protesters made the exact same point.

In reality, 40,000 young adults died of COVID in the pandemic's first 2.5 years, nearly 6 times the number of soldiers who've died fighting in wars since 9/11, and during many months, COVID was the number 1 or 2 leading cause of death amongst young adults. Nearly all of them would be alive today had they been fully vaccinated and boosted.

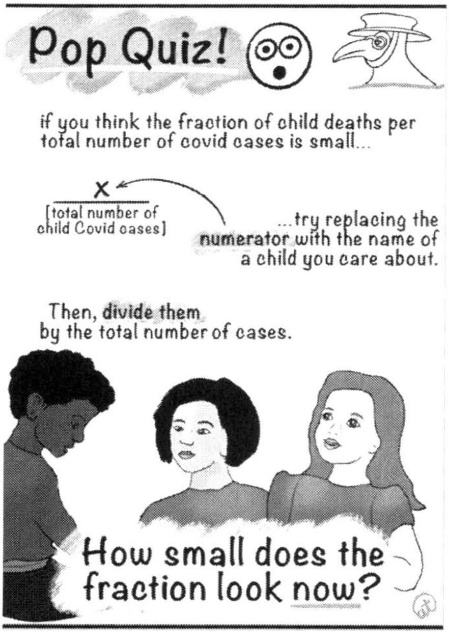

Courtesy of Peste Magazine

Dr. Vinay Prasad took this technique a step further and used the entire population of the U.S. to try to numb people to dead children. Arguing against pediatric vaccination, he said, "In April 2021, 19 kids died of COVID19 in a country of 330 million."[188]

Sometimes, the numerator matters more than the denominator. 19 children is a large number of children to die of a vaccine-preventable disease in a single month, and an average of 83 children would die of COVID in the ensuing 12-months.[5]

Of course, young people rarely die of anything, and framing their deaths using the entire population could be used to minimize deaths from cancer, car accidents, gun violence and suicide. However, a small percentage of a large number is still a significant number. As of December 2022, 43,500 adults aged 19-44 years have died of COVID.[4] As with anything else, it's tragic that this many young people died of COVID, even though tens of millions of them didn't die this way.

No one objected to the AAP's attempt to stop 1,000 children from drowning because only 0.0013% of children die this way annually. In fact, in 25 years of medicine, I've never seen doctors use this technique used to minimize *anything* that kills young people. It's only with COVID that doctors sought to diminish their deaths by using the entire population as the denominator.

#7 ~ "Natural Immunity wins again"

"Natural immunity" is a loaded phrase. As religion professor Alan Levinovitz wrote in his article "How the Phrase 'Natural Immunity' Misleads Us About Real Risks and Dangers":

> *Although scientific authorities widely use "natural immunity" as a neutral description of immunity acquired through infection, it has different significance outside of medical journals. That's because people often treat naturalness as synonymous with purity and goodness, even holiness. "God gave us a natural immunity," said an announcer recently on Victory TV, a popular Christian network. "I personally choose God-given natural immunity over the new experimental vaccine for the safety and protection of myself and my family," writes a chiropractor at Infinite Wellness Natural Healing Center. "How about you?"*
>
> *The language of naturalness short-circuits clear thinking about vaccines, substituting a theological binary – natural immunity vs. unnatural immunity*

> *– for empirical evidence. The standard vocabulary of medical science thus unwittingly undermines the very public health goals it is meant to serve by implicitly endorsing immunity that doesn't come from vaccines.*[189]

Of course, the immune response to vaccines is completely natural, and vaccines have the advantage of not being deadly.

Unsurprisingly, anti-vaxxers have long extolled the benefits of "natural immunity", arguing that the best way to avoid being harmed by a virus is to catch that virus. Dr. Kelly Brogan expressed this belief in her article, "Can Pharma Improve on Nature? HPV Vaccine vs Natural Infection," in which she wrote:

> *Natural HPV infectious exposures actually protect against the progression of HPV linked cervical changes to cancer.*[190]

This makes as much sense as shaving your head to prevent yourself from going bald. Anti-vaccine doctor Sherri Tenpenny also voiced this sentiment, writing:

> *We've got to stop calling chickenpox and measles diseases, because they're not. They're infections, and infections come and go in a week to ten days, and leave behind a lifetime of immunity. A disease is something that comes and stays, and frequently can't be cured. So when you vaccinate to avoid an infection, what you potentially are doing is causing a disease.*[191]

Using "natural immunity" as a reason not to vaccinate children remained popular in anti-vaccine circles during the pandemic. An article on Robert F. Kennedy, Jr.'s anti-vaccine website titled "FDA Used 'Critically Flawed' Risk-Benefit Analysis to 'Justify' COVID Vaccines for Children" said:

> *The FDA's risk-benefit assessment failed to account for the large proportion of children in the United States who already had COVID-19, recovered from it and now have natural immunity. For these millions of children, the risks of COVID-19 vaccination*

outweigh the benefits, as studies show natural immunity is superior to vaccine-induced immunity.[182]

During the pandemic, contrarian doctors also became cheerleaders for "natural immunity", and few of them sang its praises louder than Dr. Marty Makary. Dr. Makary published an article titled "Natural Immunity to COVID is Powerful. Policymakers Seem Afraid to Say So"[192] in *The Washington Post*, and others titled "The Power of Natural Immunity"[193] and "The High Cost of Disparaging Natural Immunity to COVID"[194] in *The Wall Street Journal*. "Natural Immunity wins again,"[195] he said on *Twitter*, one of many such tweets. In an article from March 24, 2021, titled "Herd Immunity Is Near, Despite Fauci's Denial," he wrote:

Undercounting or removing the many Americans with natural immunity from any tally of herd immunity is a scientific error of omission.[196]

Historians will not look back on our pandemic response and conclude, "They sure paid a high cost for disparaging natural immunity."

Elsewhere, Dr. Makary spoke of the advantages of "natural immunity" versus the vaccine saying that with "natural immunity, the body develops antibodies to the entire surface of the virus, not just a spike protein constructed from a vaccine."[197] He was so enamored with natural immunity, he wrote an article in February 2021 titled, "We'll Have Herd Immunity by April."[198]

We did not have herd immunity by April.

Despite this, Dr. Makary's admiration for the "natural immunity" was unshaken. When the Omicron variant arrived, with its ability to evade the immune system and cause reinfections, Dr. Makary sounded like a publicity agent for the virus. He called it "omi-cold"[199] and "nature's vaccine".[200] 300,000 Americans died of COVID in the ensuing year.[201] However, instead of wondering if he overvalued natural immunity, Dr. Makary continued to lambast those who lacked his admiration for it. In June 2022, he again complained:

Natural immunity has consistently and inexplicably been dismissed by the medical establishment.[202]

Dr. Makary feels that the "medical establishment" has been

inappropriately dismissive of natural immunity, though it is created only by SARS-CoV-2, the same virus that filled up hospitals and morgues.

When vaccines were approved for babies and toddlers in June 2022, Dr. Makary repeatedly tried to negate their value by arguing that most children already had "natural immunity." He said on Fox News:

> *The CDC reported that, as of February 2022, 75% of children 0-17 years-old already had COVID-19. Given how rampant the Omicron strain has circulated since then, upwards of 80-90% of children have likely had COVID-19. There is absolutely zero clinical evidence to support vaccinating healthy children who already had COVID. Natural immunity, inexplicably ignored by public health officials, confers strong protection against severe disease.*[203]

In another Fox News interview, he said:

> *They're about to authorize this COVID vaccine for 16 million children, 90-plus percent of whom have already had COVID, based on a small study of kids who did not have COVID. That was the condition to be in that study. So ignoring natural immunity is actually having significant implications now.*[204]

Dr. Makary was one of many doctors who was not at all concerned that an unvaccinated child might get COVID, but who vaguely felt there would be "significant implications" if a child with natural immunity got vaccinated.

In an article opposing pediatric vaccination, Dr. Vinay Prasad used the fact that most children had already contracted COVID as his top reason why they should not get vaccinated, writing:

> *Most kids already had COVID-19. CDC estimates 75% as of February, but this number is an underestimate, as millions have been infected since.*[205]

These doctors weren't wrong that this many children contracted COVID. While Dr. Prasad argued against pediatric vaccines in 2021 because pediatric "cases are FALLING PRECIPITOUSLY"[206] and Dr. Makary predicted herd immunity in April that year, what actually happened is that tens of millions of children got infected. The CDC estimated that 86% of children had contracted COVID at least once by August 2022.[207]

It's also true that viral-induced immunity confers protection against reinfection, though this depends on the variant and interval between infection. A study from England of nearly 700,000 children (before the arrival of the Omicron variant) found only 1 in 300 children suffered a reinfection.[208] While 2.4% of children with reinfections were hospitalized, the same as an initial infection, no children died.

Unfortunately, neither the vaccine nor the virus produces durable immunity against the Omicron variant in children, though they both blunt severe COVID. A study of children ages 5-11 when the Omicron variant was dominant found:

> *Both the BNT162b2 (Pfizer) vaccine and previous infection were found to confer considerable immunity against omicron infection and protection against hospitalization and death. The rapid decline in protection against omicron infection that was conferred by vaccination and previous infection provides support for booster vaccination.*[50]

Nearly all children who were hospitalized in this study were unvaccinated, as were the 7 children who died.

While "natural immunity" is not useless, there's no evidence that a child who had COVID in April 2020 will have lifelong immunity to all future variants, nor is there evidence that repeated exposures to the virus are safe for developing children, especially if they are unvaccinated. This virus has only been here for 3 years, and it has been a shapeshifter. We shouldn't dismiss natural immunity, but we should be humble and honest about its value and its cost. Many doctors were rightly worried about making "natural immunity" sound like a wonderful option. We didn't feel like praising the virus too much.

Meanwhile, there is evidence that vaccination after infection can limit reinfections, at least in the short term. A study from September 2022 titled "Effects of Vaccination and Previous Infection on Omicron Infections in Children" found that "among previously infected children, vaccine effectiveness reached 69.6%."[50] Yet another study of children ages 5-11 years found that:

> *Two doses of mRNA vaccine effectively prevented the occurrence of COVID-19 in participants with previous severe SARS-CoV-2 infection.*[209]

Beyond this, there are several very obvious reasons as to why a high rate of "natural immunity" is not a valid argument against pediatric vaccination. If 86% of children have contracted COVID, that means 14% have not. This translates to over 10 million children in the U.S. Doctors should embrace the opportunity to protect all children from rare but severe outcomes with a simple vaccine.

In addition to the millions of children who have not yet contracted COVID, nearly 10 million babies have been born since the start of the pandemic in the U.S. 10,000 newborns arrive every day. Newborns don't come with "natural immunity" and the pediatricians who care for them want to keep it that way.

History teaches us why this is important. Prior to the vaccine, measles cases would rise and fall at predictable intervals as it infected a new crop of children who then became immune.

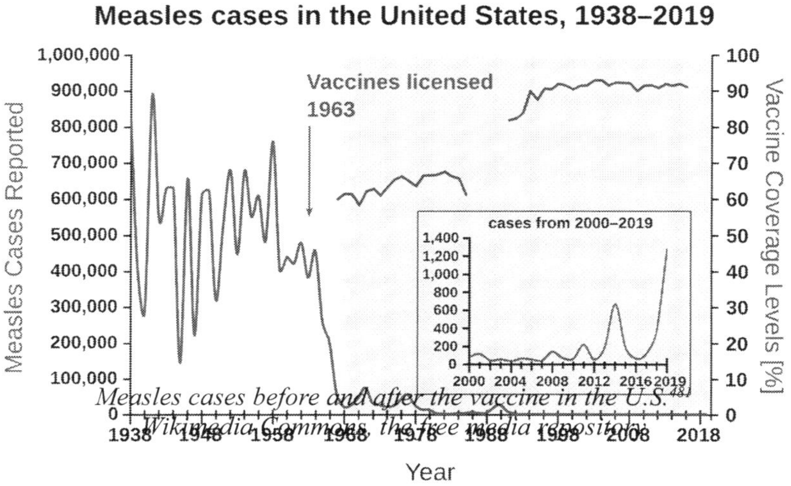

Measles cases before and after the vaccine in the U.S.[481]
Wikimedia Commons, the free media repository

If children are not vaccinated against COVID, this pattern will repeat indefinitely with tragic consequences. Babies have the highest risk of dying of all children by far, though neither Dr. Makary nor Dr. Prasad shared this simple fact in their many discussions of this subject. So far, COVID has killed 650 children aged 0-4 years[5] and hospitalized many thousands more, some needing mechanical ventilation in the ICU.

The notion that children should remain unvaccinated because they have "natural immunity" had consequences in the real world. In explaining their decision not to vaccinate healthy children, the Florida Department of Health quoted Dr. Tracy Høeg, who said:

> *The argument for vaccinating children for that for the societal benefit is not what it used to be. We need to look at children who have already been infected – and we know according to the CDC that that's at least 58% of children, it's probably more by now. Especially for healthy children, we don't know if they've benefitted from being vaccinated on top of already having infection.*[137]

Dr. Høeg had nothing to say about the 575 babies born in Florida every day who are on an inevitable collision course with SARS-CoV-2 without "natural immunity".

There are obviously still vulnerable children out there and there always will be, no matter how many times contrarian doctors repeat the mantra "natural immunity". As a result, the CDC keeps slowly increasing its grim pediatric death tally, and the number of hospitalized children also continues to rise.

#8 ~ "The risks are so low. You cannot see them."

Anti-vaxxers make bad graphs. They know that viruses can be made to look harmless and vaccines useless in an instant through misleading visuals.[210] A typical example comes courtesy of Dr. Raymond Obomsawin, who was described as "an early pioneer calling out the injuries and deaths that follow mass vaccination programs,"[211] on Robert F. Kennedy Jr.'s anti-vaccine website. In 2009, Dr. Obomsawin created a series of graphs that supposedly showed the incidence of measles was in a smooth, steady decline long before the measles vaccine arrived. His graphs made it appear as if measles was nearly gone when the vaccine showed up and took credit.

However, there were some problems. As Dr. David Gorski observed, "the decline in measles incidence is far too smooth. Measles incidence typically varies greatly from year to year."[210]

Dr. Gorski was right. Before the vaccine, measles cases would spike and fall as children who never encountered the virus were infected. In the years before the vaccine was made available in Canada, measles was not a reportable disease and Dr. Obomsawin filled in the gap by drawing a straight line down. Looking at the actual incidence of measles in Canada shows the vaccine made

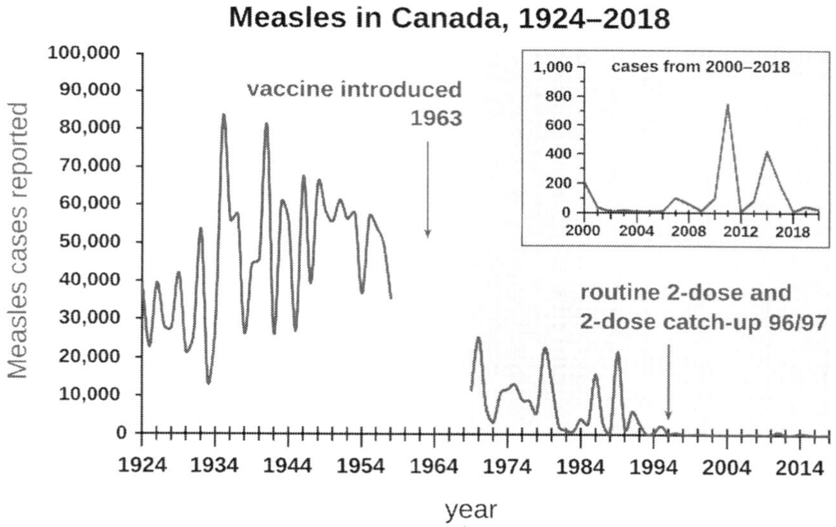

Measles cases rose and fell prior to the measles vaccine.471 - Wikimedia Commons, the free media repository

a huge difference. As Dr. Gorski said, "it doesn't get much more intellectually dishonest than that."

During the pandemic, contrarian doctors similarly rearranged data to make misleading graphs, minimizing the value of vaccines. In an article titled "Kids Vaccine is Low Risk Either Way," Dr. Vinay Prasad discussed a study from Singapore that was published in *The New England Journal of Medicine*. This study estimated vaccine effectiveness was 65.3% against PCR-confirmed SARS-CoV-2 infection, while vaccine effectiveness against hospitalization was 83% in children ages 5-11 years while the Omicron variant was circulating.[48] The study lasted just 10-weeks and examined 255,936 children, very few of whom were hospitalized. This allowed Dr. Prasad to create a graph, purporting to show that the vaccine's benefits were minimal to non-existent. He said, "The risks are so low. You cannot see them."[212]

Dr. Prasad then produced another graph and said, "Now let me blow it up. This is way below 1%. In fact, one quarter of 1%."[212] He shared this graph on *Twitter*, with a comment that pediatric COVID vaccination advocates were "off their rocker."[88]

Other doctors immediately noticed some obvious problems. It's not at all clear what Dr. Prasad's graphs are showing. Dr. Kyle Sheldrick observed that Dr. Prasad didn't provide any units for his graphs, rendering them uninterpretable. He said:

> *There are different ways to express data. Hospitalisation per infection, risk per child per year, RRR (relative risk reduction), all good. "Here's risk as a unitless number with no denominator" is not one of them.*[213]

Dr. Kristen Panthagani, an emergency medicine resident, said Dr. Prasad's work was "a case study in graphs that crush my soul."[214] Her *Twitter* comments are worth repeating in their entirety:

> *A case study in graphs that crush my soul, and why appropriate axes (and axis labels) are the lifeblood of data visualization.*
>
> *You can't even see the data (which seems to be the intended point.) This graph misleadingly suggests that the risk of hospitalization by COVID for kids is *so small* that getting vaccinated or not doesn't matter. It's basically 0!*
>
> *First, the y-axis is distorted by setting the max value too high. This is one of the oldest tricks in the book of how to mislead with graphs: if you would like your data to seem small, just set the axis to an*

*inappropriately large number, and it will look tiny! By plotting pediatric COVID hospitalizations on a graph that extends to 100% risk, it suggests that hospitalizations from COVID only *really* matter if the risk is high enough to show up on this graph. By plotting pediatric COVID hospitalizations on a graph that extends to 100% risk, it suggests that hospitalizations from COVID only *really* matter if the risk is high enough to show up on this graph.*

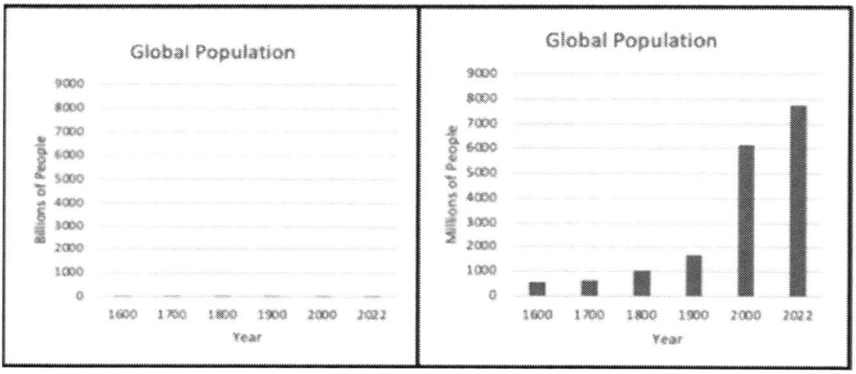

Dr. Prasad's graph with note by Dr. Panthagani regarding y-axis manipulation - Courtesy of Dr. Panthagani

Dr. Panthagani created these graphs of the world population in

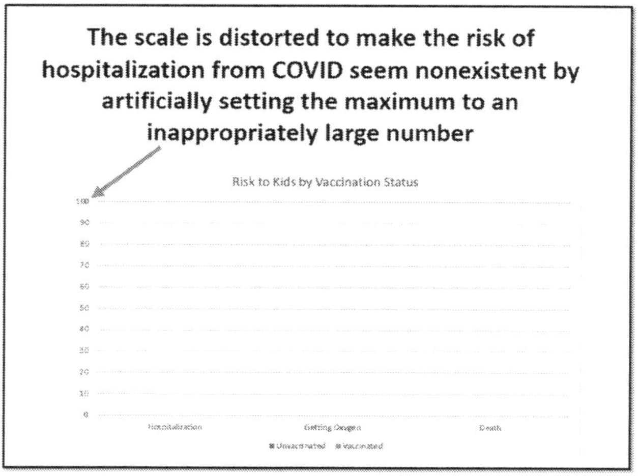

Dr. Panthagani's example graphs to demonstrate y-axis manipulation - Courtesy of Dr. Panthagani

billions and millions to show how an inappropriate y-axis can be used to obscure meaningful differences in numbers. Our eyes can be tricked in a heartbeat.

Dr. Panthagani was not done exposing the flaws in Dr. Prasad's graphs. She also noticed he had not labeled his graphs. She continued:

> *But risk of what? Hospitalization each day? Over the course of the whole study? For those who tested positive? For all kids in the study? The calculated risk (and thus where it shows up on the graph) will vary dramatically depending on the answers to these questions. And there is no axis label to tell us which*

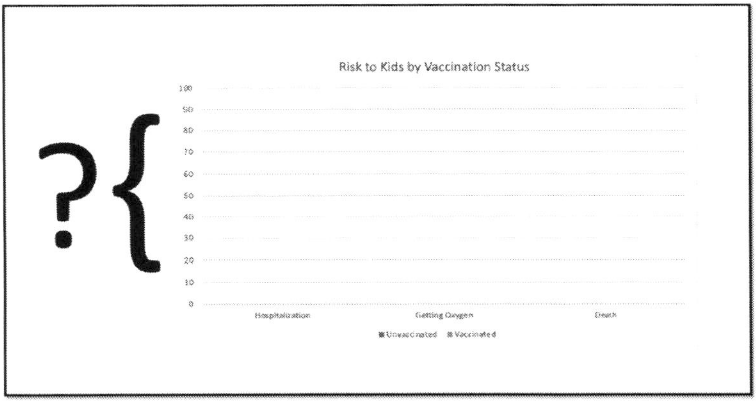

Dr. Prasad's graph with lack of y-axis label noted by Dr. Panthagani - Courtesy of Dr. Panthagani

> *risk the graph is referencing.*[214]
> *The calculated risk (and thus where it shows up on the graph) will vary dramatically depending on the answers to these questions. And there is no axis label to tell us which risk the graph is referencing. Which illustrates a key point: when you're assessing risk, you can't just say "oh that percentage is less than 1%, the risk is super low!" -- you have to know what population and time period you're talking about.*
>
> *The "zoomed up" version of the graph is also missing the axis label. To figure out what risk this graph is*

*referencing, I tried to match the data presented here with the results reported in the NEJM study, and the only analysis that seemed to fit this graph came from dividing total hospitalizations in each group by the total number of vaxxed and unvaxxed kids at the end of the study. This is not the correct way to analyze the data (and not the way the study did it) because it fails to account for the many kids who got vaccinated *during* the study.*

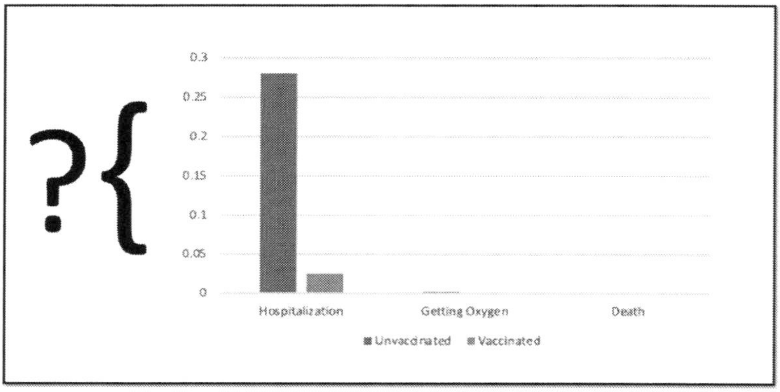

Dr. Prasad's graph with lack of y-axis label noted by Dr. Panthagani - Courtesy of Dr. Panthagani

If I'm correct, then this graph doesn't faithfully represent anything meaningful in the paper. But I don't know for sure, because, again, we have no axis label to tell us what data we're looking at.

Let's say for a second that this graph truly represented the risk of hospitalization from COVID over the course of the study period (about 2.5 months). Is a quarter of a percent risk so small that we should not worry about it? To answer this question, you need context. You can make the risk of practically anything "seem" small or big depending on how you slice and dice the data.

For example, the average risk of all cause death for everyone in the US over the same time period (2.5 mo) is about 0.2%. That's hundreds of thousands of

> *deaths, but the percentage "seems" small because we're looking across the entire population.*
>
> *To assess if a quarter of a percent of kids getting hospitalized with COVID over 2.5 months is a "big deal", you have to compare to other risks to kids over the same time period. You can't just look at a single number and say "that's super small!" and decide it's insignificant.*
>
> *This plays into a theme that has circulated widely in COVID times: the idea that if a risk isn't attached to a "big number", then it doesn't really matter. For example, a common refrain circulating in 2020 was "The risk of death from COVID is small, 98% survive!"*
>
> *I understand why people gravitate towards these interpretations. Assessing risk is complex, and deciding if the percentage seems "big" or "small" makes the job easier. But this often inaccurate, because a small percentage of a very very big number can still be a very big number.*
>
> *In conclusion, inappropriate axis scales are misleading, unlabeled data is largely useless, risk depends on the population and time period, and determining if risk is significant requires putting it into context, not just deciding if the percentage seems like a small number.*[214]

Again, Dr. Prasad was trying to convince people that the COVID vaccine won't help *that many* children. Dr. Sheldrick disagreed with him, saying:

> *The denominator in that table is person DAYS at risk, not people. His graph is the ABSOLUTE risk PER DAY. This translates to about 16,000 fewer kids aged 5-11 in hospital per year in Australia with*

vaccination. That's a massive reduction.[215]

In other words, when Dr. Prasad said "The risks are so low. You cannot see them,"[212] it's because sometimes those risks are purposefully hidden.

#9 ~ "A tremendous number of government and private policies affecting kids are based on one number: 335"

In an article posted to her blog, "First They Came for the Anti-Vaxxers," Dr. Kelly Brogan sarcastically stated, "Whatever you do though, make sure you don't accidentally show them this graph."[109] Dr. Brogan then shared a graph showing that even before the measles vaccine was approved in 1963, many fewer people were dying of measles than ever before. While measles used to kill around 10,000 Americans at the start of the 20th century, by the 1940s, this number had dropped to less than 1,000 deaths.

Anti-vaxxers claim this decline in pediatric fatalities proves the measles vaccine was of no use. An article on the anti-vaccine website *GreenMedInfo* titled "Measles: The New Red Scare" said:

> *The death rate for all infectious diseases had plummeted* ***before*** *the introduction of vaccines for all those diseases. For example, in the United States the mortality rate for measles decreased by more than 98% before the introduction of the measles vaccine in 1963*[216]

Surprisingly, this is not entirely wrong. The overall health of children was better in 1963 than it was in 1915, as was medical care. As such, many fewer children died from measles. However, Dr. Brogan thinks this proves the measles vaccine was of no benefit. Her attitude is essentially – *that which does not kill you does not matter* – and she is wrong. According to the CDC:

> *In the decade before 1963 when a vaccine became available, nearly all children got measles by the time they were 15 years of age. It is estimated 3 to 4 million people in the United States were infected each year.*

> *Also each year, among reported cases, an estimated 400 to 500 people died, 48,000 were hospitalized, and 1,000 suffered encephalitis (swelling of the brain) from measles.*[217]

The vaccine made all that go away.

Dr. Brogan's graph really shows that many more children would have been saved had the vaccine come out in 1900. However, that wasn't a good reason not to use it in 1963. It's still amazing that the measles vaccine saves 500 children per year. Moreover, while death is the worst outcome from measles, it is not the only bad one. 48,000 hospitalizations is a lot of really sick children. Measles used to be a common cause of deafness and encephalitis. It's good that the vaccine wiped all that away, but Dr. Brogan wants her readers to think that's no big deal.

In his essay, "The Flimsy Evidence Behind the CDC's Push to Vaccinate Children," Dr. Marty Makary made the same argument as Dr. Brogan. He wrote:

> *A tremendous number of government and private policies affecting kids are based on one number: 335. That is how many children under 18 have died with a COVID diagnosis code in their record, according to the and Prevention. Yet the CDC, which has 21,000 employees, hasn't researched each death to find out whether COVID caused it or if it involved a pre-existing medical condition.*[114]

This is false, and it makes no sense. The CDC had already published data that 25% of COVID deaths in people under age 21 years occurred in those without pre-existing medical conditions.[126] Additionally, while it is important for the CDC to report accurate numbers, even if COVID's exact pediatric death toll at that time was "only" 200 children, this is not an argument against the vaccine. We vaccinate children for diseases that are less dangerous than this. That the vaccine won't save the lives of *that many* children is not a valid reason to oppose it.

Moreover, as with measles, death is not the only bad outcome from COVID and Dr. Makary was wrong that recommendations to vaccinate children were based solely on the number of pediatric fatalities. In fact, the week before Dr. Makary wrote his article, the Advisory Committee on Immunization Practices was very explicit that preventing hospitalizations was a driving force behind vaccinating adolescents. As they put it:

> *The benefits (prevention of COVID-19 disease and associated hospitalizations, ICU admissions, and deaths) outweighed the risks (expected myocarditis cases after vaccination) in all populations for which vaccination has been recommended.*[218]

These hospitalizations can be severe for some children. One hospital in South Carolina had 8 intubated children and three requiring extracorporeal membrane oxygenation (ECMO) during the Delta wave in the summer of 2021.[219] These children suffered even if they didn't die.

In an article about "COVID centrist" doctors, Lydia Greene, a formerly anti-vaccine mother, explained how they echo pre-pandemic, anti-vaccine talking points by pretending that children can't be harmed by viruses that don't kill them. She said:

> *Often an antivaxxer will just look at mortality rates and completely gloss over morbidity associated with vaccine preventable disease. These "centrist" doctors do the very same thing. My 3 year old caught COVID before being vaccinated. He developed viral conjunctivitis, GI pain, ear infection, and pneumonia. He did not die. Although without medical intervention his mortality risk would have definitely been substantially higher.*
>
> *His vaccinated family had a much milder disease course by comparison. According to these centrists, I should not have vaccinated his siblings for COVID at all. After what we went through with my youngest who is a healthy and energetic young boy, I beg to differ. Vaccines prevent suffering regardless of age. I am so glad the rest of us were vaccinated for COVID,*

> *and when it did become available for my youngest, I jumped at the opportunity.*[220]

The measles and COVID vaccines saved a lot of children a lot of suffering, even if they didn't save their lives. Prior to the pandemic, only quack doctors claimed that protecting children from suffering didn't matter, so long as not that many children died.

#10 ~ "An asymptomatic child who tests positive after being injured in a bicycle accident would be counted as a 'COVID hospitalization.'"

Dr. Marty Makary has a history of understating pediatric COVID hospitalizations when communicating with the public. In an article for the *Wall Street Journal* titled "Should You Vaccinate Your 5-Year-Old?" he reported that only 562 children ages 5-11 had been hospitalized with COVID.[221] This number came from COVID-NET, a CDC surveillance system that covers approximately 10% of the U.S. population.[222] In fact, the CDC reported that over 8,300 children ages 5-11 had been hospitalized with COVID,[158] and this was just before the Omicron wave caused pediatric hospitalizations to spike to their highest levels.

Dr. Makary would have other opportunities to minimize pediatric hospitalizations. In the summer of 2021, a CDC report[223] and two studies from California, reported that nearly half of children in the hospital who tested positive for SARS-CoV-2 were deemed to be there for reasons unrelated to the virus. This high rate of incidental COVID hospitalizations added another weapon to those who sought to minimize pediatric COVID, and they wasted little time using it. An article on Robert F. Kennedy, Jr.'s website titled "5 Facts to Consider Before Vaccinating Kids for COVID" said:

> *It is well established that many hospitalized patients are found to have COVID-19 infections that are incidental to the main reason for admission.*[224]

Contrarian doctors said the same thing. On July 19, 2021, Dr. Makary published another article in the *Wall Street Journal* titled “The Flimsy Evidence Behind the CDC’s Push to Vaccinate Children.” In this article, Dr. Makary referenced the CDC study and wrote:

> *Hospitals routinely test patients being admitted for other complaints even if there’s no reason to suspect they have COVID. An asymptomatic child who tests positive after being injured in a bicycle accident would be counted as a “COVID hospitalization.”*[114]

Dr. Makary was not entirely wrong. Incidental SARS-CoV-2 infections are not rare in hospitalized children, and ignoring this would exaggerate the virus’s impact on children. That is why the CDC study he referenced excluded hospitalized children with incidental SARS-CoV-2 tests in their analysis.

However, it is not always as easy as it sounds to determine if a COVID hospitalization is incidental or not. Yes, SARS-CoV-2 is not to blame for a bike accident, but it has been found to be responsible for seizures,[225] diabetic ketoacidosis,[226] and even appendicitis[227] in children, all of which were deemed “incidental’ in some of these studies. This may be why subsequent studies found a much lower rate of incidental infections. One study during the Delta wave found that 19% of pediatric hospitalizations were incidental.[41] Another study during the Omicron wave found that 27% of pediatric hospitalizations were incidental. The authors wrote:

> *These findings suggest that incidental admissions do not account for the increase in hospitalization rates observed during the Omicron period and reinforce that children continued to experience serious COVID-19 illness.*[54]

In fact, during New York City’s Omicron wave, just 12 of 571 hospitalized children who tested positive for SARS-CoV-2 were there because of trauma,[127] though Dr. Makary made it seem as if this was a common occurrence.

Even in trauma patients, incidental SARS-CoV-2 infections may not be benign. One study found that:

> *Trauma patients who show no symptoms for COVID,*

> *yet test positive for the virus, have significantly higher rates of cardiac events, stay in the hospital longer, and incur higher hospital charges than do similar trauma patients who test negative for COVID.*[228]

Moreover, there is no guarantee that the CDC's tally captures every pediatric hospitalization. According to the CDC's COVID-Associated Hospitalization Surveillance Network:

> *The rates provided are likely to be underestimated as COVID-19-associated hospitalizations can be missed due to test availability and provider or facility testing practices.*[229]

However, beyond the mere number of pediatric hospitalizations, the results from the CDC report and two studies from California could also have been framed in a much more sobering way. All three studies showed that COVID can make some children *very sick*. About 25% of children hospitalized for COVID were admitted to an ICU, and 5% required intubation. Two children died. Dr. Makary could have written a perfectly accurate article titled "Severe COVID is Common in Hospitalized Children." Not only did he choose not to write that article, but he also neglected to even report these basic facts.

Obviously, there is no conflict between these two ways of framing the data. Some hospitalized children who test positive for SARS-CoV-2 are there for reasons unrelated to the virus, however most of them are there because of the virus, and a significant percentage of them are extremely sick. A very small percentage will die. Balanced discussions acknowledge all of these facts.

60% of a large number is still a large number. According to the CDC, over 174,000 children have been hospitalized with COVID.[65] Assuming there is no undercounting and 40% of these were incidental hospitalizations, this means that 105,000 children have been hospitalized due to COVID, and about 25,000 have needed care in the ICU. That's a lot of sick children. Given that the vaccine can dramatically lower the risk of these grave outcomes, the case to vaccinate children isn't flimsy at all.

#11 ~ "A child hospitalized for RSV may be labeled 'COVID' if they test positive for COVID."

The notion that pediatricians misdiagnose children with vaccine-preventable diseases is a standard anti-vaccine talking point. As Dr. Kelly Brogan wrote in her essay "Vaccination: Your Body. Your Baby. Their Flu":

> *Incidence of flu at the population level is grossly inflated as a fear-mongering tactic. When patients present with flu-like symptoms, they are rarely diagnostically confirmed as being Influenza type A or type B, and the vast majority of the time, may be neither.*[97]

She would go on to quote two other anti-vaccine doctors who wrote:

> *In general, most symptoms of the "flu" are not caused by influenza virus but by a variety of noninfluenza viruses, bacteria, other infectious organisms, or even noninfectious conditions. According to the CDC, only about 20% of the cases of ILI are actually caused by the influenza virus. If this is true, then theoretically only 20% of all cases of ILI are preventable by influenza vaccination, and only when there is a perfect antigenic match between the vaccine strain and the circulating virus. Furthermore, even a perfect antigenic match does not guarantee an adequate antibody titer, nor does measurable antibody assure protection.*

Similarly, an article titled "Measles and Measles Vaccines: 14 Things to Consider" on the anti-vaccine site *GreenMedInfo* declared:

> *So what about measles? A 2002 study examined 195 children with rash and high fever. Comprehensive laboratory investigation showed that none had measles or rubella. Children were determined to*

have parvovius B19, group A streptococcus (GAS), human herpes virus type 6, enterovirus, adenovirus, and group C streptococcus.

This study was similar to an earlier study that found a number of measles cases were not in fact measles. Measles incidence always relied on a doctor's clinical diagnosis with no laboratory confirmation. Now that laboratory tests are available, most "measles" cases are now found not to be measles. When you think have the "flu" you really have ILI (influenza-like illness) and when you think you have measles you really have MLI (measles-like illness.)[230]

These anti-vaccine articles sought to convince parents that vaccine-preventable diseases aren't that dangerous, and the only reason some people think they are is due to incompetent pediatricians getting their viruses confused.

Several contrarian doctors repurposed this myth during COVID. In April 2021, Dr. Tracy Høeg surveyed data from Israel and reached an optimistic conclusion that she shared on *Twitter* with her tens of thousands of followers: "There appears to be no need to vaccinate children to reach herd immunity (as anticipated),"[231] she said. While she said she was not "certain herd immunity has already been achieved in Israel,"[232] she observed that "kids cases falling w/o vaccinating them."

Reality, in the form of the Delta variant, would soon prove the worst was yet to come for children. As pediatric COVID hospitalizations rates spiked to their highest levels of the pandemic in August 2021, Dr. Høeg didn't reconsider whether her initial optimism was wrong. Instead, she wondered if a different virus, namely respiratory syncytial virus (RSV), might be responsible instead. Like SARS-CoV-2, RSV is a ubiquitous and usually mild infection, though it can be serious, even fatal, for a small number of young children. Seeking to convince her *Twitter* audience that pediatricians couldn't properly diagnose their patients, Dr. Høeg wrote:

Looking at the @CDCgov 's COVID-NET, you see

> *that it has been the 0-4 year olds driving up COVID hospitalization rates recently. 5-17 year olds have decreased/remained stable. I wonder if the recent RSV surge is resulting in some infant RSV cases being labeled COVID.*[233]

"RSV typically affects this 0-4 age group and, a child hospitalized for RSV may be labeled 'COVID' if they test positive for COVID," she said. Dr. John Mandrola amplified her message, tweeting out to his tens of thousands of followers that this was a "super-interesting observation."[234]

It was, however, not a "super-interesting observation." The graph of pediatric COVID hospitalizations available at COVID-NET showed that younger children have been hospitalized at a higher rate than older children for nearly all of the pandemic. That anyone could look at a graph and conclude that pediatricians were getting COVID and RSV confused, only shows the power of confirmation bias, especially considering that when Dr. Høeg shared her speculation, COVID hospitalization rates were decreasing in children ages 0-4 and increasing in older children, the opposite of what she claimed.

While it may not be possible to distinguish RSV from COVID on clinical grounds alone, simple tests can easily distinguish between the two viruses. As pediatrician Dr. Daniel Summers said:

> *Medical tidbit: there are tests that can be run and resulted in the span of minutes to differentiate RSV from COVID (ran several yesterday), so anyone who speculates the increase in pediatric COVID cases are misdiagnosed RSV is someone whose opinion you can disregard.*[235]

However, this obvious fact was of little relevance to those who minimize pediatric COVID. Justin Hart, the leader of the anti-vaccine organization *Rational Ground*, would latch on to Dr. Høeg's unsubstantiated speculation about pediatric COVID hospitalizations claiming that "That's likely RSV - not COVID."[236] Notably, when pediatric RSV hospitalizations spiked in fall of 2022, neither Dr. Høeg nor Dr. Mandrola wondered if children were being misdiagnosed with RSV, when they in fact had COVID.

The myth that pediatricians were misdiagnosing children with

COVID was just a drop in the ocean of COVID misinformation, but it showed contrarian doctors' ignorance of pediatric infectious diseases as well as their willingness to spread baseless rumors, minimizing pediatric COVID, and giving ammunition to anti-vaccine activists.

#12 ~ "Clinicians have a duty to rise above fear and shame-based messaging."

Anti-vaxxers and vaccine-advocates don't agree on much, but they agree on this: when it comes to vaccinating their children, parents are often more influenced by a devastating anecdote than by a scientific paper. As such, anti-vaxxers regularly share tragedies they attribute to vaccines, regardless of whether or not they are supported by science. Though it must be done with care, tact, and honesty, vaccine-advocates also share stories of children who suffered from vaccine-preventable diseases.

There's a long tradition of vaccine-advocates doing this, and research showed that "that highlighting factual information about the dangers of communicable diseases can positively impact people's attitudes to vaccination."[237] In fact, showing children who've suffered from vaccine-preventable diseases is one of the most effective techniques to counter anti-vaccine myths. The March of Dimes used such images to encourage polio vaccination, and one of the most famous and powerful images in medicine was taken by Dr. Allan Warner of the Isolation Hospital at Leicester in the UK in 1901. It showed two boys, only one of whom had been vaccinated against smallpox. I don't know how many people saw that picture at the time, but I can imagine it being very impactful.

March of Dimes image promoting polio vaccination472 - Wikimedia Commons, the free media repository

Notably, many parents of children who suffered from a vaccine-

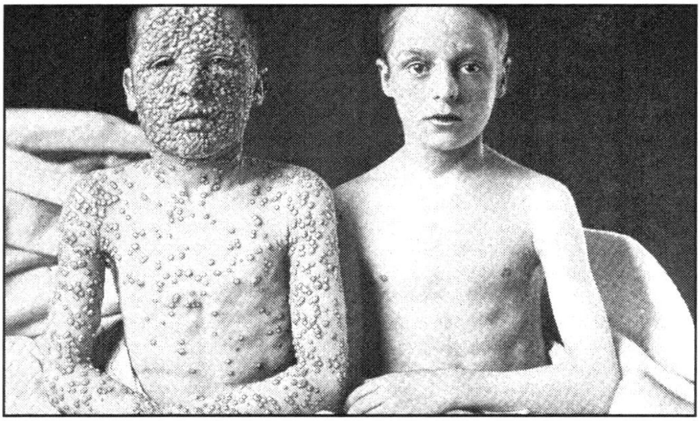

Photograph taken by Dr. Allan Warner. Archives of the Dr. Jenner's House Museum and Gardens473

preventable disease want their child's story to be told. They hope other families will be spared the unimaginable grief of losing a child. Landon Woodson's mother implored parents to "Please Please Get Vaccinated," after her 16-year-old son, a healthy football player, died of COVID.[238] Similarly, Hector Ramirez, whose unvaccinated 15-year-old-daughter Victoria died in 2021, said:

> *I don't want any other parent to go through what I did — seeing my daughter perfectly healthy one day, then following a week and a half, she's gone.*[239]

According to news reports, "He didn't get the shot for his daughter, and he regrets it."

After pleading with her to get vaccinated, the grandmother of Kennedy Stonum, a healthy 17-year-old, said "It was absolutely the worst that could happen.... I just want to say – hey, kids, don't do this to your grandparents."[240] Her husband, Kenney's grandfather, said, "We just want it so nobody has to feel this way. Nobody else." Kennedy was their only grandchild.

Teresa Sperry was a 10-year-old girl from Virginia who died of COVID in 2021 before she was eligible to be vaccinated. According to her mother, Nicole Sperry, "She loved dancing, singing, drawing, playing in the rain."[241] She was likely exposed at school as, unbelievably, her classroom job was to escort ill classmates to the nurse's office. Her parents reacted heroically to this tragedy by starting the *Our Missing Stars* foundation, whose mission is:

"Preventing unnecessary deaths by encouraging others to get vaccinated."[242] "COVID took her within five days. The only way this makes sense is if my daughter saves people. I don't want other people feeling this,"[241] her father, Jeff Sperry, said. "We definitely started with our intention of being able to honor Teresa, and not just her, but recognizing hopefully other children that have died from COVID and MIS-C," said her mother, Nicole Sperry.

It's no surprise that anti-vaxxers want to pretend these children never existed. They'll never share information of a child who dies from a vaccine-preventable disease, and several contrarian doctors suggested all medical professionals should similarly turn a blind eye to the existence of these children. Consider the reaction of Dr. Lucy McBride to the following Tweet:

Tweet by Julia Raifman to Dr. McBride regarding infant COVID death - Permission for use given by Julia Raifman

Dr. McBride responded that this was "fear-based messaging," which was a sign of communication "gone awry" and that "clinicians have a duty to rise above fear and shame-based messaging."[243] Dr. Shamez Ladhani, a pediatrician in the UK, similarly said:

> *Maybe it's just me, but as a parent and paediatrician, I think putting up the names & pictures of children who may or may not have died of #COVID19 on social media is crass & undignified. I did not include the link to those tweets out of respect for the children & their families.*[244]

I am unaware of any vaccine-advocate sharing a story of a child who "may or may not have died of #COVID19." Most vaccine-advocates are very careful to share only credible news sites about these tragedies. Indeed, the story Dr. Raifman shared was about an infant who died of COVID. It said:

> *Amelia Peyton of Iberia died from COVID-19 at University Hospital on Tuesday, Feb. 1 at 9 months*

> *old. Her twin sister, Claire, also tested positive for COVID but fortunately recovered.*[245]

"We really thought she was gonna make it," her mother said.

Dr. Alastair McAlpine, a pediatric infectious disease specialist, explained why some doctors might be averse to learning about children who died of COVID. He said, "When you've been minimizing the risk of COVID-19 for kids, seeing kids who've died is harmful to your narrative."[246] He would also add, "But pretending they don't exist isn't the way to go. They deserve to be honoured and remembered. Because we failed them."

Ms. Sperry saw Dr. Ladhani's *Twitter* post and sought to counter the narrative that sharing the existence of her child and the manner of her death was "crass & undignified." She responded by saying:

> *As a parent of 1 of the children that have died from COVID, Im proud her name Teresa is shared. Ive heard from many people that they NOW take COVID seriously hearing her story. Same w/children w/ cancer or diabetes. We share their names because their name is part of their story.*[247]

She continued:

> *Without us telling their story they would just be referred to as a child between the ages of died from COVID. Our children are more than a statistic. They will not get to grow up and have the experiences we've had because a disease that could have been lessened with people taking mitigation efforts seriously like vaccines.*
>
> *Want to do better as a parent and pediatrician? Treat any tweet that you make about COVID as if you lost your child. Would you want to see others minimize their death? No. Like I've always said it costs nothing to show compassion & empathy to others.*[248]

She's right, but sadly not alone. Kali Cook, who liked to play with worms, will never go to kindergarten. She was one of 650 American children who died before they turned 5 years old. Ryland Daic, who loved to fish, will never graduate high school. Gigi Morse will never go to a prom. Kimora Lynum, who liked shopping for clothes, will never celebrate her college graduation. Week Day will never have her first kiss. Wyatt Gibson will never get married. Dykota Morgan, a basketball player, will never hold her own child. Ethan Govan will never get the satisfaction of earning his first paycheck. Skylar Herbert, who wanted to be a pediatric dentist, will never work at all. Maybe Fabiana Zoppelli was destined to be a scientist. It's possible that Landon Woodson or Azorean Tatum would have played college football. All of these children were killed by COVID.

Teresa Sperry loved to sing. Maybe she would have been a star. Jeff and Nicole Sperry don't want any more children to suffer or die for lack of a vaccine. Had Teresa died of any virus other than SARS-CoV-2, supporting their advocacy wouldn't be controversial amongst doctors.

Reasons not to vaccinate children: The vaccine is unsafe and untested.

#13 ~ "I don't think people realize the damage continuing to push two doses in young men will do."

"Vaccines can literally change brain structures"

If half of the anti-vaccine movement is dedicated to minimizing vaccine-preventable diseases, the other half is dedicated to fear mongering about vaccine-side effects, both real and imagined, with histrionic language designed to spook parents. A typical example of fear mongering comes from Dr. Kelly Brogan's pamphlet "Vaccines and Brain Health", which said:

> *Vaccines can literally change brain structures... Analyzing data from thousands of children, researchers found that children who had been diagnosed with OCD, anorexia, anxiety, tics, or ADHD were more likely to have received a prior vaccination than their matched controls... Vaccinated children were significantly more likely to have been diagnosed*

> *with a variety of chronic diseases. Perhaps most alarmingly, children who had received vaccines had higher incidences of neurodevelopmental disorders, including learning disabilities, ADHD, and Autism Spectrum Disorder...vaccines are designed to cause inflammation.., the vaccine created antibodies that attacked brain molecule.. receiving the influenza vaccine actually hampers your immunity.*[249]

"Antibodies that attacked brain molecule" sounds more like a horror movie than something a doctor would say.

What is Vaccine-Myocarditis?

Unlike the myth that vaccines cause autism, however, COVID vaccines can cause myocarditis and pericarditis. No vaccine-advocate will deny this. However, anti-vaccine and contrarian doctors used this side effect to spook parents into believing that the vaccine was more dangerous than the virus for children. To understand why their messaging is fear mongering, first you have to understand what vaccine-myocarditis is, how often it happens, and how its clinical course differs from that of COVID itself.

Myocarditis is inflammation of the heart muscle, and pericarditis is inflammation of the pericardium, the outer lining of the heart. Both may occur at the same time in one patient. It can be caused by a wide variety of infectious agents, toxins, or autoimmune disorders. It presents with chest pain and shortness of breath, and patients typically have electrocardiographic abnormalities and elevated serum troponin levels, a marker of cardiac injury. It is more common in young males and can be quite serious, even fatal, depending on the underlying cause.

Israel was the first country to report on 148 cases of vaccine-myocarditis in June 2021, noting that it occurred most frequently in males aged 16-19 after their second vaccine dose.[250] Since then multiple reports from around the world have confirmed this pattern. Most studies found it to be more common with the Moderna vaccine than the Pfizer vaccine, which is what essentially all adolescents in the U.S. received.

There is great variability on the frequency of vaccine-myocarditis from one study to another. One study from Hong Kong reported a rate of 1 in 2,700 adolescent males after their second vaccine dose, though cases in this study were not investigated beyond the discharge diagnosis code.[251] A study from Denmark found no increased risk for males at all.[252] One review reported a rate of 1 in 7,200 to 1 in 20,000 male adolescents, though with "low certainty".[253] Even this might be a significant overestimate. A study in *The New England Journal of Medicine* of 61 patients with clinically suspected vaccine-myocarditis reported that 21 patients did not have myocarditis on biopsy.[254]

Vaccine-myocarditis is much less common in females, but it does occur. It is vanishingly rare in younger children, if it occurs at all.[255] Increasing the interval between the two vaccine doses may lower the risk. The booster vaccination also carries a risk of myocarditis, but in most studies the risk is the same or slightly lower than the second dose.[256]

While the exact rate is not known, a reasonable estimate is that vaccine-myocarditis occurs in 1 in 10,000 adolescent males after their second Pfizer vaccine. As around 15 million adolescents ages 12-17 have received two vaccine doses,[257] this translates to roughly 800 cases of vaccine-myocarditis in this age group. Since few adolescents are being vaccinated today, it's plausible that none are currently hospitalized with vaccine-myocarditis.

Fortunately, there is complete agreement about the short-term prognosis of the condition. The initial report from Israel said, "most cases have been in the hospital for up to 4 days, and 95% are considered to be mild cases."[250] Over 20 studies from around the world have confirmed this pattern. The largest systematic review f adolescents and young adults summarized 23 studies involving 854 patients. It found "low incidence rate and largely favorable early outcomes of COVID-19 mRNA vaccine–associated myopericarditis in adolescents and young adults."[258] Even in those with abnormal cardiac imaging, a systematic review of 468 cases found that "all reported cases with abnormal cardiac MRI findings showed a favorable clinical course at the acute phase."[259] Another review of 276 cases reported that "Fortunately, most myocarditis cases associated with mRNA vaccines are mild in nature and do not have serious complications and require only a few days of hospital admission."[260] Another systematic review of 28 studies stated "the prognosis of this self-limiting condition is generally good."[261]

See Table 3: Studies regarding the clinical course of vaccine-myocarditis on page 431.

Nearly all adolescents are admitted to the hospital for 2-4 days, mostly for observation, and most require only simple anti-inflammatory medications. As doctors have learned about the condition, fewer patients are being hospitalized. In the most recent report from Canada, only 44% of patients were hospitalized, mostly for one day. However, some patients are more severely affected, and one review found 23% of patients received care in the ICU, though no patients died or needed mechanical support.[258]

Most patients are advised to refrain from vigorous activity for several months, and while the majority make a quick and full recovery, not all do. In a report on 393 patients after 90 days, 81% were considered recovered by their health-care provider, though 26% were prescribed daily medication related to myocarditis.[284] Only 1% had the same cardiac status as at the initial presentation, and 68% were cleared for all physical activity. Of 249 individuals who completed a quality-of-life survey, 2% reported problems with self-care, 5% with mobility, and 20% with performing usual activities. In addition, 30% reported pain and 46% had depression. These metrics were "comparable to those in pre-pandemic and early pandemic populations of a similar age." 5.5% of patients reported missing work or school because of these symptoms.

Fortunately, the CDC and other national health agencies reported that no children are known to have died from the vaccine, though there are plausible reports of deaths in adults around the world.

In summary, the vaccine took about 800 adolescents, mostly boys, and sent them to the hospital with chest pain and markers of cardiac inflammation. None died, thankfully, but they all felt unwell, and some were more significantly affected. Though most recovered, about 150-200 adolescents still have persistent symptoms. Hopefully, they will recover over time, but they will all have to be monitored for potential cardiac scarring and arrhythmias. It's serious anytime a teenager or young adult is hospitalized, and this side-effect shouldn't be trivialized.

However, it shouldn't be magnified either. By my rough but reasonable estimate, the number of children killed by COVID (1,587) is 10 times larger than the number of adolescents with persistent symptoms after vaccine-myocarditis (160). The number of adolescents (841) killed by COVID is five-times larger than this. During the peak of the Omicron wave in January 2022, over 900 children were hospitalized with COVID daily, and 181 children died of COVID that month alone.[5] Of course, death is not the only bad outcome from COVID.

Moreover, a study of 6 million vaccinated men younger than 40-years found that "the risk of infection-associated myocarditis was higher compared to the risk of vaccine-associated myocarditis."[285] Another study of 40 health care systems from the CDC found that:

> *The incidence of cardiac outcomes after mRNA COVID-19 vaccination was highest for males aged 12-17 years after the second vaccine dose; however, within this demographic group, the risk for cardiac outcomes was 1.8-5.6 times as high after SARS-CoV-2 infection than after the second vaccine dose.*[286]

Another systematic review and meta-analysis of 58 million people found the risk of myocarditis was over seven times higher in those who contracted COVID than in those who were vaccinated. It concluded "These findings support the continued use of mRNA COVID-19 vaccines among all eligible persons."[287] COVID myocarditis is more common than vaccine-myocarditis even in young males. One study found:

> *Among males aged 12 to 17 years, the incidence of myocarditis or pericarditis after infection with SARS-CoV-2 was about twice as high as after vaccination with 2 doses of an mRNA-based COVID-19 vaccine. When MIS, a post–COVID-19 syndrome that often includes cardiac complications, was included in the comparison, the risk of cardiac problems was about 2 to 6 times higher after infection than after 2 doses of vaccine. Men aged 18 to 29 years had a 7 to 9 times greater risk of cardiac complications after infection than after 2 doses of vaccine.*[479]

In contrast to the favorable prognosis of vaccine-myocarditis, COVID can cause severe cardiac complications, especially in those with Multisystem Inflammatory Syndrome in Children (MIS-C). Though most children recover well, a systematic review of found that 75% of children with MIS-C develop myocarditis,[288] and cardiac complications of this can include coronary artery aneurysms, shock, cardiac arrhythmias, pericardial effusion, and coronary artery dilatation.[289] Cardiac arrhythmias have led "to hemodynamic collapse and need for extracorporeal membrane oxygenation support [ECMO]" in some children,[290] while others have experienced acute heart failure.[291] A study that compared classic myocarditis, myocarditis due to MIS-C and vaccine-myocarditis in children found that:

> *COVID-19 vaccine-related myocarditis generally had a milder clinical course, with a lower likelihood of cardiac dysfunction at presentation and more rapid recovery when present...COVID-19 vaccine-related myocarditis is mild, and patients typically have evidence of normal ventricular function recovery at discharge from the hospital.*[292]

Another study, though not limited to children, found that 17.6% of patients with COVID-myocarditis died, while 100% of patients with vaccine-myocarditis recovered.[264] This paper also found that children with vaccine-myocarditis had improved cardiac outcomes compared to older patients. It said:

> *Although patients under 20 years experienced more fever and myalgia, they had better ejection fraction and less prominent myocardial inflammation in magnetic resonance imaging than older patients.*

Of course, vaccine-myocarditis can't be separated from the vaccine's real and significant benefits in keeping children safe and out of the hospital. Researchers on the condition universally conclude that "the benefits of vaccination against SARS-CoV-2 in reducing the severity of COVID-19, hospital admission and deaths far outweigh the risk of developing myocarditis."[280] As such, over

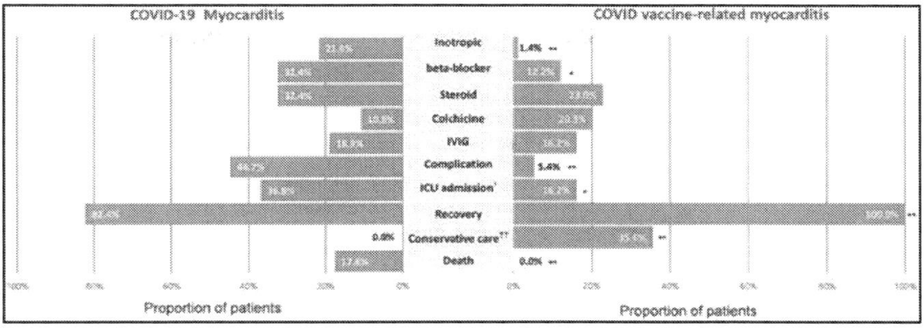

COVID-myocarditis versus vaccine-myocarditis (Woo et al., figure 2)[264]

a dozen medical organizations, including the American Heart Association and the American Academy of Pediatrics released a statement that said:

> *The facts are clear: this is an extremely rare side effect, and only an exceedingly small number of people will experience it after vaccination. Importantly, for the young people who do, most cases are mild, and individuals recover often on their own or with minimal treatment. In addition, we know that myocarditis and pericarditis are much more common if you get COVID-19, and the risks to the heart from COVID-19 infection can be more severe.*[293]

The reality on the ground tells an unambiguous story; while hospitals across the country were deluged with sick children, most of them unvaccinated, during the Delta and Omicron waves and again in fall 2022, no hospital in the entire world had to open a vaccine-injury unit.

"While our health authorities are shrugging off this risk saying cases are 'mild,' that's a frightening lie."
~ Dr. Joseph Mercola

Anti-vaccine doctors didn't see it this way, however. Dr. Joseph Mercola, who has long been America's leading anti-vaccine doctor, wrote about vaccine-myocarditis in his article, "Children at Risk for Lifelong Health Problems from COVID Vaccine," which was published on Robert F. Kennedy, Jr.'s anti-vaccine website. Dr. Mercola said:

While our health authorities are shrugging off this risk saying cases are "mild," that's a frightening lie. The damage to the heart is typically permanent, and the three- to five-year survival rate for myocarditis has historically ranged from 56% to 83%.

Patients with acute fulminant myocarditis (characterized by severe left ventricular systolic dysfunction requiring drug therapy or mechanical circulatory support) who survive the acute stage have a survival rate of 93% at 11 years, whereas those with acute nonfulminant myocarditis (left ventricular systolic dysfunction, but otherwise hemodynamically stable) have a survival rate of just 45% at 11 years.

This could mean that anywhere from 7% to 55% of the teens injured by these shots today might not survive into their late 20s or early 30s. Some might not even make it into their early 20s!

How is this possibly an acceptable tradeoff for a virus you have practically zero risk of dying from as a child or adolescent?
So, is it actually true that "For adolescents and young adults, the risk of myocarditis caused by COVID infection is much higher than after mRNA vaccination."? I doubt it.[294]

In contrast, Dr. Mercola said this about the risk of the virus:

The COVID shot is becoming even more inverted with the emergence of Omicron, as this variant produces far milder illness than previous variants, putting children at even lower risk of hospitalization or death from infection than they were before, and their risk was already negligible.

Dr. Mercola also quoted a nurse who said:

We are potentially sacrificing our children for fear of MAYBE dying, getting sick of a virus — a virus

> *with a 99% survival rate. As of now, we have more children that died from the COVID vaccine than COVID itself.*

None of this is true, of course. Vaccine-myocarditis is a different entity than viral myocarditis. Vaccine-myocarditis has a drastically improved prognosis compared to non-COVID, viral-myocarditis. One study of patients 12-years and older followed for 180-days, found:

> *1 death (1.0%) of 104 patients with postvaccination myocarditis and 84 deaths (11.0%) of 762 patients with viral infection–related myocarditis.*[276]

By highlighting the potential complications of viral-myocarditis, Dr. Mercola unintentionally provided a *very good* reason for children to get vaccinated and avoid COVID.

Characteristic	Myocarditis associated with mRNA COVID-19 vaccination*,†	Viral myocarditis‡
Inciting exposure	mRNA COVID-19 vaccination • Dose 2 > Dose 1	Viral illness • 30–60% with asymptomatic viral course
Demographics	Most cases in adolescents and young adults, males > females	Males > females, male incidence peaks in adolescence and gradually declines
Symptom onset	A few days after vaccination, most within a week	1–4 weeks after viral illness
Fulminant course	Rare¶	23%
ICU level support	~2%	~50%
Mortality/transplant	Rare¶	11–22%
Cardiac dysfunction	12%	60%
Recovery of cardiac function	Nearly all	~75%
Time to recovery of cardiac function (ejection fraction on cardiac echo), if initially poor	Hours to days	Days to weeks to months

* https://www.cdc.gov/vaccines/acip/meetings/index.html, https://www.cdc.gov/vaccinesafety/research/publications/index.html
† Oster et al. JAMA. 2022;327:331-340.
‡ Law et al. Circulation. 2021;144:e123-e135. Ghelani et al. Circ Cardiovasc Qual Outcomes. 2012;5:622-7. Kim et al. Korean Circ J. 2020;50:1013-1022. Messroghli et al. Am Heart J. 2017;187:133-144. Patel et al. J Am Heart Assoc. 2022;11:e024393.
¶ There are rare reports in the literature, especially from other countries, but it is unclear to what extent such cases were investigated
5

Vaccine-myocarditis versus viral myocarditis[255]

"No one says 'vaccine induced myocarditis is mostly mild' like someone who just saw a graph that 20% of people 37 weeks later have not fully recovered. We are talking healthy boys who are mostly getting a 2nd or 3rd dose here. Truly unacceptable."

~ Dr. Vinay Prasad

Dr. Mercola was not the only doctor who used dramatic, frightening language to discuss the risks of the vaccine, but calm, reassuring words when speaking about the virus, and no doctor became more synonymous with vaccine-side effects than Dr. Vinay Prasad. Dr. Prasad, an adult oncologist, who had no obvious interest or expertise in pediatric cardiology before the pandemic, spoke ceaselessly about vaccine-side effects during the pandemic. This started months before a single child had been vaccinated, when Dr. Prasad claimed that post-vaccination fevers and muscle aches made the vaccine an unappealing option for most parents.

When vaccine-myocarditis emerged, Dr. Prasad developed a laser-like focus on the topic. He wrote numerous articles and long *Twitter* threads about this side-effect. He made over a dozen videos about it and discussed it often with Dr. Zubin Damania.

Notably, Dr. Prasad would generally only discuss the *frequency* of vaccine-myocarditis and how this compared to the *frequency* of COVID-myocarditis. "Sorry to break it to you, vaccines can have risks of myocarditis EXCEEDING risks of myocarditis from infection,"[295] he wrote on December 26, 2021, just before the Omicron wave ripped through the pediatric population. Dr. Prasad's framing echoed Dr. Mercola, who said:

> *So, is it actually true that "For adolescents and young adults, the risk of myocarditis caused by COVID infection is much higher than after mRNA vaccination."? I doubt it.*[294]

Although doctors who've treated these children universally report that vaccine-myocarditis nearly always has a "mild, self-resolving clinical course,"[277] Dr. Prasad only rarely shared this information with his audience. He was also loath to mention the potentially severe course of COVID-myocarditis or that COVID's harm are not limited to myocarditis.

On the rare occasions when Dr. Prasad discussed the clinical course of vaccine-myocarditis, it was always framed to make the vaccine sound as frightening as possible. For example, although literally every study on the subject reports that the clinical course is nearly always favorable, Dr. Prasad felt these researchers were wrong about their own patients and their own studies. In an article titled "We Need to Talk About the Vaccines" he made it seem as if it was the "media" who called vaccine-myocarditis "mild" when, in fact, it was the doctors who cared for these patients and published their findings in the medical literature. He wrote:

> *The media dismisses concerns over myocarditis by claiming that most cases are "mild", when in fact it is too early for us to know the full effects.*[296]

Additionally, after the CDC reported that 81% of people with the condition had fully or probably recovered, Dr. Prasad reported the glass was 20% empty. He said:

> *No one says "vaccine induced myocarditis is mostly mild" like someone who just saw a graph that 20% of people 37 weeks later have not fully recovered. We are talking healthy boys who are mostly getting a 2nd or 3rd dose here. Truly unacceptable.*[297]

This histrionic language was the norm whenever Dr. Prasad discussed vaccine-myocarditis. "It is clear that the second dose brings WAY more hospitalizations from myocarditis than can possibly be prevented,"[298] he said on September 13, 2021, after the Delta wave had killed several teenage boys who were eligible to be vaccinated.[299] On a podcast, he acknowledged that "most will self-resolve" but said:

> *We don't really have the full implications. Will some lead to chronic arrhythmia, chronic cardiac disturbance? Will some lead to shortened life expectancy down the road? But what we do know for sure is that it does have the potential to have catastrophic short-term failure and death as in this case report from Israel and that should give people some caution that it's not all mild.*[300]

This is exactly how Dr. Mercola spoke about myocarditis, so long as it was caused by the vaccine.

Like Dr. Mercola, Dr. Prasad discussed harms caused by the virus in a completely different manner. He scolded doctors who warned of serious, even fatal COVID complications such as MIS-C. He tweeted that "the rate of multi-inflammatory syndrome is vanishingly low.--

although you wouldn't know that from the breathless news coverage and tweets."[301] In reality, over 9,100 American children have had MIS-C, roughly 10 times greater than the number of children who have suffered vaccine-myocarditis.[15]

Dr. Prasad was *much less* concerned about COVID's cardiac effects. On May 14, 2021, Dr. Prasad co-wrote an article titled "Setting the Record Straight: There is No 'COVID heart'." Even though the severe cardiac complications of pediatric MIS-C had been known for over a year and thousands of children had been affected by it, this article did not mention MIS-C at all.[302]

While Dr. Prasad felt that it was "too early for us to know the full effects"[296] of vaccine-myocarditis, he wrote that "people who have recovered from COVID-19 have no special reason to worry about their hearts."[302] He described on study by saying, "Cardiac magnetic resonance scans done during convalescence showed that nearly half of the individuals had no major heart abnormalities," though, of course, this means that just over half of the individuals did have major heart abnormalities. "Even in the sickest of the sick, COVID-19's effect on the heart appears to be modest," he added. However, his reference for this claim found that:

> *Myocardial infarction was found in 19% (28/148) and inducible ischaemia in 26% (20/76) of those undergoing stress perfusion (including 7 with both infarction and ischaemia). Of patients with ischaemic injury pattern, 66% (27/41) had no past history of coronary disease.*

The article concluded that "The issue of COVID-19 induced cardiac problems was massively overblown," and advised that "science communication in times of crisis must keep a level head."

It was only with COVID's harms that Dr. Prasad managed to keep a level head. Dr. Prasad wrote that it was "truly unacceptable" that approximately 160 adolescents had persistent symptoms from vaccine-myocarditis. In contrast, after 1,000 children had died of COVID, he said we should accept such deaths as a "matter of course". He wrote:

> *While the death of any child is a tragedy, COVID-19*

> *is less deadly to children than many other risks we accept as a matter of course, including drowning, vehicle accidents, and even cardiovascular disease.*[82]

Dr. Prasad complained about the "breathless coverage of rare anecdotes of MIS-C & death in kids."[303] He said that providing parents with accurate information about the potential risks of COVID only "sabotaged school reopening." "Perhaps some anecdotes should not be covered by the news,"[304] he added. In April 2021 he tweeted, "media's breathless coverage of MIS-C and variants has been a disservice."[480] The Delta and Omicron variants would arrive in less than a year causing unprecedented illness in unvaccinated children. In contrast, he excoriated *The Atlantic* for not covering "the human story of a 22 year boy with myocarditis."[305] "It won't be pretty," he said, breathlessly.

"I don't think people realize the damage continuing to push two doses in young men will do,"[306] he wrote on June 23, 2021, just before the Delta variant caused unprecedented illness in children. "We feel that even the slightest bit of inflammation in the heart should be treated seriously,"[474] he wrote with Dr. John Mandrola when discussing the vaccine. In contrast, when discussing children *killed* by COVID, he minimized their loss by writing, "In April 2021, 19 kids died of COVID19 in a country of 330 million."[188]

Dr. Prasad's repeated minimization of pediatric COVID deaths and his dramatization of vaccine-side effects earned him favorable coverage from Robert F. Kennedy, Jr.'s anti-vaccine website. They published several of his articles and wrote an homage to him in which they declared:

> *Vinay Prasad, M.D., MPH, in a video released this week called out what he said were the "lies and exaggerations" about COVID-19 vaccines and kids being spread by media and public health officials.*[307]

His work was also favorably shared on *The Vaccine Reaction*, a website published by America's oldest anti-vaccine organization, the National Vaccine Information Center.

Dr. Prasad was not the only doctor who developed a sudden interest in vaccine side-effects, nor was he the only doctor to treat harms caused by the virus differently than harms caused by the vaccine. Many other doctors scolded anyone perceived to be minimizing vaccine-myocarditis, while simultaneously shaming anyone who tried to prevent young people from dying of COVID, even with a simple vaccine. Dr. Anish Koka, for example, used laughing emojis to mock those who warned of the Delta variant before it arrived in full force in the summer of 2021. Though most children with MIS-C go to the ICU and some develop "hemodynamic collapse,"[294] Dr. Koka nonetheless said:

> *The good news is that MIS-C myocarditis is associated with almost no cardiac damage. But there is little question the level of cardiac damage that results from the vaccines is nothing that anyone in a non-COVID era would describe as mild.*[308]

At least 74 children have died of MIS-C.[15]

Dr. John Mandrola, who co-authored the article "Setting the Record Straight: There is No 'COVID Heart'" with Dr. Prasad, mocked studies showing the virus's cardiac impact, calling them "fear-mongering howler-science."[309] In his essay "No, Young Adults Should Not Live in Fear from Coronavirus," Dr. Mandrola also argued that "fear of death"[187] was not a valid reason for young adults to avoid COVID. "An excess of 12,000 deaths sounds bad" he wrote, but it's just a "tiny absolute increase in risk". He warned about "fear mongering howler-science (eg COVID myocarditis)" and reacted to a study showing that 1.4% of athletes had evidence COVID-myocarditis on cardiac MRI by saying this was "More good news on #COVID19 and athletes".[475] This rate is over 100 times higher than the rate of vaccine-myocarditis in adolescents.

Like Dr. Prasad, Dr. Mandrola changed his tone dramatically when discussing vaccine-myocarditis, treating it as a fate worse than anything COVID could do. Less than two months after writing that COVID's cardiac effects are "modest" and "overblown", he penned an article titled "Vaccine-Induced Myocarditis Concerns Demand Respect, Not Absolutism" in which he said, "humans have only one heart; inflaming it at a young age is not a small thing."[310]

On *Twitter*, Dr. Mandrola said that in order to maintain trust, doctors had to minimize the risk of COVID and exaggerate the harms of the vaccine. Even though COVID has killed some healthy young males, and over 20 studies on vaccine-myocarditis universally report that it has "largely favorable early outcomes,"[258] Dr. Mandrola felt it was inappropriate for doctors to accurately quote the medical literature. He said, "denoting vaccine-myocarditis in healthy boys at low risk from COVID as mild is a trust shredder."[311] He would further say, "Mild myocarditis only occurs in other folks' kids."[312] Of course, Dr. Mandrola had previously argued that myocarditis was "modest" and "overblown" even in the "sickest of the sick", so long as it was caused by the virus, not the vaccine.

Dr. Marty Makary was even more dramatic, suggesting that the vaccine would kill children, even though no children are known to have died from the vaccine. He said on a podcast that "maybe the rate of death from the vaccine parallels the rate of death from COVID in a healthy child"[313] and tweeted:

> *Vax deaths could approximate COVID deaths in boys 5-11 w/no comorbid...Based on the data of kids w/ NO comorbid, an estimated 0-10 kids 5-11 have ever died of COVID VS. Approx 15 would die from the vax 2nd dose (extrap from adolescents).*[314]

This is similar to Dr. Mercola's anti-vaccine nurse who said, "As of now, we have more children that died from the COVID vaccine than COVID itself."[294]

Even though vaccine-myocarditis doesn't occur in younger children, this didn't stop Dr. Makary from fear mongering about this side effect when the vaccine became available for babies and toddlers. He wrote:

> *The small size of the studies in children under 5 makes it nearly impossible to observe rates of rare complications such as myocarditis, which occurs in 1 in 2,650 12-17 year-ol boys after the 2nd dose. This complication has been associated with EKG changes in children and even concerning MRI findings months after recovering from myocarditis. The New England Journal of Medicine reported one case of vaccine-associated myocarditis death in a 22-year-old in an*

> *Israeli population study. Keep in mind that babies can't tell you when they have myocarditis.*[203]

Note that Dr. Makary reported only the study that had by far the highest reported rate of vaccine-myocarditis. Moreover, when his article was published on June 23, 2022, at least 500 children under 5-years had died of COVID,[116] a fact that went unmentioned in Dr. Makary's article. Dr. Makary also didn't mention that babies can't tell you when they have complications of COVID.

Unfortunately, this sort of misinformation made its way into the medical literature as well. On August 30, 2021, Allison Krug, Dr. Tracy Høeg, and Dr. John Mandrola posted a paper titled "SARS-CoV-2 mRNA Vaccination-Associated Myocarditis in Children Ages 12-17: A Stratified National Database Analysis."[315] Josh Stevenson, a data analyst linked with the anti-vaccine organization Rational Ground,[316] was also an author. The study was posted as a preprint, which means it had not undergone peer-review, only after it had been rejected from three journals.[317] It was finally published by the *European Journal of Clinical Investigation* online in February 2022 though Dr. Mandrola was mysteriously missing from the list of authors.[318] The final version of the paper garnered a fraction of the attention as the thrice-rejected preprint.

This preprint purported to calculate the rate of vaccine-myocarditis by examining reports made to the Vaccine Adverse Events Reporting System (VAERS), one of several vaccine-safety monitoring systems. Beyond this, it concluded that the vaccine would send more healthy adolescent boys to the hospital than the virus over a 120-day period.

The preprint had many problems. While VAERS is useful as a warning signal to detect potentially rare side-effects, anyone can file a report. The VAERS website specifically warns:

> *VAERS accepts and analyzes reports of possible health problems—also called "adverse events"—after vaccination. As an early warning system, VAERS cannot prove that a vaccine caused a problem. Specifically,* ***a report to VAERS does not mean that a vaccine caused an adverse event.*** *But VAERS can give CDC and FDA important information. If it looks*

as though a vaccine might be causing a problem, FDA and CDC will investigate further and take action if needed.

Anyone can submit a report to VAERS – healthcare professionals, vaccine manufacturers, and the general public. VAERS welcomes all reports, regardless of seriousness, and regardless of how likely the vaccine may have been to have caused the adverse event.[319]

As such, it is not possible to determine from a VAERS report if the information is accurate or if the vaccine is to blame without a detailed review of the medical records. In 2004, anesthesiologist James Laidler reported that his flu shot turned him into the Incredible Hulk, and had it accepted into VAERS for a period. Unsurprisingly, anti-vaxxers have long abused VAERS reports to blame vaccines for an assortment of maladies, most commonly autism, and one study found "a rise in the number of reports to the VAERS related to pending litigation for vaccine injury."[320] Dr. David Gorski has called this tactic "dumpster diving", and it is very familiar to vaccine-advocates.

Even though Dr. Høeg's preprint calculated a rate of vaccine-myocarditis that was higher than nearly all studies, but not the highest, it used VAERS in an inappropriate way. Some of the VAERS reports they included had other infections – including SARS-CoV-2 – while others were children who were too young to be vaccinated at the time.[321] As Dr. David Goldberg said in a comment on the preprint:

When the question is so important and politically charged, incomplete/invalid data is sometimes worse than no data. Unless the authors can have two-party adjudication with record review, and classification using standard techniques (e.g., definite vaccine-induced myocarditis, highly likely, probable, possible, not) then there are major methodological concerns with the outcome, and the overall validity of the study.[322]

No matter the rate of vaccine-myocarditis it calculated, Dr. Høeg's study was a massive outlier in concluding the vaccine was more dangerous than the virus for a subset of children. To make its case, the study contained strategic omissions and dubious statistics, minimizing the virus's harms, of course. Though the pre-print said the risk of vaccine-myocarditis would exceed the risk of the virus over a 120-day period, the virus didn't disappear after 120-days. While the efficacy of the vaccine wanes over time, its efficacy against severe disease has held so far, especially when augmented by boosters.

While Dr. Høeg's preprint acknowledged that the clinical course of vaccine-myocarditis "was reported to be relatively benign,"[315] the preprint neglected to mention the virus is not always "relatively benign" for hospitalized children. 10-year-old Dae'shun Jamison had all four limbs amputated due to MIS-C,[323] showing the folly of merely comparing hospitalization rates from the vaccine and the virus without accounting for the relative severity. Moreover, Dr. Høeg's preprint said:

> *The reported mortality rate in England has so far been 2/million children which may translate to around 6/ million infections based on a prior infection rate of 1/3.*[315]

Over 425 American children had died of COVID when the preprint posted.[116] A death rate of 6 in a million children would necessitate 71 million pediatric infections, which is 97% of children in the U.S. All it took was basic math and basic knowledge to know that the pediatric death rate was greater than 6 per million. Over 1,000 children died after Dr. Høeg's study was posted on *MedRxiv*,[4] including healthy young males who were eligible to be vaccinated.

Despite its dubious methods and obvious flaws, the preprint received international attention. Though he explicitly rejected these kinds of studies when they support vaccines, Dr. Prasad lauded this study as a "bombshell finding from dream team of authors."[324] A headline from *The Guardian* declared "Boys More at Risk from Pfizer Jab Side-Effect Than COVID, Suggests Study," and this message was spread widely on social media by anti-vaccine politicians, such as Congresswoman Marjorie Taylor Greene, who said in a now deleted Tweet:

> *When boys and young men are at a higher risk of being hospitalized from side effect of taking the COVID vaccine than actually being hospitalized from COVID itself, there is every reason to stop the COVID vaccine mandates. Stop the insanity.*

Dr. Mercola even referenced this study in his article, saying "Cases of myocarditis explode after the second shot, Høeg found, and disproportionally affect boys."[294]

This is how many parents and young adults were misled into believing that vaccine-myocarditis was both more common and severe than COVID, whose harms are not limited to myocarditis, of course. Tyler Gilreath was an unvaccinated, healthy 20-year-old college student who died of COVID in September 2021. Tyler's mother, Tamra Demello, later said:

> *I cajoled, encouraged, threatened, and nagged for him to get vaccinated. I did everything I could possibly think. I think he did some research where he was thinking that it was going to hurt his heart long-term or something... I'm not even sure where he was getting his information which is super frustrating.*[325]

I don't know where Tyler got his information from either, but it's plausible he got it from doctors who spoke about myocarditis in starkly different terms dependent entirely on whether the cause was the virus or the vaccine and in inverse proportion to both the severity and frequency of the damage, all while having no real-world responsibility for treating children who suffered from either.

#14 ~ "Some proportion of sudden cardiac death is from subclinical myocarditis."

The notion that vaccines hurt children in invisible ways that will only manifest years in the future is a common anti-vaccine trope. Since anti-vaxxers can't point to actual studies showing vaccines are more dangerous than the diseases they prevent, they instead fearmonger about "toxins" and scary-sounding chemicals. In her pamphlet "Vaccines and Brain Health" Dr. Kelly Brogan demonstrated this technique by writing:

> *All the flu vaccine components are potentially toxic; thimerosal is a mercury based preservative, formaldehyde is a known carcinogen, gelatin and egg proteins are allergens, antibiotics are literally designed to kill cells, and I can't even imagine how muscle cells respond to an influx of straight sugar... Mercury, another of the most common vaccine ingredients, is a known neurotoxin. The 'safe dose' of mercury recommended by the EPA is 2 parts per billion (ppb) per liter of drinking water. Amazingly, the flu vaccine contains 50,000 ppb of mercury! Even in very low concentrations, mercury can be toxic to brain cells. In one study, a dose of 0.5 ppb was enough to kill human brain cells. A person who complies with the current vaccine requirements will develop a staggering toxic burden, since mercury is in several vaccines, including whooping cough, tetanus, meningococcal, and Hepatitis B.*[249]

It's true that thimerosal is a mercury-based preservative that was used in some vaccines. Even though research does "not support a causal relationship between childhood vaccination with thimerosal-containing vaccines and development of autistic-spectrum disorders,"[326] it was removed from childhood vaccines in 2001 in the U.S. out of an abundance of caution.

Despite this, Dr. Brogan wants parents to think that mercury and other sinister, spooky chemicals in the bloodstream translates to brain damage, which will lead to autism. This sort of balderdash, which is ubiquitous in anti-vaccine messaging, obviates the need to show that vaccines actually hurt children and instead conveys a terrifying message to parents: *vaccines hurt your child in ways you can't even see, and the harms will only appear years from now.*

Anti-vaxxers continued to embrace the notion that pediatric COVID vaccines would cause invisible, potentially fatal damage to children. In his essay "Children at Risk for Lifelong Health Problems from COVID Vaccine," which was published on Robert F. Kennedy, Jr.'s anti-vaccine site, Dr. Joseph Mercola said:

> *Researchers have also found Pfizer and Moderna mRNA COVID-19 shots dramatically increase biomarkers associated with thrombosis, cardiomyopathy and other vascular events following injection. People who had received two doses of the mRNA jab more than doubled their five-year risk of acute coronary syndrome (ACS), the researchers found, driving it from an average of 11% to 25%. ACS is an umbrella term that includes not only heart attacks, but also a range of other conditions involving abruptly reduced blood flow to your heart.*[294]

As he is unable to find evidence the vaccine has caused catastrophic outcomes in large numbers of adolescent boys, Dr. Mercola wants parents to think that "biomarkers" in the bloodstream translate to heart damage, which will lead to heart attacks years from now.

Many anti-vaxxers claim that the silent harms of COVID vaccines are already killing people. Anti-vaxxers were eager to impugn the COVID vaccine for the on-field collapse of NFL player Damar Hamlin, and Stew Peters, a right-wing podcaster and COVID conspiracy-theorist, made a horrible disinformation movie called *Died Suddenly* that claimed young people were dying from blood clots due to the vaccine. The trailer for the film showed footage of a college basketball player collapsing on the court, though this occurred in December 2020 before anyone had been vaccinated, and the player is alive and well. The film's website said it will "present the truth about the greatest ongoing mass genocide in human history" and that "the global elite have broadcast their intentions to depopulate the world."[327]

Contrarian doctors used similar techniques to dissuade parents from vaccinating their children. In August 2022 a study on vaccine-myocarditis from Thailand confirmed what all other studies on the subject have found. It said, "The clinical presentation of myopericarditis after vaccination was usually mild and temporary, with all cases fully recovering within 14 days."[279]

The paper also found that 4 out of 301 children had elevated troponin levels, which is a marker of cardiac injury, even though they had no symptoms. This allowed contrarian doctors to communicate a *very different* message about this study: *COVID vaccines hurt your child in ways you can't even see, and the harms will only appear decades from now.*

Dr. Tracy Høeg tweeted, "Stunning prospective study from Thailand...3.5% (7/202) males & 0 females developed myoperi/peri or subclinical myocarditis."[328] Though he had previously signed a letter of concern "about overdiagnosis" of subclinical myocarditis from COVID, Dr. Vinay Prasad felt very differently the vaccine, tweeting "7/202 boys had overt or subclinical myocarditis (3.5%) or roughly 2 orders of magnitude more common than prior reports from passive adverse event reporting of myocarditis."[329] He wrote an article and made a *YouTube* video about this study as well.

In an article titled "Vaccine Myocarditis Update from Thailand" Dr. Anish Koka, warned that young people were already dying from this. He wrote:

> *I can assure you, and the mostly ER doctor contingent on twitter that brays about "mild myocarditis", that there are no cardiologists who want to see their child have a cardiac troponin that is 2x normal or 40x normal after administration of some therapeutic. What exactly does one to do with an adolescent with a troponin that is 2x normal that is asymptomatic? Given the theoretical risk of malignant cardiac arrhythmias I would imagine most cardiologists would follow the current guidelines for myocarditis and advise against strenuous cardiac activity for some months. Sudden cardiac death in young athletes is obviously a fearsome complication that is very real and it is likely some proportion of sudden cardiac death is from subclinical myocarditis....*
>
> *There are potentially a number of cases of children with chest pain that are never brought to the attention of the health care system, and are thus never captured. There is also the issues of myocardial damage that may occur without any overt, severe symptoms. The young baseball player with an ache in his left shoulder for a few days that is shrugged off. Even*

> *more concerning given the marked cardiac injury demonstrated in some vaccine myocarditis cases that presented to the hospital, it is entirely possible that there are severe cases of myocarditis that result in out of hospital death that are never labeled as myocarditis.*[330]

Like Dr. Mercola, Dr. Koka also wants parents to think that troponin in the bloodstream translates to myocarditis, which has possibly already killed young, healthy athletes. This is a barely watered-down version of the claims made by the "Died Suddenly" documentarians. Dr. Koka provided no evidence COVID vaccines were to blame for sudden cardiac death and to make his case that some proportion of sudden cardiac death is due subclinical myocarditis, Dr. Koka linked to studies from 2007 and 2019. This only proves the point that viral myocarditis is much more severe than vaccine-myocarditis, and Dr. Koka inadvertently provided a strong rationale for COVID vaccination.

Not every cardiologist agreed with his sort of baseless speculation. Pediatric cardiologist Dr. Frank Han, who actually published a report on 63 patients with vaccine-myocarditis and is continuing to study the subject, said:

> *Cardiologists have formalized the criteria for myocarditis to avoid diagnosing every person with troponin in the blood with myocarditis. This would be misdiagnosis and, unnecessarily frighten the patient.*[331]

Dr. Han, who believes children should be vaccinated against COVID, likely knew the test for troponin is very sensitive and that a vigorous game of soccer can elevate troponin levels in children[332] He was also likely aware that in a study of 61 patients who were sick enough to undergo heart biopsies, 21 of them did not have myocarditis.[254]

Though very few vaccines truly carry any long-term risk, the long-term risks of the COVID vaccine will only become known over the long term. I'm certain the vaccine will be blamed for a wide assortment of maladies for the foreseeable future. However, it's certainly possible some children will suffer long-term consequences from the vaccine.

Of course, that's also true for the virus. If subclinical myocarditis from the vaccine is concerning, then the virus is a much bigger cause for concern. One study found elevated troponin in 7% of children who presented to the ER with COVID,[333] which was double the rate found in the Thailand study. Indeed, if subclinical myocarditis might lead to sudden cardiac death in the future, the virus is much more dangerous than the vaccine. However, that study concluded:

> *Routine troponin screening does not yield much information in previously healthy paediatric COVID-19 patients without any sign of myocardial dysfunction. Elevated troponin levels may be observed but it is mostly a sign of myocardial injury without detectable myocardial dysfunction in this group of patients.*

Additionally, the virus can often cause overt, clinical myocarditis in children. A study of nearly 60,000 children found that "myocarditis was the condition with the strongest association with SARS-CoV-2 infection."[17] Another study found that an elevated troponin level in children with COVID wasn't always clinically benign. It found:

> *Out of 7 patients with high troponin levels, 3 (42.9%) of them were admitted to the pediatric intensive care unit (PICU), 2 (28.6%) required oxygen support, and 1 (14.3%) required a mechanical ventilator.*[334]

Moreover, myocarditis can be especially serious in children with Multisystem Inflammatory Syndrome in Children (MIS-C), which has affected over 9,100 American children.[15] One report of 95 patients with MIS-C found elevated troponin levels in 71% of the patients, and 53% had myocarditis.[335] 62% of these patients received vasopressor support, 80% were admitted to an intensive care unit, and 2 died.

Drs. Høeg, Prasad, or Koka did not mention these severe cardiac outcomes due to COVID, nor did they mention the "extremely favorable outcome" of children with clinical myocarditis in the Thailand study. Like Drs. Brogan and Mercola, they lacked evidence children will suffer permanent harm from the vaccine, and so were only able to fear monger about theoretical, invisible harms that might occur at some point in the future.

And though their paper was unfortunately used to scare parents about the COVID vaccine, the authors of the Thailand study concluded:

> *In this study, the disease course was mild... treated with Ibuprofen for 2 weeks and cardiac enzymes returned to normal after 1–2 weeks of outpatient treatment... Overall, COVID-19 mRNA vaccination has an extremely favorable outcome and should be recommended for adolescents.*[279]

Contrarian doctors chose not to mention this either.

#15 ~ "If the risk is higher @CDCDirector will try to hide it and Peter Marks will simply ignore it."

Anti-vaxxers love nothing more than a good conspiracy, especially one that posits that vaccine experts, government regulatory agencies, and pharmaceutical industries are all collaborating to hide the link between vaccines and autism. Every few years, one of them picks up traction and it becomes all the rage in anti-vaccine circles.

In her essay "CDC: You're Fired. Autism Coverup Exposed," Dr. Kelly Brogan wrote about such a conspiracy saying:

> *After Dr. Brian Hooker's requests through the Freedom of Information Act for original MMR study documentation, a CDC Immunization Safety Researcher, Dr. William Thompson has buckled under the pressure of his conscience, and come forth as a whistleblower.*[336]

Dr. Brogan's comment is in reference to a conspiracy from 2014 that the CDC altered and hid data to cover up a link between autism and vaccines in Black boys. As Dr. Brogan explained:

These documents demonstrated a 3.4 fold increase in the incidence of autism in African American boys, expunged from the final study results in a violent act of scientific fraud. Dr. Thompson has since corroborated the CDC's retroactive alteration of the data to eliminate the signal of harm. In light of a 2004 letter confirming CDC awareness and suppression of these findings, CDC head, Dr. Julie Gerberding committed perjury before moving onto her position at Merck in the Vaccine Division. Dr. Hooker has published the unadulterated finding here.

As parents around the world have known for 7 decades, and basic science has supported, vaccines do cause autism.

The "CDC Whistleblower" scandal was a major event in anti-vaccine circles at this time, though of course, vaccines do not cause autism.

During the pandemic, several contrarian doctors similarly tried to convince parents the CDC was suppressing information about vaccine-myocarditis. Dr. Marty Makary tweeted:

Last yr, the NEJM described a 22-yr-old that died from vax-induced myocarditis & I've heard of many more cases. I have never heard of a young healthy person with nat immunity dying from COVID. Our gov't doctors have not been honest about the risks:benefit in young healthy people.[337]

Beyond saying "I've heard of many more cases," Dr. Makary presented no evidence that young people were dying from vaccine-myocarditis, even as he accused "government doctors" of lying about the topic. Dr. Makary also published an article titled "The CDC – Which is Withholding Information – Has a Hidden Agenda" in which he lambasted the CDC for "pushing boosters for young people."[338] "The American people realize public health officials have been lying to them," he wrote.

Though Dr. Makary said "I have never heard of a young healthy person with nat immunity dying from COVID"[337], it's trivially easy to find examples of this, and according to an article titled "COVID-19 Surges Linked to Spike in Heart Attacks":

> *Spikes in heart attack deaths have tracked with surges of COVID-19 infection—even during the presumed less-severe Omicron phase of the pandemic. Furthermore, the data showed the increase was most significant among individuals ages 25-44, who are not usually considered at high risk for heart attack.*[339]

Dr. Makary was not the only doctor who accused health officials of lying for not exaggerating vaccine side-effects. In a now deleted tweet, Dr. Ramin Farzaneh-Far wrote:

> *We have no idea whether or not variant spike mRNA vaccines cause a 1/10, 1x, or 10x rate of myocarditis as compared with Wuhan strain. But we know for sure from prior experience that IF the risk is higher @CDCDirector will try to hide it and Peter Marks will simply ignore it.*

Dr. Vinay Prasad agreed, saying "the wisest comment that few appreciate."[340]

If the CDC director, Dr. Rochelle Walensky, was trying to hide vaccine-myocarditis, she did a terrible job of it. The Advisory Committee on Immunization Practices held many public meetings on the subject that received attention in the national media. Dr. Walensky gave an interview to ABC News in June 2021 titled "CDC Director Weighs in on Risk of Myocarditis From COVID-19 Vaccine."[341] Dr. Peter Marks, the FDA's chief vaccine regulator, also did a poor job of ignoring vaccine-myocarditis. He's written about it, and under his leadership:

> *Myocarditis and pericarditis were added as important identified risks in the pharmacovigilance plan and included in the Warnings sections of the vaccine Fact Sheets and EUA Prescribing Information.*[342]

Dr. Prasad also told parents that pediatricians wouldn't level with them in his article "Doctors Must be Honest with Parents About Unknown Risks of COVID-19 Emergency Vaccine." Although pediatricians have been honestly counseling patients on the risks and benefits of vaccines their entire careers, Dr. Prasad told them "it is absolutely essential that we communicate about this vaccine in an informative and nuanced way and, for the moment, resist uninformative persuasion."[343] Echoing pre-pandemic anti-vaccine rhetoric about pediatricians, Dr. Prasad warned parents they might be coerced into vaccinating their children, writing, "Applying pressure or force is not appropriate at this time." Dr. Prasad never suggested that doctors honestly present the risks – known and unknown – of COVID itself, and in fact worked ceaselessly to obscure these harms.

The CDC and FDA are not beyond reproach. However vague insinuations that "they" are hiding a vaccine-side effect, especially one they've widely publicized, only serves to undermine confidence in the pediatric COVID vaccine, which again, was the point. Prior to the pandemic, only quack doctors accused regulatory agencies and pediatricians of hiding vaccine harms and "forcing" parents to vaccinate their children.

#16 ~ "The CDC is already investigating one possible death associated with a 2nd dose of Pfizer vaccine in a 13 year old."

Anti-vaxxers know that nothing scares parents more than a sad story of a child who dies some time after getting a vaccine. These tragedies get sensationalized, distorted, and shared widely on social media. Any eventual correction receives a fraction of the attention as the original story.

A typical example is the tragedy of 12-year-old Meredith Prohaska, who was found dead in her home several hours after receiving the HPV vaccine in 2014. Her distraught mother blamed the vaccine, and this claim was repeated both in the mainstream media and on anti-vaccine websites.

But Meredith did not die from the vaccine. The medical examiner found that she died from an overdose of an antihistamine.[344] However, that did not stop the rumors and her story is still circulated as a vaccine-related death. The strong evidence against the alleged vaccine link makes this case a great example of how problematic these stories are. The truth does not concern anti-vaxxers. They know the power of these stories and make liberal use of them in propaganda movies such as *The Greater Good*, *Vaxxed*, and *Vaccine Roulette*.

Fast forward to May 10, 2021. On that date, I published a rebuttal to an article titled "COVID Vaccines for Children Should Not Get Emergency Use Authorization" which was published in the *BMJ* and written by Drs. Wesley Pegden, Vinay Prasad, and Stefan Baral. The central thesis of this article was that "severe outcomes or death associated with COVID-19 infection is very low for children, undermining the appropriateness of an emergency use authorization for child COVID-19 vaccines."[67]

In my rebuttal, I wrote the following.

> *Unfortunately, those of us who are familiar with the anti-vaccine movement know what is about to happen. Millions of children ages 12-15 years will soon be vaccinated against COVID-19. Horrible, improbable things will happen to a few of them. The media will write emotionally powerful stories about some [of] these children. Parents of these children will implore others "not to make the same mistake I did". The anti-vaccine movement will amplify and distort these tragedies to implicate the vaccine, though of course we must always keep an open-mind and consider that the vaccine is responsible. Anti-vaccine activists will claim the COVID-19 vaccines were "rushed" and "not properly studied". Parents will be frightened. Of course, this has been the pattern with nearly every vaccine for years before COVID-19 emerged.*[345]

I was right. Robert F. Kennedy, Jr.'s anti-vaccine site was soon publishing articles titled such as "8-Year-Old Boy Dies of MIS 7 Days After Pfizer Vaccine, VAERS Report Shows" and "9-Year-Old with No Pre-existing Conditions Died 2 Weeks After Pfizer Shot, Latest VAERS Data Show."

Anti-vaxxers were not the only ones to publicize these unverified tragedies. In June 2021, Dr. Pegden, a mathematician who thinks children should not be vaccinated under the emergency use authorization, wrote an article about vaccine-myocarditis that concluded by saying:

> *In the meantime, the mortality rate of vaccine-associated myocarditis cases remains uncertain. Under questioning during the meeting, Matthew Oster reported that for myocarditis unrelated to COVID-19 or COVID-19 vaccines, mortality rates are estimated in the range of 4%–9% in the literature. Fortunately, it seems likely that the rate is not so high for vaccine or COVID-19 associated myocarditis. But the rate is likely not zero, and the CDC is already investigating one possible death associated with a 2nd dose of Pfizer vaccine in a 13 year old, over a time period where no deaths would be expected to be avoided from 2nd doses of mRNA vaccines in this age group.*[346]

Dr. Pegden linked to an article about a 13-year-old boy who died three days after receiving his second dose of the COVID vaccine.[347] However, a subsequent CDC investigation, including a complete forensic and medical autopsy, found no evidence the vaccine was to blame, and the cause of his death was not determined.[348]

On *Twitter,* Dr. Tracy Høeg also shared the story of a 24-year-old who died after receiving the Pfizer vaccine. According to Dr. Høeg:

> *I believe this is the 1st confirmed post-vax myocarditis death in the US: "Because he wanted to take his classes in person, George Jr. needed to be fully vaccinated" "An autopsy report ... shows George Jr. died from "COVID-19 vaccine-related myocarditis"*[349]

However, this man died six weeks after receiving the vaccine, well outside the timeframe of a vaccine-side effect. He never complained of any cardiac symptoms and was diagnosed with a sinus infection prior to his death. The coroner who blamed the vaccine had to look up the meaning of "myocarditis" and could not pronounce it properly.[350] Upon learning this information, Dr. Høeg responded, "This case and autopsy for a 22 year old South Korean is more clear cut."[351] Dr. Høeg wasn't bothered that she shared blatant misinformation about a supposed vaccine death. She was bothered that someone might walk away from her *Twitter* feed not knowing she had an even "more clear cut" example of someone who died from the vaccine.

Mr. Kennedy's website also publicized the tragic deaths of these two young men before there was any evidence the vaccine was to blame.[352,353] As I predicted, parents were frightened, which was the point.

#17 ~ "You're talking about maybe 14,000 kids suffering grade three fevers, and maybe 880 suffering grade four fevers, which is more than one day. And I guess when you add in the myalgia, when you add in the arthralgia, when you add in the sort of headache, the fogginess, all these things, I mean, I think you have a tough sell."

Vaccines can be annoying. Everyone has a sore arm and some people, including children, feel really rotten the next day. Though this can be miserable, most people recognize the alternative is far worse. Anti-vaxxers have long argued against vaccines by claiming these side effects are worse than the diseases they prevent. For example, in her essay "Vaccination: Your Body. Your Baby. Their Flu," Dr. Brogan discouraged the flu vaccine by writing:

> *Common side effects include symptoms like fatigue, fever, body and headaches (aka...the flu!)*[97]

Obviously, side effects after a vaccine are not the same as getting the flu itself.

Anti-vaccine doctors continued to use these side effects to fear monger about COVID vaccines. An article on Robert Kennedy, Jr.'s anti-vaccine website titled "55% of Babies, Toddlers Had 'Systemic Reaction' After COVID Vaccine, CDC Survey Shows" highlighted that vaccinated children experienced "fatigue, fever, irritability and crying."[354] It quoted Dr. Meryl Nass, an anti-vaccine doctor, as saying:

> *Those reactions may, in fact, be harbingers of more serious reactions, but nobody to my knowledge has published anything looking at whether these acute local or systemic reactions are indicators of a later problem.*

Contrarian doctors also used such mundane effects to stoke fear about the pediatric vaccine. In a podcast titled "Should We Vaccinate Kids for COVID?" from February 4, 2021, before a single child had been vaccinated, Dr Vinay Prasad spread misinformation, minimizing COVID's risk to children, and expressed his opposition to the pediatric Emergency Use Authorization saying:

> *We're talking about grade three fevers, which is like, I think, 104 degrees for less than 24 hours, and grade four, which is 104 degrees for two days, for more than 24 hours. We're talking about of a million kids, you might take that risk of death from one, and let's say you drop it to zero, because there's a 95% reduction in COVID, and there appears to be almost a full protection against severe COVID. So let's say to save that one life, you gotta inoculate a million kids with vaccination to save one life. And you're talking about maybe 14,000 kids suffering grade three fevers, and maybe 880 suffering grade four fevers, which is more than one day. And I guess when you add in the myalgia, when you add in the arthralgia, when you add in the sort of headache, the fogginess, all these things, I mean, I think you have a tough sell.*[66]

Of course, COVID can cause fevers, myalgias, arthralgias, headache, and fogginess, but that never concerned Dr. Prasad. In fact, when talking about children made ill by viruses, Dr. Prasad said this was beneficial. "For children, getting sick and recovering is part of a natural and healthy life,"[82] he said in his article "Should We Let Children Catch Omicron?" Why are fevers, myalgias, arthralgias, headache, and fogginess problematic when a vaccine is the cause, but "natural and healthy" when a virus is the cause?

Prior to the pandemic, nearly all doctors agreed that a day of fevers, muscle aches, and fatigue in many children was a small price to pay for preventing a lifetime of severe harms in others. Only anti-vaccine doctors felt otherwise.

#18 ~ "If Pfizer and Moderna want these vaccines to be given to children, they should first conduct a randomized controlled trial that shows that they reduce hospitalization and all-cause mortality."

What are Randomized-Controlled Trials (RCTs)?

Randomized-controlled trials (RCTs) are the gold-standard for evaluating medical interventions. Because they randomly assign study subjects to an experimental or control group, they can isolate the intervention under investigation and minimize bias. In a fantasy world with unlimited time and money, but without ethics, an RCT would yield the optimal answer to nearly all medical questions. I firmly believe that every intervention that can be studied via an RCT should be, and there should have been more RCTs during the pandemic. My dedication to vaccine RCTs is so deep that I volunteered for the trial of the AstraZeneca vaccine, skipping an opportunity to get an mRNA vaccine in December 2021.

However, in the real world there are many reasons why medical interventions, including vaccines, can't be studied in enormous RCTs of many years duration.

- The safety of the subjects in RCTs is paramount. Basic ethics and Institutional Review Boards (IRBs) strictly limit what can be studied via an RCT.[355] Once there is reasonable evidence a vaccine is safe and effective, it would be unethical to allow children to continue to receive the placebo.

- RCTs are slow. It takes time to design the trial, to get funding, to have it evaluated and approved by an IRB, to set up the infrastructure, to enroll patients, to run the study, and to synthesize the data. Most RCTs take many years from the time they are conceived to when the final data changes clinical care.[356]

- RCTs are expensive and funding can be hard to come by, especially for studies where no one can profit based on the outcome. Every dollar spent on an RCT is money not spent elsewhere.[357]

- An RCT can sound perfect right until the moment someone actually has to enroll patients into it. A proposed RCT of hydroxychloroquine and azithromycin run by the NIH closed after enrolling *just 20 patients*, or 1% of their goal.[358] Graveyards are full of dead RCTs, and recruiting patients into them during a raging pandemic was especially hard. One researcher said about the experience: "*I think of what my clinical research team went through to enroll people in that trial, and I thought my nurses were going to die. One of them got COVID and got sick. Imagine trying to do that on a daily basis, multiple patients, some of them facing intubation, none of them have their families.*"

- RCTs require an enormous infrastructure and multiple experts with different skills. The protocol for one of the pediatric vaccine trials was 460 pages of dense text outlining exactly how the trial should be run.[359] Most RCTs occur at multiple locations, and trained teams have to be in place at every site. The COVID vaccine RCTs weren't just a scientific triumph, they were also a logistical marvel. However, this complex infrastructure naturally limits the size of RCTs.

- Given their complexity, RCTs don't always go smoothly. Serious problems can sometimes arise, and small hiccups are more common than not.[360] Vaccine trials in particular have to be flawless. Those who enjoy spreading fear about vaccines will magnify the *slightest* imperfection to cast doubt on the whole project. This happened with one site of the Pfizer adult mRNA trial, much to the delight of anti-vaxxers.[361] A rushed or sloppy RCT would do much more harm than good

- Only the largest RCTs can reliably detect rare vaccine harms or benefits. The rarer the event, the larger a study must be to detect it, something termed a study's power. Generally, rare events can only be detected once the studied treatment has been given to large numbers of people outside an RCT. This is true of nearly all medical treatments, not just vaccines.

- RCT participants, who have to be savvy enough to learn about the trial in the first place, are rarely representative of the general population. RCT participants are generally healthy and motivated enough to travel back and forth to the study site on a regular basis. I didn't have to leave my hospital to participate in a vaccine RCT. The most vulnerable people, those who benefit from the COVID vaccine the most, are underrepresented in RCTs, thus skewing the results. Racial and ethnic minorities have been underrepresented in clinical trials, as have pregnant women.

- RCTs are of relatively short duration. Any vaccine harm or benefit that occurs years later is unlikely to be detected via an RCT, though essentially all vaccine side-effects occur in the first few days after vaccination.

- Unlike any other condition in medicine, the disease and study population change rapidly in a pandemic. The adult vaccine RCTs were done with a variant that is long gone and when many people lacked viral-induced immunity. Though the vaccine was 95% effective at stopping COVID in the original mRNA RCTs, new variants rapidly made these trials historical relics. An RCT that started in the spring of 2020 would have no bearing on variants circulating today.

Given these limitations, researchers use several different types of observational studies to investigate topics that are difficult or impossible to study via an RCT. Though they aren't as rigorous as RCTs, they can provide invaluable information once vaccines and other products have been released in the real world and taken by hundreds of millions of people. If you think smoking kills and seat belts save lives, your beliefs are derived from observational studies. There has never been an RCT of these measures.

Because they don't select patients randomly, however, observational studies have a greater potential for spurious associations due to random chance and confounding variables. Researchers try to control for this bias and most openly acknowledge their limitations in their papers. While these limitations can be magnified out of proportion by those who wish to cast doubt on the validity of studies showing vaccines work, there are a lot of really bad observational studies.

Anti-Vaxxers and Methodolatry

At first blush, it may not seem that a doctor who calls for larger and longer RCTs is spreading misinformation. "We need better evidence" seems like an unobjectionable comment. However, RCTs are not the only study design that can teach us about vaccines, and those who claim otherwise are guilty of something called methodolatry. Anti-vaxxers use methodolatry to signal that vaccines haven't *really* been tested, and therefore we can't *really* know if they are safe and effective.

Most commonly anti-vaxxers have used this technique to cast doubt about the efficacy of HPV vaccine. As the article "The New Gardasil: Is It Right for Your Daughter?" posted by Dr. Kelly Brogan put it:

> *In the marketing and licensure of the HPV vaccine, changes to cervical cells have been equated with death. This is called using a "surrogate marker" and in vaccine research, this is considered acceptable because we can't otherwise prove a non-event is attributable to an intervention. There are leaps in logic and in science inherent in this practice, that render conclusions nothing more than false marketing. In fact, none of the HPV vaccines have*

> *ever been proven to prevent a single case of cervical cancer.*[362]

Dr. Brogan is not entirely wrong. There is no evidence from an RCT showing that the HPV vaccine prevents cervical cancer. The RCTs of the HPV vaccine used a surrogate endpoint, cervical intraepithelial neoplasia, which can be a cancer precursor.[363] As HPV-related cancers take many years to develop, this outcome would not be possible to study in the timeframe of an RCT, nor would it be ethical to let people remain in the placebo group once evidence emerged of the vaccine's safety and efficacy. Doctors used the HPV vaccine before they knew for sure that it would prevent cancers.

Of course, it was never a great leap to surmise that if the HPV vaccine prevented HPV infections and cervical intraepithelial neoplasia, it would also prevent cervical cancer itself. Indeed, there is now clear evidence from multiple large observational studies showing the HPV vaccine is very effective at preventing cervical cancer.[364] A study of 1.7 million women found that the HPV vaccine reduced cervical cancer incidence by 90% in girls vaccinated before age 17 years.[365] So yes, the HPV vaccine has been proven to prevent cancer.

Dr. Brogan rejects all of this. She'll *never* admit the vaccine prevents cancer.

I'm confident a massive RCT lasting 20-years could have also proven the HPV vaccine prevents cervical cancer, but there would have been a real cost of waiting. Countless millions are protected against HPV-related cancers because doctors used common sense and gave the vaccine based on solid, but less-than-perfect data.

Doctors used common sense and less-than-perfect data with the COVID vaccines too. Only one person died of COVID in the adult mRNA vaccine RCTs, and there was no evidence they saved lives when they were given to hundreds of millions of Americans. However, the RCTs showed the vaccine was very effective at stopping SARS-CoV-2 infections and preventing severe COVID. Of course, it was never a great leap to surmise that if a vaccine did this, it would also stop people from dying of COVID. As with the HPV vaccine, doctors' embrace of the extremely obvious paid off. Countless lives have been saved because doctors didn't wait until there was pristine evidence the vaccine saved lives before using the vaccine to save lives.

None of this was controversial amongst doctors previously. Only those like Dr. Brogan, who wrote articles titled "The Truth is Out: Gardasil Vaccine Coverup Exposed," opposed the HPV vaccine because there was no evidence from an RCT showing it reduced cancer and all-cause mortality.[366]

Anti-vaxxers also use methodolatry to convince parents that vaccines are dangerous. Prior to the pandemic, anti-vaccine cardiologist Dr. Jack Wolfson said, "To all the pediatricians in the world, please show me the study that found 69 doses of 16 vaccines do not cause cancer, auto-immune disease, and brain injury."[367] This simply is not how science works. It makes as much sense as demanding studies that show turmeric does not cause lung cancer and that coconut oil does not cause strokes. While there are plenty of RCTs showing vaccines are safe, anti-vaxxers will always say they didn't last long enough or weren't large enough. The perfect RCT is always the one yet to be done.

A frequent bit of anti-vaccine sophistry is to bemoan that there has never been an RCT of the entire vaccine schedule, and therefore RCTs showing the safety of individual vaccines are useless. They say in essence – *We all agree that RCTs are the gold-standard. If only lazy scientists enrolled millions of children in a simple RCT of the entire vaccine-schedule lasting the entire human lifespan looking at every possible outcome, my fears about vaccines would be assuaged.* A typical example comes from Dr. Brogan's pamphlet, "Vaccines and Brain Health," in which she wrote:

> *The vaccine schedule is a one-size-fits-all approach that has never (not once) been studied in its ever-growing entirety...The current vaccine schedule requires multiple inflammatory chemicals to be injected with little to no time in between, with people (especially babies!) often getting multiple shots in a single office visit. This barrage of antigens and inflammatory chemicals can over-activate the psychoneuroimmune system for years. Amazingly, the MMR vaccine package inserts clearly state that coadministration with other vaccines has not*

> *been studied. And only one longitudinal study has been done to assess the whole vaccine schedule in primates.*[249]

Anti-vaxxers are fully aware that an RCT of the entire vaccine schedule looking at every imaginable outcome would require hundreds of thousands of children and would take decades to perform. They further know that no parent would sign their infant up for such an RCT, no ethical scientist would conduct it, it wouldn't be approved by an IRB, and no one would fund it. It would be literally impossible to actually carry out such an RCT, and *that's the point.* Anti-vaxxers don't like that studies overwhelmingly show that vaccines are safe and effective, so they call for *impossible* RCTs to diminish the credibility of the perfectly good RCTs that exist.

Anti-vaxxers are always able to move the goalposts, identifying gaps that they feel only an enormous RCT could fill. The RCTs that have been done are deemed fatally flawed. Frequently, they are felt to be too small in size or too short in duration. Though there are many studies showing vaccines are safe and effective, the only study that matters to anti-vaxxers is just one more, forever undone RCT. However, demanding impossible RCTs while rejecting the perfectly good studies that have already been done is the entire point for those who wish to spread fear about vaccines and fetishize "natural" immunity. In contrast, when an observational study claims to reveal vaccine imperfections, anti-vaxxers suddenly have no issue with this study design, even when the methods are extremely dubious. In fact, these studies are lauded as bombshells.

Anti-Vaxxers, Contrarian Doctors, and Methodolatry

Even though nearly 25,000 children were enrolled in the COVID vaccine RCTs, which is not a small number, anti-vaxxers unsurprisingly continued to use methodolatry to belittle their value, pointing out that there are no RCTs showing the vaccine prevents severe outcomes in children. An article titled "Pfizer COVID Vaccine Fails Risk-Benefit Analysis in Children 5 to 11" from Robert F. Kennedy, Jr.'s anti-vaccine website stated:

> *One could vaccinate every child age 5 to 11 in the U.S. and not prevent a single hospitalization, ICU*

admission, or death from coronavirus — according to Pfizer's own clinical trial data as submitted to the FDA. It appears Pfizer was not even trying to conduct a responsible clinical trial of its mRNA shot in kids ages 5 to 11. Pfizer submitted an EUA application to the FDA showing no health benefit in children ages 5 to 11 and the FDA's Vaccines and Related Biologics Products Advisory Committee approved it anyway.[152]

Many contrarian doctors were similarly unimpressed with the pediatric vaccine trials. In an article on *Medscape*, Dr. John Mandrola spread misinformation about the adolescent RCT saying:

After a "positive" trial in which just over 1100 kids aged 12 to 15 years received an mRNA vaccine, a movement arose to vaccinate young and old alike. I put "positive" in quotes for two reasons: The first is that this trial measured noninferiority of the immune response, not clinical outcomes. That was necessary because so few kids get sick with COVID-19. The other reason is that the authors claimed a favorable safety profile, but 1100 kids is not enough to inform the safety of a vaccine that will be given to many millions.[310]

In fact, the adolescent RCT measured the efficacy of the vaccine,[28] something that is clearly stated in the title of the study – "Safety, Immunogenicity, and Efficacy of the BNT162b2 COVID-19 Vaccine in Adolescents." Sixteen children got COVID during this trial, all in the placebo group. Dr. Mandrola did not mention this to his readers. He apparently did not believe it was a "clinical outcome" when an adolescent got COVID in a trial of a vaccine designed to prevent them from getting COVID.

Many contrarian doctors felt that vaccines should have been authorized for children only after RCTs demonstrated their efficacy against severe disease. In an essay titled "The Triumph of Natural Immunity," Dr. Martin Kulldorff wrote:

The medical establishment used to push for evidence-

> *based medicine as a counterweight to "alternative medicine." It is tragic how that philosophy has now been thrown out the window. If Pfizer and Moderna want these vaccines to be given to children, they should first conduct a randomized controlled trial that shows that they reduce hospitalization and all-cause mortality. They failed to do so for adults. They should not get away with that for our children.*[368]

Similarly, in an essay titled "The CDC Is Breaking Trust in Childhood Vaccination," Drs. Leslie Bienen and Tracy Beth Høeg wrote:

> *With rates of severe disease now much lower in children than at the start of the pandemic—due to higher levels of natural immunity and lower rates of severe disease caused by omicron—trials would have needed to enroll hundreds of thousands of children, if not over a million, in order to detect a significant impact of the pediatric vaccine against severe disease. Vaccine companies could have conducted such time-consuming and costly trials, especially if there had been interest in international collaboration. But there was no economic incentive to do so, and every economic incentive not to: Speed, not providing meaningful information to parents and physicians about safety and efficacy, was the priority of U.S. regulatory agencies...*
>
> *The trials, in other words, enrolled only a fraction of the number of participants that would have been required to determine efficacy against end points like severe disease, hospitalization, and rare adverse events such as myocarditis, which has been linked to COVID vaccination in males in the 12- to 17-year-old age group at a rate of up to 1 in 2,700. Furthermore, the follow-up time after the second dose of Moderna and the third dose of Pfizer was only 1-3 months...*[369]

They protested that the pediatric RCTs:

> *Did not assess protection from severe disease, hospitalization, or multisystem inflammatory syndrome in children (MIS-C), important outcomes that parents worry about.*

At first glance, these doctors' objections seem valid. We all agree that RCTs are the gold standard, and before giving a vaccine to tens of millions of children, it seems reasonable to demand evidence from an RCT showing that the vaccine limits severe outcomes. But would it have been possible to run such an RCT, and would the information gained be worth the wait?

Fortunately, children rarely die from COVID or anything else. As such, it would take one of the largest and longest RCTs in the history of medicine to evaluate the vaccine's effect on all-cause mortality as Dr. Kulldorff demanded. Drs. Bienen and Høeg rightly state that such a trial would need to "enroll hundreds of thousands of children, if not over a million."

Such an enormous study cannot simply be willed into existence, and some obvious questions arise. Would hundreds of thousands, if not over a million parents enroll their children into an RCT? Would anyone fund it? Are there enough properly trained research personnel to conduct such a study? Would an IRB approve a study where children are purposefully left unvaccinated, potentially for many years? Would ethical doctors work for this study or enroll their patients in it? Should pediatric vaccines be taken off the market until this study is done? Would previously infected children be allowed in the study? If not, where would the uninfected children come from? Would the results be available in a useful timeframe? Given how quickly the virus mutates, would the results have any relevance by the time the study was over? Most importantly, what would be the consequences of leaving unvaccinated children vulnerable during this time?

None of the doctors who've proposed a million-child RCT gave a moment's thought to these important questions. This is because they didn't expect anyone to actually take them seriously. As with anti-vaxxers calling for an RCT of the entire vaccine schedule, they know there's no way an RCT hundreds of thousands of children, if not over a million, could be run in a useful time frame.

This may explain why I never saw contrarian doctors promote

pediatric RCTs. They never encouraged parents to enroll their children in them. Instead, they told parents that COVID was harmless while the vaccine had unpleasant and potentially deadly side effects. Though contrarian doctors demanded larger RCTs, they gave parents every reason to avoid them, undermining the scientists who actually ran these studies.

And thus, it becomes clear; a million-child RCT is just another *impossible* study and – again – that's the point. Calling for an RCT, with no regard as to whether it could actually be done, is what contrarian doctors do when they don't like the results of the many studies that show the vaccine is beneficial for children. It's a rhetorical trick that signals to parents *this vaccine hasn't really been tested.*

Notably, some of these doctors are happy to use treatments that weren't studied in RCTs of hundreds of thousands of people. For example, according to Dr. Høeg's professional profile:

> *Dr. Høeg has a special interest in harnessing the body's ability to heal itself through exercise and movement as well as by stimulating the body's ability to heal itself through orthobiologic medicine such as platelet rich plasma, proliferative therapy such as dextrose as well as bone marrow aspirate concentrate.*[370]

Dr. Høeg knows there aren't massive RCTs showing the benefits of bone marrow aspirate concentrate, yet this doesn't bother her. She also knows that doctors have to make decisions all the time in the absence of pristine evidence from a massive RCT, and repeatedly exposing unvaccinated children to the virus is such a decision. There have been zero RCTs of the virus after all. We have no data from an RCT showing that repeated exposures to SARS-CoV-2 are safe for developing children.

Though contrarian doctors frame the issue as whether or not children should be vaccinated, the real question is whether or not a child should be vaccinated before they encounter SARS-CoV-2. Only the most isolated children will be able to avoid the virus, and there would have been a severe cost had we demanded a million-child RCT. Such a trial might be 10% enrolled by now and would have no relevance to whatever variants will be circulating in 2030 when the results might finally be available. How many unvaccinated children would have suffered or died while this trial was being run? Contrarian doctors never considered this question.

While it's true we vaccinated children before we knew *for sure* the vaccine would keep them safe and alive, time is not an unlimited luxury in the middle of a raging pandemic. Given the vaccine limited severe disease in adults and that it prevented SARS-CoV-2 infections in children, it was never a great leap to imagine that it would also prevent severe COVID outcomes in some children as well. Some children are alive today because of the vaccine, and many more were spared hospitalization. This is why doctors who actually treat sick children were so eager to vaccinate their patients.

Again, there were real world consequences to such methodolatry. In their "guidance stating that healthy children from ages 5 to 17 may not benefit from receiving the currently available COVID-19 vaccine,"[137] The Florida Department of Health quoted Dr. Martin Kulldorff, who said:

> *I think in public health, it's important to be honest, not only about what we know, but also what we don't know. If you go back and look at the randomized trials for children of the Pfizer vaccine that we used for the emergency use authorization, what those trials showed – and they had about a little over 4,000 people in total in these two trials – is that there is the reduction in mild infections. If you look at serious disease, the hospitalization and deaths, there was none.*

Predictably, Dr. Kulldorff did not mention that nearly 25,000 children enrolled in one of six RCTs, nor did he discuss the many observational studies showing the vaccine limits serious disease in children.

Contrarian doctors are very familiar with the strengths and weaknesses of various study designs, and they could have used their large platforms to educate the public on this topic. They could have informed people that while all doctors agree RCTs are the gold-standard, having an idea for an RCT is infinitely easier than actually doing an RCT. Instead, they misled people into believing that only enormous RCTs can determine the value of vaccines, that such RCTs could have easily been done, and they weren't done because "the medical establishment" doesn't care about evidence.

In reality, when pandemic interventions aren't studied via an RCT, it's not because doctors are ignorant and lazy, it's because these studies are expensive, slow, and hard to do in a world of limited resources. It's no surprise that contrarian doctors always call for *someone else* to do an RCT rather than doing these trials themselves.

Contrarian doctors are always able to move the goalposts, identifying gaps that they feel only an enormous RCT could fill. The RCTs that have been done are deemed fatally flawed. Frequently, they are felt to be too small in size or too short in duration. Though there are many studies showing vaccines are safe and effective, the only study that matters to contrarian doctors is just one more, forever undone RCT. However, demanding impossible RCTs while rejecting the perfectly good studies that have already been done is the entire point for those who wish to spread fear about vaccines and fetishize "natural" immunity. In contrast, when an observational study claims to reveal vaccine imperfections, contrarian doctors suddenly have no issue with this study design, even when the methods are extremely dubious. In fact, these studies are lauded as bombshells.

#19 ~ "Observational data has been used to support vaccines, but is plagued by confounding."

So how does Dr. Brogan respond to a study that finds the HPV vaccine led to a 90% reduction in cervical cancer incidence?[371] She has a neat trick for dealing with unwanted studies like this. She just throws them away.

A corollary of the anti-vaccine notion that only randomized-controlled trials (RCTs) can demonstrate the benefits of vaccines, is that observational trials can be summarily discarded when they support vaccines. The fact that all observational studies have bias and some observational studies are fatally biased, is taken to mean that all observational studies are fatally biased, so long as they support vaccines. Anti-vaxxers thus spare themselves the difficult task of finding flaws in the many studies that show vaccines are safe and effective. They just throw these studies away.

In contrast, anti-vaxxers embrace observational studies that claim that vaccines are dangerous. With such welcome results, their previous concerns about bias and methodological flaws immediately evaporate.

In her pamphlet "Vaccines and Brain Health," Dr. Kelly Brogan was very upfront about this, saying that "scientific data has confirmed the risks, but not benefits, of vaccines."[249] She openly admits that she will reject any observational data showing vaccines are safe and effective, yet she will embrace this study design so long as the results purport to reveal vaccines' flaws.

Contrarian doctors agreed. In an article opposing pediatric COVID vaccinations, Dr. Vinay Prasad summarily dismissed over a dozen observational studies showing the COVID vaccine prevents severe disease in children with a single swoop of a hand, writing:

> *Observational data has been used to support vaccines, but is plagued by confounding. That is because parents who vaccinate their kids are different from those who don't. The same studies could show that driving a baby home from hospital in a Mercedes is better than a Ford.*[205]

That's just throwing studies away.

All observational studies have some bias, and nearly all researchers share the limitations with their work. Sometimes the bias is so severe, it renders an observational study useless. However, unless someone identifies a specific problem, every single observational study supporting vaccines can't be discarded this way. This is especially the case when over 20 studies all have the same, unsurprising result: the COVID vaccine keeps kids safe and out of the hospital. Of course, observational data has been key in ruling out the link between vaccines and autism. Are all of these studies also "plagued by confounding"? Anti-vaxxers think so. How would Dr. Prasad refute them? Are COVID vaccine observational studies unique in the history of medicine for their confounders?

Moreover, it's possible that confounders could bias studies against the COVID vaccine. It's possible that children with underlying health conditions were more likely to get vaccinated than healthy children, whose misinformed parents heard the virus posed no risk to them. Without controlling for this discrepancy, simply evaluating outcomes in vaccinated and unvaccinated children would make the vaccine appear less effective than it actually is.

Nonetheless, let's examine Dr. Prasad's commitment to reject observational studies with regards to the vaccine's ability to prevent Multisystem Inflammatory Syndrome in Children (MIS-C). At least seven studies from several countries have shown the vaccine drastically lowers the rate of MIS-C.

See Table 4: Observational trials on MIS-C and the COVID vaccine on page 433..

Most doctors would agree, this is compelling evidence that the COVID vaccine lowers the risk of MIS-C. Not to Dr. Prasad. In July 2022, after six of these studies were published, he said on *Twitter*, "Honestly still not sure vaccination lowers the risk of mis-c."[372] So far, so good, at least in terms of Dr. Prasad's commitment to rejecting observational studies.

However, Dr. Prasad adopted a Broganesque attitude towards vaccine-side effects, creating dozens of videos, articles, and tweets about vaccine-myocarditis, despite the fact that information about it comes exclusively from observational studies, which he deemed "plagued by confounding" when they "support vaccines". "It Is Now Undeniable Vaccine can cause more Myocarditis in Men Under 40 Than COVID-19,"[373] he tweeted, though his source for this statement was not an RCT. Moreover, the study upon which Dr. Prasad based his tweet also found that, for the Pfizer vaccine, which all adolescents received, "The risk of hospital admission or death from myocarditis is greater after SARS-CoV2 infection than COVID-19 vaccination."[374] Dr. Prasad did not highlight that important finding.

Dr. Prasad was not alone in embracing observational data only when it shows vaccine harms. In an essay titled "The Triumph of Natural Immunity," Dr. Martin Kulldorff sounded exactly like Dr. Brogan, writing:

> *There are no RCTs that show the vaccine prevents deaths or provides any other tangible benefit to*

> *children, while there could be harms. All vaccines come with some risks of adverse reactions, and while we know that they cause an increased risk of myocarditis (inflammation of the heart) in young people...*[368]

So, which is it? Are observational studies plagued by confounding or not? Why are Drs. Prasad and Kulldorff not bothered by the fact that there are no RCTs showing the vaccine causes myocarditis? If observational studies are hopelessly confounded when reporting vaccine benefits, how can they be trusted when reporting vaccine harms?

The answer, of course, is that contrarian doctors have overtly different standards of evidence when it comes to vaccine benefits and harms, just like Dr. Brogan.

#20 ~ "Kids vaccines were authorized based on antibody titers, a surrogate that becomes less reliable by the day."

It's true that antibodies are not a perfect surrogate marker for immunity to a particular virus. However, they are not meaningless either and there is a history of using antibody levels (termed immunobridging) to approve vaccines for children once they have proven their value in adults. Biostatistician Dr. Natalie Dean explained why:

> *Immunobridging is a common way to extend an existing vaccine into new populations. ... We leverage the extensive efficacy and safety data from other populations, and so do not need to start from scratch in generating evidence.*[375]

According to an interview with Dr. Philip Krause, former deputy FDA chief for vaccines:

> *Immunobridging between children and adults has been used to approve Vaxchora, a cholera vaccine, Krause said, and the method was also used to approve*

two HPV vaccines down to age 9. Immunobridging from a different flu vaccine tested in children also served as the basis for approving the seasonal flu vaccine Afluria in kids, he added.

Naturally, anti-vaxxers have sought to cast doubt on vaccines approved via this pathway. In her pamphlet "Vaccines and Brain Health," Dr. Kelly Brogan wrote:

Protective immunity involves parts of the immune system beyond antibodies, and studies have confirmed that the presence of antibodies doesn't directly translate into protection. For example, even though the flu vaccine creates antibodies, this vaccine is notoriously ineffective, with protection estimates ranging from 19% - 48% depending on the season.[249]

During the pandemic, the COVID vaccines for children ages 6-months to 5-years were authorized based on their ability to generate a robust immune response. Fortunately, this has been found to be a reliable marker of immunity for COVID. An article in the *New England Journal of Medicine* titled "A COVID-19 Milestone Attained — A Correlate of Protection for Vaccines" stated:

Meta-analyses have established high correlations between the standardized mean titer and vaccine efficacy, and the neutralizing antibody titer has consistently been shown to be a mechanistic correlate of protection in challenge studies in nonhuman primates.[376]

Nonetheless, several contrarian doctors, who never cared about immunobridging for other vaccines, decided the COVID vaccine was different for some reason. Dr. Marty Makary tweeted:

Inferred through "immunobridging" young adult data from another study?? This is statistical acrobatics, which appears to be done to achieve a desired outcome. There is no justification to bypass rigorous safety & efficacy clinical trials in children.[377]

In an article opposing pediatric vaccination, Dr. Vinay Prasad wrote:

> *Kids vaccines were authorized based on antibody titers, a surrogate that becomes less reliable by the day, and is not evidence they can lower rates of symptomatic Omicron, and its' sequelae.*[205]

Thankfully, regulators disagreed. In justifying the approval of pediatric vaccines for babies and toddlers, the CDC stated that, based on the immunobridging data, the vaccines "are expected to provide higher protection against severe disease"[378] in the youngest children. This was a very reasonable supposition, especially considering millions of elementary school children had already been safely vaccinated. Indeed, several months after the vaccine was approved for babies and toddlers, the FDA published data showing that the vaccine efficacy was over 70% against COVID infections.[379] Moreover, after one million children had been vaccinated, there were no reports of vaccine-myocarditis in this age group.[380]

While no one would claim that immunobridging studies are ideal, time is not an unlimited luxury in the middle of a pandemic. Doctors must make decisions with less-than-perfect information every day. It's a good thing that babies, who have the highest risk of dying from COVID, can now be protected against it once they are 6-months old.

#21 ~ "All COVID-19 vaccines target the Wuhan ancestral strain. The current prevailing strain is BA.5, which has immune escape from the vaccine."

Anti-vaxxers pretend that because viruses mutate, this means vaccines against them are useless. In her pamphlet "Vaccines and Brain Health," Dr. Kelly Brogan argued that even if vaccines induced protecting immunity at some point, evolution has since rendered them useless. She wrote:

> *Emerging science has called into question the effectiveness of vaccines, including the documentation*

> *of outbreaks in highly to completely-vaccinated populations and the finding that disease-causing microbes are quickly evolving to escape vaccine-induced immunity.*[249]

Obviously, this doesn't mean vaccines don't work. Yet, this rhetorical trick protects Dr. Brogan from the impossible task of showing that vaccines fail to protect children.

During the pandemic, the same contrarian doctors who lamented that pediatric COVID vaccines weren't studied via massive randomized-controlled trials also sought to undermine their value because they targeted the original SARS-CoV-2 strain. According to their logic, pediatric vaccines are of dubious value because they weren't studied for long enough and also because they rapidly became outdated. It's a perfect Catch-22.

In an article opposing pediatric COVID vaccination, Dr. Vinay Prasad made the same point as Dr. Brogan. He wrote, "All COVID-19 vaccines target the Wuhan ancestral strain.... The current prevailing strain is BA.5, which has immune escape from the vaccine."[205] Dr. Prasad is not wrong that the original mRNA vaccines don't work as well on variants, which is why regulators approved updated vaccines that are a better match. However, even the initial vaccines are far from useless in children. Indeed, one study found:

> *Vaccine effectiveness against death related to SARS-CoV-2 infection during omicron predominance was 66.9% (6.4% to 89.8%) in children and 97.6% (81.0% to 99.7%) in adolescents.*[38]

That's a big deal.

Whatever the future holds, the vaccine has already prevented a lot of suffering for a lot of children. It's certainly possible that future variants will render our current vaccines obsolete, but until there's evidence of that, baseless warnings that viruses are "quickly evolving to escape vaccine-induced immunity"[249] should not be used to leave children vulnerable to SARS-CoV-2 or any other vaccine-preventable disease.

#22 ~ "Norwegian authorities believe that natural infection will better protect children than vaccines that rely on out-of-date variants of the virus."

In 2018, anti-vaccine activist Robert F. Kennedy, Jr. wrote an article titled "The HPV Debacle: Suppressing Inconvenient Evidence" in which he celebrated Japan's decision to stop recommending the HPV vaccine. He said:

> *Following a public hearing (February 2014) at which scientific evidence was presented by independent scientists the Japanese government, not only rescinded its recommendation that girls receive the HPV vaccine, Japan established guidelines and special clinics for evaluating and treating illnesses caused by the vaccine.*[381]

Mr. Kennedy was correct about this history. In response to anti-vaccine misinformation, Japan stopped recommending the HPV vaccine in 2013, causing vaccination rates to fall from 70% to 1%.[382] It took nine years for the decision to be reversed, but it was too late for many women. A modeling study in 2020 estimated that Japan's failure to use the vaccine would result in 25,000 preventable cervical cancer cases and up to 5,700 deaths.[383] That's horrible.

During the pandemic, nearly all countries with abundant supply chose to recommend at least one dose of the COVID vaccine for children. However, there were some countries that were less than enthusiastic about vaccinating children, and they were predictably celebrated by anti-vaccine activists. An article on Mr. Kennedy's anti-vaccine website titled "Fauci Says Kids Under 5 Might Need 3 Shots, as Sweden Says Benefits Don't Outweigh Risks for Young Kids" proclaimed:

> *While the U.S. pushes for COVID vaccines for children as young as 6 months, Sweden's public health authorities this week announced they will not recommend the vaccines for children between the ages of 5 and 11....The Norwegian Institute of Public*

> *Health stated the risk of severe illness in children that is brought on by COVID is small, and that as a result, the need for children to receive a COVID vaccine is limited.*[384]

A week later, Dr. Vinay Prasad and Allison Krug made the exact same point in their article, "Should We Let Children Catch Omicron?" They wrote:

> *In Norway, for instance, parents of 5–11 year-olds can get vaccines for their children if they want them, but vaccines are only recommended for children with serious underlying conditions. This is not because vaccines are ineffective but because, according to the Norwegian Institute of Public Health, "the risk of a severe disease course at this age is small, and the need for vaccines for children and adolescents is limited... In fact, Norwegian authorities believe that natural infection will better protect children than vaccines that rely on out-of-date variants of the virus.*[82]

Dr. Tracy Høeg similarly made sure to let her Twitter audience know that the U.K. and many Nordic countries were reluctant to vaccinate children.[476]

Though anti-vaxxers claimed otherwise, Japan's HPV vaccine debacle shows that a wealthy country with intelligent doctors can make flawed decisions. Moreover, children in Norway had vastly improved COVID outcomes compared to American children,[385] showing the folly of basing vaccine recommendations for children in Atlanta based on the experience of children in Oslo. Prior to the pandemic, the fact that a country did not recommend a vaccine would not be accepted as a scientifically valid argument against that vaccine.

#23 ~ "We're unmasked, unboosted and unrepentant."

Like every medical intervention, vaccines are not perfect, and no one claims otherwise. No vaccine prevents every case of disease after a single shot. The preposterous belief that vaccines should be rejected unless they are perfect is known as the nirvana fallacy, and other mechanisms to prevent injury are not held to this standard. Seatbelts are not perfect. They can cause serious injuries, and the medical literature has described them in gory detail. But no rational person rejects seatbelts because they offer imperfect protection.

Anti-vaxxers are often guilty of the nirvana fallacy, claiming that vaccines are useless unless they are perfect. Sayer Ji, the founder of the anti-vaccine site *GreenMedInfo*, expressed this absurd belief about measles in 2014. He wrote:

> *The only way that the act of refraining from vaccinating could be justifiably characterized as 'insane behavior' is if vaccines were proven effective 100% of the time.*[386]

Most commonly, anti-vaxxers employ this technique against booster doses, claiming that vaccines are worthless unless they provide perfect, permanent protection after a single shot. An article titled "Measles and Measles Vaccines: 14 Things to Consider" on *GreenMedInfo* complained that:

> *The inventors of the early measles vaccines made claims that the vaccine would provide lifelong immunity to measles with a single shot...However, unlike natural measles infection, the measles vaccine does not appear to provide such long lasting protection. Protection afforded by vaccination appears to wane in number of years.*[230]

In his essay "Measles Transmitted By The Vaccinated, Gov. Researchers Confirm," Mr. Ji felt the measles vaccine was flawed for this reason. He said:

> *The vaccine's obvious fallibility is also indicated by the fact that the CDC now requires two doses.*[180]

Anti-vaxxers often use the pure number of vaccine doses to dissuade parents away from all of them. They know that nothing is scarier than images of needles in babies.

It's true that most vaccines require multiple doses. Children in the U.S. receive 4 doses of the polio vaccine,[387] and they receive the DTaP at 2, 4, and 6 months, 15-18 months, and 4-6 years with the Tdap at 11-12 years.[388] The schedule for routine pediatric vaccines changes occasionally as experts learn more about how immunity evolves over time, and changes in the vaccine schedule, even for old vaccines, are not unprecedented. A measles outbreak among vaccinated children in 1989 led to a second MMR dose, and in 2016, a dose of the HPV vaccine was removed for 11- and 12-year-olds.[389] That nearly all vaccines require multiple doses to be maximally effective is not a reasonable argument against them, and before the pandemic, any doctor who defended this position would have been correctly labeled a quack.

While we all hoped otherwise, there was never any guarantee that two doses of the COVID vaccine would provide years of robust protection against all future variants. Few vaccine experts were shocked that the COVID vaccine needed a booster, especially given how rapidly the virus mutates. Though they remained strong advocates for the first two vaccine doses for older adults, several contrarian doctors adopted Mr. Ji's attitude to the COVID boosters.

During a podcast from December 2021 called "Omicron Panic, Natural Immunity, Fluvoxamine, & More," Drs. Vinay Prasad, Marty Makary, and Zubin Damania made a display of sitting close together in a podcast booth and boisterously boasted about not having been boosted.[300] The transcript reads as follows:

> – *[**Marty**] Are you guys boosted being that close or is this an unboosted contact?*
>
> – *[**Zubin**] We're unmasked, unboosted and unrepentant, Marty.*
>
> – *[**Marty**] Well, I'm an unboosted male. That's my preferred pronoun, by the way.*
>
> – *[**Zubin**] Oh, is that your pronoun? An unboosted male? Yes, my pronouns are it, they, those and*

> *currently unboosted because I got Moderna, which apparently kicks ass….*
>
> *– [**Vinay**] …I haven't gotten my booster yet and-*
>
> *– [**Marty**] You mean this week you haven't gotten, 'cause you do weekly boosters, I'm sure.*
>
> *– [**Vinay**] Well, eventually, we're all gonna have to keep boosting.*
>
> *– [**Marty**] Yeah, boosting.*
>
> *– [**Zubin**] You know, my vaccine card looks like one of those like frequent flier like coffee cards where they punch the hole, like I boosted here and boosted here and boosted here and when I get 10 boosters, Fauci sends me a Fauci bobblehead that says I am the science.*
>
> *– [**Marty**] I'm getting my booster sent with the GNC nutrition vitamins.*
>
> *– [**Vinay**] They had the same evidence, you know.*

Dr. Makary falsely claimed that the booster's only benefit was that it would lower the hospitalization rate from 1 in 26,000 to 1 in 260,000 in people older than age 65. He said that the "the average age of a breakthrough death is 80," to which Dr. Damania would reply:

> *And if you look at a population of 80-year-olds, their time to death in general is not that long.*

My parents are in their early 80s, and I don't want them to die of COVID. I hope they have many happy years ahead of them. I took my grandmother to Las Vegas and the Grand Canyon for the first time when she was 95. She had so much fun, she returned to Las Vegas when she was 97. She lived to be 101, happy and healthy until the end. Countless families have mourned an elderly relative who died of COVID.

Dr. Makary would take his anti-booster message to a broader audience, falsely saying on Fox News there was no "scientific data" supporting the booster:

> *Well, there's no evidence to support it. And actually the few places in the world that are doing boosters are admittedly saying, we're not doing it with science, we're just doing it based on a theory that we think you might need it.*[482]

In fact, by December 2021, there was clear evidence boosters were beneficial. Though the results were only available as a press release, a randomized-controlled trial of 10,000 people showed that a booster was safe and 95% effective at preventing COVID.[390] This research has since been published in *The New England Journal of Medicine*, and it was always reasonable to assume that if the booster lowered SARS-CoV-2 infection rates, it would also lower severe COVID outcomes.[391] The results from an observational study of nearly 1.5 million people were also available when this podcast aired. It found that a booster was over 90% effective against admission to hospital and for severe disease, and 81% effective against death from COVID.[392]

Not only was there clear evidence the boosters were beneficial by December 2021, but a highly contagious variant also that evaded our immune system was on the horizon.[393] The consequences of the Omicron variant, combined with waning of the first two vaccine doses and low booster rates, were both tragic and predictable. An article in the *New York Times* titled "During the Omicron Wave, Death Rates Soared for Older People"[394] said it all.

There is now clear evidence from at least nine large studies from four countries in different countries (England,[395] UK,[396] Qatar,[397] Israel,[392] Israel,[398] Israel,[399] Israel,[400] USA,[401] USA[402]) showing that boosters are extremely effective at limiting severe disease. Two studies even showed the booster limits symptomatic COVID in adolescents.[46.53]

The second booster is also important. A CDC study reported that:

> *In a large cohort of nursing home residents, receipt of a second mRNA COVID-19 booster dose during circulation of SARS-CoV-2 Omicron subvariants was 74% effective at 60 days against severe COVID-19–related outcomes (including hospitalization or death) and 90% against death alone compared with receipt of a single booster dose.*[403]

The CDC also published data that found:

> *In June 2022, people ages 50 years and older with ≥2 booster doses had 14 times lower risk of dying from COVID-19, compared to unvaccinated people and 3 times lower risk of dying from COVID-19 than people with one booster dose.*[404]

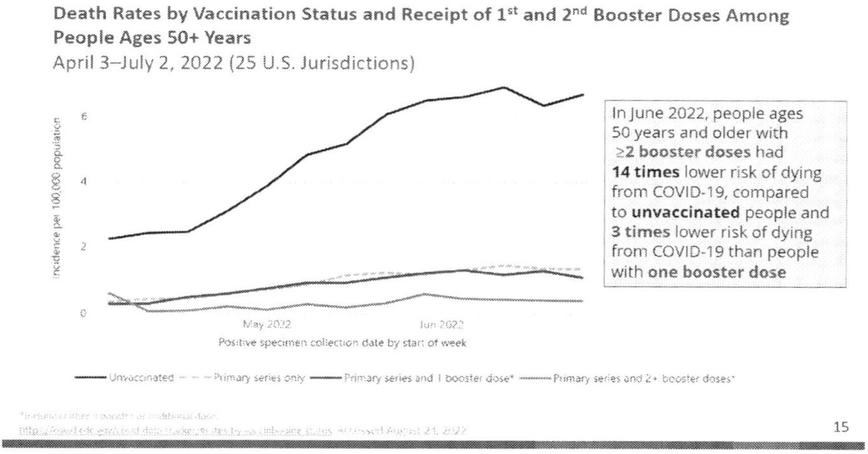

Findings presented by the CDC on September 1, 2022

Even after this data was published, Dr. Prasad continued to embrace the nirvana fallacy, mocking CDC Dr. Rochelle Walensky for her COVID infection. He wrote:

> *The CDC director getting COVID-19 one month after getting bivalent booster is a reminder she doesn't know what she is talking about. That's because she never asked Pfizer for appropriate randomized data.*[405]

The first two vaccine doses are still the most important, but there's no question that booster doses save lives and prevent suffering, especially for older people. While the booster is suboptimal at preventing COVID infections, every dose studied thus far has lowered the risk of severe outcomes. Dr. Walensky's COVID infection was likely much milder because of the bivalent booster.

Indeed, less than two months after Dr. Prasad's taunt, the CDC published two studies showing the bivalent booster protects adults against severe disease. One study concluded:

> *Among immunocompetent adults aged ≥65 years hospitalized in the multistate IVY Network, a bivalent booster dose provided 73% additional protection against COVID-19 hospitalization compared with past monovalent mRNA vaccination only.*[406]

The other concluded:

> *Bivalent booster doses provided additional protection against COVID-19–associated emergency department/urgent care encounters and hospitalizations in persons who previously received 2, 3, or 4 monovalent vaccine doses. Because of waning of monovalent vaccine-conferred immunity, relative effectiveness of bivalent vaccines was higher with increased time since the previous monovalent dose.*[407]

In addition, a study from Israel found the bivalent vaccine effectiveness was 81% for COVID- related hospitalizations and 86% for death,[477] while a different study found that "bivalent boosters provided substantial additional protection against severe omicron infection in persons who had previously been vaccinated or boosted."[478]

The third and fourth doses should just be called the third and fourth dose, and getting a COVID shot might become an annual event, which is less work than going to the dentist. Getting millions of Americans these extra doses is very low-hanging fruit for those who aim to prevent hospitalizations and save lives. Instead, contrarian doctors chose to mock and shame anyone willing to get a simple injection to gain extra protection against a dangerous, mutating virus.

#24 ~ "WOW! Paul Offit advised his own son not to get boosted."

Dr. Diane M. Harper is a professor in the departments of family medicine and obstetrics and gynecology at the University of Michigan. According to her biography, she "is an internationally recognized clinical research expert in HPV associated diseases, their prevention, early detection, and treatment for the prevention of cancer."[408] In 2009, Dr. Harper raised questions about the HPV vaccine saying:

> *If we vaccinate 11 year olds and the protection doesn't last... we've put them at harm from side effects, small but real, for no benefit. The benefit to public health is nothing, there is no reduction in cervical cancers, they are just postponed, unless the protection lasts for at least 15 years, and over 70% of all sexually active females of all ages are vaccinated.*[409]

After voicing doubts about the HPV vaccine in a TV interview with journalist Katie Couric, Dr. Harper became an unwitting hero to anti-vaxxers, and her name would invariably arise in their discussions of the HPV vaccine. To pick one example amongst many, in the essay "The New Gardasil: Is It Right For Your Daughter?" posted to her website, Dr. Kelly Brogan asked:

> *In fact, none of the HPV vaccines have ever been proven to prevent a single case of cervical cancer. Don't take my word for it, listen to what Diane Harper, one of the lead researchers for the vaccine, and a whistleblower, has to say:*
>
> *"It is silly to mandate vaccination of 11- to 12-year-old girls. There also is not enough evidence gathered on side effects to know that safety is not an issue. This vaccine has not been tested in little girls for*

efficacy. At 11, these girls don't get cervical cancer - they won't know for 25 years if they will get cervical cancer. ...To mandate now is simply to Merck's benefit, and only to Merck's benefit."[362]

Despite these comments, Dr. Harper was never a "whistleblower", and she is not anti-vaccine. In 2018, she said:

I strongly believe in cervical cancer prevention and the effects of the HPV vaccine. The vaccines will give you a higher chance of a normal screening.[410]

She's right about this. Multiple large studies have shown the HPV vaccine has the potential to eliminate cervical cancer. However, her story demonstrates that anti-vaxxers have long been eager to elevate any mainstream, credible scientist who raises any doubts about vaccines, often misrepresenting their position.

Anti-vaxxers continued this technique to cast doubt on the benefit of pediatric COVID vaccines and boosters. Three doctors served the role of Dr. Harper during the pandemic: Drs. Marion Gruber, Philip Krause, and Paul Offit. Like Dr. Harper, these are serious doctors and scientists. Dr. Krause was the former deputy director of the FDA's Office of Vaccines Research and Review, Dr. Gruber was the former director of the Food and Drug Administration's Office of Vaccines Research and Review, and Dr. Offit is a professor of pediatrics at Children's Hospital of Philadelphia and co-developer of the rotavirus vaccine.

These doctors were not opposed to the first two vaccine doses, but they felt booster doses were approved too soon and without enough evidence. In November 2021, they wrote an article titled "We Don't Need Universal Booster Shots. We Need to Reach the Unvaccinated" in which they argued:

Given that protection against serious illness is still strong from the original two doses of the mRNA vaccines, the data simply does not show that every healthy adult should get a booster.[411]

Dr. Offit advised his own son not to get boosted,[412] and Drs. Gruber and Krause resigned from their positions at the FDA in protest.

Predictably, these doctors became unwitting heroes to anti-vaxxers. Robert F. Kennedy, Jr.'s anti-vaccine website wrote an article about Drs. Gruber and Krause titled "2 Top FDA Vaccine Officials Resign, Raising Questions About Pressure from White House to Approve Boosters."[413] It similarly lauded Dr. Offit in an article "Paul Offit: It 'Felt Like the Fix Was In' Before FDA Panel Voted to Reformulate COVID Booster Shots" by saying:

> *In an interview with ZDoggMD, vaccine expert Dr. Paul Offit said the U.S. Food and Drug Administration's advisory panel's recent meeting on whether to modify COVID-19 boosters was unusual and he felt the panel was led to "vote yes" to reformulate boosters without critical data.*[414]

Whether it's Dr. Harper and the HPV vaccine or Drs. Gruber, Krause, and Offit and COVID vaccines, anti-vaxxers using their names is simply an appeal to authority, in which a claim is said to be valid not because there is evidence for it, but because experts believe it.

Contrarian doctors similarly lauded Drs. Gruber, Krause, and Offit for their opposition to boosters. Dr. Vinay Prasad tweeted:

> *WOW! Paul Offit advised his own son not to get boosted. A man who made vaccines is saying this. Hard for him to be called an 'anti-vaxxer.*[415]

In an article arguing against pediatric COVID vaccines titled "U.S. Public Health Agencies Aren't 'Following the Science,' Officials Say," Drs. Tracy Høeg and Marty Makary said.

> *The FDA's two top vaccine regulators—Dr. Marion Gruber, director of the FDA's vaccine office, and her deputy director, Dr. Philip Krause—quit the agency last year over political pressure to authorize vaccine boosters in young people. After their departure they wrote scathing commentaries explaining why the data did not support a broad booster authorization, arguing in the Washington Post that "the push for*

> *boosters for everyone could actually prolong the pandemic," citing concerns that boosting based on an outdated variant could be counterproductive.*[416]

While experts obviously should be given deference, they are not infallible. What matters is logic and evidence, not credentials and titles. This is especially true with a new, mutating virus and new mRNA vaccines. Experts are learning about all of this in real time, just like everyone else. They've never lived through a pandemic like this either. Dr. Offit's prior work on the rotavirus vaccine doesn't mean he's omniscient about this vaccine and this virus. After all, he predicted on March 2, 2020 that COVID would cause less than "one-tenth of the damage that influenza causes every year in the United States."[417]

There is now clear evidence from large studies in different countries showing that boosters are effective at limiting severe disease, especially in older people. Fortunately, cases of vaccine-myocarditis from the booster are still rare and remain "clinically mild."[269]

While anti-vaxxers and contrarian doctors were willing to share Dr. Offit's and Gruber's skepticism towards boosters, they were unwilling to share their opinion of the first two vaccine doses for children. Dr. Offit said in October 2021:

> *Now, at least the last few weeks, you'd have 200,000 cases in children a week, or 250,000 cases a week, 2,000 hospitalizations a week. And I was just on service at Children's Hospital Philadelphia last week, and I can tell you, we had our share, representing the national average, of an increased number of children with SARS-CoV-2, some of whom were in the intensive care unit, and one of whom was on ECMO, meaning extracorporeal membrane oxygenator, the heart lung machine, and is fighting for her life. So it is, certainly the answer to the question can children suffer this disease, yes. Can they be hospitalized and go to the intensive care unit? Yes. Can they die? Yes, more than 500 children have died. So if you can prevent this vaccine, I'm sorry. If you can prevent*

> *this disease safely and effectively, then prevent it.*[418]

Dr. Krause similarly supported pediatric vaccines, saying:

> *The benefits will outweigh the risk. Certainly any child who has risk factors for severe disease, it's really a no-brainer to get vaccinated. But even for children who don't have these risk factors, it's certainly a very reasonable decision to get them vaccinated.*[375]

It's good that Drs. Offit and Krause supported pediatric vaccination, though of course their expert opinion alone is not a valid argument for vaccinating children. Even Dr. Offit would eventually support a third vaccine dose in children without natural infection.[419] However, doctors should know that dropping names of famous scientists who happen to agree with them is not a substitute for science and evidence. Decisions about vaccines should be decided by evidence, not eminence, especially for a virus that no one heard of until 2020.

#25 ~ "With its unscientific push to vaccinate all infants and toddlers against COVID, the agency will harm vaccine uptake for more significant diseases."

Prior to the pandemic, around 300 American children died annually from all vaccine-preventable illnesses combined.[420] Sadly, this number may grow. The pandemic disrupted routine vaccination programs, the same way it disrupted sports, concerts, and everything else. According to news reports:

> *In a new report published Friday, the World Health Organization and UNICEF said their figures show 25 million children last year failed to get vaccinated against diptheria* [sic], *tetanus and pertussis, a marker for childhood immunization coverage, continuing a downward trend that began in 2019.*[421]

Fortunately, the pandemic's effect on routine childhood immunization has been modest thus far in the US. According to the CDC:

> *For the 2020–21 school year, coverage was approximately 94% for all required vaccines, approximately one percentage point lower than the previous school year. The exemption rate remained low at 2.2%.*[422]

However, the bigger threat to the routine vaccine schedule is the normalization of anti-vaccine mythology. Not only did the pandemic disrupt routine pediatric visits,[423] but anti-vaxxers have capitalized on mistrust of COVID vaccines to sow doubt in all vaccines. As Dr. David Gorski wrote:

> *Since the pandemic has fueled the metastasis of antivax misinformation and conspiracy theories back onto childhood vaccines, the possibility of school vaccine mandates being repealed in some states looks terrifyingly possible.*[424]

Of course, anti-vaxxers are ecstatic about this possibility. An article on Robert F. Kennedy, Jr.'s website celebrated rising mistrust in vaccines in an article titled "A COVID Silver Lining? More Parents Than Ever Questioning 'Routine' Childhood Vaccines." The article's blurb said that:

> *Children and teen vaccination rates began plummeting with the onset of the pandemic, and as concerns surfaced around the safety of COVID-19 vaccines, some parents also began questioning the need for the long list of other vaccines recommended by public health officials.*[425]

When COVID vaccines were approved for babies and toddlers, doctors who don't treat children and who hadn't shown any interest in vaccines previously, suddenly found themselves *very concerned* about the routine pediatric vaccination. They were not concerned about the rise of the anti-vaccine movement, however. They never promoted the MMR or HPV vaccines. Instead, they saw yet another opportunity to minimize pediatric COVID and discourage COVID vaccination.

Their arguments took two forms. The first argument was that pediatricians could only do one thing at a time. In an essay opposing pediatric vaccination in healthy children, Dr. Vinay Prasad wrote:

> *Doctors' time is limited. Routine childhood vaccine rates are slipping. Contrary to COVID-19 shots, the measles vaccine is sterilizing and high rates are needed to halt spread. Doctors must realize that pro-vax does not mean zealotry, but evidence first.*[205]

Pediatricians who try to vaccinate their patients are not "zealots." They are putting evidence first. Doctors are obligated to inform their patients about all vaccines that will keep them safe and out of the hospital. Moreover, at this instant, measles is not a major threat to children. A headline from 2014 said, "Washington Woman Is First U.S. Measles Death in 12 Years."[426] Yes, measles will make a rapid and deadly comeback if vaccination rates fall too low, but the happy truth is we still have herd immunity for measles. In contrast, COVID has killed and hospitalized unvaccinated children daily during the pandemic.

This is all a silly discussion because it is based on a silly premise: that the MMR and COVID vaccines are in a competition with each other where there can be only one winner. In the real world, pediatricians have been vaccinating children against multiple viruses their entire careers. Dr. Prasad presented no evidence that administration of the COVID vaccine would be such a time burden that they would be unable to simultaneously vaccinate children against measles.

Contrarian doctors' second argument was that if parents were encouraged to vaccinate their children against COVID, they would lose trust in other vaccines. In an article titled "The CDC Is Breaking Trust in Childhood Vaccination," Dr. Leslie Bienen and Tracy Høeg wrote that:

> *With its unscientific push to vaccinate all infants and toddlers against COVID, the agency will harm vaccine uptake for more significant diseases.*[369]

This itself was unscientific. Drs. Bienen and Høeg provided no evidence to support their claim, nor did they specify which diseases were "more significant" than COVID, especially considering that COVID killed and hospitalized many more American children in the past two years than all other vaccine-preventable diseases combined.

However, 2022 was the year that polio returned to America, and Dr. Prasad saw this as another opportunity to further sow doubt about the pediatric COVID vaccine. Linking to a new article about the return of polio, he tweeted:

> *A singular focus on COVID and pushing COVID shots in kids, who mostly had COVID (based on weak evidence/ w low yield <5% parents <5 has resulted in neglect for routine childhood immunization, which is disastrous. Many of us saw this coming.*[427]

While Dr. Prasad, who wants to disband the entire American Academy of Pediatrics, was eager to blame pediatricians for the return of polio, he presented no evidence that their efforts to prevent babies from dying of COVID dissuaded routine childhood vaccination.[428] This is because his belief was justified only if COVID vaccines can travel in space and time.

American's polio case occurred in an unvaccinated Orthodox Jewish 20-year-old man[429] who contracted the virus outside the U.S.[430] Had he been vaccinated on schedule he would have received his last polio vaccine 15 years ago. Unfortunately, the Orthodox Jewish community in Rockland County where he lived has long been skeptical of vaccines,[431] and prior to the pandemic, it was targeted by anti-vaccine activists. According to news reports from 2019:

> *Andrew Wakefield, Del Bigtree, and other prominent anti-vaccine advocates unleashed fear and toxic misinformation last night at a well-attended symposium in New York's Rockland County. The area is currently grappling with one of the largest and longest-standing measles outbreaks in the country, mainly in its tight-knit, ultra-Orthodox Jewish community.*[432]

Dr. Wakefield and his ilk found a receptive audience in Rockland County, where low-vaccination rates triggered a measles outbreak that sickened several hundred children in 2018 and 2019.[433] It came as no surprise that polio found a vulnerable victim there. Beyond this, polio has also been found in wastewater in London.[434] As the UK initially refused to vaccinate children against COVID – a fact Dr. Prasad celebrated[435] – this would imply that America's "singular focus on COVID and pushing COVID shots in kids"[427] led to vaccine refusal 3,400 miles away.

Dr. Blima Marcus, an Orthodox nurse practitioner and vaccine-advocate in her community, didn't have much respect for the idea that polio's return could be blamed on COVID vaccines. She said:

> *Stating that public health guidance during COVID sowed enough mistrust to cause an infectious disease outbreak is ridiculous conjecture and completely negates the dozens of outbreaks that preceded COVID. Measles outbreaks in the US occurred in 2011, 2014, and 2018-2019. Mumps outbreaks occurred in 2006, 2009-2010, and annually from 2014 through 2020. There are still tens of thousands of cases of pertussis annually, often linked to unvaccinated counties and clusters.*[436]

She's right. COVID vaccines can be blamed for the return of vaccine-preventable diseases but only if they can travel in space and time.

Moreover, spreading fear and doubt about COVID vaccines isn't the best way to instill confidence in the MMR and polio vaccines. Lydia Greene, a formerly anti-vaccine mother turned vaccine-advocate told me:

> *COVID centrists like Zdogg, Høeg, and Prasad like to blame pro-vaccine pediatricians for vaccine hesitancy. As a highly hesitant parent who was once very fearful of vaccination, I was constantly on the lookout for these centrist points of view, like Dr. Bob Sears and Dr. Paul Thomas. If these medical professionals can find something to be cautious about, then surely my reasons for not vaccinating are in plain sight and being ignored by the people I should trust the most.*

I have also noticed that the reasons the COVID centrists caution against vaccinating children for COVID, can be extrapolated to any vaccine on the schedule. I know those tropes well, and they are being recycled. If you do get a chance to look at the discussions taking place in their comment sections, you will see many vaccine myths being shared and not a single correction by the centrist doctor.

These aren't just COVID vaccine myths, they are myths about the entire childhood schedule. They offer zero correction because they know who butters their bread. Vaccine centrists breed hesitancy and validate parental fears on vaccination. As a formerly vaccine-hesitant parent who now does consultation for healthcare workers to decrease hesitancy, that is my professional opinion.

Ms. Greene is right that misinformation about the pediatric COVID vaccine is bound to spill over into other vaccines. Indeed, an article from December 2022 declared "Growing Vaccine Hesitancy Fuels Measles, Chickenpox Resurgence in U.S." It quoted Anne Zink, the chief medical officer for Alaska's health department, who said "I think there is more mistrust of the government, there's more questioning of vaccines, and we've been having a harder time getting people vaccinated."[437] Dr. Zink is right. In Florida, which is anti-pediatric COVID vaccine, a headline from December 2022 read "Immunization Rates for Florida Schoolkids at 10-Year Low."

This outcome was obvious to anyone who cared about vaccines prior to the pandemic.

#26 ~ "Are the COVID mRNA Vaccines Safe?"

The names Christopher Shaw, Lucija Tomljenovic, James Lyons-Weiler, Christopher Exley, Yehuda Shoenfeld, Gayle DeLong, Mark Geier, David Ayoub, F. Edward Yazbak, Anthony R. Mawson, Neil Miller, Gary Goldman, and Brian Hooker are very familiar to vaccine-advocates. These are a cadre of supposed researchers who publish poor, often-retracted scientific papers on vaccines. When you see one of their names on a paper, you don't have to read further. The paper will conclude that vaccines are unsafe and/or ineffective. For this reason, they are loved by anti-vaxxers.

Dr. Peter Doshi, a senior editor at the *BMJ* and Assistant Professor, Pharmaceutical Health Services Research at the University of Maryland, is also very familiar to vaccine advocates. When you see his name on a paper, you don't have to read any further. The paper will conclude that vaccines are unsafe and/or ineffective. For this reason, he is loved by anti-vaxxers. According to Dr. David Gorski, who has for years exposed Dr. Doshi's technique of starting with a conclusion and working backwards to find the evidence, Dr. Doshi has a:

> *Long history of playing footsie with the antivaccine movement since at least 2009, amplifying antivaccine conspiracy theories, downplaying the severity of influenza and thus feeding antivaccine narratives, using sleight-of-hand to downplay the effectiveness of flu vaccines, and generally playing the role of a false skeptic with respect to vaccines, as well as having signed a petition in 2006 "questioning" whether HIV causes AIDS.*[438]

During the pandemic, Dr. Doshi participated in a panel run by conspiracy-theorist Senator Ron Johnson,[439] and before the mRNA trials were published, he authored an article titled "Pfizer and Moderna's "95% Effective" Vaccines – Let's be Cautious and First See the Full Data."[440] After the trials were published showing they were 95% effective against the variant at that time, he wrote an article titled "Pfizer and Moderna's "95% Effective" Vaccines – We Need More Details and the Raw Data." In this article, he claimed the real efficacy rate was actually only 19% or 29%.[441] Unsurprisingly, Dr. Doshi has been portrayed in glowing terms on Robert F. Kennedy, Jr.'s antivaccine website *The Defender*.

Dr. Doshi's most popular pandemic paper was titled "Serious Adverse Events of Special Interest Following mRNA Vaccination in Randomized Trials," and it appeared as a preprint on June 23, 2022. The lead author was Dr. Joseph Fraiman, who had previously spread the myth that healthy children don't die of COVID, helping to convince the Florida Department of Health to recommend against vaccinating this population.[137] Dr. Fraiman also wrote an article for the anti-vaccine organization Brownstone Institute where he explained his decision to refuse the COVID vaccine because he felt its efficacy against severe disease hadn't been demonstrated in the randomized-controlled trials (RCTs) and "healthy individuals below the age of 60 without COVID-19 risk factors, the risk of hospitalization is quite rare."[442]

There was no question this paper would conclude COVID vaccines were more dangerous than the virus.

Hundreds of millions of people, if not billions of people, had received the mRNA vaccines by the time Dr. Doshi published his paper, and there was already incontrovertible evidence they kept people alive and out of the hospital. However, his paper looked at the data from the mRNA RCTs, which involved less than 100,000 people, and concluded:

> *The excess risk of serious adverse events of special interest surpassed the risk reduction for COVID-19 hospitalization relative to the placebo group in both Pfizer and Moderna trials.*[443]

Unsurprisingly, there were major problems with this conclusion. The first of these was how the harms of the virus and vaccine were tallied. A person who had abdominal pain and diarrhea after a vaccine was counted as having two adverse events, while someone hospitalized with COVID was counted as having one adverse event, even if they were intubated for a month. Even after Dr. Doshi sliced and diced the data, the findings were underwhelming. As Dr. David Robert Grimes noticed:

> *Even AFTER they tortured the data, they didn't even get a decent confession...The hazard ratios cross unity in almost every case. This is fancy statistics speak for "no effect was observed".*[444]

However, the paper's most glaring flaw was that it didn't reflect how the vaccine RCTs were designed. Simply tabulating the harms suffered by the vaccine and placebo group seems to make sense, but there are two key reasons why such this was a flawed approach for the vaccine trials. First, depending on how quickly a virus spreads, the benefits of a vaccine can take many months, even decades to accumulate. Second, nearly all vaccine harms occur in the first few days after vaccination.

In all vaccine RCTs, the harms are frontloaded, while the benefits accrue gradually over time, depending how quickly a virus spreads. Someone who analyzed the RCTs after 2 days would find the vaccine caused a bunch of people to feel sick, while preventing zero cases of COVID. The famous graphs from the COVID vaccine RCTs show how obvious this is. Every month, the benefits from the vaccine became larger and larger as more and more unvaccinated people contracted COVID, and the trials only lasted several months. In contrast, the vaccine wasn't causing any side-effects 100-days later.

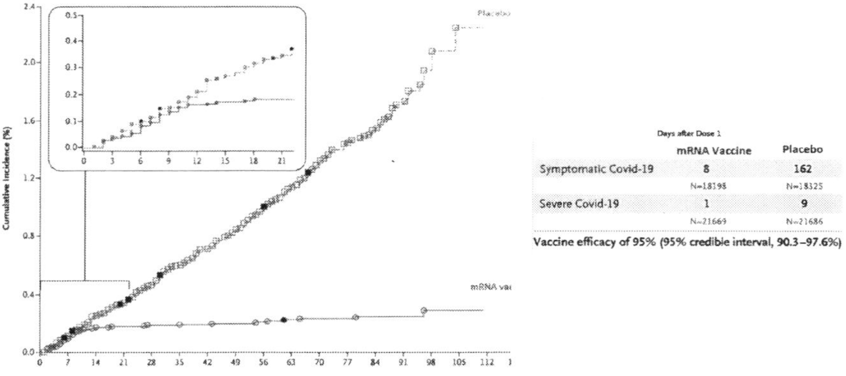

Cases of COVID in the vaccine and placebo group in the Pfizer vaccine trial. Image source: https://www.cdc.gov/library/COVID19/122220_COVIDupdate.html

As such, an RCT would have to last the entire pandemic to adequately capture the vaccine's benefits. As more and more people were exposed to the virus, the vaccine's benefits relative to placebo would grow and grow, even considering that vaccine efficacy wanes. Had the trial lasted two years, there would be many more cases of severe COVID, especially in the unvaccinated cohort.

The raw numbers from the RCTs expose the flaw with Dr. Doshi's analysis. The number of participants who received the vaccine was much larger than the number of participants who were exposed to the virus. There were about 74,000 participants in the Pfizer and Moderna trials. 37,000 of them received a vaccine, while only 366 of them had COVID. The vaccine had many more opportunities than the virus to make people feel rotten.

This was no accident. The RCTs were destined to end when a certain number of people contracted COVID. According to the Moderna study protocol, "The primary analysis will be performed when approximately 151 cases have been observed in the study".[445] The Pfizer study protocol set "a target of 164 primary-endpoint cases of confirmed COVID-19".[446] So by design, the trials concluded before the virus was allowed to harm more than several hundred people, though Dr. Doshi's paper did not acknowledge this fact.

Notably, nearly all of those harmed by the virus received placebo. There were 40 cases of severe COVID during the trials, all but one in the placebo group. That's a pretty big deal considering that most of those 74,000 trial participants have contracted COVID by now. Once this protection against severe COVID was known, it would have been unethical to continue the trials and allow people to remain unvaccinated. The RCTs clearly showed that COVID was dangerous and the vaccine very effective at curtailing these dangers.

When Dr. Doshi claimed his "results show an excess risk of serious adverse events of special interest greater than the reduction in COVID-19 hospitalizations in both Pfizer and Moderna trials,"[443] he didn't acknowledge these studies were terminated precisely because those hospitalizations began to accumulate. The trials were designed to stop once a small number of people got COVID, and Dr. Doshi spun this to claim COVID wasn't much of a threat. These trials didn't prove COVID was harmless. Rather they ended so rapidly precisely because COVID was a threat. Dr. Doshi and his many co-authors had cause and effect completely backwards.

We all know what happened once the RCTs ended, and this has great bearing on Dr. Doshi's preconceived conclusions. First, the virus spread everywhere. In the RCTs, there were 100 vaccinated people for every person who had COVID. That ratio is *very different* now, and this renders Dr. Doshi's method of counting harms completely obsolete. Dr. Doshi's "finding" was an entirely unsurprising, if not inevitable outcome from the way these trials were designed. There were *never* going to be more than several hundred people to be harmed by COVID in these studies. Dr. Doshi's study would have been of value only if the virus vanished or the vaccine ceased to be of any benefit as soon as the RCT ended.

None of these flaws mattered to anti-vaxxers. Since Dr. Doshi's paper made vaccines look bad, it was predictably celebrated in ant-vaccine circles. An article on the right-wing conspiracy site, *The Epoch Times* titled "New Study of Pfizer and Moderna Data Suggests Vaccine Harm Outweighs Benefit," stated:

> *The risk of serious adverse events from the Moderna and Pfizer vaccine exceeds the benefit of reduction of COVID-19 hospitalization.*[447]

Contrarian doctors agreed. Dr. Martin Kulldorff wrote an article for the Brownstone Institute titled "Are the COVID mRNA Vaccines Safe?" in which he said:

> *Fraiman and colleagues have produced the best evidence yet regarding the overall safety of the mRNA vaccines. The results are concerning. It is the responsibility of the manufacturers and FDA to ensure that benefits outweigh harms. They have failed to do so.*[448]

Dr. Joseph Ladapo tweeted:

> *New study published in #Vaccine shows concerning rate of serious adverse events after mRNA vaccination, but estimates are limited b/c @pfizer & @moderna_tx won't release patient-level trial data. Why are doctors blindly following Big Pharma?*[449]

Dr. Vinay Prasad also tweeted favorably about the paper and concluded, "Older, vulnerable people likely to have net gain. Younger, healthy people entirely uncertainty."[450]

Again, common sense provides a refutation to the idea that the vaccine is more dangerous than the virus. No hospital in the world opened a vaccine-injury unit. In contrast, nearly every hospital in the country was deluged with sick, dying COVID patients, often multiple times during the pandemic. Many victims were "young, healthy people". According to one news article:

> *Healthy and in their 30s, Christina and Josh Tidmore figured they were low-risk for COVID-19. With conflicting viewpoints about whether to get vaccinated against the virus filling their social media feeds and social circles, they decided to wait.*
>
> *On July 20, Josh came home from work with a slight cough initially thought to be sinus trouble. On Aug. 11, he died of COVID-19 at a north Alabama hospital as Christina Tidmore witnessed a doctor and her team frantically try to resuscitate her husband.*
>
> *"She would say, 'I need a pulse. 'I would hear, 'no pulse,' "Christina Tidmore said through tears. "They were trying so hard."*
>
> *"Nobody should go through this. He was only 36 and I'm 35 and we have three kids."*
>
> *She is now imploring young adults not to dismiss the risk and to consider getting vaccinated. "Josh was completely healthy, active, not a smoker," she said.*[451]

Unvaccinated people are still dying daily, including "not vulnerable" ones, possibly because they believe flawed studies that claim the virus is safer than the vaccine.

#27 ~ *"University booster mandates are unethical."*

Nothing enrages anti-vaxxers more than vaccine mandates. After a measles outbreak at Disneyland in 2014, California passed Senate Bill 277.[452] According to Jordan Graham:

> *Senate Bill 277, which became one of the strictest vaccine laws in the nation when it took effect in mid-2016, eliminated a loophole that allowed families to opt out of state immunization laws by saying vaccinations conflicted with their personal beliefs.*[453]

Anti-vaxxers were not happy. Robert F. Kennedy, Jr. said at the time:

> *They get the shot, that night they have a fever of a hundred and three, they go to sleep, and three months later their brain is gone. This is a holocaust, what this is doing to our country.*[454]

He did not tone down his rhetoric during the pandemic. During a January 2022 rally to "defeat the mandates," he said:

> *The minute they hand you that vaccine passport, every right that you have is transformed into a privilege contingent upon your obedience to arbitrary government dictates. It will make you a slave.*[455]

Though they used more measured language, contrarian doctors agreed with Mr. Kennedy's premises. Dr. Jay Bhattacharya raged in a tweet:

> *The discriminatory vaccine mandate/passport scheme that has violated the civil rights of countless people worldwide.*[456]

Dr. Bhattacharya also spread gross misinformation about the effects of vaccine mandates, claiming:

> *This vaccine mandate has already created all kinds of disruptions. We worried about not having enough beds, hospital beds? Many, many nurses are essentially quitting work. Yeah, I think it was like 70,000 in New York State alone. We're gonna have shortages of hospital supplies.*[457]

In reality, we never had a shortage of hospital supplies, and most large health systems with mandates lost 1-2% of their workforce due to vaccine-refusal.458 Most frontline healthcare workers supported vaccine mandates. As pediatrician Dr. Nicole Cifra said in response to Dr. Bhattacharya "None of my co-workers felt 'turned on' because of mandates. We felt supported."

Though the stakes were incredibly low, contrarian doctors also devoted great energy to opposing booster mandates. Data from Israel showed vaccine-myocarditis occurred in about 1 in 15,000 young men after the booster shot.[281] As with all other studies, it reported that "cases were clinically mild, and patients recovered after an average 3.5-days."

Nonetheless, Allison Krug, Drs. Vinay Prasad, Martin Makary, Stefan Baral, and Tracy Høeg authored an article titled "COVID-19 Vaccine Boosters for Young adults: A Risk Benefit Assessment and Ethical Analysis of Mandate Policies at Universities"[459] and another titled "COVID-19 Vaccine Boosters for Young Adults: A Risk-Benefit Assessment and Five Ethical Arguments against Mandates at Universities," both of which described how mandates are "unethical". The second article said:

> *University booster mandates are unethical because: 1) no formal risk-benefit assessment exists for this age group; 2) vaccine mandates may result in a net expected harm to individual young people; 3) mandates are not proportionate: expected harms are not outweighed by public health benefits given the modest and transient effectiveness of vaccines against transmission; 4) US mandates violate the reciprocity principle because rare serious vaccine-related harms will not be reliably compensated due to gaps in current vaccine injury schemes; and 5) mandates create wider social harms.*[460]

This is certainly more thoughtful than the ramblings of Mr. Kennedy. However, it's telling that throughout the pandemic, these doctors were only willing to share information that bolstered their ethical values. It's telling that they put a great deal of thought and effort into articles that *might* spare some college students a booster that carried little risk, during a year when over 1,000 children, nearly all of them unvaccinated, died of COVID.

"I just feel there's almost no incentive at all to give him the vaccine" ~ Anonymous parent

There is no question that the anti-vaccine movement won the battle for pediatric COVID. Thanks to their efforts, pediatric vaccination rates are abysmally low. As of September 2022, just 6% of children younger than 5 years had received a COVID vaccine.[461] For children 5-11, it's 38%, and for children ages 12-to-17-year-olds it is 70%. One woman, who had never previously questioned vaccines, revealed the success contrarian doctors had in convincing parents there was no benefit to the COVID vaccine. She said:

> *I just feel there's almost no incentive at all to give him the vaccine. Even if there was like no risk to it. It just seems why would we even get it for him? If he were to get it, he would be able to heal pretty quick. And it's unlikely that he would spread it to others.*[462]

Contrarian doctors recognized their influence and were proud of it. In an article advocating letting unvaccinated babies and toddlers get COVID, Dr. Vinay Prasad boasted of his success:

> *Parents are smart and get this. They vote with their feet. Just one in three kids 5-11 have gotten the shot and <5% of kids less than 5.*[205]

Doctors with real world responsibility for treating sick children don't see it this way. Pediatrician and vaccine-advocate Dr. Christopher Hickie said:

> *I'm really feeling like nothing COVID-19 does to children (or what it might still do) can ever make a dent in the dismissive attitude of about 60% of parents. They will tell you the kids who were hospitalized or died from COVID-19 weren't "healthy" or "had something wrong with them". They don't believe me when I tell them several hundreds of infants have died from COVID-19 (often because they haven't read of any of those deaths on social media!). The kids with long COVID are just faking it they will say. I heard one person say there's no evidence COVID-19 has long term effects in kids which was why they weren't worried. Oh, and they didn't vaccinate against*

> *COVID-19 because there's no long term studies on the vaccine.*[463]

Fortunately, grave outcomes remain extremely rare in children. But they could have been essentially zero had more children been vaccinated. There would be a national outcry if the vaccination rates for polio or measles were as low as for COVID, and yet for COVID, there's a collective shrug. Doctors convinced Americans that it's acceptable for a small number of children to suffer and die from COVID for no good reason at all.

Smart children disagree.

Jose Luis Chavez is a 17-year-old from Texas who spent 5-months in the hospital after his COVID infection. He said that "I was taking really shallow breaths; I couldn't take a deep breath."[464] He continued, "I was surprised because I play the saxophone, and I use my lungs a lot." Jose was intubated and needed ECMO to survive. Eventually, his life was saved by a double lung transplant. According to a news article about his experience:

> *"After the transplant, the first thing I did was I took a deep breath in and was like 'wow, I can finally breathe again,'" he said.*
>
> *Chavez's doctors said his new lungs are working just fine. And although he'll always have to take medications to make sure his body doesn't reject the lungs, Chavez is grateful he's alive and able to do the things he loves again, like play the saxophone and spend time with his family.*
>
> *And if he meets any teens hesitant about getting vaccinated, he said, "I always show them my scar."*

Table 1: Pediatric randomized controlled trials (BNT162b2/Pfizer & mRNA-1273/Moderna)

TRIAL NAME	STUDY POPULATION	KEY RESULTS
Safety, Immunogenicity, and Efficacy of the BNT162b2 Covid-19 Vaccine in Adolescents[28]	2,260 adolescents 12 to 15 years of age received injections; 1,131 received BNT162b2, and 1,129 received placebo	A two-dose regimen of 30 μg of BNT162b2 administered 21 days apart to adolescents 12 to 15 years of age was safe and immunogenic and resulted in an observed vaccine efficacy of 100% against Covid-19 from 7 days after dose 2.
Evaluation of mRNA-1273 SARS-CoV-2 Vaccine in Adolescents[29]	A total of 3,732 participants were randomly assigned to receive mRNA-1273 (2,489 participants) or placebo (1,243 participants).	No cases of Covid-19 with an onset of 14 days after the second injection were reported in the mRNA-1273 group, and four cases occurred in the placebo group. The mRNA-1273 vaccine had an acceptable safety profile in adolescents. The immune response was similar to that in young adults, and the vaccine was efficacious in preventing Covid-19.
Evaluation of the BNT162b2 Covid-19 Vaccine in Children 5 to 11 Years of Age[30]	A total of 2,268 children were randomly assigned to receive the BNT162b2 vaccine (1,517 children) or placebo (751 children).	Covid-19 with onset 7 days or more after the second dose was reported in three recipients of the BNT162b2 vaccine and in 16 placebo recipients (vaccine efficacy, 90.7%)A Covid-19 vaccination regimen consisting of two 10-μg doses of BNT162b2 administered 21 days apart was found to be safe, immunogenic, and efficacious in children 5 to 11 years of age.

TRIAL NAME	STUDY POPULATION	KEY RESULTS
Evaluation of mRNA-1273 Covid-19 Vaccine in Children 6 to 11 Years of Age[31]	4,016 participants were randomly assigned to receive two 50-µg injections of the mRNA-1273 vaccine or two injections of placebo	Estimated vaccine efficacy was 88.0% against Covid-19 occurring 14 days or more after the first injection, at a time when Delta was the dominant circulating variant. Two 50-µg doses of the mRNA-1273 vaccine were found to be safe and effective in inducing immune responses and preventing Covid-19 in children 6 to 11 years of age.
Pfizer press release[32]	4,526 children 6 months to less than 5 years of age. In the trial, children received the third 3-µg dose at least two months after the second dose at a time when Omicron was the predominant variant.	Following a third dose in this age group, the vaccine was found to elicit a strong immune response, with a favorable safety profile similar to placebo. No new safety signals were identified, and the frequency of adverse reactions observed in children 6 months to less than 5 years were generally lower than in children 5 to less than 12 years. Vaccine efficacy, a secondary endpoint in this trial, was 80.3% in children 6 months to under 5 years of age.
Evaluation of mRNA-1273 Vaccine in Children 6 Months to 5 Years of Age[33]	3,040 children 2 to 5 years of age and 1,762 children 6 to 23 months of age were randomly assigned to receive two 25-µg injections of mRNA-1273. 1,008 children 2 to 5 years of age and 593 children 6 to 23 months of age were randomly assigned to receive placebo.	Two 25-µg doses of the mRNA-1273 vaccine were found to be safe in children 6 months to 5 years of age and elicited immune responses that were noninferior to those in young adults.The estimated vaccine efficacy against Covid-19 was 36.8% among 2-to-5-year-olds and 50.6% among 6-to-23-month-olds, at a time when Omicron was the predominant circulating variant.

Table 2: Observational trials on the COVID vaccine for children

STUDY	RESULTS
Marks et al.[10] (Morbidity and Mortality Weekly Report)	"A higher proportion of unvaccinated adolescents (70.3%) than fully vaccinated adolescents (40.8%) had COVID-19 as a primary reason for admission. A significantly higher proportion of unvaccinated adolescents were admitted to the ICU (30.3%) than were those who were vaccinated (15.5%)."
Olson et al.[34] (The New England Journal of Medicine)	"Of the case patients, 180 (40%) were admitted to the ICU, and 127 (29%) required life support; only 2 patients in the ICU had been fully vaccinated. The overall effectiveness of the BNT162b2 vaccine against hospitalization for Covid-19 was 94%. ... The effectiveness was 98% against ICU admission and 98% against Covid-19 resulting in the receipt of life support. All 7 deaths occurred in patients who were unvaccinated."
Zambrano et al.[35] (Morbidity and Mortality Weekly Report)	"Among 102 MIS-C case-patients, five (5%) were fully vaccinated ... and 97 (95%) were unvaccinated. ...Sixty-two (61%) were admitted to an intensive care unit, and 38 (37%) received life support during hospitalization, including invasive mechanical ventilation, vasoactive infusions, or extracorporeal membrane oxygenation (ECMO). All 38 MIS-C patients requiring life support were unvaccinated; among these, nine patients required invasive mechanical ventilation, 35 received vasoactive infusions and one required ECMO." Only 1 fully vaccinated child was admitted to the ICU but did not require life support measures."

STUDY	RESULTS
Olson et al.[36] (Morbidity and Mortality Weekly Report)	In hospitalized adolescents, "179 COVID-19 case-patients, six (3%) were vaccinated and 173 (97%) were unvaccinated. Overall, 77 (43%) case-patients were admitted to an intensive care unit, and 29 (16%) critically ill case-patients received life support during hospitalization, including invasive mechanical ventilation, vasoactive infusions, or extracorporeal membrane oxygenation; two of these 29 critically ill patients (7%) died. All 77 case-patients admitted to the intensive care unit, all 29 critically ill case-patients, and both deaths occurred among unvaccinated case-patients."
LaRovere et al.[37] (JAMA Neurology)	"Of the 155 vaccine-eligible patients with neurologic involvement and confirmed vaccination status, 147 (95%) were unvaccinated, including 15 of 16 patients (94%) with life-threatening neurologic conditions."
Castelli et al.[38] (BMJ)	"Vaccine effectiveness against death related to SARS-CoV-2 infection during omicron predominance was 66.9% (6.4% to 89.8%) in children and 97.6% (81.0% to 99.7%) in adolescents. Vaccine effectiveness in preventing mortality remained high in children and adolescents regardless of the circulating variant."
Delahoy et al.[39] (Morbidity and Mortality Weekly Report)	"Hospitalization rates were 10 times higher among unvaccinated than among fully vaccinated adolescents."
Messiah et al.[40] (The Pediatric Infectious Disease Journal)	"Increased risk for persistent COVID symptoms >12 weeks included severe symptoms with initial infection, not being vaccinated and having unhealthy weight"
Wanga et al.[41] (Morbidity and Mortality Weekly Report)	"Among 272 vaccine-eligible patients hospitalized for COVID-19, one (0.4%) was fully vaccinated and 12 (4.4%) were partially vaccinated with an mRNA COVID-19 vaccine at the time of hospitalization."

STUDY	RESULTS
Lutrick et al.[42] (Morbidity and Mortality Weekly Report)	"Under real world conditions, vaccine effectiveness of full immunization (completion of the second in a 2-dose series ≥14 days earlier) was 92% against SARS-CoV-2 infections irrespective of symptom status"
Levy et al.[43] (JAMA)	"A total of 107 children with MIS-C were hospitalized … 33 were adolescents eligible for vaccination. …29 were admitted to a PICU. Among them, 0 had been fully vaccinated, 7 had received 1 dose …. and 26 had not been vaccinated."
Nygaard et al.[44] (The Lancet Child & Adolescent Health)	"We identified 51 MIS-C cases among unvaccinated individuals and one in a fully vaccinated adolescent. The incidence of MIS-C was one in 3400 unvaccinated individuals … and one in 9900 vaccinated individuals."
Chang et al.[45] (The Lancet Child & Adolescent Health)	"Reports of MIS-C after COVID-19 vaccination occurred in only 1 per million individuals aged 12–20 years who received one or more doses of a COVID-19 vaccine."
Fleming-Dutra et al.[46] (JAMA)	"Estimated booster [BNT162b2] dose effectiveness in adolescents 2 to 6.5 weeks after the booster was 71.1%."
Yousaf et al.[47] (The Lancet Child & Adolescent Health)	"The overall reporting rate for MIS-C after vaccination 1·0 case per million individuals receiving one or more doses in this age group."
Tan et al.[48] (The New England Journal of Medicine)	Vaccine effectiveness against hospitalization was 83% in children ages 5-11.
Price et al.[49] (The New England Journal of Medicine)	Vaccine effectiveness against hospitalization was 68% in children ages 5-11 during Omicron and 79% effective against critical COVID-19 for adolescents 12 to 18 years of age.
Lin et al.[50] (The New England Journal of Medicine)	Vaccine effectiveness against hospitalization was 88% in children ages 5-11, though this waned to 76% after several months. 7 children died, all unvaccinated.

STUDY	RESULTS
Cohen-Stavi et al.[51] (The New England Journal of Medicine)	This observational study of effectiveness of the BNT162b2 vaccine among children 5 to 11 years of age showed a vaccine effectiveness of 51% against documented SARS-CoV-2 infection and 48% against symptomatic Covid-19 at 7 to 21 days after the second dose. "Results also suggested that effectiveness may be greater among younger children (5 or 6 years of age) than older children (10 or 11 years of age)."
Dorabawila et al.[52] (JAMA)	"The risks of infection and hospitalization were elevated for unvaccinated vs vaccinated children aged 5 to 11 and 12 to 17 years."
Klein et al.[53] (Morbidity and Mortality Weekly Report)	"Overall, 2-dose VE [vaccine-effectiveness] against COVID-19–associated hospitalization was 73%–94%."
Shi et al.[54] (Morbidity and Mortality Weekly Report)	"During the period of Omicron predominance (December 19, 2021–February 28, 2022), COVID-19–associated hospitalization rates in children aged 5–11 years were approximately twice as high among unvaccinated as among vaccinated children. Non-Hispanic Black children represented the largest group of unvaccinated children. Thirty percent of hospitalized children had no underlying medical conditions, and 19% were admitted to an intensive care unit."
Miller et al.[55] (Clinical Infectious Diseases)	"We describe 2116 multisystem inflammatory syndrome in children (MIS-C) cases reported to the and Prevention during Delta and Omicron circulation from July 2021 through January 2022. Half of MIS-C patients were aged 5-11 years, 52% received intensive care unit-level care, and 1.1% died. Only 3.0% of eligible patients were fully vaccinated prior to MIS-C onset."
Yousaf et al.[56] (CDC & Centers for Preparedness and Response presentation)	In 1,485 children with MIS-C, 1,305 were unvaccinated, 91 were partially vaccinated, and 89 fully vaccinated. ICU treatment was required for 768 unvaccinated, 45 partially vaccinated, and 40 fully vaccinated. 21 unvaccinated children died. No deaths were recorded for partially and fully vaccinated children.

STUDY	RESULTS
Watanabe et al.[467] (JAMA Pediatrics)	In this meta-analysis of 17 studies, we demonstrated 2 important findings: (1) mRNA COVID-19 vaccination in children aged 5 to 11 years was associated with lower risks of SARS-CoV-2 infections, severe COVID-19–related illnesses, and hospitalizations due to COVID-19 and (2) while mRNA COVID-19 vaccination compared with placebo was associated with any adverse events, most of them were non-severe and transient.

Table 3: Studies regarding the clinical course of vaccine-myocarditis

STUDY	RESULTS
Gargano et al.[218] (Morbidity and Mortality Weekly Report)	Acute clinical courses were generally mild.
Israel Ministry of Health[250]	95% are considered to be mild cases.
Yasuhara et al.[258] (JAMA Pediatrics)	This systematic review and meta-analysis found low incidence rate and largely favorable early outcomes of COVID-19 mRNA vaccine–associated myopericarditis in adolescents and young adults from a wide range of populations. These findings are reassuring but continued follow-up is warranted.
Samimisedeh et al.[259] (Journal of Magnetic Resonance Imaging)	All reported cases with abnormal cardiac MRI findings showed a favorable clinical course at the acute phase.
Khan et al.[260] (Cureus)	Fortunately, most myocarditis cases associated with mRNA vaccines are mild in nature and do not have serious complications and require only a few days of hospital admission.
Ling et al.[261] (The Lancet Respiratory Medicine)	The prognosis of this self-limiting condition is generally good, long-term outcomes for affected patients after 3 months and 6 months are currently awaited.
Dionne et al.[262] (JAMA Cardiology)	All patients in this series had a benign course; none required intensive care unit admission.
Marshall et al.[263] (Pediatrics)	All 7 patients resolved their symptoms rapidly.
Woo et al. (Journal of Medical Virology)	In agreement with previous reports on these patients' relatively favorable clinical courses, symptoms of all 74 patients in this review resolved, and nearly a third (31.0%) of them recovered with conservative treatment.
Diaz et al.[265] (JAMA)	All were discharged after a median of 2 days. There were no readmissions or deaths.
Montgomery et al.[267] (JAMA Cardiology)	All patients received brief supportive care and were recovered or recovering at the time of this report.
Rosner et al.[268] (Circulation)	The clinical course of vaccine-associated myocarditis-like illness appears favorable, with resolution of symptoms in all patients.

STUDY	RESULTS
Jain et al.[266] (Pediatrics)	Hospital course is mild with quick clinical recovery and excellent short-term outcomes.
Mevorach et al.[269] (The New England Journal of Medicine)	All the cases were clinically mild, involving a mean duration of hospitalization of 3.1 days.
Nygaard et al.[270] (The Pediatric Infectious Disease Journal)	The mild phenotype of myopericarditis cases in our study were comparable with cases described in other studies, except 1 patient with myocarditis and MIS-C, who needed treatment at intensive care unit.
Witberg et al.[271] (The New England Journal of Medicine)	Most cases of myocarditis were mild or moderate in severity.
Mouch et al.[272] (Vaccine)	The clinical course was mild in all six patients.
Larson et al.[273] (Circulation)	All patients had resolution of their chest pain, were discharged from the hospital in stable condition, and were alive with preserved left ventricular ejection fraction at last contact.
Truong et al.[274] (Circulation)	Most cases of suspected COVID-19 vaccine myocarditis occurring in persons <21 years have a mild clinical course with rapid resolution of symptoms. Abnormal findings on cardiac MRI were frequent. Future studies should evaluate risk factors, mechanisms, and long-term outcomes.
Patone et al.[275] (Nature Medicine)	Most vaccine-associated myocarditis events have been mild and self-limiting.
Lai et al.[276] (Journal of the American College of Cardiology)	This study found a significantly lower rate of mortality among individuals with myocarditis after mRNA vaccination compared with those with viral infection–related myocarditis. Prognosis of this iatrogenic condition may be less severe than naturally acquired viral infection–related myocarditis.
Varma et al.[277] (The Medical Journal of Australia)	COVID-19 mRNA vaccine-associated myocarditis has a mild, self-resolving clinical course, in contrast to reported complications and long term sequelae associated with COVID-19, such as multisystem inflammatory syndrome in children, and other forms of myocarditis. The long term consequences of myocardial injury with vaccine-associated myocarditis nevertheless warrant further investigation

Table 4: Observational trials on MIS-C and the COVID vaccine

STUDY	RESULTS
Zambrano et al.[35] (Morbidity and Mortality Weekly Report)	Among critically ill MIS-C case-patients requiring life support, all were unvaccinated...97/102 children with MIS-C were unvaccinated. None of the 5 vaccinated MIS-C patients required respiratory or cardiovascular life support (invasive mechanical ventilation, vasoactive infusions, or ECMO) compared to 38/97 unvaccinated MIS-C patients.
Levy et al.[43] (JAMA)	In 33 adolescents with MIS-C eligible for vaccination...0 had been fully vaccinated, 7 had received 1 dose.
Nygaard et al.[44] (The Lancet Child & Adolescent Health)	We identified 51 MIS-C cases among unvaccinated individuals and one in a fully vaccinated adolescent.
Chang et al.[45] (The Lancet Child & Adolescent Health)	Reports of MIS-C after COVID-19 vaccination occurred in only 1 per million individuals aged 12–20 years who received one or more doses of a COVID-19 vaccine.
Yousaf et al.[47] (The Lancet Child & Adolescent Health)	The overall reporting rate for MIS-C after vaccination 1·0 case per million individuals receiving one or more doses in this age group.
Miller et al.[55] (Clinical Infectious Diseases)	We describe 2116 multisystem inflammatory syndrome in children (MIS-C) cases reported to the and Prevention during Delta and Omicron circulation from July 2021 through January 2022. Half of MIS-C patients were aged 5-11 years, 52% received intensive care unit-level care, and 1.1% died. Only 3.0% of eligible patients were fully vaccinated prior to MIS-C onset.
Yousaf et al.[56] (CDC Presentation)	In 1,485 children with MIS-C, 1,305 were unvaccinated and 768 were treated in the ICU. 91 were partially vaccinated and 89 were fully vaccinated. All 21 children who died were unvaccinated.

Conclusion: "Every time we see or hear such mistruths we need to combat them and call them out."

"These kinds of public health misinformation are deadly, especially when it comes from people who should know better."

~ Media Matters

On April 17, 2020, Dr. John Ioannidis said, "at some point we need to go back and check very carefully and try to understand what exactly did the virus do to all these people."[1]

We can begin doing that now. Around the world, the virus has sickened billions of people and killed 6.5 million of them,[2] though this a significant undercount. In the US, the virus has killed over 1.1 million people.[3] COVID is the greatest mass casualty event in American history, and our most vulnerable, marginalized citizens were hit hardest. Many millions more were hospitalized, and some survivors have been severely debilitated by strokes or amputations. Millions of others are suffering from Long COVID. A report from August 2022 estimated that as many as 4 million people are out of work due to COVID,[4] and we will be learning about long-term consequences of COVID for years.

It's not over yet.

Doctors and scientists have an obligation to choose their words very carefully when engaging with the public about a deadly virus and to openly correct the errors we will inevitably make. Yet, at every step of our pandemic tragedy, highly credentialed doctors and scientists falsely reassured Americans that only grandma needs to worry, the worst is over, and the only real danger lies in the measures to control the virus, including vaccines.

This was not just an ivory tower debate amongst academics. There are real world consequences to medical misinformation. When an American dies of COVID today – and hundreds are still dying daily – it is probable the decedent passed up an opportunity to be vaccinated or boosted. Perhaps this person heard that herd immunity had arrived, that death certificates couldn't be trusted, or that boosters had no evidence. Perhaps this person was told doctors killed patients through their "crazy," inappropriate intubations. As such, doctors couldn't be trusted when they suggested vaccination or warned against quack cures.

Unfortunately, the problem of doctors spreading misinformation is significantly larger than what I've described thus far. The doctors mentioned in this book produced countless hours of podcasts, *YouTube* videos, and interviews, as well as volumes of editorials, social media posts, and *Substack* essays. I've only reported a fraction of their misinformation here, which was not limited to vaccines. Doctors spread voluminous misinformation about masks, testing, and any and all measures to control the virus. Remember, they wanted them infected.

Other doctors I've not even mentioned became anti-vaccine celebrities during the pandemic, campaigning alongside pre-pandemic anti-vaxxers. According to an article by the anti-vaccine group Children's Health Defense titled "CHD and Robert F. Kennedy, Jr. to Join Thousands on January 23 for the Defeat the Mandates Rally in Washington, DC":

> *Prominent anti-mandate, pro-science advocates are scheduled to address the crowd including Robert F. Kennedy, Jr., Del Bigtree, Dr. Robert Malone, Dr. Peter McCullough, Dr. Pierre Kory, Dr. Paul Marik, Dr. Ryan Cole, Dr. Aaron Kheriaty…*[5]

A separate book could easily be written about these doctors and the anti-vaccine misinformation they spread.

There are still many more doctors who have spread misinformation. I've only discussed three – Drs. Marty Makary, Jay Bhattacharya, and Scott Atlas – of the top 10 doctors named in an article from *Media Matters* titled "The Dishonest Doctors Who Were Fox News' Most Frequent Medical Guests In 2021." According to this article:

> *With the help of its rotating roster of supposed medical experts, Fox News turned vaccine passports and mandates into culture war battles because it's "great for ratings." According to a Media Matters study, Fox News undermined vaccines nearly every*

> *day over a six-month period. (Ironically, Fox's own vaccine and testing policies are more stringent than those put forward by the Biden administration.)*
>
> *Guests and hosts on Fox also spread many questionable "miracle cures" for COVID-19, including bear bile, vaping, and sunlight. Notably, Fox helped fan the flames of hydroxychloroquine and ivermectin misinformation, leading to shortages of these medications which are crucial for treating other ailments.*
>
> *These kinds of public health misinformation are deadly, especially when it comes from people who should know better. The frequent bad actors listed below each have a history of spreading misleading and false medical advice on Fox News, which gives these medical misinformers a huge platform to spread that bad advice to its viewers.*[6]

The top spreader of misinformation on Fox News, Dr. Marc Siegel, blamed Haitian immigrants for spreading the virus and made specious arguments about vaccinating children ages 5-11, saying that regulators "are not factoring in natural immunity at all." "Two million kids in that age group have already had COVID, and I want that factored in," he said. "I want them to say maybe wait a while, or maybe you get one mRNA shot that cements immunity at the lower dose."

It's no surprise that an audience fed a diet a COVID misinformation rejected chances to protect themselves against it. Today, the news headlines read, "The Right's Anti-Vaxxers Are Killing Republicans and Study: More Republicans Than Democrats Likely Died Of COVID-19."[7]

There's also much to say about doctors who published or amplified junk science. From pure fraud to pure garbage, a lot of bad scientific papers were published during the pandemic, and contrarian doctors amplified them to cast doubt on measures to control the virus. One such paper was titled "Experimental Assessment of Carbon Dioxide Content in Inhaled Air With or Without Face Masks in

Healthy Children," which claimed masks harm children.[8] The paper had glaring flaws and was immediately retracted, as was another paper by the same author, Dr. Harald Walach, which claimed that COVID vaccines cause two deaths for every three deaths prevented.[9] However, this didn't stop contrarian doctors, namely Drs. Marty Makary, Vinay Prasad, and Stefan Baral, from amplifying the anti-mask paper on *Twitter*.[35] It bolstered their position that efforts to prevent children from getting COVID were harmful, and that was enough.

According to an analysis on trials of ivermectin for COVID by the BBC, "more than a third of 26 major trials of the drug for use on COVID have serious errors or signs of potential fraud."[10] A healthcare analytics company called Surgisphere, run by Dr. Sapan Desai, managed to have papers published in *The Lancet* and *The New England Journal of Medicine* based on a database of over 600 hospitals. However, this database doesn't even exist, and Surgisphere's "findings" were obviously fraudulent.[11] One critic noted that their research reported "more in-hospital deaths than had occurred in the entire country (Australia) during the study period."[12] The website *Retraction Watch* lists nearly 300 COVID papers that have been retracted for various reasons.[13] Undoubtedly, there are many more flawed papers polluting the COVID scientific landscape.

Another book could be written about the failures of our health and regulatory agencies. The World Health Organization (WHO) famously tweeted on March 28, 2020, "FACT: #COVID19 is NOT airborne,"[14] when there was already clear evidence COVID was airborne. At the start of the pandemic, the CDC sent out COVID test kits with a faulty reagent and the FDA placed regulatory hurdles in the way of scientists who developed their own tests. These early missteps allowed the virus to spread undetected until it was too late.

As the pandemic progressed, politicians also interfered with ostensibly apolitical health agencies. According to the House Select Subcommittee on the Coronavirus Crisis:

> *Trump Administration officials repeatedly sought to alter CDC and HHS press materials to promote positive news, downplay coronavirus risks, and attempt to redirect blame away from the Trump Administration for its poor handling of the coronavirus pandemic...*

The Select Subcommittee's investigation uncovered an unprecedented campaign by Trump Administration appointees to influence the process, manipulate the content, or block the dissemination of at least 19 different CDC scientific reports that they deemed to be politically harmful to President Trump…

Amid a failing coronavirus response, Trump Administration officials diverted hundreds of millions of dollars from CDC's budget to launch what amounted to a celebrity vanity campaign to "defeat despair and inspire hope" about the state of the pandemic in the direct lead up to the November 2020 presidential election.[15]

Dr. Mehmet Oz even helped push the FDA to authorize hydroxychloroquine early in the pandemic. According to news reports, he has:

Financial ties to at least two pharmaceutical companies that supply hydroxychloroquine, an anti-malaria drug that he has floated as a possible COVID-19 treatment.[16]

Indeed, there is a lot to say about the shady financial ties many of these doctors have. Some make money by selling subscriptions to their *Substack* newsletters. According to the reporting of misinformation researcher Derek Beres:

Anti-vaxxers aren't limited to Politics newsletters. In Health & Wellness, hematologist-oncologist Vinay Prasad was using social media to stoke controversies long before the pandemic and was criticized for comparing COVID mandates to Nazi Germany. Unsurprisingly, his COVID claims don't hold up. Still, thousands of subscribers pay $7/month for his "observations and thoughts" in the Health & Wellness category, while his "Sensible Medicine" Substack, which is much more COVID-focused in the

> *Science category, has hundreds of people shelling out $8/month.*[34]

Meanwhile, Dr. Zubin Damania lets strangers lets people pay to join the "ZPAC supporter tribe"[17] or buy merchandise at his online store.[18] Many doctors have gotten rich selling quack treatments. According to the House Select Subcommittee on the Coronavirus Crisis, the doctors behind the anti-vaccine disinformation group America's Frontline Doctors:

> *Have reportedly received more than $6.7 million for facilitating paid telehealth consultations and off-label prescriptions for the purported coronavirus treatments that they promote online.*[19]

Dr. Simone Gold, who founded America's Frontline Doctors, opened a telemedicine business in Florida called GoldCare Health & Wellness LLC, a "private membership association" that allows customers to pay for "medical freedom."[20] It costs $1,000 a year for an individual or $2,000 for a family. No private or government insurance is accepted. Lab tests and prescriptions are an additional cost, and hospital care is not covered. Ivermectin and hydroxychloroquine are available at "freedom pharmacies." In a delicious twist, she is also being sued by America's Frontline Doctors, as they allege that she used their funds to buy a $3.6 million mansion, luxury vehicles, and take trips on private planes.[21]

Other doctors have received significant financial support and media amplification from wealthy, right-wing donors. Unlike Dr. Martin Kulldorff,[36] I hope I never feel the need to make a video titled "The Great Barrington Declaration is NOT Koch Funded Eugenics." However, there is clearly a coordinated anti-vaccine movement involving some of the doctors I've discussed and a connected web of COVID disinformation groups from several countries, such as Pandemics Data & Analytics (PANDA), the Brownstone Institute, Health Advisory and Recovery Team (HART), Us For Them, Collateral Global, Rational Ground, Urgency of Normal, and others. Arnold Ventures, a foundation created by former Enron trader and billionaire John D. Arnold and his wife Laura Arnold has funded Drs. John Ioannidis and Vinay Prasad.

Still another book could also be written about the Biden

administration's response to COVID. While President Biden never suggested treating COVID with disinfectant and UV light, his CDC director, Dr. Rochelle Walensky, officially surrendered to the virus in December 2022 saying, "We can't stop the spread of #COVID19,"[22] prompting biologist T. Gregory Ryan to say:

> *People who think there's nothing we can do to stop mass infectious disease should not be in charge of our response to mass infectious disease.*[23]

President Biden similarly acknowledged the pandemic stopped being a priority for him, saying in January 2023, "I sometimes underestimate it because I stopped thinking about it."[37] 700,000 Americans have died of COVID since President Biden took office.[3] As NFL head coach Bill Parcells famously said, "You are what your record says you are."

"Every time we see or hear such mistruths we need to combat them and call them out." ~ Dr. David Oliver

There is no simple solution to the problem of doctors spreading misinformation. Certainly, journalists need to be more careful about whom they interview. A doctor who declared the pandemic over every month in 2021 did not deserve a large platform to repeat this message in 2022.

Government regulatory agencies have a role to play. In September 2022, California passed a bill to sanction doctors who spread gross misinformation about COVID to their patients.[24] However, this will limit only a fraction of the misinformation spread by doctors, and I am sympathetic to those who worry this would be a dangerous power to hand to malevolent forces. I don't want a Medical Misinformation Board created by a future President Ron DeSantis to have the power to punish doctors who spread "misinformation".

Additionally, The Federation of State Medical Boards' Board of Directors published a statement about doctors who spread misinformation that said:

> *Physicians who generate and spread COVID-19 vaccine misinformation or disinformation are risking*

> *disciplinary action by state medical boards, including the suspension or revocation of their medical license. Due to their specialized knowledge and training, licensed physicians possess a high degree of public trust and therefore have a powerful platform in society, whether they recognize it or not. They also have an ethical and professional responsibility to practice medicine in the best interests of their patients and must share information that is factual, scientifically grounded and consensus-driven for the betterment of public health. Spreading inaccurate COVID-19 vaccine information contradicts that responsibility, threatens to further erode public trust in the medical profession and puts all patients at risk.*[25]

Despite this strong language, formal disciplinary action against doctors for spreading misinformation is a slow, difficult process, which is rarely used. For example, Dr. Bob Sears, a California pediatrician who has long spread anti-vaccine misinformation, merely received probation as punishment for writing multiple fake vaccine exemptions.[26] In other states, politicians made it impossible for medical boards to do their job. In Tennessee, the medical licensing board was forced to remove a policy opposing COVID misinformation after a conservative member of the Tennessee House of Representatives threatened to dissolve the board and replace its members.[27]

Dr. Nick Sawyer, an emergency medicine physician, created the organization No License For Disinformation to draw attention to the timidity of state medical boards. He said:

> *The failure of state medical boards to act – and worse, to rubber-stamp the medical license renewal of doctors actively spreading dangerous and unfounded conspiracy theories – creates a COVID-19 force multiplier, leading to overwhelmed and understaffed hospitals and unnecessary suffering and death. Just as doctors have a duty to act in their patients' best interest, state medical boards have a duty to act in the public's best interest.*[28]

Most Americans agree. A survey by the de Beaumont Foundation found that 90% of Americans "believe that doctors who intentionally spread misinformation about COVID-19 should be held accountable."

However, until medical boards put teeth into their words, doctors and scientists need to take the lead role in correcting medical misinformation. We need to police ourselves. There is no virtue in greeting misinformation with a shrug, or even worse, claiming that those who spread obviously false statistics are just "independent thinkers." Famous doctors are not owed a free pass simply because they have stellar credentials and can sling scientific jargon. When the emperor has no clothes, we are obligated to tell him he is naked. Sadly, some medical students have shown more courage calling out misinformation spread by their professors than tenured department chairmen.

Doctors who corrected medical misinformation prior to the pandemic largely did so on their own time, without reward. Their efforts were viewed as a quirky hobby, not a valuable service to present to a promotion's committee. Fortunately, there is growing recognition amongst medical leaders that correcting misinformation shouldn't be left to a small number of doctors willing to do it on nights and weekends. The president of the American Medical Association (AMA), Dr. Jack Resneck, Jr., published an article titled "Turning the Tide Against Medical Disinformation Will Take All of Us" in which he said:

> *Among the enduring lessons from COVID-19 are how quickly medical misinformation and disinformation can be spread online and through social media, and the devastation they leave behind. Both can have serious consequences for our patients and the health of the nation—the distinction between the two is that disinformation is intentionally deceptive. The resulting distrust in experts, science, and medical institutions hampers our ability to respond effectively in a health crisis.*[29]

According to Dr. Resneck:

The AMA House of Delegates, representing every state and specialty, also adopted a comprehensive strategy to address health-related disinformation spread by health professionals at the 2022 Annual Meeting in June. The new policy includes nine concrete actions we can and must take to counter the spread of disinformation. These include:

- *Ensuring the widespread availability of evidence-based medical and health information for physicians and the public.*

- *Addressing the dissemination and monetization of disinformation by health professionals via social media platforms.*

- *Educating health professionals and the public on how to recognize disinformation as well as how it spreads.*

However, significant barriers still remain. Doctors who correct misinformation are frequently harassed and threatened for their efforts. Too often they are left to fend for themselves against coordinated attacks from well-funded, paranoid, hostile, anti-vaxxers.

Thu 5/6/2021 5:44 PM
To: Hotez, Peter Jay

*****CAUTION:*** This email is not from a [redacted] Source. Only click links or open attachments you know are safe.**

Peter, 75 years ago people like you were tried, convicted and hung by the neck until dead. There is a Lawyers Committee right now collecting the names of people to be indicted for Nuremberg Crimes. I am turning your name over to the Prosecutor's Legal team.

[redacted]

May The Force be with you,

One of several threatening emails received by Dr. Peter Hotez[38]
Reprint permission granted by Dr. Hotez

Such harassment was not limited to well-known scientists. Hundreds of public health officials have resigned or retired rather than face abuse and threats. According to news reports:

> *Some have become the target of far-right activists, conservative groups and anti-vaccination extremists who have coalesced around common goals: fighting mask orders, quarantines and contact tracing with protests, threats and personal attacks.*[30]

According to a survey from *The New York Times*, "Public health agencies have seen a staggering exodus of personnel, many exhausted and demoralized, in part because of abuse and threats."[31] They reported that "more than 500 top health officials who left their jobs in the past 19 months." We are likely less prepared for a pandemic now than we were at the start of 2020.

Beyond not wanting to have their lives threatened, some doctors are wary of calling out medical misinformation to avoid being accused of censorship or threatening academic freedom. This is understandable. Many of the doctors I've discussed reflexively say they are being "silenced" or "slandered" whenever they are merely corrected. Mislabeling one's critics as "censors" is a very effective way to censor one's critics.

Of course, no one wants unorthodox beliefs to be labeled as "misinformation". We need to leave room for people to have good faith disagreements without being smeared as "anti-vaccine" or "anti-science." We need to be open to outliers and mavericks. The inspirational story of Dr. Katalin Kariko, the unappreciated scientist whose work paved the way for mRNA vaccines,[32] shows why this is so. No doctor should be fearful to challenge medical orthodoxy, so long as they have evidence and are willing to admit error if their pet theory doesn't pan out.

However, doctors who said herd immunity arrived in the spring of 2021 and that it was "healthy and natural" when unvaccinated babies got COVID weren't just "thinking differently." It's not "heterodox" to humiliate people who want to avoid the virus and say they are mentally ill. Doctors who mocked the virus by calling it "omi-cold" or who said pediatric vaccine-advocates are "off their rocker" aren't challenging the "conventional wisdom".

These doctors are endangering lives. They shouldn't be treated any differently than a doctor who opposes the MMR, HPV, or any other vaccine, even if they have stellar reputations, fancy titles, and claim to be driven by evidence and data. The misinformation they spread diminishes trust in the entire medical profession and precludes informed debate. Misinformation is censorship.

To quote Dr. David Oliver,

> *Every time we see or hear such mistruths we need to combat them and call them out. They are used to play down the seriousness and consequences of COVID-19 and undermine health protection efforts.*[33]

Indeed.

References

Chapter One

1. Cabrera, J. (2021, July 27). DeSantis holds roundtable on masks in schools: "This should absolutely not be imposed." *Alachua Chronicle*. https://alachuachronicle.com/desantis-holds-roundtable-on-masks-in-schools-this-should-absolutely-not-be-imposed/

2. DeSantis, R. (2021, August 1). "We have protected the vulnerable by vaccinating the older population." - Dr. Jay Bhattacharya, Professor of Medicine at Stanford University [Facebook post; image attached]. Facebook. https://www.facebook.com/GovRonDeSantis/photos/a.4187528271305201/4378021065589253/

3. Hodgson, I. (2021, August 11). Florida vaccinations climb during delta surge, but half the state is still unvaccinated: Vaccinations surged among school-aged Floridians. But 12 to 19 year-olds are still the least protected age group in the state. *Tampa Bay Times*. https://www.tampabay.com/news/health/2021/08/11/florida-vaccinations-climb-during-delta-surge-but-half-the-state-is-still-unvaccinated/

4. Brink, G., Day, S., Dortch, S., Hill, J., Verhulst, J., & Gallaty, C. (2022, September 9). Why are so many Floridians still dying from COVID? How Florida's COVID death rate compares to other states, including California, Texas and New York. *Tampa Bay Times*. https://www.tampabay.com/opinion/2022/09/09/floridas-tough-COVID-summer-now-what-editorial/

5. Kennedy, K., & Marcelo, P. (2021, August 5). *'There are only so many beds': COVID-19 surge hits hospitals.* AP News. https://apnews.com/article/joe-biden-health-florida-coronavirus-pandemic-38917e4fd073c8142df15de2d8102a24

6. and Prevention. (n.d.). *United States COVID-19 cases and deaths by state* [Interactive dataset]. U.S. Department of Health and Human Services. Retrieved December 28, 2022, from https://data.cdc.gov/Case-Surveillance/United-States-COVID-19-Cases-and-Deaths-by-State-o/9mfq-cb36/data

7. Zitser, J. (2021, August 28). Florida hospitals order mobile morgues to deal with COVID-19 death overflow, report says: AdventHealth said that is has "begun utilizing" mobile morgues at 10 campuses throughout Florida. *Insider*. https://www.businessinsider.com/florida-hospitals-order-mobile-morgues-COVID-19-death-overflow-2021-8

8. Preidt, R., & Foster, R. (2021, August 26). Record high COVID cases and deaths reported in Florida. *U.S. News & World Report*. https://www.

usnews.com/news/health-news/articles/2021-08-26/record-high-COVID-cases-and-deaths-reported-in-florida

9. Haughey, J. (2021, September 17). *Florida leads nation in nursing home resident, staff deaths: AARP*. Yahoo! News. https://news.yahoo.com/florida-leads-nation-nursing-home-123000761.html

10. NBC 6 South Florida. (2021, September 4). *15 Miami-Dade educators die from COVID-19 in 10 days*. WLWT5 Cincinnati. https://www.wlwt.com/article/15-miami-dade-educators-die-from-COVID-19-in-10-days/37481919

11. Sah, P., Moghadas, S. M., Vilches, T. N., Shoukat, A., Singer, B. H., Hotez, P. J., Schneider, E. C., & Galvani, A. P. (2021). Implications of suboptimal COVID-19 vaccination coverage in Florida and Texas. *The Lancet Infectious Diseases*, *21*(11), 1493-1494. https://doi.org/10.1016/S1473-3099(21)00620-4

12. Sachs, S. (2021, September 2). *Florida child hospitalizations at 68 per day with children's hospitals 'under an unprecedented strain'*. WFLA News Channel 8. https://www.wfla.com/news/florida/florida-child-hospitalizations-at-68-per-day-as-childrens-hospitals-under-an-unprecedented-strain/

13. *Florida teen on ventilator after COVID diagnosis; Had not yet received COVID-19 vaccine. Teen's mother who had COVID vaccine suffering milder case of disease*. (2021, July 27). ABC11. https://abc11.com/COVID-COVID-19-vaccine-paulina-velasquez/10912013/

14. Sarkissian, A. (2021, September 10). Child COVID deaths more than doubled in Florida as kids returned to the classroom. *Politico*. https://www.politico.com/states/florida/story/2021/09/09/child-COVID-fatalities-nearly-double-in-florida-1390807

15. Piggott, J. (2021, September 7). *UF Health medical leaders express concern over increased rate of COVID child deaths*. News4JAX. https://www.news4jax.com/health/2021/09/07/uf-health-medical-leaders-express-concern-over-increased-rate-of-COVID-child-deaths/

16. Hodgson, I., & O'Donnell, C. (2021, September 10). 4 kids among Florida's COVID death toll as state sets another record for fatalities: The number of new infections is falling, but cases are increasingly concentrated among children and adolescents, weekly state report shows. *Tampa Bay Times*. https://www.tampabay.com/news/health/2021/09/10/4-kids-among-floridas-COVID-death-toll-as-state-sets-another-record-for-fatalities/

17. Long, C. (2021, September 9). *Florida dad regrets not getting COVID*

vaccine after 15-year-old daughter's death. WAVY.com. https://www.wavy.com/COVID-19-vaccine/florida-dad-regrets-not-getting-COVID-vaccine-after-15-year-old-daughters-death/

18. Kulldorff, M., & Bhattacharya, J. (2021, June 17). The ill-advised push to vaccinate the young. *The Hill*. https://thehill.com/opinion/healthcare/558757-the-ill-advised-push-to-vaccinate-the-young/

19. Sarkissian, A. (2022, June 16). DeSantis says Florida is 'affirmatively against' COVID-19 vaccines for young kids. "You are free to choose — that's not the issue," he also said. *Politico*. https://www.politico.com/amp/news/2022/06/16/desantis-COVID-vaccine-florida-kids-fda-00040191

20. Persaud, C. (2022, June 25). COVID wave may be peaking in Florida as cases start to level off, but deaths spike. *Palm Beach Post*. https://www.palmbeachpost.com/story/news/coronavirus/2022/06/25/COVID-cases-florida-leveling-off-while-deaths-start-increase/7724180001/

21. Johns Hopkins University. (2020, February 27). *Here's the Johns Hopkins study President Trump referenced in his coronavirus news conference*. JHU Hub. https://hub.jhu.edu/2020/02/27/trump-johns-hopkins-study-pandemic-coronavirusCOVID-19-649-em0-art1-dtd-health/

22. Rabin, R. C. (2022, August 31). U.S. life expectancy falls again in 'historic' setback. The decline during the pandemic is the sharpest in nearly 100 years, hitting Native American and Alaska Native communities particularly hard. *The New York Times*. https://www.nytimes.com/2022/08/31/health/life-expectancy-COVID-pandemic.html

23. Hui, M. (2022, September 1). *China's life expectancy is now higher than that of the US. US life expectancy at birth is now at 76.1 years, versus 77.1 for China*. Quartz. https://qz.com/china-life-expectancy-exceeds-us-1849483265

24. Kuehn, B. M. (2022). Lowest US life expectancy since 1996 linked to COVID-19. *JAMA*, *328*(14), 1389. https://doi.org/10.1001/jama.2022.15455

25. Kulldorff, M. (2022, May 6). *The triumph of natural immunity*. Brownstone Institute. https://brownstone.org/articles/the-triumph-of-natural-immunity/

26. Makary, M. [@MartyMakary]. (2022, June 12). *Natural immunity wins again. New England Journal study: natural immunity "protection was higher than that conferred after the same time* [Tweet; thumbnail link to article]. Twitter. https://twitter.com/MartyMakary/

status/1536112474113683459

27. Brown School of Public Health. (2022). *Vaccinations: Vaccine preventable deaths analysis* [Interactive dataset]. Global Epidemics. Retrieved December 28, 2022 from https://globalepidemics.org/vaccinations/

28. Hiltzik, M. (2022, November 30). COVID boosted anti-vaccine propaganda. Now measles and other childhood diseases are on the march. *Los Angeles Times*. https://www.latimes.com/business/story/2022-11-30/the-anti-vax-movement-is-fostering-a-measles-epidemic

29. Valerio, M., & Wainman, L. (2021, October 19). *Virginia couple die of COVID 2 weeks apart, leave 5 children behind. The family of Kevin and Misty Mitchem say the parents regretted their choice to not get a COVID-19 vaccine*. WUSA9. https://www.wusa9.com/article/news/health/coronavirus/unvaccinated-parents-5-kids-die-regret-not-getting-vaccine-last-words/65-9e2da979-c911-446b-8d39-c655795e33ac

30. Center for Countering Digital Hate. (2021, March 24). *The disinformation dozen. Why platforms must act on twelve leading online anti-vaxxers*. https://counterhate.com/wp-content/uploads/2022/05/210324-The-Disinformation-Dozen.pdf

31. Frankel, J. (2017, December 6). HIV doesn't cause AIDS according to Gwyneth Paltrow Goop 'trusted expert' doctor Kelly Brogan. *Newsweek*. https://www.newsweek.com/hiv-doesnt-cause-aids-according-gwyneth-paltrow-goop-doctor-kelly-brogan-735645

32. Brogan, K., & Ji, S. (2014, March 23). HPV vaccine maker's study proves natural HPV infection beneficial, not deadly. *GreenMedInfo*. https://greenmedinfo.com/blog/hpv-vaccine-maker-s-study-shows-natural-hpv-infection-beneficial-not-deadly

33. Brogan, K. (n.d.). Vaccination: Your body. Your baby. Their flu. *Kelly Brogan, MD*. Retrieved December 28, 2022 from https://www.kellybroganmd.com/blog/vaccination-your-body-your-baby-their-flu

34. Brogan, K. (n.d.). Choose your Path: Symptom suppression or health transformation? *Kelly Brogan, MD*. Retrieved December 28, 2022 from https://www.kellybroganmd.com/blog/choose-your-path-symptom-suppression-or-health-transformation

35. Remski, M. (2020, September 15). Inside Kelly Brogan's COVID-denying, vax-resistant conspiracy machine. Alt-health meets alt-right in the 'conspirituality' movement. *GEN-Medium*. https://gen.medium.com/inside-kelly-brogans-COVID-denying-vax-resistant-conspiracy-machine-28342e6369b1

36. Di Filippo, E. (2020, March 25). *'Very, very dangerous' Goop 'expert' slammed for bizarre coronavirus video*. Yahoo! Style. https://www.yahoo.com/now/kelly-brogan-doubts-existance-of-coronavirus-in-new-video-164034780.html

37. Henderson, D. K., Lee, L. M., & Palmore, T. N. (2014, June 1). The contemporary Semmelweis Reflex: History as an imperfect educator. *Infection Control Today*. https://www.infectioncontroltoday.com/view/contemporary-semmelweis-reflex-history-imperfect-educator

38. Brogan, K., & Ji, S. (n.d.). Could this be driving the epidemic of Sudden Infant Death? *Kelly Brogan, MD*. Retrieved December 18, 2022 from https://www.kellybroganmd.com/blog/driving-epidemic-sudden-infant-death-sids

39. White, J. B., & Benton, R. (2015, October 17). Robert Kennedy Jr. warns of vaccine-linked 'holocaust'. *The Sacramento Bee*. http://www.sacbee.com/news/politics-government/capitol-alert/article17814440.html

40. Diaz, J., Donio, M., Grant, J., Stone, M., & Zeck, A. (2022, August 5). *Debunking the nonsense* [Video presentation]. Health Freedom for Humanity 2022. https://healthfreedomforhumanity.org/debunking-the-nonsense-presentation-copy/

41. Kalichman, S. C., Eaton, L. A., Earnshaw, V. A., & Brousseau, N. (2022). Faster than warp speed: Early attention to COVD-19 by anti-vaccine groups on Facebook. *Journal of Public Health*, *44*(1), e96-e105. https://doi.org/10.1093/pubmed/fdab093

42. Miller, M. E. (2015, June 29). Anti-vaccine doctor behind 'dangerous' autism therapy found dead. Family cries foul. *The Washington Post*. https://www.washingtonpost.com/news/morning-mix/wp/2015/06/29/anti-vaccine-doctor-behind-dangerous-autism-therapy-found-dead-family-cries-foul/

43. Kestenbaum, S. (2022, May 9). Christiane Northrup, once a New Age health guru, now spreads COVID disinformation. *The Washington Post*. https://www.washingtonpost.com/religion/2022/05/03/COVID-christiane-northrup/

44. Brogan, K. (n.d.). Health as spiritual warfare. *Kelly Brogan, MD*. Retrieved December 18, 2022 from https://www.kellybroganmd.com/blog/health-as-spiritual-warfare

45. Satija, N., & Sun, L. H. (2019, December 20). A major funder of the anti-vaccine movement has made millions selling natural health products. *The Washington Post*. https://www.washingtonpost.com/

investigations/2019/10/15/fdc01078-c29c-11e9-b5e4-54aa56d5b7ce_story.html

46. Brogan, K. (n.d.). *Join Vital Life Project*. Kelly Brogan, MD. Retrieved December 2, 2022, from https://www.kellybroganmd.com/vital-life-project-offer-old

47. Lessem, M. A. (2015, May 3). Deconstructing "200 evidence based reasons not to vaccinate". *Science-Based Medicine*. https://sciencebasedmedicine.org/deconstructing-200-evidence-based-reasons-not-to-vaccinate/

48. Sugerman, D. E., Barskey, A. E., Delea, M. G., Ortega-Sanchez, I. R., Bi, D., Ralston, K. J., Rota, P. A., Waters-Montijo, K., & Lebaron, C. W. (2010). Measles outbreak in a highly vaccinated population, San Diego, 2008: Role of the intentionally undervaccinated. *Pediatrics*, *125*(4), 747-755. https://doi.org/10.1542/peds.2009-1653

49. Southern Poverty Law Center. (2000, Summer). The Neo-Confederates. *Intelligence Report*. https://www.splcenter.org/fighting-hate/intelligence-report/2000/neo-confederates

50. Howard, J. (2018). *Cognitive errors and diagnostic mistakes: A case-based guide to critical thinking in medicine*. Springer International Publishing. https://doi.org/10.1007/978-3-319-93224-8

51. Howard, J. (2022, August 12). Can COVID vaccines travel in space and time? *Science-Based Medicine*. https://sciencebasedmedicine.org/space-and-time/

52. Amygator. [@AmyA1A]. (2021, May 26). *Oh, @MonicaGandhi9's relentless optimism and positivity buoyed me up so many times during this whole mess. She never abandoned science* [Tweet]. Twitter. https://twitter.com/AmyA1A/status/1397660588583624709

53. Martin, R. (2021, December 30). *The dishonest doctors who were Fox News' most frequent medical guests in 2021: These 10 guests made nearly 700 combined appearances on Fox this year – and often spread medical misinformation on-air*. Media Matters for America. https://www.mediamatters.org/fox-news/dishonest-doctors-who-were-fox-news-most-frequent-medical-guests-2021-0

54. Falun Gong. (2022). In *Wikipedia*. https://en.wikipedia.org/w/index.php?title=Falun_Gong&oldid=1118928351

55. Roose, K. (2021, March 9). How The Epoch Times created a giant influence machine: Since 2016, the Falun Gong-backed newspaper has used aggressive Facebook tactics and right-wing misinformation to create

an anti-China, pro-Trump media empire. *The New York Times*. https://www.nytimes.com/2020/10/24/technology/epoch-times-influence-falun-gong.html

56. Urgency of Normal. (2022, February 18). *Children, COVID, and the urgency of normal: An advocacy toolkit for parents, students, mentors, teachers, and administrators*. https://tulip-chartreuse-stwk.squarespace.com/s/Urgency-of-Normal-Toolkit.pdf

57. Prasad, V. (2021, February 3). Kids don't need COVID-19 vaccines to return to school. *STAT*. https://www.statnews.com/2021/02/03/kids-dont-need-COVID-19-vaccines-to-return-to-school/

58. Prasad, V. (2021, September 2). The downsides of masking young students are real. *The Atlantic*. https://www.theatlantic.com/ideas/archive/2021/09/school-mask-mandates-downside/619952/

59. Bhattacharya, J., & Kulldorff, M. (2020, September 3). The case against COVID tests for the young and healthy. *Wall Street Journal*. https://www.wsj.com/articles/the-case-against-COVID-tests-for-the-young-and-healthy-11599151722

60. Diamond, D. (2020, December 16). 'We want them infected': Trump appointee demanded 'herd immunity' strategy, emails reveal. Then-HHS science adviser Paul Alexander called for millions of Americans to be infected as means of fighting COVID-19. *Politico*. https://www.politico.com/news/2020/12/16/trump-appointee-demanded-herd-immunity-strategy-446408

61. KaraJelly. (2022, September 16). *InfoWars: COVID jab is a bio-weapon* [Video]. Bitchute. https://www.bitchute.com/video/rfGDXbJ1K7Pr/

62. Alexander, P. (2022, November 25). Unvaccinated blood: It is your right to demand and source unvaccinated blood now for yes, Igor is right, the blood supply is damaged now and high risk; I won't want blood from a vaccinated person. *Alexander COVID news - Dr. Paul Alexander's newsletter*. https://palexander.substack.com/p/unvaccinated-blood-it-is-your-right

63. Alexander, P. (n.d.). *COVID research stipend support*. GiveSendGo. Retrieved December 23, 2022, from https://www.givesendgo.com/G2BC6

64. Offit, P. (2020, March 2). *Dr. Paul Offit: Why the coronavirus will be hard to contain* [Video interview]. Amanpour & Co. https://www.pbs.org/wnet/amanpour-and-company/video/dr-paul-offit-why-coronavirus-will-be-hard-to-contain/

65. Szabo, L. (2020, December 21). *Many US health experts underestimated the coronavirus ... Until it was too late*. Kaiser Health News. https://khn.org/news/article/many-us-health-experts-underestimated-the-coronavirus-until-it-was-too-late/

66. Howard, J. [@19joho]. (2020, August 23). *Given that COVID is benign in the vast majority of young children, I doubt it will become a major killer* [Tweet]. Twitter. https://twitter.com/19joho/status/1297678334789406720

67. Bergstrom, C. T. [@CT_Bergstrom]. (2021, March 15). *How can you advocate for herd immunity in October but oppose vaccination in March? Sadly predictable: many those previously opposed* [Tweet; thumbnail link to tweet]. Twitter. https://twitter.com/ct_bergstrom/status/1371649675174940674

68. Prasad, V. (2021, October 2). How democracy ends: COVID19 policy shows a (potential) path to the end of America. *Vinay Prasad's Observations and Thoughts*. https://vinayprasadmdmph.substack.com/p/how-democracy-ends

69. Jamison, P. (2020, December 16). A top scientist questioned virus lockdowns on Fox News. The backlash was fierce. *The Washington Post*. https://www.washingtonpost.com/dc-md-va/2020/12/16/john-ioannidis-coronavirus-lockdowns-fox-news/

70. Rickard, S. (2021, August 31). *'COVID is no joke': Unvaccinated Texas teenager dies in hospital from COVID-19*. Spectrum News. https://spectrumlocalnews.com/tx/south-texas-el-paso/news/2021/09/01/-COVID-is-no-joke---unvaccinated-texas-teenager-dies-in-hospital-from-COVID-19

71. Yager, P. (2021, August 30). *19-year-old Navarro College student dies from COVID-19*. FOX 4 News Dallas-Fort Worth. https://www.fox4news.com/news/19-year-old-navarro-college-student-dies-from-COVID-19

72. Brogan, K. (n.d.). CDC: You're fired. Autism coverup exposed. *Kelly Brogan, MD*. https://www.kellybroganmd.com/blog/cdc-youre-fired-autism-coverup-exposed

73. DeSantis, Ron. [@GovRonDeSantis]. (2021, August 1). *"We have protected the vulnerable by vaccinating the older population." – Dr. Jay Bhattacharya, Professor of Medicine at Stanford University* [Tweet; image attached]. Twitter. https://twitter.com/GovRonDeSantis/status/1421919960142581782

Chapter Two

1. Parrotta, E., Kister, I., Charvet, L., Sammarco, C., Saha, V., Charlson, R. E., Howard, J., Gutman, J. M., Gottesman, M., Abou-Fayssal, N., Wolintz, R., Keilson, M., Fernandez-Carbonell, C., Krupp, L. B., & Ryerson, L. Z. (2020, September). COVID-19 outcomes in MS: Observational study of early experience from NYU Multiple Sclerosis Comprehensive Care Center. *Neurology: Neuroimmunology & Neuroinflammation*, *7*(5), Article 835. https://doi.org/10.1212/NXI.0000000000000835

2. Frontera, J. A., Sabadia, S., Lalchan, R., Fang, T., Flusty, B., Millar-Vernetti, P., Snyder, T., Berger, S., Yang, D., Granger, A., Morgan, N., Patel, P., Gutman, J., Melmed, K., Agarwal, S., Bokhari, M., Andino, A., Valdes, E., Omari, M., … Galetta, S. (2021). A prospective study of neurologic disorders in hospitalized patients with COVID-19 in New York City. *Neurology*, *96*(4), e575-e586. https://doi.org/10.1212/WNL.0000000000010979

3. von Hehn, C., Howard, J., Liu, S., Meka, V., Pultz, J., Mehti, D., Prada, C., Ray, S., Edwards, M. R., & Sheikh, S. I. (2018, January). Immune response to vaccines is maintained in patients treated with dimethyl fumarate. *Neurology: Neuroimmunology & Neuroinflammation*, *5*(1), Article 409. https://doi.org/10.1212/NXI.0000000000000409

4. MedlinePlus. (2020, August 2). *Subacute sclerosing panencephalitis*. https://medlineplus.gov/ency/article/001419.htm

5. Glenn, K. (2017, July 5). Shingles increases risk of heart attack, stroke: Study says it's important patients with shingles are made aware of heart disease risk. *American College of Cardiology*. https://www.acc.org/about-acc/press-releases/2017/07/05/09/53/shingles-increases-risk-of-heart-attack-stroke

6. Farhat, N., Dauod, S., Hdiji, O., Sakka, S., Damak, M., & Mhiri, C. (2021). Myelopathy after zoster virus infection in immunocompetent patients: A case series. *The Journal of Spinal Cord Medicine*, *44*(2), 334-338. https://doi.org/10.1080/10790268.2019.1607053

7. Barshak, M. (2021, January 27). Shingles of the eye can cause lasting vision impairment. *Harvard Health Publishing*. https://www.health.harvard.edu/blog/shingles-of-the-eye-can-cause-lasting-vision-impairment-2021012721792

8. Howard, J., & Reiss, D. (2018). The anti-vaccine movement: A litany of fallacy and errors. In A. B. Kaufman & J. C. Kaufman (Eds.), *Pseudoscience: The conspiracy against science* (pp. 195-219). The MIT

Press. https://doi.org/10.7551/mitpress/10747.003.0013

9. Howard, J. (2018). *Cognitive errors and diagnostic mistakes: A case-based guide to critical thinking in medicine.* Springer International Publishing. https://doi.org/10.1007/978-3-319-93224-8

10. Howard, J. [@19joho]. (2019, November 22). *Yes. I've always said the biggest danger to my kids isn't the measles, but the thought process that leads people* [Tweet]. Twitter. https://twitter.com/19joho/status/1197959109582245889

11. Center for Countering Digital Hate. (2021, March 24). *The disinformation dozen. Why platforms must act on twelve leading online anti-vaxxers.* https://counterhate.com/wp-content/uploads/2022/05/210324-The-Disinformation-Dozen.pdf

12. Cullen, K. (2021, October 21). In the last three months, five conservative talk show hosts have died from COVID: Over the last few months, no less than five conservative radio talk show hosts who urged their audiences to avoid vaccines for COVID-19 have died from the virus. *The Boston Globe.* https://www.bostonglobe.com/2021/10/21/metro/dying-an-audience/

13. Pegden, W., Prasad, V., & Baral, S. (2021, May 7). COVID vaccines for children should not get emergency use authorization. *The BMJ opinion.* https://blogs.bmj.com/bmj/2021/05/07/COVID-vaccines-for-children-should-not-get-emergency-use-authorization/

14. Pfizer. (2021, March 31). *Pfizer-BioNTech announce positive topline results of pivotal COVID-19 vaccine study in adolescents* [Press release]. https://www.pfizer.com/news/press-release/press-release-detail/pfizer-biontech-announce-positive-topline-results-pivotal

15. Frenck, R. W., Jr., Klein, N. P., Kitchin, N., Gurtman, A., Absalon, J., Lockhart, S., Perez, J. L., Walter, E. B., Senders, S., Bailey, R., Swanson, K. A., Ma, H., Xu, X., Koury, K., Kalina, W. V., Cooper, D., Jennings, T., Brandon, D. M., Thomas, S. J., … Gruber, W. C. (2021). Safety, immunogenicity, and efficacy of the BNT162b2 COVID-19 vaccine in adolescents. *The New England Journal of Medicine, 385*, 239-250. https://doi.org/10.1056/NEJMoa2107456

16. Baral, S. [@sdbaral]. (2021, February 8). *I don't think variants are going to cause a third wave of #COVID19 in the coming weeks or months across* [Tweet]. Twitter. https://twitter.com/sdbaral/status/1358774006258798594

17. Prasad, V. [@VPrasadMDMPH]. (2021, June 23). *Myocarditis cont.*

ACIP slides are up. First, let us all remember cases are FALLING PRECIPITOUSLY The benefit side of the [Tweet; thumbnail link to infographic]. Twitter. https://twitter.com/VPrasadMDMPH/status/1407743348719316993

18. and Prevention. (n.d.). *COVID data tracker: Demographic trends of COVID-19 cases and deaths in the US reported to CDC* [Interactive dataset]. U.S. Department of Health and Human Services. Retrieved December 28, 2022, from https://COVID.cdc.gov/COVID-data-tracker/#demographics

19. Nirenberg, E., Freedman, D. A., Hoshino, R., Howard, J., & McAlpine, A. (2021, June 23). COVID-19 vaccination in children. *The BMJ Opinion*. https://blogs.bmj.com/bmj/2021/06/23/COVID-19-vaccination-in-children/

20. Howard, J. (2021, May 10). Should COVID-19 vaccines be administered to children under an emergency use authorization? *Science-Based Medicine*. https://sciencebasedmedicine.org/COVID-19-vaccine-children-under-an-emergency-use-authorization/

21. Gorski, D. (2022, June 6). "New school" COVID-19 antivaxxers are becoming less and less distinguishable from "old school" antivaxxers. *Science-Based Medicine*. https://sciencebasedmedicine.org/new-school-COVID-19-antivaxxers-are-becoming-less-and-less-distinguishable-from-old-school-antivaxxers/

22. Krauth, D. (2020, July 17). *Coronavirus News: Traveling nurses recall "It was like a medical war zone"*. ABC7 New York. https://abc7ny.com/traveling-nurses-nyc-COVID-19-news/6320577/

23. Rothfeld, M., Sengupta, S., Goldstein, J., & Rosenthal, B. M. (2020, April 14). 13 deaths in a day: An 'apocalyptic' coronavirus surge at an N.Y.C. hospital. Hospitals in the city are facing the kind of harrowing increases in cases that overwhelmed health care systems in China and Italy. *The New York Times*. https://www.nytimes.com/2020/03/25/nyregion/nyc-coronavirus-hospitals.html

24. Hanna, J., & Maxouris, C. (2020, April 7). *New York City reports a record 800-plus deaths in one day*. CNN. https://www.cnn.com/2020/04/07/health/us-coronavirus-tuesday/index.html

25. Annese, J. (2020, March 25). NYC builds massive makeshift morgue near Bellevue Hospital. *New York Daily News*. https://www.nydailynews.com/coronavirus/ny-coronavirus-city-puts-up-makeshift-morgue-outside-bellevue-hospital-20200325-raora6bqxncp5gx3qfoagyxida-story.html

26. Otterman, S. (2020, December 26). Why 530 frozen bodies sit in

a Brooklyn warehouse: In the first wave of COVID, the crush of bodies overwhelmed New York City's capacity to deal with the dead. Now, the city is prepared if a second onslaught occurs. *The New York Times*. https://www.nytimes.com/2020/12/26/nyregion/frozen-bodies-coronavirus-brooklyn.html

27. Bumsted, R., & Sisak, M. R. (2020, March 31). *Hospitals overflowing with bodies in US epicenter of virus*. AP News. https://apnews.com/article/virus-outbreak-us-news-ap-top-news-new-york-city-new-york-1b40d68e4969af9fa03e833afd24d709

28. Anderson, M. (2020, April 10). *Burials on New York Island are not new, but are increasing during pandemic*. NPR. https://www.npr.org/sections/coronavirus-live-updates/2020/04/10/831875297/burials-on-new-york-island-are-not-new-but-are-increasing-during-pandemic

29. Watkins, A., & Rashbaum, W. K. (2021, January 15). How many people have actually died from coronavirus in New York? The official statistics paint a partial picture and may understate the death toll. Here's why. *The New York Times*. https://www.nytimes.com/2020/04/10/nyregion/new-york-coronavirus-death-count.html

30. Collman, A. (2020, March 31). Shocking video shows the bodies of NYC coronavirus victims being forklifted into a refrigerated truck used as a temporary morgue. *Insider*. https://www.businessinsider.com/coronavirus-nyc-forklift-transfers-victims-bodies-refrigerated-truck-temporary-morgue-2020-3

31. Associated Press. (2021, May 8). *Bodies of 750 COVID-19 victims in New York City remain in refrigerated trucks: The bodies are inside trucks located in a Brooklyn pier while family members sort out plans for their final resting places, the city's medical examiner's office said*. NBC News. https://www.nbcnews.com/news/us-news/bodies-750-COVID-19-victims-new-york-city-remain-refrigerated-n1266762

32. Stein, R., & Kim, C. (2020, March 25). 'People are dying': 72 hours inside a N.Y.C. hospital battling coronavirus. An emergency room doctor in Elmhurst, Queens, gives a rare look inside a hospital at the center of the coronavirus pandemic. "We don't have the tools that we need." [Video]. *The New York Times*. https://www.nytimes.com/video/nyregion/100000007052136/coronavirus-elmhurst-hospital-queens.html

33. Grim, R. (2020, March 31). *Rikers Island prisoners are being offered PPE and $6 an hour to dig mass graves: New York City owns and operates a public cemetery on Hart Island, which has been tended by prison labor. Now prisoners are being asked to dig mass graves*. The

Intercept. https://theintercept.com/2020/03/31/rikers-island-coronavirus-mass-graves/

34. Otani, A. (2020, August 1). A toll of coronavirus in New York is a new group of orphans: Although statistics are hard to come by, experts say the scale of the losses is likely staggering. *Wall Street Journal*. https://www.wsj.com/articles/a-toll-of-coronavirus-in-new-york-is-a-new-group-of-orphans-11596288601

35. O'Connor, A. (2020, October 13). After a hospital stay for COVID, patients may face months of rehabilitation: Many patients who were critically ill with COVID-19 face arduous recoveries, often requiring extensive physical rehabilitation. *The New York Times*. https://www.nytimes.com/2020/10/08/well/live/COVID-19-hospital-rehabilitation.html

36. Ankel, S. (2020, April 23). Photos show how shortages are forcing doctors and nurses to improvise coronavirus PPE from snorkel masks, pool noodles, and trash bags. *Insider*. https://www.businessinsider.com/photos-show-doctors-nurses-improvising-due-to-lack-of-ppe-2020-4

37. Wan, W. (2021, April 22). Burned out by the pandemic, 3 in 10 health-care workers consider leaving the profession: After a year of trauma, doctors, nurses and other health workers are struggling to cope. *The Washington Post*. https://www.washingtonpost.com/health/2021/04/22/health-workers-COVID-quit/

38. Shapiro, A., & Eltohamy, F. (2021, March 8). *'War doesn't even compare': A year in the life of a traveling nurse*. NPR. https://www.npr.org/2021/03/08/974835141/a-year-in-the-life-of-a-traveling-nurse

39. Carrington, A. E. (2021, March 28). *How NY hospital faced COVID devastation and came back from the brink: The staff at Elmhurst Hospital Center has seen the darkest days of the pandemic*. ABC News. https://abcnews.go.com/Health/ny-hospital-faced-COVID-devastation-back-brink/story?id=76638912

40. Knoll, C., Watkins, A., & Rothfeld, M. (2020, July 11). 'I couldn't do anything': The virus and an E.R. doctor's suicide. Dr. Lorna Breen was unflappable — until she faced a new enemy. *The New York Times*. https://www.nytimes.com/2020/07/11/nyregion/lorna-breen-suicide-coronavirus.html

41. Gee, A. (2020, August 13). *Dying young: The health care workers in their 20s killed by COVID-19*. Kaiser Health News. https://khn.org/news/dying-young-the-health-care-workers-in-their-20s-killed-by-COVID-19/

42. Fuentes, G. (2020, April 27). *Hospital ship Comfort ends NYC COVID-19 mission after treating 182 patients.* USNI News. https://news.usni.org/2020/04/27/hospital-ship-comfort-ends-nyc-COVID-19-mission-after-treating-182-patients

43. Anderson, M. (2020, May 17). *'She wasn't alone,' a doctor reflects on New York City's coronavirus peak.* NPR. https://www.npr.org/2020/05/17/852719312/she-wasn-t-alone-a-doctor-reflects-on-new-york-city-s-coronavirus-peak

44. Philips, K., Uong, A., Buckenmyer, T., O'Connor, K., Shiminski-Maher, T., & Hametz, P. (2020). Rapid implementation of an adult coronavirus disease 2019 unit in a children's hospital. *The Journal of Pediatrics, 222,* 22-27. https://doi.org/10.1016/j.jpeds.2020.04.060

45. Lee, Y. J. (2020, March 27). Medical schools in New York are turning students into doctors ahead of schedule to help fight the coronavirus pandemic. *Insider.* https://www.businessinsider.com/medical-schools-graduate-students-early-coronavirus-COVID-19-2020-3

46. Roberts, G., & Golding, B. (2020, April 1). 'Somebody's got to do it': Forklift driver moves bodies of coronavirus victims. *New York Post.* https://nypost.com/2020/04/01/somebodys-got-to-do-it-forklift-driver-who-moves-coronavirus-victims/

47. BBC News. (2020, April 30). *Coronavirus kills 70 veterans at Massachusetts care home.* https://www.bbc.com/news/world-us-canada-52468287

48. Chavez, J.-C., Maan, A., & Allen, J. (2020, November 9). El Paso, Texas, Calls in Ten Morgue Trucks as Coronavirus Cases Surge. *U.S. News & World Report* https://www.usnews.com/news/top-news/articles/2020-11-09/el-paso-texas-calls-in-ten-morgue-trucks-as-coronavirus-cases-surge

49. Waller, A. (2020, December 9). Children's hospitals are pitching in to help with the flood of adult COVID-19 patients. *The New York Times.* https://www.nytimes.com/2020/12/09/us/childrens-hospitals-are-pitching-in-to-help-with-the-flood-of-adult-COVID-19-patients.html

50. Goodman, A., Perez Maestro, L., Formanek, I., Ramsay, M., & Kottasovà, I. (2020, March 24). *Spain turns ice rink into a morgue as coronavirus deaths pile up.* CNN. https://www.cnn.com/2020/03/24/europe/spain-ice-rink-morgue-coronavirus-intl/index.html

51. Horowitz, J., & Bubola, E. (2020, March 19). Italy's coronavirus victims face death alone, with funerals postponed. As morgues are inundated,

coffins pile up and mourners grieve in isolation: "This is the bitterest part." *The New York Times*. https://www.nytimes.com/2020/03/16/world/europe/italy-coronavirus-funerals.html

52. Pandey, G. (2021, May 19). *COVID-19: India's holiest river is swollen with bodies*. BBC News. https://www.bbc.com/news/world-asia-india-57154564

53. Armus, T. (2020, April 3). 'Every day it's getting worse': Bodies of coronavirus victims are left on the streets in Ecuador's largest city. *The Washington Post*. https://www.washingtonpost.com/nation/2020/04/03/ecuador-coronavirus-bodies/

54. Betancourt, S. (2021, July 22). 'It's too late': US doctor says dying patients begging for COVID vaccine. At least 99% of those in US who died of COVID in the last six months had not been vaccinated, says CDC director Dr Rochelle Walensky. *The Guardian*. https://www.theguardian.com/us-news/2021/jul/22/us-coronavirus-COVID-unvaccinated-hospital-rates-vaccines

55. Brooks, K. (2021, September 1). Verbal and physical attacks on health workers surge as emotions boil during latest COVID-19 wave: Stressed health workers are now confronting volatile visitors and patients. "The verbal abuse, the name-calling, racial slurs … we've had broken bones, broken noses," said one hospital official in Dallas. *The Texas Tribune*. https://www.texastribune.org/2021/09/01/coronavirus-texas-hospital-attacks-health-workers/

56. Karan, A. [@AbraarKaran]. (2021, October 31). *One thing I guarantee you will notice if you pay attention Doctors who have cared for #COVID19 patients will never* [Tweet]. Twitter. https://twitter.com/AbraarKaran/status/1454685110393917444

57. Naftulin, J. (2020, May 19). A New York ICU doctor who postponed his retirement to treat coronavirus patients has died from COVID-19. *Insider.* https://www.insider.com/nyc-icu-doctor-came-out-of-retirement-died-COVID-19-2020-5

Chapter Three

1. Fridenmaker, E. [@emily_fri]. (2020, February 24). *#medtwitter-are you nervous about corona?* [Tweet]. Twitter. https://twitter.com/emily_fri/status/1232091800740954113

2. Howard, J. [@19joho]. (2020, February 24). *This seems much more contagious than the flu. So yes, very concerned. Hope I'm wrong* [Tweet]. Twitter. https://twitter.com/19joho/status/1232119957028249600

3. Howard, J. [@19joho]. (2020, February 25). *Yes. I agree there is basically nothing to do. But I'm concerned. This has the potential to be an worldwide disaster* [Tweet]. Twitter. https://twitter.com/19joho/status/1232314070675705857

4. John Ioannidis. (2022, November 28). In *Wikipedia*. https://en.wikipedia.org/w/index.php?title=John_Ioannidis&oldid=1124429450

5. Ioannidis, J. P. A. (2005). Why most published research findings are false. *PLoS Medicine*, *2*(8), Article 124. https://doi.org/10.1371/journal.pmed.0020124

6. Ioannidis, J. P. A. (2020, March 17). A fiasco in the making? As the coronavirus pandemic takes hold, we are making decisions without reliable data. *STAT*. https://www.statnews.com/2020/03/17/a-fiasco-in-the-making-as-the-coronavirus-pandemic-takes-hold-we-are-making-decisions-without-reliable-data/

7. Ioannidis, J. P. A. (2020). Coronavirus disease 2019: The harms of exaggerated information and non-evidence-based measures. *European Journal of Clinical Investigation*, *50*(4), Article 13222. https://onlinelibrary.wiley.com/doi/full/10.1111/eci.13222

8. Portal: Current events/2020 March 19. (n.d.). In *Wikipedia*. Retrieved December 8, 2022. https://en.wikipedia.org/wiki/Portal:Current_events/2020_March_19

9. CBS News. (2020, March 19). *Coronavirus updates from March 19, 2020*. https://www.cbsnews.com/live-updates/coronavirus-disease-COVID-19-latest-news-2020-03-19/

10. Hamblin, J. (2020, February 24). A vaccine won't stop the new coronavirus. Most cases are not life-threatening, which is also what makes the virus a historic challenge to contain. *The Atlantic*. https://www.theatlantic.com/health/archive/2020/02/COVID-vaccine/607000/

11. Lipsitch, M. (2020, March 18). We know enough now to act decisively against COVID-19. Social distancing is a good place to start. *STAT*.

https://www.statnews.com/2020/03/18/we-know-enough-now-to-act-decisively-against-COVID-19/

12. Jamison, P. (2020, December 16). A top scientist questioned virus lockdowns on Fox News. The backlash was fierce. *The Washington Post.* https://www.washingtonpost.com/dc-md-va/2020/12/16/john-ioannidis-coronavirus-lockdowns-fox-news/

13. Warner, P. [@phwarner]. (2020, March 17). *This doesn't make any sense. Do you not see what is happening in Italy? This virus quickly almost crashed their* [Tweet]. Twitter. https://twitter.com/phwarner/status/1239987497926524935

14. Tal, M. [@ImmunoFever]. (2020, March 12). *Look at this season's flu cases that led to ICU care or death in Italy this season compared to coronavirus* [Tweet; infographic attached]. Twitter. https://twitter.com/ImmunoFever/status/1238301571483607040

15. Bastian, H. (2020, May 4). "Fiasco" rebuttal postscript: What about that 0.3% case fatality estimate? *Hilda Bastian: Scientist, blogger, cartoonist.* https://hildabastian.net/index.php/8-secondary/88

16. Will. (2020, March 19). In the same article that you use the Diamond Princess cruise ship as a case study for fatality rates, you [Comment on "A fiasco in the making?"]. *STAT*. https://www.statnews.com/2020/03/17/a-fiasco-in-the-making-as-the-coronavirus-pandemic-takes-hold-we-are-making-decisions-without-reliable-data/comment-page-46/#comment-2952676

17. Mathieu, E., Ritchie, H., Rodés-Guirao, L., Appel, C., Giattino, C., Hasell, J., Macdonald, B., Dattani, S., Beltekian, D., Ortiz-Ospina, E., & Roser, M. (2020). *Coronavirus pandemic (COVID-19)* [Interactive dataset]. Our World in Data. Retrieved December 14, 2022, from https://ourworldindata.org/COVID-deaths

18. Bendavid, E., Mulaney, B., Sood, N., Shah, S., Bromley-Dulfano, R., Lai, C., Weissburg, Z., Saavedra-Walker, R., Tedrow, J., Bogan, A., Kupiec, T., Eichner, D., Gupta, R., Ioannidis, J. P. A., & Bhattacharya, J. (2021). COVID-19 antibody seroprevalence in Santa Clara County, California. *International Journal of Epidemiology, 50*(2), 410-419. https://doi.org/10.1093/ije/dyab010

19. Offord, C. (2020, May 18). How (not) to do an antibody survey for SARS-CoV-2. *The Scientist*. https://www.the-scientist.com/news-opinion/how-not-to-do-an-antibody-survey-for-sars-cov-2-67488

20. CNN. [@CNN]. (2020, May 2). *Epidemiologist Dr. John Ioannidis says his research shows that the coronavirus is "common" and that there's*

likely been many asymptomatic [Tweet; thumbnail link to video]. Twitter. https://twitter.com/cnn/status/1256579248342564865

21. Yeung, J., Regan, H., Renton, A., Reynolds, E., & Alfonso, F., III. (2020, March 19). *March 19, 2020 coronavirus news*. CNN. https://www.cnn.com/world/live-news/coronavirus-outbreak-03-19-20-intl-hnk/index.html

22. Ioannidis, J. P. A. (2020, April 17). *Perspectives on the pandemic* [Episode 4; video podcast interview transcript]. The Press and the Public. https://www.thepressandthepublic.com/post/perspectives-on-the-pandemic-iv

23. McCormick, E. (2020, April 23). Why experts are questioning two hyped antibody studies in coronavirus hotspots. Investigations at California universities highlight challenges of research under pressure to provide quick answers. *The Guardian*. https://www.theguardian.com/world/2020/apr/23/coronavirus-antibody-studies-california-stanford

24. Claus, P. (2020, June 27). *Up to 300 million people may be infected by COVID-19, Stanford guru John Ioannidis says*. Greek Reporter. https://greekreporter.com/2020/06/27/up-to-300-million-people-may-be-infected-by-COVID-19-stanford-guru-john-ioannidis-says/

25. Zakaria, F. (2020, April 9). Why the coronavirus models aren't totally accurate. *The Washington Post*. https://www.washingtonpost.com/opinions/without-mass-testing-were-flying-blind-through-this-crisis/2020/04/09/bf61e178-7a9b-11ea-a130-df573469f094_story.html

26. Lee, S. M. (2020, July 24). *An elite group of scientists tried to warn Trump against lockdowns in March: John Ioannidis's controversial studies claim that the coronavirus isn't that big a threat. Before the Stanford scientist did any of them, he wanted to take that message to the White House*. BuzzFeed News. https://www.buzzfeednews.com/article/stephaniemlee/ioannidis-trump-white-house-coronavirus-lockdowns

27. Levin, M. (Host). (2020, April 19). *Dr. John Ioannidis on the race for real data on the coronavirus pandemic* [Video interview]. Fox News: Life, Liberty, and Levin. https://www.foxnews.com/video/6150670357001#sp=show-clips

28. Ferguson, N., Laydon, D., Nedjati Gilani, G., Imai, N., Ainslie, K., Baguelin, M., Bhatia, S., Boonyasiri, A., Cucunuba Perez, Z., Cuomo-Dannenburg, G., Dighe, A., Dorigatti, I., Fu, H., Gaythorpe, K., Green, W., Hamlet, A., Hinsley, W., Okell, L., Van Elsland, S., … Ghani, A. (2020, March 16). Impact of non-pharmaceutical interventions (NPIs) to reduce COVID-19 mortality and healthcare demand (Report 9). *Imperial College*. https://doi.org/10.25561/77482

29. Dean, N. E. [@nataliexdean]. (2020, April 17). *A rapid, unsolicited peer review on emerging serosurvey data from Santa Clara County, and why I remain skeptical of claims* [Tweet; thumbnail link to article]. Twitter. https://twitter.com/nataliexdean/status/1251309217215942656

30. Lee, S. M. (2020, April 24). *A Stanford professor's wife recruited people for his coronavirus study by claiming it would reveal if they could "Return to work without fear". An email sent to a Silicon Valley middle school's private listserv tried to recruit families for the antibody study, promising "peace of mind" about their immunity to the coronavirus.* BuzzFeed News. https://www.buzzfeednews.com/article/stephaniemlee/stanford-coronavirus-study-bhattacharya-email

31. Cherian, J. [@jjcherian]. (2020, April 17). *That means that if the true specificity of the test lies somewhere close to 98.3%, nearly all of the positive* [Tweet]. Twitter. https://twitter.com/jjcherian/status/1251272334629048322

32. Lee, S. M. (2020, May 15). *JetBlue's founder helped fund a Stanford study that said the coronavirus wasn't that deadly. A Stanford whistleblower complaint alleges that the controversial John Ioannidis study failed to disclose important financial ties and ignored scientists' concerns that their antibody test was inaccurate.* BuzzFeed News. https://www.buzzfeednews.com/article/stephaniemlee/stanford-coronavirus-neeleman-ioannidis-whistleblower

33. Gelman, A. (2020, April 19). Concerns with that Stanford study of coronavirus prevalence. *Statistical Modeling, Causal Inference, and Social Science*. https://statmodeling.stat.columbia.edu/2020/04/19/fatal-flaws-in-stanford-study-of-coronavirus-prevalence/

34. Kolata, G. (2020, April 21). Coronavirus infections may not be uncommon, tests suggest. Two preliminary efforts to survey citizens for antibodies to the virus have produced controversial results. *The New York Times*. https://www.nytimes.com/2020/04/21/health/coronavirus-antibodies-california.html

35. Goodman, J. D., & Rashbaum, W. K. (2021, September 3). N.Y.C. death toll soars past 10,000 in revised virus count. The city has added more than 3,700 additional people who were presumed to have died of the coronavirus but had never tested positive. *The New York Times*. https://www.nytimes.com/2020/04/14/nyregion/new-york-coronavirus-deaths.html

36. Levin, A. T., Hanage, W. P., Owusu-Boaitey, N., Cochran, K. B., Walsh, S. P., & Meyerowitz-Katz, G. (2020). Assessing the age specificity of infection fatality rates for COVID-19: Systematic review, meta-analysis,

and public policy implications. *European Journal of Epidemiology, 35*, 1123-1138. https://doi.org/10.1007/s10654-020-00698-1

37. Byambasuren, O., Cardona, M., Bell, K., Clark, J., McLaws, M.-L., & Glasziou, P. (2020). Estimating the extent of asymptomatic COVID-19 and its potential for community transmission: Systematic review and meta-analysis. *Official Journal of the Association of Medical Microbiology and Infectious Disease Canada*, *5*(4), 223-234. https://doi.org/10.3138/jammi-2020-0030

38. McNamara, D. (2020, September 28). About 80% of asymptomatic people with COVID-19 develop symptoms. *Medscape*. https://www.medscape.com/viewarticle/938195

39. Szabo, L. (2020, December 21). *Many US health experts underestimated the coronavirus ... Until it was too late*. Kaiser Health News. https://khn.org/news/article/many-us-health-experts-underestimated-the-coronavirus-until-it-was-too-late/

40. Jha, S. (2020, July 15). John Ioannidis explains his COVID views [Interview]. *Medscape*. https://www.medscape.com/viewarticle/933977#vp_5

41. Bastian, H. (2021, June 2). Posting this on behalf of John Ioannidis. Dear Hilda, Thank you for sharing this blog. It is very stimulating and [Comment on the blog post "Peering Through the Smoke at a Duel Over COVID's Infection Fatality Rate"]. *Absolutely Maybe: PLoS Blogs*. https://absolutelymaybe.plos.org/2021/05/31/peering-through-the-smoke-at-a-duel-over-COVIDs-infection-fatality-rate/#comment-27932

42. Ioannidis, J. P. A., Cripps, S., & Tanner, M. A. (2022). Forecasting for COVID-19 has failed. *International Journal of Forecasting*, *38*(2), 423-438. https://doi.org/10.1016/j.ijforecast.2020.08.004

43. Dow, J. (2020, April 9). *Latest coronavirus updates in New York: Thursday, April 9, 2020*. PIX11. https://pix11.com/news/coronavirus/latest-coronavirus-updates-in-new-york-thursday-april-9-2020/

44. New York COVID-19 nursing home scandal. (n.d.). In *Wikiwand*. Retrieved December 28, 2022, from https://www.wikiwand.com/en/New_York_COVID-19_nursing_home_scandal

45. Dienst, J., Valiquette, J., & Winter, T. (2021, February 18). *U.S. attorney, FBI investigating Cuomo's handling of nursing home deaths. In recent weeks, the administration revealed that 15,000 long-term care residents have died, up from the 8,500 previously disclosed.* NBC News. https://www.nbcnews.com/news/us-news/u-s-attorney-fbi-investigating-cuomo-

s-handling-nursing-home-n1258207

46. Doyle-Burr, N. (2022, November 19). COVID deaths still loom over NH nursing homes as outbreaks continue. *Valley News*. https://www.vnews.com/Upper-Valley-nursing-homes-see-COVID-19-deaths-amid-outbreaks-48780090

47. Ioannidis, J. P. A. (2020, March 23). *Perspectives on the pandemic* [Episode 1; video interview]. The Press and the Public. https://www.thepressandthepublic.com/post/perspectives-on-the-pandemic-i

48. Boccia, S., Ricciardi, W., & Ioannidis, J. P. A. (2020). What other countries can learn from Italy during the COVID-19 pandemic. *JAMA Internal Medicine*, *180*(7), 927-928. https://doi.org/10.1001/jamainternmed.2020.1447

49. Ioannidis, J. P. A. (2021). Over- and under-estimation of COVID-19 deaths. *European Journal of Epidemiology*, *36*, 581-588. https://doi.org/10.1007/s10654-021-00787-9

50. Prasad, V. (Host). (2021, February 9). Building a meta-research center and constructing COVID-19 health policy with Dr. John Ioannidis (Episode 3.41) [Audio podcast]. In *Plenary Session*. Apple Podcast. https://podcasts.apple.com/us/podcast/3-41-building-meta-research-career-constructing-COVID/id1429998903?i=1000508090404

51. Moses, D. (2021, February 28). *COVID-19, one year later: Elmhurst Hospital remembers the horrific dawn of the pandemic*. amNewYork. https://www.amny.com/news/COVID-19-one-year-later-elmhurst-hospital-remembers-the-horrific-dawn-of-the-pandemic/

52. Ioannidis, J. P. A. (2021). COVID-19 vaccination in children and university students. *European Journal of Clinical Investigation*, *51*(11), Article 13678. https://doi.org/10.1111/eci.13678

53. Select Subcommittee on the Coronavirus Crisis. (2022, June). *The Atlas dogma: The Trump administration's embrace of a dangerous and discredited herd immunity via mass infection strategy* [Staff report]. U.S. House of Representatives. https://coronavirus.house.gov/sites/democrats.coronavirus.house.gov/files/2022.06.21%20The%20Trump%20Administration%E2%80%99s%20Embrace%20of%20a%20Dangerous%20and%20Discredited%20Herd%20Immunity%20via%20Mass%20Infection%20Strategy.pdf

54. Select Subcommittee on the Coronavirus Crisis. (2022, January 7). *Interview of: Scott Atlas, M.D.* [Interview transcript]. U.S. House of Representatives. https://coronavirus.house.gov/sites/democrats.

coronavirus.house.gov/files/Transcribed%20Interview%20of%20 Scott%20Atlas.pdf

55. Select Subcommittee on the Coronavirus Crisis. (n.d.). *Excerpts from transcribed interview with Dr. Deborah Birx* [Interview transcript]. U.S. House of Representatives. https://coronavirus.house.gov/sites/democrats.coronavirus.house.gov/files/Birx%20TI%20Excerpts.pdf

56. Richards, W. (2021, April 20). *Ted Nugent has caught COVID-19 after calling it "not a real pandemic"*. NME. https://www.nme.com/news/music/ted-nugent-has-caught-COVID-19-after-calling-it-not-a-real pandemic-2924035

57. Gorski, D. [Orac]. (2020, August 31). The "only 6%" gambit: the latest viral COVID-19 disinformation. *Respectful Insolence*. https://respectfulinsolence.com/2020/08/31/only-six-percent-gambit-latest-viral-COVID-19-disinformation/

58. Hsu, T. (2020, September 24). Right-wing media stars mislead on COVID-19 death toll. Using a bogus interpretation of C.D.C. data, radio hosts like Mark Levin cast doubt on 200,000 pandemic deaths. *The New York Times*. https://www.nytimes.com/2020/09/24/business/media/right-wing-media-stars-mislead-on-COVID-19-death-toll.html

59. Di Filippo, E. (2020, March 25). *'Very, very dangerous' Goop 'expert' slammed for bizarre coronavirus video*. Yahoo! Style. https://www.yahoo.com/now/kelly-brogan-doubts-existance-of-coronavirus-in-new-video-164034780.html

60. Reuters. (2020, October 30). Trump falsely tells Michigan rally: 'Our doctors get more money if someone dies of COVID' [Video]. *The Guardian*. https://www.theguardian.com/us-news/video/2020/oct/30/trump-falsely-tells-michigan-rally-our-doctors-get-more-money-if-someone-dies-of-COVID-video

61. Henley, J., & McIntyre, N. (2020, October 26). Survey uncovers widespread belief in 'dangerous' COVID conspiracy theories. False claims that pandemic is a hoax or was started deliberately are attracting adherents around world. *The Guardian*. https://www.theguardian.com/world/2020/oct/26/survey-uncovers-widespread-belief-dangerous-COVID-conspiracy-theories

62. The BMJ. (2021, March 11). *Is zero COVID possible?* [Video]. YouTube. https://www.youtube.com/watch?v=HBd5Q8NpvoI

63. Prasad, V. (2022, July 28). John Ioannidis: The pandemic as of 7/28/2022. *Sensible Medicine*. https://sensiblemed.substack.com/p/john-

ioannidis-the-pandemic-as-of?utm_source=twitter&utm_campaign=auto_share&s=w

64. Ioannidis, J. P. A. (2022, March 30). I did not 'mock' those who were worried about COVID-19 [Letter]. *The Guardian*. https://www.theguardian.com/world/2022/mar/30/i-did-not-mock-those-who-were-worried-about-COVID-19

Chapter Four

1. Ioannidis, J. P. A. (2020, April 17). *Perspectives on the pandemic* [Episode 4; video podcast interview transcript]. The Press and the Public. https://www.thepressandthepublic.com/post/perspectives-on-the-pandemic-iv

2. Ioannidis, J. P. A. (2020, March 17). A fiasco in the making? As the coronavirus pandemic takes hold, we are making decisions without reliable data. *STAT*. https://www.statnews.com/2020/03/17/a-fiasco-in-the-making-as-the-coronavirus-pandemic-takes-hold-we-are-making-decisions-without-reliable-data/

3. and Prevention. (n.d.). *Comorbidities and other conditions* [Interactive dataset]. U.S. Department of Health & Human Services. Retrieved December 28, 2022, from https://www.cdc.gov/nchs/nvss/vsrr/COVID_weekly/index.htm#Comorbidities

4. Gillespie, C. (2020, September 2). The CDC's 6% COVID-19 deaths stat is causing confusion on social media—Here are the facts. No, 94% of coronavirus deaths were not actually caused by something else. *Health*. https://www.health.com/condition/infectious-diseases/coronavirus/cdc-6-percent-COVID-deaths

5. Levin, M. (Host). (2020, April 19). *Dr. John Ioannidis on the race for real data on the coronavirus pandemic* [Video interview]. Fox News: Life, Liberty, and Levin. https://www.foxnews.com/video/6150670357001#sp=show-clips

6. Ioannidis, J. P. A. (2020, March 23). *Perspectives on the pandemic* [Episode 1; video interview]. The Press and The Public. https://www.thepressandthepublic.com/post/perspectives-on-the-pandemic-i

7. Spector, J. (2020, May 9). 3 children have died in New York from a coronavirus-linked inflammatory disease, Cuomo says. *USA Today*. https://www.usatoday.com/story/news/health/2020/05/09/coronavirus-new-york-children-die-disease-similar-kawasaki/3103395001/

8. Gundlapalli, A. V., Lavery, A. M., Boehmer, T. K., Beach, M. J., Walke, H. T., Sutton, P. D., & Anderson, R. N. (2021). Death certificate-based ICD-10 diagnosis codes for COVID-19 mortality surveillance - United States, January-December 2020. *Morbidity and Mortality Weekly Report, 70*(14), 523-527. http://dx.doi.org/10.15585/mmwr.mm7014e2

9. Ioannidis, J. P. A. (2021). Over- and under-estimation of COVID-19 deaths. *European Journal of Epidemiology, 36*, 581-588. https://doi.org/10.1007/s10654-021-00787-9

10. Juyal, D., Kumar, A., Pal, S., Thaledi, S., Jauhari, S., & Thawani, V. (2020). Medical certification of cause of death during COVID-19 pandemic – a challenging scenario. *Journal of Family Medicine and Primary Care*, *9*(12), 5896-5898. https://doi.org/10.4103/jfmpc.jfmpc_1435_20

11. and Prevention. (2004, August). *Instructions for completing the cause-of-death section of the death certificate* [Publication #04-0377 (8/04)]. U.S. Department of Health and Human Services. https://www.cdc.gov/nchs/data/dvs/blue_form.pdf

12. National Center for Health Statistics. (2020). Guidance for certifying deaths due to coronavirus disease 2019 (COVID-19). *Vital Statistics Reporting Guidance* (Report No. 3). U.S. Department of Health and Human Services. https://www.cdc.gov/nchs/data/nvss/vsrg/vsrg03-508.pdf

13. Watkins, A., & Rashbaum, W. K. (2021, January 15). How many people have actually died from coronavirus in New York? *The New York Times*. https://www.nytimes.com/2020/04/10/nyregion/new-york-coronavirus-death-count.html

14. BBC News. (2020, August 12). *Coronavirus: England death count review reduces UK toll by 5000*. https://www.bbc.com/news/health-53722711

15. Balram, N. (2021, June 4). *Alameda county updates COVID-19 death calculation to align with state definitions.* County of Alameda, California. https://COVID-19.acgov.org/COVID19-assets/docs/press/press-release-2021.06.04.pdf

16. Ioannidis, J. P. A., Cripps, S., & Tanner, M. A. (2022). Forecasting for COVID-19 has failed. *International Journal of Forecasting*, *38*(2), 423-438. https://doi.org/10.1016/j.ijforecast.2020.08.004

17. Fletcher, E. R. (2020, March 18). *Worldwide shortage of COVID-19 test agents plagues health systems - Even as infections surpass 200,000.* Health Policy Watch. https://healthpolicy-watch.news/worldwide-shortage-of-COVID-19-test-agents-plagues-health-systems-even-as-infections-surpass-200000/

18. and Prevention. (2022, October 26). *Symptoms of COVID-19*. U.S. Department of Health and Human Services. https://www.cdc.gov/coronavirus/2019-ncov/symptoms-testing/symptoms.html

19. Oliver, D. (2021). David Oliver: mistruths and misunderstandings about COVID-19 death numbers. *BMJ*, *372*, n352. https://doi.org/10.1136/bmj.n352

20. BBC News. (2020, February 7). *Li Wenliang: Coronavirus kills Chinese whistleblower doctor*. https://www.bbc.com/news/world-asia-china-51403795

21. Begley, S. (2020, July 20). Trump said more COVID-19 testing 'creates more cases.' We did the math. *STAT*. https://www.statnews.com/2020/07/20/trump-said-more-COVID19-testing-creates-more-cases-we-did-the-math/

22. *Manhattan woman, 39, is NYC's first COVID-19 case; Husband's test results are pending*. (2020, March 1). NBC New York. https://www.nbcnewyork.com/news/coronavirus/person-in-nyc-tests-positive-for-COVID-19-officials/2308155/

23. Claus, P. (2020, June 27). *Up to 300 million people may be infected by COVID-19, Stanford guru John Ioannidis says*. Greek Reporter. https://greekreporter.com/2020/06/27/up-to-300-million-people-may-be-infected-by-COVID-19-stanford-guru-john-ioannidis-says/

24. Ellis, R. (2021, November 25). *Unvaccinated 14 times more likely to die from COVID*. WebMD. https://www.webmd.com/vaccines/COVID-19-vaccine/news/20211124/unvaccinated-14-times-more-likely-to-die-from-COVID

25. Baker, M. G., Wilson, N., & Anglemyer, A. (2020). Successful elimination of COVID-19 transmission in New Zealand. *The New England Journal of Medicine, 383*, e56. https://doi.org/10.1056/nejmc2025203

26. Our World in Data. (n.d.). *Excess mortality: Deaths from all causes compared to average over previous years* [Interactive chart]. Retrieved December 28, 2022, from https://ourworldindata.org/grapher/excess-mortality-p-scores-average-baseline?country=NZL~GBR~USA

27. Aizenman, N. (2020, May 21). *U.S. could have saved thousands of lives if lockdown started earlier, study finds*. NPR. https://www.npr.org/2020/05/21/859991296/u-s-could-have-saved-thousands-of-lives-if-lockdown-started-earlier-study-finds

28. Johnson, M. (2020, November 27). The young die as well from COVID-19, even as many engage in denial. *Milwaukee Journal Sentinel*. https://www.jsonline.com/story/news/2020/11/25/fighting-dangerous-myth-COVID-only-threatens-old-ill/6389206002/

29. Wu, K. J. (2021, February 18). The coronavirus has claimed 2.5 million years of potential life in the U.S., study finds. A Harvard researcher added up the number of years that Americans who died from COVID-19

might have lived had they reached a typical life expectancy. *The New York Times*. https://www.nytimes.com/2020/10/21/health/coronavirus-statistics-deaths.html

30. Elledge, S. J. (2020, October 27). *2.5 million person-years of life have been lost due to COVID-19 in the United States*. Medrxiv. https://doi.org/10.1101/2020.10.18.20214783

31. Quast, T., Andel, R., Gregory, S., & Storch, E. A. (2022). Years of life lost associated with COVID-19 deaths in the USA during first year of the pandemic. *Journal of Public Health*, *44*(1), e20-e25. https://doi.org/10.1093/pubmed/fdab123

32. Prasad, V. (Host). (2021, February 9). Building a meta-research center and constructing COVID-19 health policy with Dr. John Ioannidis (Episode 3.41) [Audio podcast]. In *Plenary Session*. https://podcasts.apple.com/us/podcast/3-41-building-meta-research-career-constructing-COVID/id1429998903?i=1000508090404

33. Begley, S. (2020, April 8). With ventilators running out, doctors say the machines are overused for COVID-19. *STAT*. https://www.statnews.com/2020/04/08/doctors-say-ventilators-overused-for-COVID-19/

34. Preidt, R. (2020, April 22). *Study: Most N.Y. COVID patients on ventilators died*. WebMD. https://www.webmd.com/lung/news/20200422/most-COVID-19-patients-placed-on-ventilators-died-new-york-study-shows#1

35. Brod, M., Kongsø, J. H., Lessard, S., & Christensen, T. L. (2009). Psychological insulin resistance: patient beliefs and implications for diabetes management. *Quality of Life Research*, *18*(1), 23-32. https://doi.org/10.1007/s11136-008-9419-1

36. Papoutsi, E., Giannakoulis, V. G., Xourgia, E., Routsi, C., Kotanidou, A., & Siempos, I. I. (2021). Effect of timing of intubation on clinical outcomes of critically ill patients with COVID-19: A systematic review and meta-analysis of non-randomized cohort studies. *Critical Care*, *25*, 121. https://doi.org/10.1186/s13054-021-03540-6

37. Parish, A. J., West, J. R., Caputo, N. D., Janus, T. M., Yuan, D., Zhang, J., & Singer, D. J. (2021). Early intubation and increased coronavirus disease 2019 mortality: a propensity score-matched retrospective cohort study. *Critical Care Explorations*, *3*(6), Article 0452. https://doi.org/10.1097/CCE.0000000000000452

38. Zirpe, K. G., Tiwari, A. M., Gurav, S. K., Deshmukh, A. M., Suryawanshi, P. B., Wankhede, P. P., Kapse, U. S., Bhoyar, A. P.,

Khan, A. Z., Malhotra, R. V., Kusalkar, P. H., Chavan, K. J., Naik, S. A., Bhalke, R. B., Bhosale, N. N., Makhija, S. V., Kuchimanchi, V. N., Jadhav, A. S., Deshmukh, K. R., & Kulkarni, G. S. (2021). Timing of invasive mechanical ventilation and mortality among patients with severe COVID-19-associated acute respiratory distress syndrome. *Indian Journal of Critical Care Medicine*, *25*(5), 493-498. https://doi.org/10.5005/jp-journals-10071-23816

39. Lowe, Y. (2021, February 1). UK COVID-19 patients dying needlessly due to unfounded fears about ventilators. Some critically ill people are refusing intubation, wrongly associating it with higher risk of death, say doctors. *The Guardian*. https://www.theguardian.com/world/2021/jan/31/uk-COVID-patients-are-dying-needlessly-due-to-unfounded-fears-about-ventilators

40. Goldhill, O. (2021, January 25). Undercounting of COVID-19 deaths is greatest in pro-Trump areas, analysis shows. *STAT*. https://www.statnews.com/2021/01/25/undercounting-COVID-19-deaths-greatest-in-pro-trump-areas-analysis-shows/

41. Bergin, D., Ladyzhets, B., Kincaid, J., Kravitz, D., Haselhorst, S., White, A., Capps, A., Keller, R., & Hassanein, N. (2021, December 26). Uncounted: Inaccurate death certificates across the country hide the true toll of COVID-19. In some counties, half of the spike in deaths during the pandemic is attributed to COVID-19. Researchers say that points to a massive undercount. *USA Today*. https://www.usatoday.com/in-depth/news/nation/2021/12/22/COVID-deaths-obscured-inaccurate-death-certificates/8899157002/

42. Finucane, M. (2022, May 5). BU professor: True death toll of COVID-19 pandemic could now be as high as 1.22 million in United States. *The Boston Globe*. https://www.bostonglobe.com/2022/05/05/nation/bu-professor-true-death-toll-COVID-19-pandemic-could-now-be-high-122-million-united-states/

43. Sidik, S. M. (2022, February 10). Heart-disease risk soars after COVID — even with a mild case. Massive study shows a long-term, substantial rise in risk of cardiovascular disease, including heart attack and stroke, after a SARS-CoV-2 infection. *Nature*. https://www.nature.com/articles/d41586-022-00403-0

44. Gale, J. (2022, October 24). COVID-19 tied to higher risk of deadly blood clots in large study: Clots more common in COVID patients across severity spectrum. Study shows virus's propensity to stoke cardiovascular disease. *Bloomberg*. https://www.bloomberg.com/news/articles/2022-10-24/COVID-s-heart-effects-infections-raise-clotting-death-risks-in-large-study

45. Meyerowitz-Katz, G. (2021, April 19). How many people have died of COVID-19? Why the true number of deaths is probably higher than our official count. *Medium Coronavirus Blog*. https://coronavirus.medium.com/how-many-people-have-died-of-COVID-19-60243f60bc25

46. Msemburi, W., Karlinsky, A., Knutson, V., Aleshin-Guendel, S., Chatterji, S., & Wakefield, J. (2022). The WHO estimates of excess mortality associated with the COVID-19 pandemic. *Nature*. https://doi.org/10.1038/s41586-022-05522-2

47. Payne, S. (2022, December 14). *COVID-19 responsible for 14.83 million deaths, World Health Organization says*. ABC. https://www.abc.net.au/news/2022-12-15/who-COVID-19-excess-deaths/101770442

48. Faust, J. (2023, January 22). Data snapshot: Unnatural deaths like accidents, trauma, and overdose rarely attributed to COVID. Debunking a misleading talking point about COVID death certificates and unnatural causes. *Inside Medicine*. https://insidemedicine.substack.com/p/data-snapshot-unnatural-deaths-like

49. New York City Department of Health and Mental Hygiene COVID-19 Response Team. (2020). Preliminary estimate of excess mortality during the COVID-19 outbreak - New York City, March 11-May 2, 2020. *Morbidity and Mortality Weekly Report*, *69*(19), 603–605. http://dx.doi.org/10.15585/mmwr.mm6919e5

50. Czeisler, M. É., & Czeisler, C. A. (2023). Shifting mortality dynamics in the United States during the COVID-19 pandemic as measured by years of life lost. *Annals of Internal Medicine*, *176*(1), 141-143. https://doi.org/10.7326/M22-2226

51. Nolley, E. P., Sahetya, S. K., Hochberg, C. H., Hossen, S., Hager, D. N., Brower, R. G., Stuart, E. A., & Checkley, W. (2023). Outcomes among mechanically ventilated patients with severe pneumonia and acute hypoxemic respiratory failure from SARS-CoV-2 and other etiologies. *JAMA Network Open*, *6*(1), Article 2250401. https://doi.org/10.1001/jamanetworkopen.2022.50401

Chapter Five

1. D'Souza, G., & Dowdy, D. (2021, September 13). *Rethinking herd immunity and the COVID-19 response end game*. Johns Hopkins Bloomberg School of Public Health. https://www.jhsph.edu/COVID-19/articles/achieving-herd-immunity-with-COVID19.html

2. Hamblin, J. (2020, July 13). A new understanding of herd immunity: The portion of the population that needs to get sick is not fixed. We can change it. *The Atlantic*. https://www.theatlantic.com/health/archive/2020/07/herd-immunity-coronavirus/614035/

3. Prater, E., & Williams, T. (2022, December 5). Thanksgiving kicked off a COVID surge, and it's slamming U.S. hospitals already battling the tripledemic: 'It's the perfect storm for a terrible holiday season'. *Fortune*. https://fortune.com/well/2022/12/05/thanksgiving-COVID-surge-us-tripledemic-hospitalizations-rising-coroanvirus-omicron-perefct-storm-holiday-season-vaccination-rsv-flu/

4. Barshak, M. (2021, January 27). Shingles of the eye can cause lasting vision impairment. *Harvard Health Publishing*. https://www.health.harvard.edu/blog/shingles-of-the-eye-can-cause-lasting-vision-impairment-2021012721792

5. Glenn, K. (2017, July 5). Shingles increases risk of heart attack, stroke: Study says it's important patients with shingles are made aware of heart disease risk. *American College of Cardiology*. https://www.acc.org/about-acc/press-releases/2017/07/05/09/53/shingles-increases-risk-of-heart-attack-stroke

6. Forbes, H., Douglas, I., Finn, A., Breuer, J., Bhaskaran, K., Smeeth, L., Packer, S., Langan, S. M., Mansfield, K. E., Marlow, R., Whitaker, H., & Warren-Gash, C. (2020). Risk of herpes zoster after exposure to varicella to explore the exogenous boosting hypothesis: Self controlled case series study using UK electronic healthcare data. *BMJ*, *368*, l6987. https://doi.org/10.1136/bmj.l6987

7. Leung, J., Dooling, K., Marin, M., Anderson, T. C., & Harpaz, R. (2022). The impact of universal varicella vaccination on herpes zoster incidence in the United States: Comparison of birth cohorts preceding and following varicella vaccination program launch. *The Journal of Infectious Diseases*, *226*(Suppl. 4), S470-S477. https://doi.org/10.1093/infdis/jiac255

8. Immunization Action Coalition. (2018). *Varicella (chickenpox): questions and answers* [P4202]. https://www.immunize.org/catg.d/p4202.pdf

9. Lopez, A., Harrington, T., & Marin, M. (2021, September 20). *Varicella.*

and Prevention. https://www.cdc.gov/vaccines/pubs/pinkbook/varicella.html

10. Haelle, T. (2019, June 11). Two-for-one: Chickenpox vaccine lowers shingles risk in children. Immunization reduces the likelihood of a painful reemergence of the virus in kids. *Scientific American.* https://www.scientificamerican.com/article/two-for-one-chickenpox-vaccine-lowers-shingles-risk-in-children/

11. Bunce-Mason, A. (2012, September 10). *Could the death of my daughter have been prevented?* Vaccines Today. https://www.vaccinestoday.eu/stories/could-the-death-of-my-daughter-have-been-prevented/

12. Matthews, S. (2022, October 20). *Chickenpox now rare in U.S. due to routine vaccination.* Infectious Diseases Society of America. https://www.idsociety.org/news--publications-new/articles/2022/chickenpox-now-rare-in-u.s.-due-to-routine-vaccination/

13. Krug, A., & Prasad, V. (2022, February 2). *Should we let children catch Omicron? Restrictions in schools must never return.* UnHerd. https://unherd.com/2022/02/should-we-let-children-catch-omicron/

14. Ioannidis, J. P. A. (2021). COVID-19 vaccination in children and university students. *European Journal of Clinical Investigation, 51*(11), Article 13678. https://doi.org/10.1111/eci.13678

15. Howard, J. (2021, October 30). The JCVI speaks: "Natural infection in children could have substantial long-term benefits on COVID-19 in the UK". The UK's Joint Committee on Vaccination and Immunisation suggested using sick children as human shields to protect adults. *Science-Based Medicine.* https://sciencebasedmedicine.org/jcvi/

16. Dingwall, R. (2020, March 18). *Coronavirus UK – Why closing schools is (generally) a bad idea.* Social Science Space. https://www.socialsciencespace.com/2020/03/coronavirus-uk-why-closing-schools-is-generally-a-bad-idea/

17. Steerpike. (2021, August 5). Revealed: Robert Dingwall axed as government advisor. *The Spectator.* https://www.spectator.co.uk/article/revealed-robert-dingwall-axed-as-government-advisor

18. *Expert reaction to plans for self isolation for over 70s that may be implemented in the UK in the coming weeks.* (2020, March 15). Science Media Centre. https://www.sciencemediacentre.org/expert-reaction-to-plans-for-self-isolation-for-over-70s-that-may-be-implemented-in-the-uk-in-the-coming-weeks/

19. Howard, J. (2022, February 11). Should an infectious disease epidemiologist comment on child vaccination? Yes! *Science-Based Medicine*. https://sciencebasedmedicine.org/unkind-largely-unqualified-and-highly-judgmental/

20. Balloux, F. [@BallouxFrancois]. (2022, January 22). *This is an interesting question. Vaccinating healthy ≤12 year olds makes hardly difference to them directly, however we look at* [Tweet]. Twitter. https://twitter.com/BallouxFrancois/status/1486468926762541059

21. Lavine, J. S., Bjornstad, O., & Antia, R. (2021). Vaccinating children against SARS-CoV-2. *BMJ*, *373*, n1197. https://doi.org/10.1136/bmj.n1197

22. AIER Library. (2020, October 6). *Reaching immunity | A private summit of epidemiologists against lockdowns* [Video]. YouTube. https://www.youtube.com/watch?v=jtiInz1DWuA

23. Baral, S. [@sdbaral]. (2021, December 23). *I hear that and don't have an answer for anyone other than myself. I talk to most people as I* [Tweet; thumbnail link to tweet]. Twitter. https://twitter.com/sdbaral/status/1474075127981776903

24. Gorski, D., & Yamey, G. (2021, September 23). COVID-19 and the new merchants of doubt. *The BMJ Opinion*. https://blogs.bmj.com/bmj/2021/09/13/COVID-19-and-the-new-merchants-of-doubt/

25. John Locke Foundation. (2020, October 12). *AIER's Jeffrey Tucker discusses the Great Barrington Declaration* [Video]. YouTube. https://www.youtube.com/watch?v=I5gXS6z6NGY

26. Jeffery Tucker. (2022, December 9). In *Wikipedia*. https://en.wikipedia.org/w/index.php?title=Jeffrey_Tucker&oldid=1126391557

27. Tucker, J. A. (2016, November 3). *Let the kids work*. Foundation for Economic Education. https://fee.org/articles/let-the-kids-work/

28. Tucker, J. (2015, May 3). *How I quit smoking and why I'm glad I did*. Beautify Anarchy. https://tucker.liberty.me/how-i-quit-smoking-and-why-im-glad-i-did/

29. Kulldorff, M., Gupta, S., & Bhattacharya, J. (2020, October 4). *The Great Barrington Declaration*. https://gbdeclaration.org/

30. Bhattacharya, J., Gupta, S., & Kulldorff, M. (2020, November 25). *Focused protection*. Great Barrington Declaration. https://gbdeclaration.org/focused-protection/

31. Great Barrington Declaration. (n.d.). *Frequently asked questions*. Retrieved November 14, 2022, from https://gbdeclaration.org/frequently-asked-questions/

32. Kulldorff, M. [@MartinKulldorff]. (2020, December 24). *If the young live normal lives, some will be infected, but their risk is less than from lockdown collateral damage* [Tweet]. Twitter. https://twitter.com/MartinKulldorff/status/1342239762258808832

33. Great Barrington Declaration [@gbdeclaration]. (2021, April 13). *We have to go back to the basic principles of public health that was thrown out the window a year* [Tweet; thumbnail link to article]. Twitter. https://twitter.com/gbdeclaration/status/1381983341344342023

34. Kulldorff, M. [@MartinKulldorff]. (2020, August 15). *The best way to get herd immunity is through a vaccine* [Tweet]. Twitter. https://twitter.com/MartinKulldorff/status/1294830690492715009

35. Reaction Team. (2020, July 21). *We may already have herd immunity - an interview with Professor Sunetra Gupta*. Reaction. https://reaction.life/we-may-already-have-herd-immunity-an-interview-with-professor-sunetra-gupta/

36. Kulldorff, M. (2020, August 8). Herd immunity is still key in the fight against COVID-19. *The Spectator*. https://www.spectator.co.uk/article/herd-immunity-is-still-key-in-the-fight-against-COVID-19

37. PA Media. (2020, October 9). Herd immunity letter signed by fake experts including 'Dr Johnny Bananas'. *The Guardian*. https://www.theguardian.com/world/2020/oct/09/herd-immunity-letter-signed-fake-experts-dr-johnny-bananas-COVID

38. KCBS Radio Staff. (2020, October 20). *Physicians make controversial call for return to normalcy*. Audacy. https://www.audacy.com/kcbsradio/news/physicians-make-controversial-call-for-return-to-normalcy

39. Mathieu, E., Ritchie, H., Rodés-Guirao, L., Appel, C., Giattino, C., Hasell, J., Macdonald, B., Dattani, S., Beltekian, D., Ortiz-Ospina, E., & Roser, M. (2020). *Coronavirus pandemic (COVID-19)* [Interactive dataset]. Our World in Data. Retrieved December 30, 2022, from https://ourworldindata.org/COVID-deaths

40. Ioannidis, J. P. A. (2020, April 17). *Perspectives on the pandemic* [Episode 4; video podcast interview transcript]. The Press and the Public. https://www.thepressandthepublic.com/post/perspectives-on-the-pandemic-iv

41. Ioannidis, J. P. A. (2020, March 17). A fiasco in the making? As the coronavirus pandemic takes hold, we are making decisions without reliable data. *STAT*. https://www.statnews.com/2020/03/17/a-fiasco-in-the-making-as-the-coronavirus-pandemic-takes-hold-we-are-making-decisions-without-reliable-data/

42. Rational Ground. (2020, September 28). *Governor DeSantis' roundtable experts advocate for "normal" life for young people* [Video meeting transcript]. https://rationalground.com/governor-desantis-roundtable-experts-advocate-for-normal-life-for-young-people/

43. Sayburn, A. (2020). COVID-19: Experts question analysis suggesting half UK population has been infected. *BMJ*, *368*, m1216. https://doi.org/10.1136/bmj.m1216

44. Sayers, F. (2020, May 21). *Sunetra Gupta: COVID-19 is on the way out. The author of the Oxford model defends her view that the virus has passed through the UK's population*. UnHerd. https://unherd.com/2020/05/oxford-doubles-down-sunetra-gupta-interview/

45. Chivers, T. (2021, August 7). Scientists need scrutiny over COVID, too. *The Times*. https://www.thetimes.co.uk/article/scientists-need-scrutiny-over-COVID-too-t5db88mq2

46. Bendavid, E., & Bhattacharya, J. (2020, March 24). Is the Coronavirus as deadly as they say? Current estimates about the COVID-19 fatality rate may be too high by orders of magnitude. *Wall Street Journal*. https://www.wsj.com/articles/is-the-coronavirus-as-deadly-as-they-say-11585088464

47. Bhattacharya, J. [@DrJBhattacharya]. (2022, March 14). *I never called it the flu. The standard errors, properly calculated, do not include 0 in the CI. That would* [Tweet]. Twitter. https://twitter.com/DrJBhattacharya/status/1503587344565571584

48. Robinson, P. (Host). (2020, March 27). Questioning conventional wisdom in the COVID-19 crisis, with Dr. Jay Bhattacharya [Video podcast episode]. In *Uncommon knowledge with Peter Robinson*. https://www.youtube.com/watch?v=-UO3Wd5urg0

49. D'Ambrosio, A. (2020, October 30). Seeking common ground in 'herd immunity' debate – Scientists agree that lockdowns are harmful, but abandoning them has costs too. *MedPage Today*. https://www.medpagetoday.com/infectiousdisease/COVID19/89432

50. Royal, D., & Flores, R. (2020, July 26). *A 9-year-old who died of coronavirus had no known underlying health issues, family says*. CNN. https://www.cnn.com/2020/07/25/us/kimora-lynum-dies-of-coronavirus/index.html

51. and Prevention. (2022, September 27). *Obesity, race/ethnicity, and COVID-19*. U.S. Department of Health and Human Services. https://www.cdc.gov/obesity/data/obesity-and-COVID-19.html

52. Ortaliza, J., Amin, K., & Cox, C. (2022, November 10). *COVID-19 leading cause of death ranking*. Peterson-KFF Health System Tracker. https://www.healthsystemtracker.org/brief/COVID-19-leading-cause-of-death-ranking/#Age-specific%20rank%20of%20COVID-19%20deaths%20among%20leading%20causes%20of%20death%20in%20the%20U.S.,%20by%20month,%20January%202021%20-%20September%202022

53. Steensma, D. P., & Kyle, R. A. (2022). Dr Li Wenliang: Wuhan "whistleblower" and early COVID-19 victim. *Mayo Clinic Proceedings: Stamp Vignette on Medical Science, 97*(7), 1409-1410. https://doi.org/10.1016/j.mayocp.2022.05.033

54. Cha, A. E. (2020, April 25). Young and middle-aged people, barely sick with COVID-19, are dying of strokes: Doctors sound alarm about patients in their 30s and 40s left debilitated or dead. Some didn't even know they were infected. *The Washington Post*. https://www.washingtonpost.com/health/2020/04/24/strokes-coronavirus-young-patients/

55. Paulson, M. (2020, July 5). Nick Cordero, nominated for Tony as tap-dancing tough guy, dies at 41: The Broadway actor's battle with the coronavirus was followed closely by many as his wife chronicled his experience on social media. *The New York Times*. https://www.nytimes.com/2020/07/05/obituaries/nick-cordero-dead-coronavirus.html

56. Guardian Staff. (2020, July 5). Nick Cordero: Broadway star dies aged 41 of coronavirus complications. Tony-nominated actor spent more than 90 days in hospital and had his right leg amputated. *The Guardian*. https://www.theguardian.com/world/2020/jul/06/nick-cordero-broadway-star-dies-aged-41-of-coronavirus-complications

57. Louis-Ferdinand, N. (2022, May 27). Lockdowns were voluntary, reasonable, and effective. *A [Heart] For Lives*. https://aloveforlives.substack.com/p/lockdowns-were-voluntary-reasonable

58. Bhattacharya, J. (2021, October 21). *What happened: Dr. Jay Bhattacharya on 19 months of COVID* [Interview]. Hoover Institution. https://www.hoover.org/research/what-happened-dr-jay-bhattacharya-19-months-COVID-1

59. Louis-Ferdinand, N. (2022, May 27). The GBD lacked popular support. *A [Heart] For Lives*. https://aloveforlives.substack.com/p/the-gbd-lacked-

popular-support

60. Lee, C., & Palosky, C. (2021, September 28). *Surging Delta variant cases, hospitalizations, and deaths are biggest drivers of recent uptick in U.S. COVID-19 vaccination rates*. Kaiser Family Foundation. https://www.kff.org/coronavirus-COVID-19/press-release/surging-delta-variant-cases-hospitalizations-and-deaths-are-biggest-drivers-of-recent-uptick-in-u-s-COVID-19-vaccination-rates/

61. Kilduff, L. (2021, December 22). *Which U.S. states have the oldest populations?* Population Reference Bureau. https://www.prb.org/resources/which-us-states-are-the-oldest/

62. Melamed, M., & Rivera, T. (2021, June 1). Nearly one-third of U.S. coronavirus deaths are linked to nursing homes. *The New York Times*. https://www.nytimes.com/interactive/2020/us/coronavirus-nursing-homes.html

63. Yates, K. [@Kit_Yates_Maths]. (2022, April 26). *For example, because shielding in real populations would have been imperfect, infections in the lower-risk population would have leaked through* [Tweet]. Twitter. https://twitter.com/Kit_Yates_Maths/status/1519013625729634305

64. Boehmer, T. K., DeVies, J., Caruso, E., van Santen, K. L., Tang, S., Black, C. L., Harnett, K. P., Kite-Powell, A., Dietz, S., Lozier, M., & Gundlapalli, A. V. (2020). Changing age distribution of the COVID-19 pandemic - United States, May-August 2020. *Morbidity and Mortality Weekly Report, 69*(39), 1404-1409. http://dx.doi.org/10.15585/mmwr.mm6939e1

65. Kulldorff, M., Gupta, S., & Bhattacharya, J. (2020, October 30). We should focus on protecting the vulnerable from COVID infection. *Newsweek*. https://www.newsweek.com/we-should-focus-protecting-vulnerable-COVID-infection-opinion-1543225

66. Bhattacharya, J. (2020, October 29). It's time for an alternative to lockdown. *The Spectator*. https://www.spectator.co.uk/article/it-s-time-for-an-alternative-to-lockdown/

67. Kulldorff, M., & Bhattacharya, J. (2020, November 2). Lockdown isn't working. *The Spectator*. https://www.spectator.co.uk/article/lockdown-isn-t-working

68. American Academy of Pediatrics & Children's Hospital Association. (2020, November 12). *Children and COVID-19: State data report*. American Academy of Pediatrics. https://downloads.aap.org/AAP/PDF/AAP%20and%20CHA%20-%20Children%20and%20COVID-19%20

State%20Data%20Report%2011.12.20%20FINAL.pdf

69. and Prevention. (n.d.). *Influenza-associated pediatric mortality* [Interactive dataset]. U.S. Department of Health and Human Services. Retrieved December 3, 2022, from https://gis.cdc.gov/grasp/fluview/pedfludeath.html

70. Walter, E. B., Talaat, K. R., Sabharwal, C., Gurtman, A., Lockhart, S., Paulsen, G. C., Barnett, E. D., Muñoz, F. M., Maldonado, Y., Pahud, B. A., Domachowske, J. B., Simões, E. A. F., Sarwar, U. N., Kitchin, N., Cunliffe, L., Rojo, P., Kuchar, E., Rämet, M., Munjal, I., … Gruber, W. C. (2022). Evaluation of the BNT162b2 COVID-19 vaccine in children 5 to 11 years of age. *The New England Journal of Medicine, 386*, 35-46. https://doi.org/10.1056/NEJMoa2116298

71. Ochieng, N., Chidambaram, P., & Musumeci, M. (2022, April 4). *Nursing facility staffing shortages during the COVID-19 pandemic*. Kaiser Family Foundation. https://www.kff.org/coronavirus-COVID-19/issue-brief/nursing-facility-staffing-shortages-during-the-COVID-19-pandemic/

72. Kinner, K. (2022, October 16). *CDC: Over 212 nursing home workers have died from COVID-19 since August*. World Socialist Web Site. https://www.wsws.org/en/articles/2022/10/17/ryab-o17.html

73. Dawson, L., & Kates, J. (2021, November 4). *Rapid home tests for COVID-19: Issues with availability and access in the U.S. - Issue brief.* Kaiser Family Foundation. https://www.kff.org/report-section/rapid-home-tests-for-COVID-19-issues-with-availability-and-access-in-the-u-s-issue-brief/

74. Meyerowitz-Katz, G. (2022, March 2). Focused protection from the Great Barrington Declaration never made sense: Why focused protection was never a real strategy for reducing the impact of COVID-19. *Gideon M-K; Health Nerd*. https://gidmk.medium.com/focused-protection-from-the-great-barrington-declaration-never-made-sense-416b86ac5f06

75. Cohn, D., Menasce Horowitz, J., Minkin, R., Fry, R., & Hurst, K. (2022, March 24). Demographics of multigenerational households. *Pew Research Center*. https://www.pewresearch.org/social-trends/2022/03/24/the-demographics-of-multigenerational-households/

76. Lock, S. (2021, April 27). *US hotel room count by chain scale segment 2020*. Statista. https://www.statista.com/statistics/245864/us-hotel-rooms-by-chain-scale-segment/

77. Tucker, J. A., & Younes, J. (2021, April 15). *Medical journal warns about masks' potentially devastating consequences*. American Institute

for Economic Research. https://www.aier.org/article/medical-journal-warns-about-maskss-potentially-devastating-consequences/

78. Verno, L. (2021, March 19). *Fact-checking claims made by DeSantis' COVID response experts*. News4JAX. https://www.news4jax.com/news/local/2021/03/18/fact-checking-claims-made-by-experts-brought-in-by-desantis-analyze-his-COVID-response/?utm_source=twitter&utm_medium=social&utm_campaign=snd&utm_content=wjxt4

79. Sood, N., & Bhattacharya, J. (2021, July 13). Mandatory masking of school children is a bad idea. *Orange County Register*. https://www.ocregister.com/2021/07/13/mandatory-masking-of-school-children-is-a-bad-idea/

80. Bhattacharya, J., & Kulldorff, M. (2020, September 3). The case against COVID tests for the young and healthy. *Wall Street Journal*. https://www.wsj.com/articles/the-case-against-COVID-tests-for-the-young-and-healthy-11599151722

81. Gateway Bible Baptist Church et al. v Manitoba et al. (2021 MBQB 219). https://www.jccf.ca/wp-content/uploads/2021/10/Gateway-Bible-Baptist-Church-et-al.-v.-Manitoba-et-al.-2021-MBQB-219.pdf

82. Bhattacharya, J. (2022, November 2). *Jay Bhattacharya on COVID Policy Missteps - Publications* [Interview; audio podcast]. The Technology Policy Institute. https://techpolicyinstitute.org/publications/miscellaneous/jay-bhattacharya-on-responses-of-public-health-and-economic-experts-to-COVID-19/

83. Farberman, R., & Krawchenko, K. (2022, July 28). *The impact of chronic underfunding on America's public health system: Trends, risks, and recommendations, 2022*. Trust for America's Health. https://www.tfah.org/report-details/funding-report-2022/

84. *Great Barrington Declaration Scientists with Gov. DeSantis in Florida*. (2021, March 18). American Institute for Economic Research. https://www.aier.org/article/great-barrington-declaration-scientists-with-gov-desantis-in-florida/

85. Thomas, N. (2020, August 4). *Jails can spread coronavirus to nearby communities, study finds*. CNN. https://www.cnn.com/2020/08/04/health/jails-nearby-communities-coronavirus-spread-study/index.html

86. Colello, K. J. (2020, April 1). *Senior nutrition programs' response to COVID-19* [IN11266, version 5]. Congressional Research Service. https://crsreports.congress.gov/product/pdf/IN/IN11266

87. Coronavirus Aid, Relief, and Economic Security Act, S. 3548, 116th Cong., 2d Sess. (2020) (enacted). https://www.congress.gov/116/bills/s3548/BILLS-116s3548is.pdf

88. Families First Coronavirus Response Act, H.R. 6201, 116th Cong., 2d Sess. (2020) (enacted). https://www.govinfo.gov/content/pkg/PLAW-116publ127/pdf/PLAW-116publ127.pdf.

89. Parlapiano, A., Solomon, D. B., Ngo, M., & Cowley, S. (2022, March 11). Where $5 trillion in pandemic stimulus money went. *The New York Times*. https://www.nytimes.com/interactive/2022/03/11/us/how-COVID-stimulus-money-was-spent.html

90. Javers, E., & Zamost, S. (2021, December 21). *Criminals have stolen nearly $100 billion in COVID relief funds, Secret Service says*. CNBC. https://www.cnbc.com/2021/12/21/criminals-have-stolen-nearly-100-billion-in-COVID-relief-funds-secret-service.html

91. Van Oot, T. (2022, September 21). *Federal prosecutors allege "brazen" fraud involving federal food program for needy kids in Minnesota*. Axios: Twin Cities. https://www.axios.com/local/twin-cities/2022/09/21/feeding-our-future-indictment-minnesota

92. Romo, V. (2020, November 19). *Tyson managers suspended after allegedly betting if workers would contract COVID*. NPR. https://www.npr.org/2020/11/19/936905707/tyson-managers-suspended-after-allegedly-betting-if-workers-would-contract-COVID

93. Chidambaram, P. (2022, February 3). *Over 200,000 residents and staff in long-term care facilities have died from COVID-19*. Kaiser Family Foundation. https://www.kff.org/policy-watch/over-200000-residents-and-staff-in-long-term-care-facilities-have-died-from-COVID-19/

94. Kulldorff, M. [@MartinKulldoff]. (2022, December 14). *Faucism and Fascism are not the same, but there are some similarities - Blind belief in an all-knowing leader - Government-corporate partnership* [Tweet]. Twitter. https://twitter.com/MartinKulldorff/status/1603043029887160320

95. Impelli, M. (2021, April 16). Stanford Doctor Jay Bhattacharya calls Dr. Fauci 'number one anti vaxxer'. *Newsweek*. https://www.newsweek.com/stanford-doctor-jay-bhattacharya-calls-dr-fauci-number-one-anti-vaxxer-1584181

96. Kulldorff, M. [@MartinKulldorff]. (2021, December 22). *If we had done focused protection, as outlined in the Great Barrington Declaration, the pandemic would have been over now* [Tweet]. Twitter. https://twitter.com/

MartinKulldorff/status/1473633920939868163

97. Schreiber, M. (2022, March 11). A fifth of all US child COVID deaths occurred during Omicron surge. *The Guardian*. https://www.theguardian.com/world/2022/mar/11/us-child-COVID-deaths-omicron-surge

98. Ollove, M. (2021, August 5). *The pandemic has devastated the mental health of public health workers*. The Pew Charitable Trusts. https://www.pewtrusts.org/en/research-and-analysis/blogs/stateline/2021/08/05/the-pandemic-has-devastated-the-mental-health-of-public-health-workers

99. Prasad, V. (2021, December 23). At a time when the U.S. needed COVID-19 dialogue between scientists, Francis Collins moved to shut it down. *STAT*. https://www.statnews.com/2021/12/23/at-a-time-when-the-u-s-needed-COVID-19-dialogue-between-scientists-francis-collins-moved-to-shut-it-down/

100. Bhattacharya, J. [@DrJBhattacharya]. (2021, December 17). *So now I know what it feels like to be the subject of a propaganda attack by my own government* [Tweet; image attached]. Twitter. https://twitter.com/drjbhattacharya/status/1471986453823459330

101. Editorial Board. (2021, December 21). How Fauci and Collins shut down COVID debate. *Wall Street Journal*. https://www.wsj.com/articles/fauci-collins-emails-great-barrington-declaration-COVID-pandemic-lockdown-11640129116

102. Stolberg, S. G., & Mandavilli, A. (2020, October 23). A viral theory cited by health officials draws fire from scientists: A manifesto urging reliance on "herd immunity" without lockdowns was warmly received by administration officials. But the strategy cannot stem the pandemic, many experts say. *The New York Times*. https://www.nytimes.com/2020/10/19/health/coronavirus-great-barrington.html

103. Walker, M. (2020, October 15). Researchers blast 'dangerous' COVID-19 herd immunity strategy. *MedPage Today*. https://www.medpagetoday.com/infectiousdisease/COVID19/89127

104. Ahmed, N. (2020, October 9). *Climate science denial network behind Great Barrington Declaration*. Byline Times. https://bylinetimes.com/2020/10/09/climate-science-denial-network-behind-great-barrington-declaration/

105. Hanage, W. (2020, March 15). I'm an epidemiologist. When I heard about Britain's 'herd immunity' coronavirus plan, I thought it was satire. *The Guardian*. https://www.theguardian.com/commentisfree/2020/mar/15/epidemiologist-britain-herd-immunity-coronavirus-COVID-19

106. Butler, K. (2020, October 9). *The "Great Barrington" plan for reopening is championed as good for the poor. It's not.* Mother Jones. https://www.motherjones.com/politics/2020/10/the-great-barrington-plan-for-re-opening-is-championed-as-good-for-the-poor-its-not/

107. O'Brien, N. [@NeilDotObrien]. (2020, October 16). *Taking the Great Barrington Declaration seriously - a thread* [Tweet]. Twitter. https://twitter.com/NeilDotObrien/status/1317046902605729792

108. BBC News. (2021, December 8). *First person to get COVID vaccine is happy to inspire others*. https://www.bbc.com/news/uk-england-coventry-warwickshire-59566578

109. Tenforde, M. W., Self, W. H., Gaglani, M., Ginde, A. A., Douin, D. J., Keipp Talbot, H., Casey, J. D., Mohr, N. M., Zepeski, A., McNeal, T., Ghamande, S., Gibb, K. W., Files, D. C., Hager, D. N., Shehu, A., Prekker, M. E., Frosch, A. E., Gong, M. N., Mohamed, A., … IVY Network. (2022). Effectiveness of mRNA vaccination in preventing COVID-19–Associated invasive mechanical ventilation and death — United States, March 2021–January 2022. *Morbidity and Mortality Weekly Report*, *71*(12), 459-465. http://dx.doi.org/10.15585/mmwr.mm7112e1

110. Cowen, T. (2020, October 15). A dangerous libertarian strategy for herd immunity. *Bloomberg*. https://www.bloomberg.com/opinion/articles/2020-10-15/great-barrington-declaration-is-wrong-about-herd-immunity

111. Murphy, J., Wu, J., Chiwaya, N., & Muccari, R. (2020, April 7). *Graphic: coronavirus deaths in the U.S., per day* [Dataset]. NBC News. Retrieved October 25, 2022, from https://www.nbcnews.com/health/health-news/coronavirus-deaths-united-states-each-day-2020-n1177936

112. Goldman, J. D., Wang, K., Röltgen, K., Nielson, S. C. A., Roach, J. C., Naccache, S. N., Yang, F., Wirz, O. F., Yost, K. E., Lee, J.-Y., Chun, K., Wrin, T., Petropoulos, C. J., Lee, I., Fallen, S., Manner, P. M., Wallick, J. A., Algren, H. A., Murray, K. M., … Heath, J. R. (2020, September 25). *Reinfection with SARS-CoV-2 and failure of humoral immunity: A case report*. Medrxiv. https://doi.org/10.1101/2020.09.22.20192443

113. Kher, S. (2021, December 12). Our ability to block COVID infections, even with vaccines, is short-lived: Dr Sunetra Gupta. *Times of India*. https://timesofindia.indiatimes.com/home/sunday-times/all-that-matters/our-ability-to-block-COVID-infections-even-with-vaccines-is-short-lived-dr-sunetra-gupta/articleshow/88228611.cms

114. Gupta, S. (2021, October 31). Waning immunity should not alarm us.

The Telegraph. https://www.telegraph.co.uk/news/2021/10/31/waning-immunity-should-not-alarm-us/

115. Paul, L. A., Daneman, N., Schwartz, K. L., Science, M., Brown, K. A., Whelan, M., Chan, E., & Buchan, S. A. (2021). Association of age and pediatric household transmission of SARS-CoV-2 infection. *JAMA Pediatrics*, *175*(11), 1151-1158. https://doi.org/10.1001/jamapediatrics.2021.2770

116. and Prevention. (n.d.). *COVID data tracker: Demographic trends of COVID-19 cases and deaths in the US reported to CDC* [Interactive dataset]. U.S. Department of Health and Human Services. Retrieved December 28, 2022, from https://COVID.cdc.gov/COVID-data-tracker/#demographics

117. Kulldorff, M., & Bhattacharya, J. (2021, June 17). The ill-advised push to vaccinate the young. *The Hill*. https://thehill.com/opinion/healthcare/558757-the-ill-advised-push-to-vaccinate-the-young/

118. Howard, J. [@19joho]. (2021, November 24). *It's worse than that* [Tweet; image attached]. Twitter. https://twitter.com/JHowardBrainMD/status/1463540124407451659

119. Prosser Scully, R. (2022, August 26). COVID vaccines slash risk of spreading Omicron — and so does previous infection: But the benefit of vaccines in reducing Omicron transmission doesn't last for long. *Nature*. https://doi.org/10.1038/d41586-022-02328-0

120. Giubilini, A., Gupta, S., & Heneghan, C. (2021). A focused protection vaccination strategy: Why we should not target children with COVID-19 vaccination policies. *Journal of Medical Ethics*, *47*(8), 565-566. https://doi.org/10.1136/medethics-2021-107700

121. Gupta, S. (2022, January 20). Why it's time to end COVID self-isolation. *The Telegraph*. https://www.telegraph.co.uk/news/2022/01/20/time-end-self-isolation/

122. Impelli, M. (2021, March 8). Jay Bhattacharya, Stanford doctor, calls lockdowns the 'biggest public health mistake we've ever made'. *Newsweek*. https://www.newsweek.com/stanford-doctor-calls-lockdowns-biggest-public-health-mistake-weve-ever-made-1574540

123. Kulldorff, M. [@MartinKulldorff]. (2021, August 12). *By arguing for impossible #ZeroCOVID, with devastating lockdown carnage on children, workers, and the poor, the left is committing political* [Tweet; thumbnail link to article]. Twitter. https://twitter.com/MartinKulldorff/status/1425940909959516161

124. Kulldorff, M. [@MartinKulldorff]. (2020, November 23). *Yes Lee. True for the #COVID19 lockdown strategy that protects professionals, while it is the worst assault on the working* [Tweet; thumbnail link to website]. Twitter. https://twitter.com/MartinKulldorff/status/1331042585977233412

125. Jordan, M., & Dickerson, C. (2021, January 28). Poultry worker's death highlights spread of coronavirus in meat plants: Some employees are coming in sick, and one woman died after being ordered back to work. "Our work conditions are out of control," a longtime Tyson employee said. *The New York Times*. https://www.nytimes.com/2020/04/09/us/coronavirus-chicken-meat-processing-plants-immigrants.html

126. Kulldorff, M. [@MartinKulldorff]. (2021, December 28). *Lockdowns: - postpone infections, prolonging the pandemic - generate more contagious variants, increasing herd immunity threshold needed for endemic stage, so more* [Tweet]. Twitter. https://twitter.com/MartinKulldorff/status/1475920572525780994

127. Jha, A. K. [@ashishkjha]. (2021, January 28). *So let's talk about where variants ARE coming from and under what circumstances Variants arise when infections run wild And* [Tweet]. Twitter. https://twitter.com/ashishkjha/status/1354995266143875072

128. Kulldorff, M. [@MartinKulldorff]. (2022, January 3). *As the laptop class is now getting infected with COVID, it is nice to hear more voices arguing against shaming* [Tweet]. Twitter. https://twitter.com/MartinKulldorff/status/1478157702685728769

129. American Institute for Economic Research. (2021, April 5). *A conversation on COVID and lockdowns: Drs. Prasad and Kulldorff.* https://www.aier.org/article/a-conversation-on-COVID-and-lockdowns-drs-prasad-and-kulldorff/

130. Kibbe, M. (2022, August 3). Lockdowns threw 100 million people into poverty [Episode 187; video podcast]. *Kibbe on Liberty*. https://youtu.be/bX54aMZr-4U

131. Faust, J. S., Renton, B., Chen, A. J., Du, C., Liang, C., Li, S-X., Lin, Z., & Krumholz, H. M. (2022). Uncoupling of all-cause excess mortality from COVID-19 cases in a highly vaccinated state. *The Lancet*, *22*(10), 1419-1420. https://doi.org/10.1016/S1473-3099(22)00547-3

132. Kulldorff, M. [@MartinKulldorff]. (2020, September 19). *Hi Rupert. Countries like S Korea and NZ have mainly kept number low through lockdowns, including nation-wide isolation, which can* [Tweet]. Twitter. https://twitter.com/MartinKulldorff/status/1307388904077692929

133. Fitzpatrick, M. C., Moghadas, S. M., Pandey, A., & Galvani, A. P. (2022, December 13). Two years of U.S. COVID-19 vaccines have prevented millions of hospitalizations and deaths. *Commonwealth Fund.* https://www.commonwealthfund.org/blog/2022/two-years-COVID-vaccines-prevented-millions-deaths-hospitalizations

134. Salcedo, A. (2021, August 18). A mom of 4 who died of COVID days after her husband makes one final wish: 'Make sure my kids get vaccinated'. *The Washington Post.* https://www.washingtonpost.com/nation/2021/08/18/texas-couple-declined-COVID-19-vaccine-died-orphans/

135. Staten, A. (2022, January 26). Unvaccinated father texted 'I really regret not getting the vaccine' before COVID death. *Newsweek.* https://www.newsweek.com/unvaccinated-father-texted-i-really-regret-not-getting-vaccine-before-COVID-death-1673210

136. Graff, A., & Madrigal-Yankowski, N. (2021, August 23). 21 stories of people who regret not getting a COVID-19 vaccine. *SFGATE.* https://www.sfgate.com/nation/article/regret-COVID-unvaccinated-hospital-coronavirus-16378317.php

137. Edwards, E. (2021, July 8). *Unvaccinated hospitalized patients say they regret not getting the shot.* NBC News. https://www.nbcnews.com/health/health-news/unvaccinated-hospitalized-patients-say-they-regret-not-getting-shot-n1273342

138. Ortaliza, J., Amin, K., & Cox, C. (2022, November 10). *COVID-19 leading cause of death ranking.* Kaiser Family Foundation. https://www.kff.org/coronavirus-COVID-19/issue-brief/COVID-19-leading-cause-of-death-ranking/

139. Cabrera, J. (2021, July 27). DeSantis holds roundtable on masks in schools: "This should absolutely not be imposed." *Alachua Chronicle.* https://alachuachronicle.com/desantis-holds-roundtable-on-masks-in-schools-this-should-absolutely-not-be-imposed/

140. Kelly, M. (Host). (2021, December 1). Why no one should panic about the Omicron variant, with Dr. Bhattacharya and Dr. Dowdy [Video podcast]. In *The Megyn Kelly Show.* https://www.youtube.com/watch?v=jlqjMfRPzmA

141. Mueller, B., & Lutz, E. (2022, May 31). During the Omicron wave, death rates soared for older people. *The New York Times.* https://www.nytimes.com/2022/05/31/health/omicron-deaths-age-65-elderly.html

142. The Londoner: Let children be exposed to viruses, says Professor Gupta.

(2020, September 2). *Evening Standard.* https://www.standard.co.uk/news/londoners-diary/the-londoner-let-children-be-exposed-to-viruses-says-professor-gupta-a4538386.html

143. Kulldorff, M. [@MartinKulldorff]. (2021, December 29). *The pandemic ends when enough people have natural immunity after COVID recovery. With herd immunity, we then enter the endemic* [Tweet]. Twitter. https://twitter.com/MartinKulldorff/status/1476267273199493120

144. Kulldorff, M. [@MartinKulldorff]. (2022, February 10). *The denial of natural immunity after COVID disease is the worst unscientific folly in the past 75 years. How will* [Tweet]. Twitter. https://twitter.com/MartinKulldorff/status/1491760864063488003

145. Kulldorff, M. [@MartinKulldorff]. (2022, June 14). *Study after study have shown that natural immunity after COVID infection is superior to vaccine immunity. Just as one would* [Tweet; thumbnail link to tweet]. Twitter. https://twitter.com/MartinKulldorff/status/1536675759825338370

146. Kulldorff, M. (2022, May 6). *The triumph of natural immunity.* Brownstone Institute. https://brownstone.org/articles/the-triumph-of-natural-immunity/

147. Brogan, K. (n.d.). Can pharma improve on nature? HPV vaccine vs natural infection. *Kelly Brogan, MD.* https://www.kellybroganmd.com/blog/can-pharma-improve-nature-hpv-vaccine-vs-natural-infection

148. Bowe, B., Xie, Y., & Al-Aly, Z. (2022). Acute and postacute sequelae associated with SARS-CoV-2 reinfection. *Nature Medicine*, *28*, 2398–2405. https://doi.org/10.1038/s41591-022-02051-3

149. Lapid, N. (2022, November 10). *Repeat COVID is riskier than first infection, study finds.* Reuters. https://www.reuters.com/business/healthcare-pharmaceuticals/repeat-COVID-is-riskier-than-first-infection-study-finds-2022-11-10/

150. Goldberg, Y., Mandel, M., Bar-On, Y. M., Bodenheimer, O., Freedman, L. S., Ash, N., Alroy-Preis, S., Huppert, A., & Milo, R. (2022). Protection and waning of natural and hybrid immunity to SARS-CoV-2. *The New England Journal of Medicine*, *386*, 2201-2212. https://doi.org/10.1056/NEJMoa2118946

151. Krishnamoorthi, R. (2021, November 17). *Congressman Krishnamoorthi reveals Republican witness in COVID-19 misinformation hearing has been repeatedly discredited by courts for promoting misinformation* [Press release]. United States Congressman Raja Krishnamoorthi. https://krishnamoorthi.house.gov/media/press-releases/congressman-

krishnamoorthi-reveals-republican-witness-COVID-19-misinformation

152. Timms, M., Mangrum, M., & Gang, D. W. (2021, October 22). Gov. Bill Lee's mask order violates federal law, remains blocked in Williamson County, judge rules. *The Tennessean.* https://www.tennessean.com/story/news/politics/2021/10/22/tennessee-gov-bill-lees-mask-opt-out-order-violates-federal-law-judge-rules/8449956002/

153. Brodkin, J. (2020, August 25). Florida order requiring all schools to reopen was illegal, judge rules: Florida disregarded COVID-19 risks, judge finds. Governor appeals court loss. *Ars Technica.* https://arstechnica.com/tech-policy/2020/08/judge-rules-florida-cant-force-all-schools-to-reopen-amid-pandemic/

154. Gilmore, R. (2022, October 20). *'Freedom convoy' forced kids' chemo delays, rescheduling for 13 families.* Global News. https://globalnews.ca/news/9209533/freedom-convoy-chemo-children-appointments-cheo/

155. Kulldorff, M. [@MartinKulldorff]. (2022, February 13). *At my local truck stop in Massachusetts, this is now the only posted public health restriction. Nice to see some* [Tweet; image attached]. Twitter. https://twitter.com/MartinKulldorff/status/1492863070644932610

156. Bhattacharya, J. [@DrJBhattacharya]. (2022, July 1). *Happy Canada Day to all my amazing Canadian friends! A day is coming when Canada's biomedical security state recedes and* [Tweet]. Twitter. https://twitter.com/DrJBhattacharya/status/1543075028941426689

157. Romero, L. (2022, June 16). *Dr. Simone Gold, leading anti-vax figure, sentenced for storming Capitol on Jan. 6.* ABC News. https://abcnews.go.com/US/dr-simone-gold-leading-anti-vax-figure-sentenced/story?id=85445732

158. Howard, J. [@19joho]. (2022, September 23). *Lol. @Michigan_Noah* [Tweet; image attached]. Twitter. https://twitter.com/19joho/status/1573449047746269201

159. Bodnar, N. (2021, November). *A discussion with Dr. Jay Bhattacharya.* [Interview]. Columbia University. https://www.cuw.edu/academics/schools/business/_assets/quaestus-journal/2022-quaestus-journal/Bhattacharya-Disscussion-Summery.pdf

160. DeSantis, R. [@GovRonDeSantis]. (2022, December 13). *Florida will hold the medical establishment accountable by: • Creating a grand jury to investigate mRNA shots & Big Pharma • Investigating cardiac-related* [Tweet]. Twitter. https://twitter.com/GovRonDeSantis/status/1602763432788635651

161. News Service of Florida. (2022, December 23). *The Florida Supreme Court impanels a grand jury to investigate COVID vaccines*. WFSU News. https://news.wfsu.org/state-news/2022-12-22/the-florida-supreme-court-impanels-a-grand-jury-to-investigate-COVID-vaccines

162. Stripling, J. (2023, January 4). Fla. surgeon general used 'flawed' vaccine science, faculty peers say: But the University of Florida declined to discipline Joseph A. Ladapo, who is a tenured professor of medicine there. *The Washington Post*. https://www.washingtonpost.com/education/2023/01/04/ladapo-surgoen-general-university-florida/

163. Dailey, R. (2022, December 5). Non-COVID vaccine rates for Florida school children are lowest in more than 10 years. *Miami Herald*. https://www.miamiherald.com/news/local/education/article269616331.html

164. Brownstone Institute. (2022). *About Brownstone Institute*. Retrieved November 14, 2022, from https://brownstone.org/about/

165. Tucker, J. A. (2022, October 2). *The 70 seconds that shook the world*. Brownstone Institute. https://brownstone.org/articles/the-70-seconds-that-shook-the-world/

166. Tucker, J. A. [@jeffreyatucker]. (2022, January 1). *I used to feel enough clarity on issues to know for sure that crazy was not correct. These days, I* [Tweet]. Twitter. https://twitter.com/jeffreyatucker/status/1477384740634304515

167. Tucker, J. A. [@jeffreyatucker]. (2022, September 14). *So 88% of those forced on ventilators died. These people are fathers, mothers, grandfathers, most of them far younger than* [Tweet; thumbnail link to article]. Twitter. https://twitter.com/jeffreyatucker/status/1570227635082661888

168. Hockett, J. (2022, November 4). *More questions about Spring 2020 COVID in New York City hospitals*. Brownstone Institute. https://brownstone.org/articles/more-questions-about-spring-2020-COVID-in-new-york-city-hospitals/

169. McCool, A., & Wepukhulu, K. S. (2022, January 21). *US conservatives spreading anti-vax misinformation to unvaccinated Uganda*. OpenDemocracy. https://www.opendemocracy.net/en/5050/us-conservatives-spread-anti-vaccine-COVID-misinformation-uganda/

170. Bhattacharya, J. (2022, August 7). *Zero COVID has cost New Zealand dearly*. Spiked. https://www.spiked-online.com/2022/08/07/zero-COVID-has-cost-new-zealand-dearly/

171. Our World in Data. (n.d.). *Excess mortality: Deaths from all causes compared to average over previous years* [Interactive chart]. Retrieved December 13, 2022, from https://ourworldindata.org/grapher/excess-mortality-p-scores-average-baseline?country=NZL~GBR~USA

172. U.S. Bureau of Labor Statistics. (2022, November 2). *Labor force statistics from the current population survey: Supplemental data measuring the effects of the coronavirus (COVID-19) pandemic on the labor market.* United States Department of Labor. https://www.bls.gov/cps/effects-of-the-coronavirus-COVID-19-pandemic.htm

173. Romei, V., & Smith, A. (n.d.). *Global inflation tracker: see how your country compares on rising prices* [Interactive dataset]. Financial Times. Retrieved December 15, 2022, from https://www.ft.com/content/088d3368-bb8b-4ff3-9df7-a7680d4d81b2

174. Fenton, R., & Golding, B. (2020, March 31). Brooklyn hospital resumes use of forklift to move bodies amid coronavirus. *New York Post*. https://nypost.com/2020/03/31/nyc-hospital-resumes-use-of-forklift-to-move-bodies-amid-coronavirus/

175. Bach, K. (2022, August 24). *New data shows long COVID is keeping as many as 4 million people out of work*. Brookings Institution. https://www.brookings.edu/research/new-data-shows-long-COVID-is-keeping-as-many-as-4-million-people-out-of-work/

176. Bhattacharya, J. [@DrJBhattacharya]. (2022, August 13). *Now that @CDCgov has finally adopted focused protection as its COVID strategy, it's crucial for people at the local level* [Tweet]. Twitter. https://twitter.com/DrJBhattacharya/status/1558503906593820672

177. File: Waterpokken.JPG. (2021, August 10). *Wikimedia Commons, the free media repository*. Retrieved from https://commons.wikimedia.org/w/index.php?title=File:Waterpokken.JPG&oldid=579504723

178. File: Herps zoster ophthalmicus.jpg. (2020, September 16). *Wikimedia Commons, the free media repository*. Retrieved from https://commons.wikimedia.org/w/index.php?title=File:Herps_zoster_ophthalmicus.jpg&oldid=460836624

179. File: 1918 Headlines from Chicago newspapers - Spanish flu - 1918 influenza pandemic.jpg. (2020, November 24). *Wikimedia Commons, the free media repository*. Retrieved from https://commons.wikimedia.org/w/index.php?title=File:1918_Headlines_from_Chicago_newspapers_-_Spanish_flu_-_1918_influenza_pandemic.jpg&oldid=514615183

Chapter Six

1. Martin, R. (2021, December 30). *The dishonest doctors who were Fox News' most frequent medical guests in 2021: These 10 guests made nearly 700 combined appearances on Fox this year – and often spread medical misinformation on-air.* Media Matters for America. https://www.mediamatters.org/fox-news/dishonest-doctors-who-were-fox-news-most-frequent-medical-guests-2021-0

2. UnHerd. (2020, October 5). *Dissenting scientists issue COVID-19 herd immunity declaration* [Video]. YouTube. https://www.youtube.com/watch?v=rz_Z7Gf1aRE&t

3. Lee, S. M. (2020, July 24). *An elite group of scientists tried to warn Trump against lockdowns in March: John Ioannidis's controversial studies claim that the coronavirus isn't that big a threat. Before the Stanford scientist did any of them, he wanted to take that message to the White House*. BuzzFeed News. https://www.buzzfeednews.com/article/stephaniemlee/ioannidis-trump-white-house-coronavirus-lockdowns

4. Diamond, D. (2020, December 16). 'We want them infected': Trump appointee demanded 'herd immunity' strategy, emails reveal. Then-HHS science adviser Paul Alexander called for millions of Americans to be infected as means of fighting COVID-19. *Politico*. https://www.politico.com/news/2020/12/16/trump-appointee-demanded-herd-immunity-strategy-446408

5. Alexander, P. (2022, December 18). The greatest crime in GLOBAL history, GREATEST, without exception, is the fraud COVID pandemic, lockdowns & the vaccine; all of it was a pure lie, all of it; TRUMP was devastatingly MISLED! You were! *Alexander COVID News - Dr. Paul Elias Alexander's Newsletter*. https://palexander.substack.com/p/the-greatest-crime-in-history-greatest

6. Abutaleb, Y., & Dawsey, J. (2020, August 31). New Trump pandemic adviser pushes controversial 'herd immunity' strategy, worrying public health officials. *The Washington Post*. https://www.washingtonpost.com/politics/trump-coronavirus-scott-atlas-herd-immunity/2020/08/30/925e68fe-e93b-11ea-970a-64c73a1c2392_story.html

7. Select Subcommittee on the Coronavirus Crisis. (2022, June). *The Atlas dogma: The Trump administration's embrace of a dangerous and discredited herd immunity via mass infection strategy* [Staff report]. U.S. House of Representatives. https://coronavirus.house.gov/sites/democrats.coronavirus.house.gov/files/2022.06.21%20The%20Trump%20Administration%E2%80%99s%20Embrace%20of%20a%20

Dangerous%20and%20Discredited%20Herd%20Immunity%20via%20Mass%20Infection%20Strategy.pdf

8. Ioannidis, J. P. A. (2020, March 17). A fiasco in the making? As the coronavirus pandemic takes hold, we are making decisions without reliable data. *STAT*. https://www.statnews.com/2020/03/17/a-fiasco-in-the-making-as-the-coronavirus-pandemic-takes-hold-we-are-making-decisions-without-reliable-data/

9. Atlas, S. W. (2020, April 22). The data is in – stop the panic and end the total isolation. *The Hill*. https://thehill.com/opinion/healthcare/494034-the-data-are-in-stop-the-panic-and-end-the-total-isolation/

10. Atlas, S. W. (2020, June 29). *Fox news: Tucker Carlson tonight* [Video interview]. MediaMatters. https://www.mediamatters.org/media/3889611

11. Atlas, S. W. (2020, July 9). *Dr. Scott Atlas: There is no risk to children from COVID-19, I don't know why people deny this* [Audio interview]. Brian Kilmeade Show: Fox News Radio. https://radio.foxnews.com/2020/07/09/dr-scott-atlas-there-is-no-risk-to-children-from-COVID-19-i-dont-know-why-people-deny-this/

12. Bump, P. (2020, December 1). Scott Atlas will forever be the face of surrender to the coronavirus. *The Washington Post*. https://www.washingtonpost.com/politics/2020/12/01/scott-atlas-will-forever-be-face-surrender-coronavirus/

13. Alex Azar. (2022, November 17). In *Wikipedia*. https://en.wikipedia.org/w/index.php?title=Alex_Azar&oldid=1122479788

14. Stolberg, S. G. (2020, October 13). White House embraces a declaration from scientists that opposes lockdowns and relies on 'herd immunity'. *The New York Times*. https://www.nytimes.com/2020/10/13/world/white-house-embraces-a-declaration-from-scientists-that-opposes-lockdowns-and-relies-on-herd-immunity.html

15. Romo, V. (2020, November 30). *Dr. Scott Atlas, special coronavirus adviser to Trump, resigns*. NPR. https://www.npr.org/2020/11/30/940376041/dr-scott-atlas-special-coronavirus-adviser-to-trump-resigns

16. Office of Science and Technology. (2020, October 27). Trump administration releases science and technology accomplishments from first term. *Politico*. https://www.politico.com/f/?id=00000175-6bc5-d2df-adff-6fdfff5c0000

17. Mathieu, E., Ritchie, H., Rodés-Guirao, L., Appel, C., Giattino, C., Hasell, J., Macdonald, B., Dattani, S., Beltekian, D., Ortiz-Ospina, E., & Roser, M. (2020). *Coronavirus pandemic (COVID-19)* [Interactive dataset]. Our World in Data. Retrieved December 14, 2022, from https://ourworldindata.org/COVID-deaths

18. Atlas, S. W. (2021). *A plague upon our house: My fight at the Trump White House to stop COVID from destroying America*. Bombardier Books.

19. Atlas, S. W. (2022, December 29). When will academia account for its COVID failures? We need universities to be robust centers of debate, not rigid enforcers of ideological conformity. *Wall Street Journal*. https://www.wsj.com/articles/when-will-academia-account-for-its-COVID-failures-pandemic-lockdowns-stanford-ivy-league-elite-narrative-ideology-11672346923

20. McNally, A. (2020, December 14). Backers of 'herd immunity' shouldn't have been allowed near Boris Johnson: The fringe view that we should avoid coronavirus restrictions was presented to the PM as he weighed a crucial decision. *The Guardian*. https://www.theguardian.com/commentisfree/2020/dec/14/herd-immunity-boris-johnson-coronavirus

21. Clarke, K. E. N., Jones, J. M., Deng, Y., Nycz, E., Lee, A., Iachan, R., Gundlapalli, A. V., Hall, A. J., & MacNeil, A. (2022). Seroprevalence of infection-induced SARS-CoV-2 antibodies - United States, September 2021-February 2022. *Morbidity and Mortality Weekly Report*, *71*(17), 606-608. http://dx.doi.org/10.15585/mmwr.mm7117e3

22. Holder, J. (2021, October 29). Children drive Britain's longest-running COVID surge. *The New York Times*. https://www.nytimes.com/interactive/2021/10/29/world/europe/uk-britain-COVID-surge.html

23. Weale, S. (2022, March 22). COVID absences in schools in England triple in two weeks: Data shows 202,000 pupils off sick on 17 March, raising fears of disruption before summer exams. *The Guardian*. https://www.theguardian.com/world/2022/mar/22/COVID-absences-schools-england-triple-in-two-weeks

24. Aguilar García, C., & Duncan, P. (2022, August 23). Twice as many people died with COVID in UK this summer compared with 2021: Higher figure fuelled by Omicron subvariants and contrasts with lower overall numbers for year to date. *The Guardian*. https://www.theguardian.com/world/2022/aug/23/twice-as-many-people-died-with-COVID-in-uk-this-summer-compared-with-2021

25. Vogel, G. (2020, October 6). Sweden's gamble: The country's pandemic

policies came at a high price – and created painful rifts in its scientific community. *Science*. https://doi.org/10.1126/science.abf1247

26. Brusselaers, N., Steadson, D., Bjorklund, K., Breland, S., Stilhoff Sörensen, J., Ewing, A., Bergmann, S., & Steineck, G. (2022). Evaluation of science advice during the COVID-19 pandemic in Sweden. *Humanities and Social Sciences Communications*, *9*, 91. https://doi.org/10.1057/s41599-022-01097-5

27. Ludvigsson, J. F. (2020). Children are unlikely to be the main drivers of the COVID-19 pandemic – A systematic review. *Acta Paediatrica*, *109*(8), 1525-1530. https://doi.org/10.1111/apa.15371

28. Ludvigsson, J. F., Engerström, L., Nordenhäll, C., & Larsson, E. (2021). Open schools, COVID-19, and child and teacher morbidity in Sweden. *The New England Journal of Medicine*, *384*, 669-671. https://doi.org/10.1056/NEJMc2026670

29. Vogel, G. (2021, March 2). Critics slam letter in prestigious journal that downplayed COVID-19 risks to Swedish schoolchildren: Researchers omitted data suggesting child mortality went up in the spring of 2020. *Science*. https://doi.org/10.1126/science.abh3416

30. VOA News. (2020, December 3). *Sweden closes high schools until early January to stem COVID-19 infections*. (2020, December 3). https://www.voanews.com/a/COVID-19-pandemic_sweden-closes-high-schools-until-early-january-stem-COVID-19-infections/6199141.html

31. Henley, J. (2020, December 17). King of Sweden blasts country's 'failed' coronavirus response: Criticism of anti-lockdown stance comes as hospitals struggle to cope with surge in cases. *The Guardian*. https://www.theguardian.com/world/2020/dec/17/king-sweden-failed-COVID-strategy-rare-royal-rebuke-lockdown-hospitals-cases

32. BBC News. (2020, December 17). *Coronavirus: Swedish King Carl XVI Gustaf says coronavirus approach 'has failed'*. https://www.bbc.com/news/world-europe-55347021

33. Levitt, M. [@MLevitt_NP2013]. (2020, July 25). *US COVID19 will be done in 4 weeks with a total reported death below 170,000. How will we know* [Tweet; thumbnail link to tweet]. Twitter. https://twitter.com/MLevitt_NP2013/status/1287036738565738496

34. Downey, R. (2020, September 25). *'Herd immunity' the phrase of the day at Gov. DeSantis' panel of scientists: Herd immunity is misunderstood, Gov. Ron DeSantis says*. Florida Politics. https://floridapolitics.com/archives/369647-herd-immunity-the-phrase-of-the-day-at-gov-desantiss-

panel-of-scientists/

35. *Great Barrington Declaration Scientists with Gov. DeSantis in Florida.* (2021, March 18). American Institute for Economic Research. https://www.aier.org/article/great-barrington-declaration-scientists-with-gov-desantis-in-florida/

36. Cabrera, J. (2021, July 27). DeSantis holds roundtable on masks in schools: "This should absolutely not be imposed." *Alachua Chronicle.* https://alachuachronicle.com/desantis-holds-roundtable-on-masks-in-schools-this-should-absolutely-not-be-imposed/

37. Pipitone, T. (2021, October 29). *Florida Delta wave cases plunge, leaving record deaths in its wake: Despite most Floridians being vaccinated, the delta wave was by far the deadliest, coming as many shed masks and sought return to normalcy.* NBC 6 South Florida. https://www.nbcmiami.com/news/local/florida-delta-wave-cases-plunge-leaving-record-deaths-in-its-wake/2598705/

38. Brink, G., Day, S., Dortch, S., Hill, J., Verhulst, J., & Gallaty, C. (2022, December 1). What to do now that seniors account for 9 in 10 Florida COVID deaths. Florida has a lot of older residents. We should not forget that in our day to day living. *Tampa Bay Times.* https://www.tampabay.com/opinion/2022/12/01/what-do-now-that-seniors-account-9-10-florida-COVID-deaths-editorial/

39. Kulldorff, M. (2021, October 12). COVID, lockdown and the retreat of scientific debate. *The Spectator.* https://www.spectator.co.uk/article/COVID-lockdown-and-the-retreat-of-scientific-debate

40. Bhattacharya, J. (2021, October 21). *What happened: Dr. Jay Bhattacharya on 19 months of COVID* [Interview]. Hoover Institution. https://www.hoover.org/research/what-happened-dr-jay-bhattacharya-19-months-COVID-1

41. Louis-Ferdinand, N. (2022, May 27). The logistical shortcomings of focused protection. *A [Heart] For Lives.* https://aloveforlives.substack.com/p/the-logistical-shortcomings-of-focused

42. and Prevention. (n.d.). *COVID data tracker: Trends in number of COVID-19 cases and deaths in the US reported to CDC, by state/territory* [Interactive dataset]. U.S. Department of Health and Human Services. Retrieved December 28, 2022, from https://COVID.cdc.gov/COVID-data-tracker/#trends_weeklydeaths_7daydeathsper100k_12

Chapter Seven

1. Hall, H. (2021, June 29). A new COVID-19 myth? *Science-Based Medicine*. https://sciencebasedmedicine.org/a-new-COVID-19-myth/

2. Zubin Damania. (2022, November 19). In *Wikipedia*. https://en.wikipedia.org/w/index.php?title=Zubin_Damania&oldid=1122695599

3. Damania, Z. (Host). (2020, March 17). COVID-19: is our cure worse than the disease? [Video podcast episode]. In *ZDoggMD: Slightly funnier than placebo*. https://zdoggmd.com/paul-offit-COVID/

4. Damania, Z. (Host). (2020, October 11). How to stop living in fear of COVID [Video podcast episode]. In *ZDoggMD: Slightly funnier than placebo*. https://zdoggmd.com/monica-gandhi-2/

5. Damania, Z. (Host). (2021, February 22). The end of the epidemic [Video podcast episode]. In *ZDoggMD: Slightly funnier than placebo*. https://zdoggmd.com/monica-gandhi-3/

6. Gandhi, M. (2022, February 4). Mehdi Hasan questions doctor on COVID predictions [Video interview]. In *The Mehdi Hasan Show*. https://www.youtube.com/watch?v=VaSTb5kNT4s

7. Damania, Z. (Host). (2022, May 15). Living with COVID [Video podcast episode]. In *ZDoggMD: Slightly funnier than placebo*. https://zdoggmd.com/living-with-COVID/

8. Damania, Z. [ZDoggMD]. (2022, December 11). *A better pandemic playbook* [Video podcast]. YouTube. https://www.youtube.com/watch?v=6j0u2n_kubw

9. Ortaliza, J., Amin, K., & Cox, C. (2022, November 10). *COVID-19 leading cause of death ranking*. Kaiser Family Foundation. https://www.kff.org/coronavirus-COVID-19/issue-brief/COVID-19-leading-cause-of-death-ranking/

10. Fisher, M. (2021, September 4). The COVID endgame: Is the pandemic over already? Or are there years to go? *The Washington Post*. https://www.washingtonpost.com/politics/COVID-how-will-it-end/2021/09/04/44bdd69a-fed7-11eb-a664-4f6de3e17ff0_story.html

11. Koka, A. [@anish_koka]. (2021, June 30). *Is it possible Howard & co. Are correctly predicting Armageddon unless the kids aren't forced to be vaxxed ? Maybe.. (we'll know* [Tweet]. Twitter. https://twitter.com/anish_koka/status/1410346527290179590

12. Goodman, B. (2021, August 17). *Pediatric hospitals in U.S. in peril*

as Delta hits children. WebMD. https://www.webmd.com/COVID/news/20210817/pediatric-hospitals-us-in-peril-delta-hits-children

13. Backhaus, A. [@AndreasShrugged]. (2021, April 9). *I thought about writing a paper that estimates how long it takes for a country or region to suffer from* [Tweet; thumbnail link to tweet]. Twitter. https://twitter.com/AndreasShrugged/status/1380653456227196928

14. Damania, Z. (Host). (2021, April 14). Focused protection for COVID [Video podcast episode]. In *ZDoggMD: Slightly funnier than placebo*. https://zdoggmd.com/jay-bhattacharya-2/

15. Bhattacharya, J. (2021, May 3). *The Ingraham Angle* [Video interview transcript]. Fox News. https://www.foxnews.com/transcript/ingraham-left-doesnt-want-to-debate-they-want-to-dominate

16. Hill, Z. K. (2021, July 21). Stanford doc Jay Bhattacharya calls vaccine mandates 'unethical,' says patients can choose. *Newsweek*. https://www.newsweek.com/stanford-doc-jay-bhattacharya-calls-vaccine-mandates-unethical-says-patients-can-choose-1611938

17. Polumbo, B. (2021, July 28). *Despite 'Delta' alarmism, US COVID deaths are at lowest level since March 2020, Harvard and Stanford Professors explain*. Foundation for Economic Education. https://fee.org/articles/despite-delta-alarmism-us-COVID-deaths-are-at-lowest-level-since-march-2020-harvard-and-stanford-professors-explain/

18. Arnold, J. (2022, January 6). *Pandemic of obsolete talking points*. Family Research Council. https://www.frc.org/updatearticle/20220106/pandemic-points

19. Howard, J. (2021, July 25). "We'll have herd immunity by April": Reflections on a failed prediction. *Science-Based Medicine*. https://sciencebasedmedicine.org/well-have-herd-immunity-by-april-reflections-on-a-failed-prediction/

20. Mathieu, E., Ritchie, H., Rodés-Guirao, L., Appel, C., Giattino, C., Hasell, J., Macdonald, B., Dattani, S., Beltekian, D., Ortiz-Ospina, E., & Roser, M. (2020). *Coronavirus pandemic (COVID-19)* [Interactive dataset]. Our World in Data. Retrieved December 14, 2022, from https://ourworldindata.org/COVID-deaths

21. Ioannidis, J. P. A. (2020). Coronavirus disease 2019: The harms of exaggerated information and non-evidence-based measures. *European Journal of Clinical Investigation*, *50*(4), Article 13222. https://onlinelibrary.wiley.com/doi/full/10.1111/eci.13222

22. Ioannidis, J. P. A. (2020, April 17). *Perspectives on the pandemic*

[Episode 4; video podcast interview transcript]. The Press and the Public. https://www.thepressandthepublic.com/post/perspectives-on-the-pandemic-iv

23. Mandrola, J. [@drjohnm]. (2020, May 1). *I recoil against the idea that moderation of distancing measures in places in the US and Sweden is akin to* [Tweet]. Twitter. https://twitter.com/drjohnm/status/1256332884714983425

24. Mandrola, J. [@drjohnm]. (2020, May 4). *We disagree. Each of your tweets has a rebuttal 1) US hospitals not close to being overrun. It's the opposite* [Tweet]. Twitter. https://twitter.com/drjohnm/status/1257306077764317184

25. Mandrola, J. (2020, May 5). Can we discuss flatten-the-curve in COVID19? My eight assertions. *Dr John M.* https://www.drjohnm.org/2020/05/can-we-discuss-flatten-the-curve-in-COVID19-my-eight-assertions/

26. Mandrola, J. [@drjohnm]. (2020, May 7). *As I said in the piece, May is different from March. People are not stupid. Public health surveillance is better* [Tweet]. Twitter. https://twitter.com/drjohnm/status/1258408784399159297

27. Atlas, S. W. (2020, June 29). *Fox news: Tucker Carlson tonight* [Video interview]. MediaMatters. https://www.mediamatters.org/media/3889611

28. Bump, P. (2020, December 1). Scott Atlas will forever be the face of surrender to the coronavirus. *The Washington Post*. https://www.washingtonpost.com/politics/2020/12/01/scott-atlas-will-forever-be-face-surrender-coronavirus/

29. Levitt, M. [@MLevitt_NP2013]. (2020, July 25). *US COVID19 will be done in 4 weeks with a total reported death below 170,000. How will we know* [Tweet; thumbnail link to tweet]. Twitter. https://twitter.com/MLevitt_NP2013/status/1287036738565738496

30. Cha, A. E. (2020, August 8). 40% of people with coronavirus have no symptoms; might they be the key to ending the pandemic? *The Seattle Times*. https://www.seattletimes.com/nation-world/40-of-people-with-coronavirus-have-no-symptoms-might-they-be-the-key-to-ending-the-pandemic/

31. Ioannidis, J. P. A., Cripps, S., & Tanner, M. A. (2022). Forecasting for COVID-19 has failed. *International Journal of Forecasting*, *38*(2), 423-438. https://doi.org/10.1016/j.ijforecast.2020.08.004

32. Rational Ground. (2020, September 28). *Governor DeSantis' roundtable*

experts advocate for "normal" life for young people [Video meeting transcript]. https://rationalground.com/governor-desantis-roundtable-experts-advocate-for-normal-life-for-young-people/

33. Mandrola, J. [@drjohnm]. (2020, December 15). *Barring something (very)unforeseen the #COVID19 pandemic is over soon. Such good news! [backhand index pointing down]* [Tweet; thumbnail link to deleted account tweet]. Twitter. https://twitter.com/drjohnm/status/1338899854962135040

34. Crump, J. (2020, December 22). Doctor claims US could reach herd immunity if 20 per cent of population get COVID vaccine: 'The reality is that about 25 to 50 per cent of Americans have already had the infection,' Dr Marty Makary claims. *The Independent*. https://www.independent.co.uk/news/world/americas/COVID-vaccine-us-herd-immunity-b1777527.html

35. Kulldorff, M. [@MartinKulldorff]. (2020, December 24). *If the young live normal lives, some will be infected, but their risk is less than from lockdown collateral damage* [Tweet]. Twitter. https://twitter.com/MartinKulldorff/status/1342239762258808832

36. Claus, P. (2020, December 28). *'Don't panic over new coronavirus strain,' says Stanford's John Ioannidis*. Greek Reporter. https://greekreporter.com/2020/12/28/new-coronavirus-strain-stanford-professor-john-ioannidis-interview/

37. Makary, M. [@MartyMakary]. (2021, January 1). *Good question. Everyone should get vaccinated, but to hit herd immunity this spring, we may only need 20-30% of people* [Tweet]. Twitter. https://twitter.com/MartyMakary/status/1345210715167186944

38. Prasad, V. [@VPrasadMDMPH]. (2021, January 13). *Let me be perfectly clear: children DO NOT NEED a sars-cov-2 vaccine before they are permitted to return to normal* [Tweet]. Twitter. https://twitter.com/VPrasadMDMPH/status/1349427724834664448

39. Makary, M. [@MartyMakary]. (2021, January 17). *I believe herd immunity is closer than people think I predict April The old guard medical establishment has been dismissive* [Tweet]. Twitter. https://twitter.com/MartyMakary/status/1350897859013570563

40. Makary, M. [@MartyMakary]. (2021, January 22). *COVID daily cases are DOWN 27% in the last 13 days! Natural Immunity is slowing the spread [backhand index pointing down x2]. We will see* [Tweet; thumbnail link to article]. Twitter. https://twitter.com/MartyMakary/status/1352800725043208192

41. Makary, M. [@MartyMakary]. (2021, January 24). *We may be starting to see the early signs of herd immunity. There has been a 32% decrease in daily* [Tweet; thumbnail link to article]. Twitter. https://twitter.com/MartyMakary/status/1353542185988329472

42. Gandhi, M. [@MonicaGandhi9]. (2021, January 29). *you only have to live like this until summer. Please listen to all of the optimism and try to phase* [Tweet]. Twitter. https://twitter.com/MonicaGandhi9/status/1355049509995208704

43. Gandhi, M. [@MonicaGandhi9]. (2021, January 31). *Thanks. Helpful. What will happen with vaccines is that - when we see the hospitalizations go away (100% effective for this* [Tweet; thumbnail link to tweet]. Twitter. https://twitter.com/MonicaGandhi9/status/1356101355169927168

44. Makary, M. (2021, February 18). We'll have herd immunity by April: COVID cases have dropped 77% in six weeks. Experts should level with the public about the good news. *Wall Street Journal*. https://www.wsj.com/articles/well-have-herd-immunity-by-april-11613669731

45. Gandhi, M. [@MonicaGandhi9]. (2021, February 23). *Doom & gloom seems to be part of the narrative from many in the scientific community because they got politicized in* [Tweet]. Twitter. https://twitter.com/MonicaGandhi9/status/1364375493525401603

46. Ting, E. (2021, February 23). Stop panicking about the COVID-19 variants, says UCSF's Monica Gandhi. *SFGATE*. https://www.sfgate.com/news/editorspicks/article/COVID-19-variants-vaccines-effective-San-Francisco-15961073.php#

47. McBride, L. (2021, March 2). *I'm a doctor seeing patients with coronaphobia. Here's what you need to know.* HuffPost. https://www.huffpost.com/entry/coronavirus-phobia-side-effects-anxiety_n_603d18eec5b6829715023334

48. Gandhi, M. [@MonicaGandhi9]. (2021, March 4). *I genuinely with all my heart apologize for anyone who continues to try to scare you about variants; we have* [Tweet; thumbnail link to tweet]. Twitter. https://twitter.com/monicagandhi9/status/1367500383820648453

49. McBride, L. (2021, March 9). I've been yearning for an end to the pandemic. Now that it's here, I'm a little afraid. *The Washington Post*. https://www.washingtonpost.com/opinions/2021/03/09/weve-adjusted-pandemic-life-now-we-face-anxiety-leaving-it-behind/

50. Mandrola, J. [@drjohnm]. (2021, March 10). *The more that people ride bikes, the more hip fractures and cranial bleeds we will see. The*

pandemic is essentially [Tweet; thumbnail link to tweet]. Twitter. https://twitter.com/drjohnm/status/1369810654626988032

51. Mandrola, J. [@drjohnm]. (2021, March 10). *Ky has vaccinated about 1 in 3 older people. CT has done even better. The vaccine squelches severe cases Millions* [Tweet]. Twitter. https://twitter.com/drjohnm/status/1369820360791711744

52. Mandrola, J. [@drjohnm]. (2021, March 11). *I think ALB makes a good point. I wish I had wrote "almost done here in the US." Frustration with* [Tweet; thumbnail link to tweet]. Twitter. https://twitter.com/drjohnm/status/1369979642699014146

53. Makary, M. [@MartyMakary]. (2021, March 11). *The reason Biden's timeline to normal is staggered out to July 4th is that his medical advisor puts low numbers* [Tweet; thumbnail link to tweet]. Twitter. https://twitter.com/MartyMakary/status/1370195502373949444

54. McBride, L. [@drlucymcbride]. (2021, March 23). *It's what some medical professionals, including myself, are calling "post-pandemic stress" which is not an official diagnosis (nor does it* [Tweet]. Twitter. https://twitter.com/drlucymcbride/status/1506702727300190215

55. Makary, M. (2021, March 24). Herd immunity is near, despite Fauci's denial: His estimate that it'll take a 70% to 85% vaccination rate ignores those who have already been infected. *Wall Street Journal*. https://www.wsj.com/articles/herd-immunity-is-near-despite-faucis-denial-11616624554?mod=e2fb

56. May, O. (2021, March 25). *Risk of asymptomatic spread minimal. Variants over-hyped. Masks pointless. An interview with Professor Jay Bhattacharya*. The Daily Sceptic. https://dailysceptic.org/archive/risk-of-asymptomatic-spread-minimal-variants-over-hyped-masks-pointless-an-interview-with-professor-jay-bhattacharya/

57. Prasad, V. (2021, March 30). The COVID endgame: A look into Prasad's crystal ball – Predictions on the future of vaccines, schools, media, science, and more. *MedPage Today*. https://www.medpagetoday.com/opinion/vinay-prasad/91860

58. Gandhi, M. [@MonicaGandhi9]. (2021, April 1). *I have a new saying. Even the most doom-filled, pessimistic, variant-steeped expert is no match for the vaccines!* [Tweet]. Twitter. https://twitter.com/MonicaGandhi9/status/1377841139051425796

59. Høeg, T. [@TracyBethHoeg]. (2021, April 2). *The same trend continues in Israel. As of yesterday, just over 60% of the population has received*

the first dose [Tweet; Thumbnail to infographic]. Twitter. https://twitter.com/TracyBethHoeg/status/1378010361933176840

60. McBride, L. (2021, April 3). Wired and tired after months of COVID-19 distress, it's time to recover our mental health: To fully bounce back from COVID, we need a dose of reassurance and a plan for recovery. We need science under our feet and doctors at our back. *USA Today*. https://www.usatoday.com/story/opinion/2021/04/03/COVID-anxiety-depression-time-for-mental-health-recovery-column/4807342001/

61. McBride, L. [@drlucymcbride]. (2021, April 3). *Well there is always a risk — even after vaccination — of getting COVID. But as you know, once you've been vaccinated* [Tweet]. Twitter. https://twitter.com/drlucymcbride/status/1378488612250136578

62. Makary, M. [@MartyMakary]. (2021, April 3). *Alaska had zero COVID deaths in the last 10 days. They are #2 in the nation in their vax rate* [Tweet]. Twitter. https://twitter.com/MartyMakary/status/1378488581388296194

63. McBride, L. (2021, April 5). *Preparing for post-pandemic life: a doctor's guide. As we look ahead to post-vaccination life, primary care physician, Dr. Lucy McBride, lays out a plan to get back into the driver's seat of your own well-being*. MSNBC News. https://www.msnbc.com/know-your-value/feature/preparing-post-pandemic-life-doctor-s-guide-ncna1262699

64. McBride, L. [@drlucymcbride]. (2021, April 6). *After a year under duress, many of us will have a hard time with re-entry. Some degree of #anxiety is* [Tweet; thumbnail link to article]. Twitter. https://twitter.com/drlucymcbride/status/1379607153036697606

65. McBride, L. [@drlucymcbride]. (2021, April 6). *The risks of getting #COVID19 and transmitting #SARSCoV2 both drop significantly after #vaccination. Neither risk is zero (zero isn't even* [Tweet]. Twitter. https://twitter.com/drlucymcbride/status/1379563724185436160

66. McBride, L. [@drlucymcbride]. (2021, April 13). *The risk of my vaccinated patient & their vaccinated doctor infecting each other in my exam room? Close to zero. The* [Tweet]. Twitter. https://twitter.com/drlucymcbride/status/1382016934967922689

67. McBride, L. [@drlucymcbride]. (2021, April 19). *You nailed it, Derek. I've been using the "off-ramp" analogy with patients — both for how restrictions should END & how we* [Tweet]. Twitter. https://twitter.com/drlucymcbride/status/1384116198606966787

68. Talpos, S. (2021, April 20). *Do kids really need to be vaccinated for COVID? Yes. No. Maybe: Many experts argue that COVID-19 cannot be curbed without vaccinating children. But others aren't so sure*. Undark. https://undark.org/2021/04/20/do-kids-really-need-to-be-vaccinated-for-COVID/

69. Gandhi, M. [@MonicaGandhi9]. (2021, April 21). *Think we are getting closer and closer to that inflection point when things turn around in these regions of the* [Tweet; thumbnail link to article]. Twitter. https://twitter.com/MonicaGandhi9/status/1384984717393502209

70. Redford, G. (2021, April 21). *Is herd immunity closer than we think? real world data trickling in from other countries sheds light on how quickly the United States might contain the coronavirus through a combination of natural infection and vaccination*. AAMC. https://www.aamc.org/news-insights/herd-immunity-closer-we-think

71. McBride, L. [@drlucymcbride]. (2021, April 21). *You are correct -- it wasn't resistant at all; the #vaccine crushed it. Vaccines aren't 100% effective (though these are close!)* [Tweet]. Twitter. https://twitter.com/drlucymcbride/status/1384925788898799616

72. McBride, L. [@drlucymcbride]. (2021, April 22). *My (humble) impression is this: nothing in life is risk-free. Certainly the risk of COVID transmission is higher w/ the* [Tweet]. Twitter. https://twitter.com/drlucymcbride/status/1385299929615278088

73. Gandhi, M. [@MonicaGandhi9]. (2021, April 25). *We certainly seemed to have reached inflection point in US with ~32,000 cases today (lowest since June); see inflection on* [Tweet; thumbnail link to infographic]. Twitter. https://twitter.com/MonicaGandhi9/status/1386479236710428673

74. Gandhi, M. [@MonicaGandhi9]. (2021, April 29). *Indeed, SF may be at herd immunity now with 21 cases in city of 896K despite massive testing, 70% 1st* [Tweet; thumbnail link to infographic]. Twitter. https://twitter.com/MonicaGandhi9/status/1387780487305850881

75. Daugherty, E. H. (2021, May 4). *Q&A: Dr. Lucy McBride '95 on COVID-19, risk, and mental health*. Princeton Alumni Weekly. https://paw.princeton.edu/article/qa-dr-lucy-mcbride-95-COVID-19-risk-and-mental-health

76. Makary, M. (2021, May 4). Don't buy the fearmongering: The COVID-19 threat is waning. *New York Post*. https://nypost.com/2021/05/04/dont-buy-the-fearmongering-the-COVID-19-threat-is-ending/

77. Prasad, V. [@VPrasadMDMPH]. (2021, May 4). *I have been out and about in the USA lately. At least here, COVID is ending. It's visible. I can* [Tweet]. Twitter. https://twitter.com/VPrasadMDMPH/status/1389762926647541761

78. Sierra, S. (2021, May 5). *California 'weeks away' from reaching herd immunity, UCSF doctors say*. ABC7. https://abc7.com/herd-immunity-sf-san-francisco-COVID-19-cases-california/10586281/

79. Prasad, V. [@VPrasadMDMPH]. (2021, May 8). *Vast majority of kids recover quickly from SARS cov 2. And after all adults are vaccinated their risk of COVID* [Tweet; thumbnail link to tweet]. Twitter. https://twitter.com/vprasadmdmph/status/1391196541705097224

80. Gandhi, M. [@MonicaGandhi9]. (2021, May 10). *What I have seen in this pandemic is that experts start saying same thing: we need boosters; immunity won't be* [Tweet]. Twitter. https://twitter.com/MonicaGandhi9/status/1391757056152014854

81. Makary, M. (2021, May 21). Risk of COVID is now very low — It's time to stop living in fear: Doctor. *New York Post*. https://nypost.com/2021/05/21/risk-of-COVID-is-now-very-low-its-time-to-stop-living-in-fear-doctor/

82. Gandhi, M. (2021, May 24). *7 reasons why we should not need boosters for COVID-19*. Leaps.Org. https://leaps.org/booster-shot/particle-1

83. Gandhi, M. [@MonicaGandhi9]. (2021, May 25). *I wanted to explain what it feels like to be an ID doctor in the US with measles. Once we* [Tweet]. Twitter. https://twitter.com/MonicaGandhi9/status/1397348188063862784

84. Gandhi, M. [@MonicaGandhi9]. (2021, May 25). *Results of Moderna trial in teens 12-17, 3700 so half got Moderna vaccine; half got placebo. 4 cases in those* [Tweet]. https://twitter.com/MonicaGandhi9/status/1397351011866464257.

85. Gandhi, M. [@MonicaGandhi9]. (2021, May 26). *Oh, hard to see - California really has the lowest in-person learning in entire US (although we have likely reached herd* [Tweet; thumbnail link to article]. Twitter. https://twitter.com/MonicaGandhi9/status/1397723110393073666

86. McBride, L. [@drlucymcbride]. (2021, May 26). *Thx, Cat & @MikaKYV365. Parents need to role model confidence and optimism about the end of the pandemic. Masking outdoors* [Tweet; thumbnail link to tweet]. Twitter. https://twitter.com/drlucymcbride/status/1397555380637605893

87. Høeg, T. B., McBride, L., Krug, A., & Gandhi, M. (2021, May 26). It's time for children to finally get back to normal life. *The Washington Post.* https://www.washingtonpost.com/opinions/2021/05/26/its-time-children-finally-get-back-normal-life/

88. Makary, M. [@MartyMakary]. (2021, May 27). *They are moving the goal posts. Now that 80-85% of the adult U.S. population is immune (vax + natural immunity)* [Tweet]. Twitter. https://twitter.com/MartyMakary/status/1397960596734283777

89. Gandhi, M. [@MonicaGandhi9]. (2021, June 4). *Thanks @LetOregonLearn - yes, and with the vaccines+ natural immunity getting us to population immunity (herd immunity), it is so* [Tweet; thumbnail link to tweet]. Twitter. https://twitter.com/MonicaGandhi9/status/1400859894731870210

90. Makary, M. (2021, June 8). The power of natural immunity. *Wall Street Journal.* https://www.wsj.com/articles/the-power-of-natural-immunity-11623171303

91. Gandhi, M. [@MonicaGandhi9]. (2021, June 8). *San Francisco on track to be 1st CA metro city to reach full herd immunity, UCSF doctors say like George* [Tweet; thumbnail link to article]. Twitter. https://twitter.com/MonicaGandhi9/status/1402395400976232450

92. Gandhi, M. [@MonicaGandhi9]. (2021, June 8). *Right @BotondBallo, highly effective vaccines (Israel only had a 3.8% seroprevalence rate in Sept so not a lot of prior* [Tweet; thumbnail link to tweet]. Twitter. https://twitter.com/MonicaGandhi9/status/1402387731624255490

93. Mandrola, J. (Host). (2021, June 11). Jun 11, 2021 this week in cardiology [Audio podcast]. *Medscape.* https://www.medscape.com/viewarticle/952895#vp_2

94. Gandhi, M. [@MonicaGandhi9]. (2021, June 17). *San Francisco nears herd immunity- I and others on CGTN. When you get to herd immunity, those unvaccinated protected by* [Tweet; link to article]. Twitter. https://twitter.com/MonicaGandhi9/status/1405420592132624388

95. Gandhi, M. [@MonicaGandhi9]. (2021, June 22). *And cases continue to go lower despite 20% being delta, so it is okay to want to motivate vaccination, but* [Tweet; thumbnail link to infographic]. Twitter. https://twitter.com/MonicaGandhi9/status/1407550039233163268

96. Gandhi, M. [@MonicaGandhi9]. (2021, June 23). *Know we are all delta variant right now but look- plummeting cases since April 14 when we passed 40% 1st* [Tweet; thumbnail link to tweet]. Twitter. https://twitter.com/MonicaGandhi9/status/1407727163365683203

97. Prasad, V. [@VPrasadMDMPH]. (2021, June 23). *Myocarditis cont. ACIP slides are up. First, let us all remember cases are FALLING PRECIPITOUSLY The benefit side of the* [Tweet; thumbnail link to infographic]. Twitter. https://twitter.com/VPrasadMDMPH/status/1407743348719316993

98. Harris, M. (2021, June 24). *Why you shouldn't worry about the Delta variant (if you're vaccinated).* Slate. https://slate.com/technology/2021/06/delta-variant-COVID-vaccines-risk-monica-gandhi.html

99. Kulldorff, M., & Bhattacharya, J. (2021, June 27). A COVID commission Americans can trust: The country has lost faith in experts, but a thorough review free from conflicts of interest could help. *Wall Street Journal.* https://www.wsj.com/articles/a-COVID-commission-americans-can-trust-11624823367

100. Swaggering Towards Bethlehem [@KindAndUnblind]. (2021, December 13). *Gandhi, June 29, 2021: "I actually do not wear masks unless the business asks me to, bc I feel really* [Tweet; embedded video interview of M. Gandhi recorded June 29, 2021]. Twitter. https://twitter.com/KindAndUnblind/status/1470487789196259329

101. Bienen, L., & Gandhi, M. (2021, July 15). The reassuring data on the Delta variant. *Wall Street Journal.* https://www.wsj.com/articles/delta-variant-hospitalizations-COVID-coronavirus-vaccine-immunity-11626374706

102. Gandhi, M. [@MonicaGandhi9]. (2021, July 15). *but to public, the delta will become the dominant variant if more fit. So, 2nd question is whether the delta* [Tweet; thumbnail link to infographic]. Twitter. https://twitter.com/MonicaGandhi9/status/1415827834388422656

103. Cabrera, J. (2021, July 27). DeSantis holds roundtable on masks in schools: "This should absolutely not be imposed." *Alachua Chronicle.* https://alachuachronicle.com/desantis-holds-roundtable-on-masks-in-schools-this-should-absolutely-not-be-imposed/

104. Mandrola, J. [@drjohnm]. (2021, July 29). *If you were vaccinated and had mild to moderate URI symptoms, why on earth would you get a COVID test?* [Tweet; thumbnail link to tweet]. Twitter. https://twitter.com/drjohnm/status/1420913802095304705

105. Levitt, M. [@MLevitt_NP2013]. (2021, August 1). *Should we be concerned or is this just another mis-informed report to at get attention? With no move in added* [Tweet; thumbnail link to photos; link to article]. Twitter. https://twitter.com/MLevitt_NP2013/

status/1421750391801323524

106. Damania, Z. (Host). (2021, August 17). Turning COVID into the common cold [Video podcast episode]. In *ZDoggMD: Slightly funnier than placebo*. https://zdoggmd.com/pandemic-endemic/

107. Bhattacharya, J. (2021, August 26). The war on COVID should be over - We do not need lockdowns. *Daily Express*. https://www.express.co.uk/comment/expresscomment/1480182/COVID-war-over-no-more-lockdowns-coronavirus-comment

108. Bhattacharya, J. [@DrJBhattacharya]. (2021, September 8). *Now that we have (mostly) vaccinated the vulnerable, the pandemic will end when the people say it is over. At* [Tweet]. Twitter. https://twitter.com/DrJBhattacharya/status/1435486161007304706

109. Gandhi, M. (2021, September 21). We won't eradicate COVID. The pandemic will still end. *The Washington Post*. https://www.washingtonpost.com/outlook/2021/09/21/COVID-pandemic-end/

110. Gandhi, M. (2021, September 30). COVID will soon be endemic, thank goodness. *Wall Street Journal*. https://www.wsj.com/articles/COVID-endemic-vaccines-measles-smallpox-pandemic-coronavirus-11633015316

111. Billups, E. (2021, October 6). *Could Delta be the variant to end the pandemic? Experts say maybe*. Spectrum News. https://spectrumlocalnews.com/nys/central-ny/exploring-your-health/2021/10/06/could-delta-be-the-variant-to-end-the-pandemic-

112. Gandhi, M. [@MonicaGandhi9]. (2021, October 25). *NYC's high rates of vax, some prior infection and precautions keeping the worst outcomes of COVID-19 in check: "We're on* [Tweet; thumbnail link to article]. Twitter. https://twitter.com/MonicaGandhi9/status/1452760664129224707

113. Gandhi, M. (2021, November 3). It's time to contemplate the end of the crisis. *The Atlantic*. https://www.theatlantic.com/ideas/archive/2021/11/children-vaccines-pandemic-endemic/620594/

114. Bhattacharya, J. [@DrJBhattacharya]. (2021, November 15). *This emotionally manipulative message by a political leader is premised on bad science. The vaccine does not stop disease transmission* [Tweet; thumbnail link to tweet]. Twitter. https://twitter.com/DrJBhattacharya/status/1460405757405327361

115. Kelly, M. (Host). (2021, December 1). Why no one should panic

about the Omicron variant, with Dr. Bhattacharya and Dr. Dowdy [Video podcast]. In *The Megyn Kelly Show*. https://www.youtube.com/watch?v=jlqjMfRPzmA

116. Makary, M. (2021, December 16). *Dr. Makary on 'Kilmeade Show': Omicron fear fueling a 'second pandemic of lunacy'* [Video interview]. Fox News. https://www.foxnews.com/media/omicron-COVID-fear-pandemic-lunacy-makary-kilmeade

117. Bhattacharya, J. [@DrJBhattacharya]. (2021, December 16). *Almost one year to the day I published this piece with @SunetraGupta. It has held up well. Focused protection by* [Tweet; thumbnail link to article]. Twitter. https://twitter.com/DrJBhattacharya/status/1471569842750705666

118. Bhattacharya, J. (2021, December 17). We cannot stop the spread of COVID, but we can end the pandemic: Protect the old and vulnerable, forget lockdowns - and learn to live with the virus, writes Dr. Jay Bhattacharya, Stanford University of Medicine professor. *Daily Mail*. https://www.dailymail.co.uk/news/article-10321143/We-stop-viral-spread-COVID-end-pandemic-writes-Dr-Jay-Bhattacharya.html

119. Wall, J. (2022, January 2). *Updated science: Omicron called 'nature's vaccine' by Johns Hopkins professor Dr. Marty Makary*. TAPinto. https://www.tapinto.net/towns/hazlet-and-keyport/sections/health-and-wellness/articles/updated-science-omicron-called-nature-s-vaccine-by-johns-hopkins-professor-dr-marty-makary

120. Damania, Z. (Host). (2022, January 5). Omicron & the endemic phase of COVID. In *ZDoggMD: Slightly funnier than placebo*. https://zdoggmd.com/omicold/

121. McBride, L. [@drlucymcbride]. (2022, January 11). *More ppl are becoming immune to COVID, but *no one* is immune to the stress of the pandemic. Myself included!* [Tweet; thumbnail link to mailing list]. Twitter. https://twitter.com/drlucymcbride/status/1481019000557551617

122. Claus, P. (2022, January 17). *Dr. John Ioannidis: Transition from pandemic to endemic now happening*. Greek Reporter. https://greekreporter.com/2022/01/17/ioannidis-transition-pandemic-endemic/

123. Risch, H., Bhattacharya, J., & Alexander, P. E. (2022, January 23). *The emergency must be ended, now*. Brownstone Institute. https://brownstone.org/articles/the-emergency-must-be-ended-now/

124. Bhattacharya, J. [@DrJBhattacharya]. (2022, January 29). *Damian, to me the term pandemic no longer has any epidemiological definition. It is a political term to designate whatever* [Tweet]. Twitter. https://twitter.com/

DrJBhattacharya/status/1487659305629192196

125. Bhattacharya, J. [@DrJBhattacharya]. (2022, January 31). *This seems like big news -- Joining Jared Polis (D), NJ Gov. Phil Murphy (D) said it is time to* [Tweet; thumbnail link to article]. Twitter. https://twitter.com/DrJBhattacharya/status/1488294222960619521

126. Damania, Z. [ZDoggMD]. (2022, February 13). *Sunday LIVE w/Dr. Z: Time to end pandemic restrictions* [Video podcast]. YouTube. https://www.youtube.com/watch?v=77BSPcPeX5g

127. Bhattacharya, J. [@DrJBhattacharya]. (2022, March 12). *It is far past time to end the state of emergency in California, end the rule of the technocrats, and* [Tweet; thumbnail link to tweet]. Twitter. https://twitter.com/DrJBhattacharya/status/1502760764687327233

128. Bhattacharya, J. (2022, March 20). Two years later, be honest about what worked and what didn't. *Orange County Register*. https://www.ocregister.com/2022/03/20/two-years-later-be-honest-about-what-worked-and-what-didnt/

129. Ioannidis, J. P. A. (2022). The end of the COVID-19 pandemic. *European Journal of Clinical Investigation, 52*(6), Article 13782. https://doi.org/10.1111/eci.13782

130. Makary, M. [@MartyMakary]. (2022, May 2). *Hospitals are virtually empty of COVID-ill patients, yet the pandemic of fear continues [two backhand index pointing down] Forced cloth masking of toddlers is still* [Tweet; thumbnail link to tweet]. Twitter. https://twitter.com/martymakary/status/1521175536827092993

131. Gandhi, M. [@MonicaGandhi9]. (2022, May 15). *TOOLS TO KEEP COVID ENDEMIC NOW HERE: Long thread to explain that we now have all the tools necessary in* [Tweet]. Twitter. https://twitter.com/MonicaGandhi9/status/1525710894495174656

132. Bhattacharya, J. [@DrJBhattacharya]. (2022, May 26). *It's far past time for the COVID state of emergency to end. No more biomedical security state. No more state* [Tweet; thumbnail link to tweet]. Twitter. https://twitter.com/DrJBhattacharya/status/1529834619109093378

133. Prasad, V. [@VPrasadMDMPH]. (2022, June 2). *COVID-19 is really over when the New York Times health section returns to hard-hitting coverage such as: How many blueberries* [Tweet]. Twitter. https://twitter.com/VPrasadMDMPH/status/1532370301077495808

134. Howard, J. [@19joho]. (2022, September 10). *Can someone search his*

2018 timeline to see how much he talked about the flu? Cause that's how much he [Tweet; thumbnail image of tweet]. Twitter. https://twitter.com/19joho/status/1568771918290886657

135. Bhattacharya, J. [@DrJBhattacharya]. (2022, July 12). *The virus is endemic and will circulate forever. Most of the population has been infected and recovered and is protected* [Tweet]. Twitter. https://twitter.com/DrJBhattacharya/status/1547056728004386818

136. Mandrola, J. [@drjohnm]. (2022, July 27). *I work in a hospital every week. Anil is correct. We now have a diff disease: many if not most* [Tweet]. Twitter. https://twitter.com/drjohnm/status/1552223720290263040

137. Bhattacharya, J. [@DrJBhattacharya]. (2022, August 16). *It's far past time for the US COVID state of emergency declaration to end. Many states have already ended theirs* [Tweet; thumbnail link to tweet]. Twitter. https://twitter.com/DrJBhattacharya/status/1559605819015962624

138. Miltimore, J. (2022, August 22). *The CDC finally admits it was wrong about natural immunity. Why did it take so long?* Foundation for Economic Education. https://fee.org/articles/the-cdc-finally-admitted-the-science-on-natural-immunity-why-did-it-take-so-long/

139. Egli, A. [@Adrian7745]. (2022, September 10). *Oh it isn't over yet. Now @MonicaGandhi9 is parroting the "good news". [weary face] See, Dr. Makam has "only" seen one patient* [Tweet; picture of tweet]. Twitter. https://twitter.com/Adrian7745/status/1568731886201217024

140. Prasad, V. (2022, September 11). A good doctor and researcher makes a factual statement, at his peril. *Vinay Prasad's Observations and Thoughts*. https://vinayprasadmdmph.substack.com/p/a-good-doctor-and-researcher-makes?sd=pf

141. Stein, R. (2022, September 16). *Scientists debate how lethal COVID is. Some say it's now less risky than flu.* NPR. https://www.npr.org/sections/health-shots/2022/09/16/1122650502/scientists-debate-how-lethal-COVID-is-some-say-its-now-less-risky-than-flu

142. Prasad, V. [@VPrasadMDMPH]. (2022, September 18). *I do think it is important he says it [backhand index pointing down] The emergency or pandemic phase is over. COVID will be around* [Tweet; thumbnail link to video]. Twitter. https://twitter.com/VPrasadMDMPH/status/1571660852356587520

143. Bhattacharya, J. [@DrJBhattacharya]. (2022, September 19). *Pres. Biden is right. The pandemic emergency is over. Research for better treatments*

should continue, but the lockdowns, restrictions, and [Tweet]. Twitter. https://twitter.com/DrJBhattacharya/status/1571831550458859520

144. Daignault, M., & Gandhi, M. (2022, December 13). The case for cautious COVID optimism this winter. *Time*. https://time.com/6240524/COVID-19-optimism-this-winter/

145. Agarwal, S., & Bhattacharya, J. (2021, January 11). *Majority Indians have natural immunity. Vaccinating entire population can cause great harm*. ThePrint. https://theprint.in/opinion/majority-indians-have-natural-immunity-vaccinating-entire-population-can-cause-great-harm/582174/

146. Refutations to Anti-Vaccine Memes. [@RtAVM]. (2021, July 8). *yep* [Tweet; thumbnail link to image]. Twitter. https://twitter.com/RtAVM/status/1413211091774152716

147. Pandey, G. (2021, May 19). *COVID-19: India's holiest river is swollen with bodies*. BBC News. https://www.bbc.com/news/world-asia-india-57154564

148. Gandhi, M. [@MonicaGandhi9]. (2021, April 25). *3) Mistake I, others made in India (I made huge error, so sorry) is assuming seroprevalence studies from slums in* [Tweet; thumbnail link to article]. Twitter. https://mobile.twitter.com/MonicaGandhi9/status/1386371806605451267

149. Kulldorff, M. [@MartinKulldorff]. (2020, May 23). *Antibodies in Spain vs Sweden, by age 0-19: 3.3% vs 4.7% 20-64: 5.3% vs 6.7% 65-69 6.2% vs 2.7% Deaths/million* [Tweet]. Twitter. https://twitter.com/MartinKulldorff/status/1264223771684200448

150. Kulldorff, M. [@MartinKulldorff]. (2021, August 8). *Essentially #ZeroCOVID deaths in Sweden for a month now* [Tweet; thumbnail link to infographic]. Twitter. https://twitter.com/MartinKulldorff/status/1424340615446384645

151. Kulldorff, M. [@MartinKulldorff]. (2021, July 13). *With vaccine generated #FocusedProtection of the old, UK #COVID case are mostly among young people with miniscule risk of death* [Tweet; thumbnail link to infographic]. Twitter. https://twitter.com/MartinKulldorff/status/1414842781584044034

152. Edmunds, D. R. (2020, March 20). Nobel laureate: surprised if Israel has more than 10 coronavirus deaths. *The Jerusalem Post*. https://www.jpost.com/israel-news/nobel-laureate-israel-will-have-no-more-than-ten-coronavirus-deaths-621407

153. Levitt, M. [@MLevitt_NP2013]. (2020, April 22). *Looks like Sweden has*

done the right thing after all. Herd immunity, intact economy, little social hardship [Tweet; thumbnail link to article]. Twitter. https://twitter.com/MLevitt_NP2013/status/1252988382470438918

154. Qimron, U., Gavish, U., Abadi-Korek, I., Shahar, E., & Levitt, M. (2020, July 20). Countering the second wave with facts, not misconceptions [Trans.]. *Ha'aretz*. https://www.dropbox.com/s/znxy6flxtusxgaw/Haaretz_20Jul20_ENGLISH%2012082020%20v4.pdf

155. Urgency of Normal. (n.d.). *About*. Retrieved November 16, 2022, from https://www.urgencyofnormal.com/about

156. Urgency of Normal. (2022, February 18). *Children, COVID, and the urgency of normal: An advocacy toolkit for parents, students, mentors, teachers, and administrators*. https://tulip-chartreuse-stwk.squarespace.com/s/Urgency-of-Normal-Toolkit.pdf

157. and Prevention. (n.d.). *Influenza-associated pediatric mortality* [Interactive dataset]. U.S. Department of Health and Human Services. Retrieved December 3, 2022, from https://gis.cdc.gov/grasp/fluview/pedfludeath.html

158. and Prevention. (n.d.). *COVID data tracker: Demographic trends of COVID-19 cases and deaths in the US reported to CDC* [Interactive dataset]. U.S. Department of Health and Human Services. Retrieved December 28, 2022, from https://COVID.cdc.gov/COVID-data-tracker/#demographics

159. Høeg, T. [@TracyBethHoeg]. (2021, March 21). *Also, children have not been found to be superspreaders and since there is high over dispersion of this disease schools* [Tweet]. Twitter. https://twitter.com/TracyBethHoeg/status/1373718832494211073

160. Johnson, K. (2022, October 3). Schools are significant sites of COVID transmission. *Medscape*. https://www.medscape.com/viewarticle/981770

161. Prasad, V. (2021, September 2). The downsides of masking young students are real. *The Atlantic*. https://www.theatlantic.com/ideas/archive/2021/09/school-mask-mandates-downside/619952/

162. Chernozhukov, V., Kasahara, H., & Schrimpf, P. (2021). The association of opening K–12 schools with the spread of COVID-19 in the United States: County-level panel data analysis. *PNAS*, *118*(42), Article 2103420118. https://doi.org/10.1073/pnas.2103420118

163. Urgency of Normal. (n.d.). *Main page*. Retrieved November 16, 2022, from https://www.urgencyofnormal.com/

164. Waller, A., Huang, K., & Cai, M. (2021, September 3). At least 45 districts shut down in-person classes due to COVID-19 cases, affecting more than 40,000 students. *The Texas Tribune*. https://www.texastribune.org/2021/09/03/texas-COVID-school-districts-shut-down/

165. Associated Press. (2021, August 12). *4 Georgia districts stop in-person classes due to COVID*. WIS-TV. https://www.wistv.com/2021/08/12/4-georgia-districts-stop-in-person-classes-due-COVID/

166. Elsen-Rooney, M. (2022, January 8). A record number of NYC kids have missed the last two weeks of school. *New York Daily News*. https://www.nydailynews.com/new-york/education/ny-student-absences-COVID-surge-testing-schools-20220109-3bm2t36we5hqnhytgwhudfsvky-story.html

167. *Coronavirus news: 30 teachers among 74 DOE employees to die of COVID-19*. (2020, May 11). ABC7 New York. https://abc7ny.com/teacher-deaths-doe-department-of-education-schools/6173896/

168. Maxwell, L. A. (2022, December 16). Educators we've lost to the coronavirus: Some of the teachers, principals, coaches, counselors, and other staff members who've died. *Education Week*, *39*(37), 1. https://www.edweek.org/teaching-learning/educators-weve-lost-to-the-coronavirus/2020/04

169. Black, T. [@tylerblack32]. (2022, February 1). *New version: Now that suicides not useful, just remove it! It just disappears. That's awful & unscientific. It should keep the* [Tweet; image attached]. Twitter. https://twitter.com/tylerblack32/status/1488729829897695239

170. Charpignon, M-L., Ontiveros, J., Sundaresan, S., Puri, A., Chandra, J., Mandl, K. D., & Shahnaz Majumder, M. (2022). Evaluation of suicides among US adolescents during the COVID-19 pandemic. *JAMA Pediatrics*, *176*(7), 724-726. https://doi.org/10.1001/jamapediatrics.2022.0515

171. Curtin, S. C., Garnett, M. F., & Ahmad, F. B. (2022). Provisional numbers and rates of suicide by month and demographic characteristics: United States, 2021. *Vital Statistics Rapid Report, No. 24*. https://dx.doi.org/10.15620/cdc:120830

172. Hansen, B., Sabia, J. J., & Schaller, J. (n.d.). *In-person schooling and youth suicide: Evidence from school calendars and pandemic school closures*. National Bureau of Economic Research. https://doi.org/10.3386/w30795

173. Black, T. [@tylerblack32]. (2022, January 25). */2 I'm skipping the first*

line (for now), but the second part, about "deaths from child suicide vastly outnumbering deaths [Tweet; image attached]. Twitter. https://twitter.com/tylerblack32/status/1486111659483713540

174. Chatterjee, R. (2022, July 24). *Losing a parent can derail teens' lives. A high school grief club aims to help.* NPR. https://www.npr.org/sections/health-shots/2022/07/24/1110916298/losing-a-parent-can-derail-teens-lives-a-high-school-grief-club-aims-to-help

175. Pierce, C. A., Herold, K. C., Herold, B. C., Chou, J., Randolph, A., Kane, B., McFarland, S., Gurdasani, D., Pagel, C., Hotez, P., Cobey, S., & Hensley, S. E. (2022, September 8). COVID-19 and children. *Science, 377*(6611), 1144-1149. https://doi.org/10.1126/science.ade1675

176. Chuck, E., Breslauer, B., & McFadden, C. (2022, March 7). *More than 200,000 kids have lost a parent or caregiver to COVID. Efforts to help them have been haphazard.* NBC News. https://www.nbcnews.com/news/us-news/200000-us-children-lost-parent-caregiver-COVID-efforts-help-haphazard-rcna16140

177. Khan, F. (2022, April 20). *1 in every 200 NYC children have lost a parent or caregiver to COVID. That's almost twice the national rate.* The City. https://www.thecity.nyc/2022/4/20/23033998/1-in-every-200-children-nyc-lost-parent-COVID-twice-national-rate

178. Van Beusekom, M. (2022, September 6). *COVID-19 may have orphaned 7.5 million kids worldwide.* Center for Infectious Disease Research and Policy. https://www.cidrap.umn.edu/news-perspective/2022/09/COVID-19-may-have-orphaned-75-million-kids-worldwide

179. Requarth, T. (2022, April 6). America's pandemic orphans are slipping through the cracks. *The Atlantic.* https://www.theatlantic.com/health/archive/2022/04/COVID-orphan-kids-lost-parent/629436/

180. Damania, Z. (Host). (2021, May 24). Least wrong about COVID? [Video podcast episode]. In *ZDoggMD: Slightly funnier than placebo.* https://zdoggmd.com/marty-makary-3/

181. Rivera, M. [@manuriv93285316]. (2021, March 11). *Thank you for the positivity, I see so many other people cheering on a 4th surge like it was a* [Tweet]. Twitter. https://twitter.com/manuriv93285316/status/1370214810881683457

182. Cifu, A., & Prasad, V. (2022, July 26). A pro-con debate: Should doctors encourage healthy kids 11 and under be vaccinated against COVID-19? *Sensible Medicine.* https://sensiblemed.substack.com/p/a-pro-con-debate-should-doctors-encourage

183. Baral, S. [@sbbaral]. (2021, February 8). *I don't think variants are going to cause a third wave of #COVID19 in the coming weeks or months across* [Tweet]. Twitter. https://twitter.com/sdbaral/status/1358774006258798594

184. Gandhi, M. [@MonicaGandhi9]. (2021, February 8). *completely agree* [Tweet; thumbnail link to tweet]. Twitter. https://twitter.com/MonicaGandhi9/status/1358859188789604353

185. Mandrola, J. [@drjohnm]. (2021, February 13). *The good news on #COVID19 continues* [Tweet; thumbnail link to tweet]. Twitter. https://twitter.com/drjohnm/status/1360587368739258373

186. Mandrola, J. [@drjohnm]. (2021, February 14). *Good news on #COVID19 is getting to be a routine now.* [Tweet; thumbnail link to tweet]. Twitter. https://twitter.com/drjohnm/status/1361069454659051521

187. Prasad, V. [@VPrasadMDMPH]. (2021, February 18). *This NYTimes story on Jan 24th "Vaccines alone won't end pandemic" Did not age well (as of Feb 18)* [Tweet; thumbnail link to dataset]. Twitter. https://twitter.com/VPrasadMDMPH/status/1362593239056801792

188. Prasad, V. (Host). (2021, March 2). COVID-19 vaccine results, messaging on a patient level, & schools with Dr. Monica Gandhi (Episode 3.47) [Audio podcast]. In *Plenary Sessions*. https://soundcloud.com/plenarysession/ep347

189. Makary, M. [@MartyMakary]. (2021, April 3). *Herd immunity has many definitions, but that looks like herd immunity to me* [Tweet; thumbnail link to tweet]. Twitter. https://twitter.com/MartyMakary/status/1378461823255650305

190. Makary, M. [@MartyMakary]. (2021, May 15). *Nice herd immunity, Eric* [Tweet; thumbnail link to tweet]. Twitter. https://twitter.com/MartyMakary/status/1393695456060903428

191. Makary, M. [@MartyMakary]. (2021, June 30). *The term is herd immunity [smiling face with smiling eyes] But that was before the human immune became politicized. We now say high population immunity* [Tweet; thumbnail link to tweet]. Twitter. https://twitter.com/MartyMakary/status/1410429600082153473

192. Kulldorff, M. [@MartinKulldorff]. (2020, April 19). *Extremely surprising if past infection does not give some immunity. Around 1/3 of ppl in Stockholm has now had COVID-19* [Tweet; thumbnail link to article]. Twitter. https://twitter.com/MartinKulldorff/status/1251913905653403651

193. Makary, M. [@MartyMakary]. (2021, April 3). *U.K. has now vaccinated 60% of adults with 1 dose by delaying 2nd doses a few months--a winning strategy* [Tweet; thumbnail link to article]. Twitter. https://twitter.com/MartyMakary/status/1378461383772225536
194. Davis, N. (2021, June 11). Delta variant causes more than 90% of new COVID cases in UK. *The Guardian.* https://www.theguardian.com/world/2021/jun/11/delta-variant-is-linked-to-90-of-COVID-cases-in-uk

Chapter Eight

1. Sears, B. (2014, March 18). *Measles epidemic . . . NOT! Why is it every time there are a few cases of measles, everyone panics? I just don't* [Status update]. Facebook. https://www.facebook.com/permalink.php?story_fbid=684812428223911&id=116317855073374

2. Bystrianyk, R. (2019, March 1). Measles: The new red scare. *GreenMedInfo*. https://greenmedinfo.com/blog/measles-new-red-scare

3. Benatar, O. (2022, December 12). *Ohio measles outbreak reaches more than 70 cases*. NBC4 WCMH-TV. https://www.nbc4i.com/news/local-news/columbus/ohio-measles-outbreak-reaches-more-than-70-cases/

4. Nugent, T. (2020, April 23). *Why do I have to stay home just because you are scared? How about you stay home....you stay in* [Status update]. Facebook. https://www.facebook.com/tednugent/posts/10157423794732297/

5 Ji, S. (2020, March 11). Sayer Ji: Beyond the coronavirus [Episode 34; audio podcast interview]. *A New and Ancient Story*. https://charleseisenstein.org/podcasts/new-ancient-story-podcast/sayer-ji-beyond-the-coronavirus-e45/

6. Remski, M. (2020, September 15). Inside Kelly Brogan's COVID-denying, vax-resistant conspiracy machine. Alt-health meets alt-right in the 'conspirituality' movement. *GEN-Medium*. https://gen.medium.com/inside-kelly-brogans-COVID-denying-vax-resistant-conspiracy-machine-28342e6369b1

7. Mercola, J. (2022, January 7). *Children at risk for lifelong health problems from COVID vaccine*. The Defender: Children's Health Defense News & Views. https://childrenshealthdefense.org/defender/children-risk-lifelong-health-problems-COVID-vaccine/

8. Ioannidis, J. P. A. (2020, April 17). *Perspectives on the pandemic* [Episode 4; video podcast interview transcript]. The Press and the Public. https://www.thepressandthepublic.com/post/perspectives-on-the-pandemic-iv

9. Carrington, A. E. (2021, March 28). *How NY hospital faced COVID devastation and came back from the brink: The staff at Elmhurst Hospital Center has seen the darkest days of the pandemic*. ABC News. https://abcnews.go.com/Health/ny-hospital-faced-COVID-devastation-back-brink/story?id=76638912

10. Finley, A. (2020, April 24). The bearer of good coronavirus news. *Wall Street Journal*. https://www.wsj.com/articles/the-bearer-of-good-

coronavirus-news-11587746176

11. Mandrola, J. [@drjohnm]. (2020, March 5). *Late on this, but strikingly calm words on #COVID19, from the PM of Singapore "The real test to our social* [Tweet; thumbnail link to Facebook post]. Twitter. https://twitter.com/drjohnm/status/1235531026878746624

12. Mathieu, E., Ritchie, H., Rodés-Guirao, L., Appel, C., Giattino, C., Hasell, J., Macdonald, B., Dattani, S., Beltekian, D., Ortiz-Ospina, E., & Roser, M. (2020). *Coronavirus pandemic (COVID-19)* [Interactive dataset]. Our World in Data. Retrieved December 14, 2022, from https://ourworldindata.org/COVID-deaths

13. Mandrola, J. [@drjohnm]. (2020, September 7). *Lately, I am seeing lots of fear-mongering in #COVID19 Let's be clear: the virus deserves respect. The 5 big recs* [Tweet; thumbnail link to infographics]. Twitter. https://twitter.com/drjohnm/status/1303010231484665856

14. Mandrola, J., & Foy, A. (2020, December 29). No, young adults should not live in fear from coronavirus. *Dr John M.* https://www.drjohnm.org/2020/12/no-young-adults-should-not-live-in-fear-from-coronavirus/

15. Mandrola, J. [@drjohnm]. (2021, March 11). *I think ALB makes a good point. I wish I had wrote "almost done here in the US." Frustration with* [Tweet; thumbnail link to tweet]. Twitter. https://twitter.com/drjohnm/status/1369979642699014146

16. Prasad, V. [@VPrasadMDMPH]. (2021, January 23). *I want to write a children's book about a bear who didn't want to leave home till it was perfectly* [Tweet]. Twitter. https://twitter.com/vprasadmdmph/status/1353119932263788544

17. Gorski, D. [Orac]. (2022, September 7). Caution over COVID-19 is "irrational anxiety"? *Respectful Insolence.* https://www.respectfulinsolence.com/2022/09/07/vp-accuses-public-health-of-legitimizing-irrational-anxiety/

18. Prasad, V. (2022, September 16). When scientists' anxiety disorder interferes with other people's lives. *Vinay Prasad's Observations and Thoughts*. https://vinayprasadmdmph.substack.com/p/when-scientists-anxiety-disorder

19. Prasad, V. (2022, November 21). STAT's ID experts are not good thinkers. *Vinay Prasad's Observations and Thoughts*. https://vinayprasadmdmph.substack.com/p/stats-id-experts-are-not-good-thinkers

20. Sharff, K. (2022, October 1). Reflections of an infectious disease physician: Where COVID-19 and my personal world collide. *Sensible*

Medicine. https://sensiblemed.substack.com/p/reflections-of-an-infectious-disease

21. Di Filippo, E. (2020, March 25). *'Very, very dangerous' Goop 'expert' slammed for bizarre coronavirus video*. Yahoo! Style. https://www.yahoo.com/now/kelly-brogan-doubts-existance-of-coronavirus-in-new-video-164034780.html

22. Bhattacharya, J. (2021, May 12). *Tucker Carlson Tonight* [Video interview]. Fox News. https://www.foxnews.com/transcript/tucker-carlson-on-COVID-vaccine-passports-nyc-mayoral-race-inflation-concerns

23. Bhattacharya, J. [@DrJBhattacharya]. (2022, December 12). *If you live life as if there are no respiratory viruses, you'll sometimes get sick, and you'll live your life* [Tweet]. Twitter. https://twitter.com/DrJBhattacharya/status/1602528043309858817

24. Makary, M. (2021, May 4). Don't buy the fearmongering: The COVID-19 threat is waning. *New York Post*. https://nypost.com/2021/05/04/dont-buy-the-fearmongering-the-COVID-19-threat-is-ending/

25. Makary, M. (2021, May 21). Risk of COVID is now very low — It's time to stop living in fear: Doctor. *New York Post*. https://nypost.com/2021/05/21/risk-of-COVID-is-now-very-low-its-time-to-stop-living-in-fear-doctor/

26. Pletka, D., & Thiessen, M. (2021, July 28). WTH is going on with breakthrough infections? Dr. Marty Makary explains why renewed panic over COVID-19 is unwarranted (Episode #113) [Audio podcast transcript]. *What the Hell is Going On?* https://www.aei.org/wp-content/uploads/2021/07/Makary-Final-Transcript-7.28.21.pdf

27. Makary, M. (2021, December 16). *Dr. Makary on 'Kilmeade Show': Omicron fear fueling a 'second pandemic of lunacy'* [Video interview]. Fox News. https://www.foxnews.com/media/omicron-COVID-fear-pandemic-lunacy-makary-kilmeade

28. Damania, Z. (Host). (2020, March 28). Hacking our anxious brain in uncertain times [Video podcast episode]. In *ZDoggMD: Slightly funnier than placebo*. https://zdoggmd.com/jud-brewer/

29. Damania, Z. (Host). (2020, March 17). COVID-19: is our cure worse than the disease? [Video podcast episode]. In *ZDoggMD: Slightly funnier than placebo*. https://zdoggmd.com/paul-offit-COVID/

30. Damania, Z. (Host). (2020, June 26). COVID-19 live update: should

we panic? [Video podcast episode]. In *ZDoggMD: Slightly funnier than placebo*. https://zdoggmd.com/COVID-june-26/

31. Yan, H. (2020, September 22). *200,000 people have died from COVID-19 in the US. That's more than the US battle deaths from 5 wars combined.* CNN. https://www.cnn.com/2020/09/22/health/us-coronavirus-deaths-200k/index.html

32. Ortaliza, J., Amin, K., & Cox, C. (2022, November 10). *COVID-19 leading cause of death ranking*. Kaiser Family Foundation. https://www.kff.org/coronavirus-COVID-19/issue-brief/COVID-19-leading-cause-of-death-ranking/

33. Damania, Z. (Host). (2020, October 11). How to stop living in fear of COVID [Video podcast episode]. In *ZDoggMD: Slightly funnier than placebo*. https://zdoggmd.com/monica-gandhi-2/

34. Emmert, M. (2020, May 13). Iowa native Michael Osterholm, a world-renowned epidemiologist, saw the pandemic coming. Now, he wants you to be worried. *The Des Moines Register*. https://www.desmoinesregister.com/story/news/2020/05/13/iowa-native-michael-osterholm-predicted-COVID-19-pandemic-uses-medical-expertise-try-guide-response/3102428001/

35. Shapiro, A., & Eltohamy, F. (2021, March 8). *'War doesn't even compare': A year in the life of a traveling nurse*. NPR. https://www.npr.org/2021/03/08/974835141/a-year-in-the-life-of-a-traveling-nurse

36. Damania, Z. (Host). (2021, February 22). The end of the epidemic [Video podcast episode]. In *ZDoggMD: Slightly funnier than placebo*. https://zdoggmd.com/monica-gandhi-3/

37. Scott, D., Raina, P., & Sitlhou, M. (2021, August 19). *The long road to India's unparalleled pandemic catastrophe*. Vox. https://www.vox.com/coronavirus-COVID19/22628806/india-COVID-19-cases-deaths-delta-variant

38. Damania, Z. (Host). (2021, May 24). Least wrong about COVID? [Video podcast episode]. In *ZDoggMD: Slightly funnier than placebo*. https://zdoggmd.com/marty-makary-3/

39. Damania, Z. (Host). (2021, April 14). Focused protection for COVID [Video podcast episode]. In *ZDoggMD: Slightly funnier than placebo*. https://zdoggmd.com/jay-bhattacharya-2/

40. Bendavid, E., & Bhattacharya, J. (2020, March 24). Is the Coronavirus as deadly as they say? Current estimates about the COVID-19 fatality rate may be too high by orders of magnitude. *Wall Street Journal*.

https://www.wsj.com/articles/is-the-coronavirus-as-deadly-as-they-say-11585088464

41. Damania, Z. (Host). (2021, December 4). Omicron panic, natural immunity, fluvoxamine, & more [Episode 4] (Video podcast). In *The VPZD Show*. https://zdoggmd.com/podcasting/vpzd-4/

42. McBride, L. (2021, March 2). *I'm a doctor seeing patients with coronaphobia. Here's what you need to know.* HuffPost. https://www.huffpost.com/entry/coronavirus-phobia-side-effects-anxiety_n_603d18eec5b6829715023334

43. McBride, L. (2021, March 9). I've been yearning for an end to the pandemic. Now that it's here, I'm a little afraid. *The Washington Post*. https://www.washingtonpost.com/opinions/2021/03/09/weve-adjusted-pandemic-life-now-we-face-anxiety-leaving-it-behind/

44. McBride, L. (2021, August 13). Fear of COVID-19 in kids is getting ahead of the data. *The Atlantic*. https://www.theatlantic.com/ideas/archive/2021/08/children-delta-COVID-19-risk-adults-overreact/619728/

45. Goodman, B. (2021, August 17). *Pediatric hospitals in U.S. in peril as Delta hits children*. WebMD. https://www.webmd.com/COVID/news/20210817/pediatric-hospitals-us-in-peril-delta-hits-children

46. Kuehn, B. M. (2021). Delta variant linked with spike in youth hospitalizations. *JAMA*, *326*(14), 1366. https://doi.org/10.1001/jama.2021.16667

47. McBride, L. (2022, March 23). *Dealing with 'post-pandemic stress': a doctor's guide*. MSNBC News. https://www.msnbc.com/know-your-value/health-mindset/COVID-19-post-pandemic-stress-how-deal-anxiety-life-gets-n1292798

48. McBride, L. [@drlucymcbride]. (2022, May 14). *I'm finding that the "cure" for some of my patients' outsize fear of COVID is ... COVID. "Coronaphobia" can be* [Tweet; thumbnail link to article]. Twitter. https://twitter.com/drlucymcbride/status/1525519994565672960

49. Ioannidis, J. P. A. (2020, March 17). A fiasco in the making? As the coronavirus pandemic takes hold, we are making decisions without reliable data. *STAT*. https://www.statnews.com/2020/03/17/a-fiasco-in-the-making-as-the-coronavirus-pandemic-takes-hold-we-are-making-decisions-without-reliable-data/

50. McBride, L. [@drlucymcbride]. (2022, February 16). *Thank you. I fully realize that people are suffering a lot more than he is. Everyone is exhausted & worn* [Tweet]. Twitter. https://twitter.com/drlucymcbride/

status/1494166256206942209

51. Makary, M. [@MartyMakary]. (2022, February 11). *I applaud @ Surgeon_General for calling out the devastation to children-TY. But this harm from a political CDC that still, today* [Tweet; thumbnail link to article]. https://twitter.com/MartyMakary/status/1492276812524793860.

52. Kulldorff, M. [@MartinKulldorff]. (2022, May 14). *A local medical officer, Dr. @strauss_matt, was heavily criticized for resisting Canada's draconian pandemic policies. The COVID mortality numbers have* [Tweet; thumbnail link to article]. Twitter. https://twitter.com/ MartinKulldorff/status/1525595954476466185

53. Prasad, V. [@VPrasadMDMPH]. (2021, January 21). *Just read one of the most important papers of the COVID19 pandemic by @sdbaral and colleagues [backhand index pointing down] Pls read COVID19 & how* [Tweet; thumbnail link to article]. Twitter. https://twitter.com/ VPrasadMDMPH/status/1351411478083997697

54. Bhattacharya, J. [@DrJBhattacharya]. (2022, September 28). *Mary, we did not adopt 'let it rip', we adopted lockdown and civil liberties restrictions. The public sacrificed itself to* [Tweet]. Twitter. https://twitter. com/DrJBhattacharya/status/1575178460682604544

55. Bhattacharya, J. [@DrJBhattacharya]. (2022, July 1). *Happy Canada Day to all my amazing Canadian friends! A day is coming when Canada's biomedical security state recedes and* [Tweet]. Twitter. https://twitter. com/DrJBhattacharya/status/1543075028941426689

56. Bhattacharya, J. [@DrJBhattacharya]. (2022, August 5). *Lockdown-by-stealth: policies that aim to keep people physically distant from one another by force or fear. [diamond shape with dot inside] mass asymptomatic testing & quarantines* [Tweet]. Twitter. https://twitter.com/ drjbhattacharya/status/1555726858515202048

57. Damania, Z. [@ZDoggMD]. (2020, March 17). *Are we doing more harm than good with our current draconian approach to COVID-19 mitigation? A brand new interview with* [Tweet; thumbnail link to video]. Twitter. https://twitter.com/ZDoggMD/status/1240023453966585856

58. and Prevention. (n.d.). *COVID data tracker: Health department-reported cases of multisystem inflammatory syndrome in children (MIS-C) in the United States* [Interactive dataset]. U.S. Department of Health and Human Services. Retrieved December 22, 2022, from https://COVID. cdc.gov/COVID-data-tracker/#mis-national-surveillance

59. Mandrola, J. [@drjohnm]. (2020, October 25). *Way to gain followers*

during the pandemic: bash the US. Promote fear. Consider every #COVID19 case as a stab in [Tweet]. Twitter. https://twitter.com/drjohnm/status/1320465216430288896

60. Mandrola, J. [@drjohnm]. (2021, February 19). *More good news to report on #COVID19: poorly thought out virtual-signaling Tweets seem to be getting less attention. #progress* [Tweet]. Twitter. https://twitter.com/drjohnm/status/1362935304118755330

61. Gandhi, M. [@MonicaGandhi9]. (2021, March 12). *I think it's an addition to fear, an addition to doom, and perhaps an addiction to being on TV or* [Tweet]. Twitter. https://twitter.com/MonicaGandhi9/status/1370274158689480706

62. Refutations to Anti-Vaccine Memes. [@RtAVM]. (2021, November 5). *So gross* [Tweet; image attached]. Twitter. https://twitter.com/RtAVM/status/1456689789806252051

63. Brogan, K. (n.d.). Health as spiritual warfare. *Kelly Brogan, MD*. https://www.kellybroganmd.com/blog/health-as-spiritual-warfare

64. Prasad, V. (2022, August 27). The AAP (American Academy of Pediatrics) is broken, failed organization: Kids need a new advocate who puts kids first. *Sensible Medicine*. https://sensiblemed.substack.com/p/the-aap-american-academy-of-pediatrics

65. Prasad, V. (2021, October 2). How democracy ends. *Vinay Prasad's Observations and Thoughts*. https://vinayprasadmdmph.substack.com/p/how-democracy-ends

66. Shaffer, B. (2015, April 24). First they came for the anti-vaxxers. *Age of Autism*. https://www.ageofautism.com/2015/04/first-they-came-for-the-anti-vaxxers-by-bretigne-schaffer.html

67. Brunner, J. (2021, June 30). Washington lawmaker wears yellow Star of David, evoking Nazi persecution, to protest COVID vaccine mandates. *The Seattle Times*. https://www.seattletimes.com/seattle-news/politics/washington-lawmaker-wears-gold-star-of-david-evoking-nazi-persecution-to-protest-COVID-vaccine-mandates/

68. Gorski, D. [Orac]. (2022, September 6). COVID-19 vaccines and the Nuremberg Code, revisited. *Respectful Insolence*. https://www.respectfulinsolence.com/2022/09/06/COVID-19-vaccines-and-the-nuremberg-code-revisited/

69. Luna, T. (2019, October 2). Vaccine bill protester threw blood on California senators, investigation confirms. *Los Angeles Times*. https://www.latimes.com/california/story/2019-10-02/vaccine-law-protester-

blood-california-state-senate

70. Gorski, D. [Orac]. (2016, July 19). The violent rhetoric of the antivaccine movement, VAXXED edition. *Respectful Insolence*. https://respectfulinsolence.com/2016/07/19/the-violent-rhetoric-of-the-antivaccine-movement-vaxxed-edition/

71. Kaiser Health News, Sable, B., & Miller, A. (2021, October 11). America stopped treating health-care workers like heroes. *The Atlantic*. https://www.theatlantic.com/health/archive/2021/10/pandemic-might-be-making-hospital-violence-worse/620409/

72. Associated Press. (2020, December 14). *At least 181 public health leaders nationwide have resigned, retired or been fired amid pandemic*. KTLA. https://ktla.com/news/coronavirus/at-least-181-public-health-leaders-nationwide-have-resigned-retired-or-been-fired-amid-pandemic/

73. Baker, M., & Ivory, D. (2021, October 20). Why public health faces a crisis across the U.S. *The New York Times*. https://www.nytimes.com/2021/10/18/us/coronavirus-public-health.html

74. Nogrady, B. (2021, October 13). 'I hope you die': how the COVID pandemic unleashed attacks on scientists. *Nature*. https://www.nature.com/articles/d41586-021-02741-x

75. Novella, S. (2021, October 20). Experts abused for talking to the public. *Science-Based Medicine*. https://sciencebasedmedicine.org/experts-abused-for-talking-to-the-public/

76. Vazquez, M. (2020, March 14). *How Dr. Anthony Fauci became Trump's coronavirus truth teller*. CNN. https://www.cnn.com/2020/03/14/politics/anthony-fauci-trump-coronavirus/index.html

77. Newburger, E. (2020, August 5). *Dr. Fauci says his daughters need security as family continues to get death threats*. CNBC. https://www.cnbc.com/2020/08/05/dr-fauci-says-his-daughters-need-security-as-family-continues-to-get-death-threats.html

78. Gray, L. (2021, May 7). Online trolls take anti-vaxx hate speech to a new level, attacking Houston's Dr. Peter Hotez. *Houston Chronicle*. https://www.houstonchronicle.com/news/houston-texas/health/article/Trolls-take-anti-vaxx-hate-speech-to-a-new-level-16160138.php

79. Whitfield, S. (2021, May 9). *Dr. Peter Hotez targeted by anti-vaxx hate mail*. KHOU. https://www.khou.com/article/news/health/coronavirus/vaccine/hotez-anti-vaxx-hate-mail/285-dd0df03e-ac56-41e3-9ff6-189a67ec3759

80. Farzan, A. N. (2019, August 22). 'Yeah, I pushed you': anti-vaxxer cited for assaulting lawmaker while live-streaming on Facebook. *The Washington Post*. https://www.washingtonpost.com/nation/2019/08/22/yeah-i-pushed-you-anti-vaxxer-cited-assaulting-lawmaker-while-live-streaming-facebook/

81. Lipson, P. (2016, May 5). Alleged medical expert Mike Adams attacks respected cancer doctor. *Forbes*. https://www.forbes.com/sites/peterlipson/2016/05/05/alleged-medical-expert-mike-adams-attacks-respected-cancer-doctor/?sh=331f74495d47

82. Austen, I. (2021, September 21). Vaccine passports roll out, and so do unruly anti-vaccine protests. *The New York Times*. https://www.nytimes.com/2021/09/03/world/canada/vaccine-passports-protests.html

83. D'Emilio, F. (2021, October 13). *Neo-fascists exploit 'no-vax' rage, posing dilemma for Italy*. AP News. https://apnews.com/article/coronavirus-pandemic-europe-italy-rome-violence-2f61aafb5a9c219f5856c3ea4b3273aa

84. Charlton, A., & Gouvy, C. (2021, July 19). *Anger as French protesters compare vaccines to Nazi horrors*. AP News. https://apnews.com/article/europe-health-government-and-politics-coronavirus-pandemic-race-and-ethnicity-e3757c1c51abd7ce56473c455f6f880d

85. O'Connor, P. (2021, September 21). *Australian anti-vaccine, extreme right demonstrators target construction industry*. World Socialist Web Site. https://www.wsws.org/en/articles/2021/09/22/cfme-s22.html

86. BBC News. (2021, April 13). *The anti-vax movement targeting German children*. https://www.bbc.com/news/blogs-trending-56675874

87. Thomasson, E. (2021, August 29). *Thousands protest in Berlin against COVID curbs, vaccines*. Reuters. https://www.reuters.com/world/europe/german-region-plans-tougher-restrictions-unvaccinated-2021-08-29/

88. KTLA Digital Staff. (2021, September 2). *1 arrested in stabbing at anti-vaccine protest outside L.A. City Hall*. KTLA. https://ktla.com/news/local-news/1-arrested-in-stabbing-at-anti-vaccine-protest-outside-l-a-city-hall/

89. Lozano, A. V. (2021, January 30). *Anti-vaccine protest briefly shuts down Dodger Stadium vaccination site*. NBC News. https://www.nbcnews.com/news/us-news/anti-vaccine-protest-briefly-shuts-down-dodger-stadium-vaccination-site-n1256283

90. Salcedo, A. (2021, September 1). A Georgia vaccine site had to

close after protesters bullied health-care workers: 'This is absolutely wrong'. *The Washington Post*. https://www.washingtonpost.com/nation/2021/09/01/georgia-vaccination-site-shuts-down/

91. Sicha, C. (2021, October 4). *Marchers attack coronavirus testing station in Union Square*. Curbed. https://www.curbed.com/2021/10/anti-vaccine-mandate-protest-new-york-city.html

92. Sarkar, A. R. (2021, October 7). Anti-vaxxer killed brother and sister-in-law for 'killing people' with the COVID shot. *The Independent*. https://www.independent.co.uk/news/world/americas/crime/maryland-anti-vaxxer-kills-pharmacists-b1933825.html

93. Planas, A., & Ciechalski, S. (2021, September 3). *Three men with zip ties confront Arizona principal after student told to quarantine*. NBC News. https://www.nbcnews.com/news/us-news/three-men-zip-ties-confront-arizona-principal-after-student-told-n1278504

94. Sarteschi, C., & Blotcky, A. D. (2021, September 8). *Anti-maskers and anti-vaxxers now present a real threat of violence*. Salon.com. https://www.salon.com/2021/09/08/anti-maskers-and-anti-vaxxers-now-present-a-real threat-of-violence/

95. Associated Press. (2021, August 21). *More anti-vaccine, anti-mask demonstrations across U.S. descend into violence and harassment*. KTLA. https://ktla.com/news/nationworld/more-anti-vaccine-anti-mask-demonstrations-across-u-s-descend-into-violence-and-harassment/

96. Paybarah, A. (2021, June 14). Man kills Georgia grocery worker in mask argument, police say. *The New York Times*. https://www.nytimes.com/2021/06/14/us/georgia-shooting-grocery-store-mask.html

97. Madani, D. (2021, January 26). *Wisconsin pharmacist who tried to destroy 500 COVID vaccine doses agrees to plead guilty*. NBC News. https://www.nbcnews.com/news/us-news/wisconsin-pharmacist-who-tried-destroy-500-COVID-vaccine-doses-agrees-n1255770

98. Hollingsworth, H., & Schulte, G. (2021, September 29). *From heroes to the harassed: Health workers being threatened, attacked*. 13NewsNow. https://www.13newsnow.com/article/news/health/coronavirus/virus-outbreak-threatened-health-workers/507-a5b1b5c1-18cc-4e6a-a09a-0321dc6f3c6c

99. Burke, M. (2021, September 28). *Missouri hospital to give staff panic buttons to protect them from violent patients*. NBC News. https://www.nbcnews.com/news/us-news/missouri-hospital-give-staff-panic-buttons-protect-them-violent-patients-n1280245

100. Ebrahimji, A. (2021, September 24). Man attacked female nurse after his wife is vaccinated for COVID without his permission. *The Mercury News*. https://www.mercurynews.com/2021/09/24/man-attacked-female-nurse-after-his-wife-is-vaccinated-for-COVID-without-his-permission/

101. BBC News. (2021, October 5). *Guatemala: Anti-vaccine villagers attack and hold nurses with COVID jabs*. https://www.bbc.com/news/world-latin-america-58801096

102. Morgan, Z. (2021, October 9). *COVID: Anti-vax protesters intimidate teen outside jab centre*. BBC. https://www.bbc.com/news/uk-wales-58856068

103. McDougall, A. J. (2021, October 6). *Beverly Hills anti-vaxxers follow kids, parents to school, shouting 'child abuse'*. The Daily Beast. https://www.thedailybeast.com/beverly-hills-anti-vaxxers-follow-kids-parents-to-school-shouting-child-abuse

104. Wade, P. (2021, August 6). Rep. Taylor Greene encourages greeting vaccine door knockers with guns. *Rolling Stone*. https://www.rollingstone.com/politics/politics-news/marjorie-taylor-greene-vaccine-guns-1208939/

105. Castronuovo, C. (2021, July 9). Cawthorn: Biden door-to-door vaccine strategy could be used to 'take' guns, Bibles. *The Hill*. https://thehill.com/homenews/house/562372-cawthorn-biden-door-to-door-vaccine-strategy-could-be-used-to-take-guns-bibles

106. Skolnik, J. (2021, September 21). *Tucker Carlson warns Pentagon's vaccine mandate is attempt to weed out "men with high testosterone"*. Salon.com. https://www.salon.com/2021/09/21/tucker-carlson-warns-pentagons-vaccine-mandate-is-attempt-to-weed-out-men-with-high-testosterone/

107. Baragona, J. [@justinbaragona]. (2021, September 2). *Tucker Carlson straight up advocates for unvaccinated people to get fake vaccine cards to avoid mandates: "Buying a fake vaccination* [Tweet; thumbnail link to video]. Twitter. https://twitter.com/justinbaragona/status/1433588541745999873?s=11

108. Swenson, A. (2021, April 14). *COVID-19 vaccines are not called 'Luciferase'*. AP News. https://apnews.com/article/fact-checking-afs:Content:10051582995

109. Seddiq, O. (2021, August 3). Top Florida RNC official calls the COVID-19 vaccine a 'mark of the beast' and a 'false god,' report says. *Business Insider*. https://www.businessinsider.com/rnc-official-calls-

vaccine-mark-of-beast-false-god-report-2021-8

110. Mazza, E. (2021, October 5). *GOP lawmaker links coronavirus vaccine to Satan, tentacle monsters and 5G*. Yahoo! News. https://news.yahoo.com/gop-lawmaker-links-coronavirus-vaccine-044628728.html

111. Gleeson, S., & Gilbert, A. C. (2021, September 27). Some say COVID-19 vaccine is the 'mark of the beast.' Is there a connection to the Bible? *USA Today*. https://www.usatoday.com/story/news/nation/2021/09/26/COVID-vaccine-mark-beast-what-book-revelation-says/8255268002/

112. Machicao, M., Limachi, S., & Limachi, S. (2021, May 20). *'Vaccines are satanic': Bolivia battles fake news in inoculation drive*. Reuters. https://www.reuters.com/world/americas/vaccines-are-satanic-bolivia-battles-fake-news-inoculation-drive-2021-05-20/

113. Bischoff, L. A. (2021, August 25). Anti-vaccine protests in Ohio drawing extremists, conspiracy theorists. *The Columbus Dispatch*. https://www.dispatch.com/story/news/2021/08/25/anti-vaccine-protests-ohio-drawing-extremists-conspiracy-theorists/8246980002/

114. Montgomery, B. (2021, September 4). *Three schools forced into lockdown after anti-masker Proud Boys try to infiltrate*. The Daily Beast. https://www.thedailybeast.com/anti-mask-protests-and-proud-boys-shut-down-three-schools-in-vancouver

115. Casiano, L. (2021, September 14). *Los Angeles bars protests at homes after anti-vaccine rally supporters show up at officials' residences*. Fox News. https://www.foxnews.com/us/los-angeles-protests-private-residences-ban

116. Ross, J. (2021, October 13). *'I can't wait for the shooting to start': Texas anti-vaxxer charged with threatening doctor*. The Daily Beast. https://www.thedailybeast.com/scott-eli-harris-charged-with-threatening-to-shoot-doctor-who-urged-public-to-take-coronavirus-vaccine

117. Holzer, H., & Mascareñas, X. (2021, September 30). Rocklin school board meeting shows Placer County tensions. *The Sacramento Bee*. https://www.sacbee.com/opinion/article254625807.html

118. Owens, T. (2021, July 23). *Breast cancer patient attacked by violent anti-mask protest outside clinic*. VICE. https://www.vice.com/en/article/pkbxmg/breast-cancer-patient-attacked-anti-mask-protest

119. O'Rourke, C. (2022, October 19). *Video shows Dr. Anthony Fauci admitting "he failed Americans during the pandemic when unnecessarily forcing masks."* Politifact: The Poynter Institute. https://www.politifact.

com/factchecks/2022/oct/19/instagram-posts/video-shows-fauci-reflecting-early-recommendations/

120. Gillies, R. (2022, February 1). *Swastikas and public urination: anti-vaccine protest draws outrage in Canada.* PBS. https://www.pbs.org/newshour/world/swastikas-and-public-urination-anti-vaccine-protest-draws-outrage-in-canada

121. Torrago, L. [@Loretta_Torrago]. (2022, September 23). *The previous 2 Tweets tell the story of why the Biden Administration is intent on gaslighting: they are going after* [Tweet]. Twitter. https://twitter.com/Loretta_Torrago/status/1573349636181528578

122. Richards, W. (2021, April 29). *Ted Nugent says he's "never been so scared in all my life" than battling COVID-19.* NME. https://www.nme.com/news/music/ted-nugent-says-hes-never-been-so-scared-in-all-my-life-than-battling-COVID-19-2930419

123. File: A man taunts Assembly Member Forrest Dunbar, who is Jewish, with a yellow Star of David at the September 29, 2021 Anchorage Assembly meeting.jpg. (2021, November 7). Wikimedia Commons, the free media repository. Retrieved from https://commons.wikimedia.org/w/index.php?title=File:A_man_taunts_Assembly_Member_Forrest_Dunbar,_who_is_Jewish,_with_a_yellow_Star_of_David_at_the_September_29,_2021_Anchorage_Assembly_meeting.jpg&oldid=606086197

Chapter Nine

1. and Prevention. (n.d.). *COVID data tracker: Nationwide commercial lab pediatric antibody seroprevalence* [Interactive dataset]. U.S. Department of Health and Human Services. Retrieved December 28, 2022, from https://COVID.cdc.gov/COVID-data-tracker/#pediatric-seroprevalence

2. Gundlapalli, A. V., Lavery, A. M., Boehmer, T. K., Beach, M. J., Walke, H. T., Sutton, P. D., & Anderson, R. N. (2021). Death certificate-based ICD-10 diagnosis codes for COVID-19 mortality surveillance - United States, January-December 2020. *Morbidity and Mortality Weekly Report, 70*(14), 523-527. http://dx.doi.org/10.15585/mmwr.mm7014e2

3. and Prevention. (2022, September 16). *Flu vaccines are important for children: Flu can be dangerous for children.* U.S. Department of Health and Human Services. https://www.cdc.gov/flu/highrisk/children.htm#danger

4. and Prevention. (n.d.). *COVID data tracker: Demographic trends of COVID-19 cases and deaths in the US reported to CDC* [Interactive dataset]. U.S. Department of Health and Human Services. Retrieved December 28, 2022, from https://COVID.cdc.gov/COVID-data-tracker/#demographics

5. National Center for Health Statistics. (2022, November 23). *Provisional COVID-19 deaths: Focus on ages 0-18 years* [Dataset]. and Prevention. Retrieved December 28, 2022, from https://data.cdc.gov/NCHS/Provisional-COVID-19-Deaths-Focus-on-Ages-0-18-Yea/nr4s-juj3

6. Bundock, L. (2021, October 3). *Sister of teen who died from COVID-19 says she cries herself to sleep every night.* Sky News. https://news.sky.com/story/sister-of-teen-who-died-from-COVID-19-says-she-cries-herself-to-sleep-every-night-12425395

7. Office of Disease Prevention and Health Promotion. (2022, February 6). *Immunization and infectious diseases.* Healthy People 2020. https://www.healthypeople.gov/2020/topics-objectives/topic/immunization-and-infectious-diseases

8. Gerber, J. S., & Offit, P. A. (2021). COVID-19 vaccines for children. *Science, 374*(6570), 913. https://doi.org/10.1126/science.abn2566

9. and Prevention. (n.d.). *COVID data tracker: COVID-NET Laboratory-confirmed COVID-19 hospitalizations* [Interactive dataset]. U.S. Department of Health and Human Services. Retrieved December 22, 2022, from https://COVID.cdc.gov/COVID-data-tracker/#COVIDnet-hospitalization-network

10. Marks, K. J., Whitaker, M., Anglin, O., Milucky, J., Patel, K., Pham, H., Chai, S. J., Daily Kirley, P., Armistead, I., McLafferty, S., Meek, J., Yousey-Hindes, K., Anderson, E. J., Openo, K. P., Weigel, A., Henderson, J., Tellez Nunez, V., Como-Sabetti, K., Lynfield, R., … Havers, F. P. (2022). Hospitalizations of children and adolescents with laboratory-confirmed COVID-19 — COVID-NET, 14 states, July 2021–January 2022. *Morbidity and Mortality Weekly Report*, *71*(7), 271-278. http://dx.doi.org/10.15585/mmwr.mm7107e4

11. Alberty, E. (2022, January 21). Not so mild? Hospitalizations exploding among Utah infants, children with COVID-19′s Omicron strain. *The Salt Lake Tribune*. https://www.sltrib.com/news/2022/01/21/utahs-COVID/

12. Antoon, J. W., Hall, M., Howard, L. M., Herndon, A., Freundlich, K. L., Grijalva, C. G., & Williams, D. J. (2022). COVID-19 and acute neurologic complications in children. *Pediatrics*, *150*(5), Article 2022058167. https://doi.org/10.1542/peds.2022-058167

13. and Prevention. (2021, September 20). *For parents: Multisystem inflammatory syndrome in children (MIS-C) associated with COVID-19*. U.S. Department of Health and Human Services. https://www.cdc.gov/mis/mis-c.html

14. Dufort, E. M., Koumans, E. H., Chow, E. J., Rosenthal, E. M., Muse, A., Rowlands, J., Barranco, M. A., Maxted, A. M., Rosenberg, E. S., Easton, D., Udo, T., Kumar, J., Pulver, W., Smith, L., Hutton, B., Blog, D., & Zucker, H. (2020). Multisystem inflammatory syndrome in children in New York State. *The New England Journal of Medicine*, *383*, 347-358. https://doi.org/10.1056/NEJMoa2021756

15. and Prevention. (n.d.). *COVID data tracker: Health department-reported cases of multisystem inflammatory syndrome in children (MIS-C) in the United States* [Interactive dataset]. U.S. Department of Health and Human Services. Retrieved December 22, 2022, from https://COVID.cdc.gov/COVID-data-tracker/#mis-national-surveillance

16. Edney, A., & Griffin, R. (2021, May 18). Deadly COVID-Linked syndrome may be undercounted in U.S. kids. *Bloomberg*. https://www.bloomberg.com/news/articles/2021-05-18/deadly-COVID-linked-syndrome-may-be-undercounted-in-u-s-kids

17. Rao, S., Lee, G. M., Razzaghi, H., Lorman, V., Mejias, A., Pajor, N. M., Thacker, D., Webb, R., Dickinson, K., Bailey, L. C., Jhaveri, R., Christakis, D. A., Bennett, T. D., Chen, Y., & Forrest, C. B. (2022). Clinical features and burden of postacute sequelae of SARS-CoV-2 infection in children and adolescents. *JAMA Pediatrics*, *176*(10), 1000-1009. https://doi.org/10.1001/jamapediatrics.2022.2800

18. *Hospitals open pediatric long-haul COVID units as children grapple with lingering virus effects*. (2021, April 12). CBS News. https://www.cbsnews.com/news/COVID-long-haul-hospitals-pediatric-units-children/

19. Topol, E. [@EricTopol]. (2022, September 23). *Two new independent reports, one Norway nationwide, and the other US-based, indicate increased risk of Type 1 (autoimmune) diabetes from* [Tweet; thumbnail link to articles]. Twitter. https://twitter.com/EricTopol/status/1573329404008316929

20. Yasgur, B. S. (2022, November 18). Higher risk for seizures after COVID vs influenza. *Medscape*. https://www.medscape.com/viewarticle/984325#vp_2

21. Heiss, R., Tan, L., Schmidt, S., Regensburger, A. P., Ewert, F., Mammadova, D., Buehler, A., Vogel-Claussen, J., Voskrebenzev, A., Rauh, M., Rompel, O., Nagel, A. M., Lévy, S., Bickelhaupt, S., May, M. S., Uder, M., Metzler, M., Trollmann, R., Woelfle, J., … Knieling, F. (2022). Pulmonary dysfunction after pediatric COVID-19. *Radiology*. Advance online publication. https://doi.org/10.1148/radiol.221250

22. Gottlieb, S. [@ScottGottliebMD]. (2022, June 19). *COVID is novel and pathogenic virus. Most kids will have mild course and recover fine from acute illness. But we* [Tweet]. Twitter. https://twitter.com/ScottGottliebMD/status/1538593124389466113?s=20&t=kcuilbO7FV3rMcLTg_RVnA

23. Soucheray, S. (2019, November 1). *Measles does long-term damage to immune system, studies show*. Center for Infectious Disease Research & Policy. https://www.cidrap.umn.edu/measles/measles-does-long-term-damage-immune-system-studies-show

24. HealthDay. (2022, March 16). Omicron wave had 5 times as many small kids hospitalized compared to Delta. *USNews.com*. https://www.usnews.com/news/health-news/articles/2022-03-16/omicron-wave-had-5-times-as-many-small-kids-hospitalized-compared-to-delta

25. Schreiber, M. (2022, January 5). COVID hospitalizations among US children soar as schools under pressure. *The Guardian*. https://www.theguardian.com/us-news/2022/jan/05/COVID-hospitalizations-us-children-omicron-schools-hospitals

26. Richards, E. (2022, January 4). Not 2020 again? Tell that to parents where COVID cases, test shortages are closing schools. *USA Today*. https://www.usatoday.com/story/news/education/2022/01/03/COVID-omicron-school-closings-home-test/9082871002/

27. Schreiber, M. (2022, March 11). A fifth of all US child COVID deaths occurred during Omicron surge. *The Guardian*. https://www.theguardian.com/world/2022/mar/11/us-child-COVID-deaths-omicron-surge

28. Frenck, R. W., Jr., Klein, N. P., Kitchin, N., Gurtman, A., Absalon, J., Lockhart, S., Perez, J. L., Walter, E. B., Senders, S., Bailey, R., Swanson, K. A., Ma, H., Xu, X., Koury, K., Kalina, W. V., Cooper, D., Jennings, T., Brandon, D. M., Thomas, S. J., … Gruber, W. C. (2021). Safety, immunogenicity, and efficacy of the BNT162b2 COVID-19 vaccine in adolescents. *The New England Journal of Medicine*, *385*, 239-250. https://doi.org/10.1056/NEJMoa2107456

29. Ali, K., Berman, G., Zhou, H., Deng, W., Faughnan, V., Coronado-Voges, M., Ding, B., Dooley, J., Girard, B., Hillebrand, W., Pajon, R., Miller, J. M., Leav, B., & McPhee, R. (2021). Evaluation of mRNA-1273 SARS-CoV-2 vaccine in adolescents. *The New England Journal of Medicine*, *385*, 2241-2251. https://doi.org/10.1056/NEJMoa2109522

30. Walter, E. B., Talaat, K. R., Sabharwal, C., Gurtman, A., Lockhart, S., Paulsen, G. C., Barnett, E. D., Muñoz, F. M., Maldonado, Y., Pahud, B. A., Domachowske, J. B., Simões, E. A. F., Sarwar, U. N., Kitchin, N., Cunliffe, L., Rojo, P., Kuchar, E., Rämet, M., Munjal, I., … Gruber, W. C. (2022). Evaluation of the BNT162b2 COVID-19 vaccine in children 5 to 11 years of age. *The New England Journal of Medicine*, *386*, 35-46. https://doi.org/10.1056/NEJMoa2116298

31. Creech, C. B., Anderson, E., Berthaud, V., Yildirim, I., Atz, A. M., Melendez Baez, I., Finkelstein, D., Pickrell, P., Kirstein, J., Yut, C., Blair, R., Clifford, R. A., Dunn, M., Campbell, J. D., Montefiori, D. C., Tomassini, J. E., Zhao, X., Deng, W., Zhou, H., … Schnyder Ghamloush, S. (2022). Evaluation of mRNA-1273 COVID-19 vaccine in children 6 to 11 years of age. *The New England Journal of Medicine*, *386*, 2011-2023. https://doi.org/10.1056/NEJMoa2203315

32. Pfizer. (2022, July 8). *Pfizer and BioNTech submit a variation to EMA for the vaccination of children 6 months to less than 5 years with COMIRNATY®*. Pfizer. https://www.pfizer.com/news/announcements/pfizer-and-biontech-submit-variation-ema-vaccination-children-6-months-less-than-5-years

33. Anderson, E. J., Creech, C. B., Berthaud, V., Piramzadian, A., Johnson, K. A., Zervos, M., Garner, F., Griffin, C., Palanpurwala, K., Turner, M., Gerber, J., Bennett, R. L., Ali, K., Ampajwala, M., Berman, G., Nayak, J., Chronis, C., Rizzardi, B., Muller, W. J., … Schnyder Ghamloush, S. (2022). Evaluation of mRNA-1273 vaccine in children 6 months to 5 years of age. *The New England Journal of Medicine*, *387*, 1673-1687. https://doi.org/10.1056/NEJMoa2209367

34. Olson, S. M., Newhams, M. M., Halasa, N. B., Price, A. M., Boom, J. A., Sahni, L. C., Pannaraj, P. S., Irby, K., Walker, T. C., Schwartz, S. P., Maddux, A. B., Mack, E. H., Bradford, T. T., Schuster, J. E., Nofziger, R. A., Cameron, M. A., Chiotos, K., Cullimore, M. L., Gertz, S. J., … Overcoming COVID-19 Investigators. (2022). Effectiveness of BNT162b2 vaccine against critical COVID-19 in adolescents. *The New England Journal of Medicine, 386*, 713-723. https://doi.org/10.1056/NEJMoa2117995

35. Zambrano, L. D., Newhams, M. M., Olson, S. M., Halasa, N. B., Price, A. M., Boom, J. A., Sahni, L. C., Kamidani, S., Tarquinio, K. M., Maddux, A. B., Heidemann, S. M., Bhumbra, S. S., Bline, K. E., Nofziger, R. A., Hobbs, C. V., Bradford, T. T., Cvijanovich, N. Z., Irby, K., Mack, E. H., … Overcoming COVID-19 Investigators. (2022). Effectiveness of BNT162b2 (Pfizer-BioNTech) mRNA vaccination against multisystem inflammatory syndrome in children among persons aged 12–18 Years — United States, July–December 2021. *Morbidity and Mortality Weekly Report, 71*(2), 52-58. http://dx.doi.org/10.15585/mmwr.mm7102e1

36. Olson, S. M., Newhams, M. M., Halasa, N. B., Price, A. M., Boom, J. A., Sahni, L. C., Irby, K., Walker, T. C., Schwartz, S. P., Pannaraj, P. S., Maddux, A. B., Bradford, T. T., Nofziger, R. A., Boutselis, B. J., Cullimore, M. L., Mack, E. H., Schuster, J. E., Gertz, S. J., Cvijanovich, N. Z., … Randolph, A. G. (2021, October 22). Effectiveness of Pfizer-BioNTech mRNA vaccination against COVID-19 hospitalization among persons aged 12–18 years — United States, June–September 2021. *Morbidity and Mortality Weekly Report, 70*(42), 1483–1488. http://dx.doi.org/10.15585/mmwr.mm7042e1

37. LaRovere, K. L., Poussaint, T. Y., Young, C. C., Newhams, M. M., Kucukak, S., Irby, K., Kong, M., Schwartz, S. P., Walker, T. C., Bembea, M. M., Wellnitz, K., Havlin, K. M., Cvijanovich, N. Z., Hall, M. W., Fitzgerald, J. C., Schuster, J. E., Hobbs, C. V., Halasa, N. B., Singh, A. R., … Randolph, A. G. (2022, November 7). Changes in distribution of severe neurologic involvement in US pediatric inpatients with COVID-19 or multisystem inflammatory syndrome in children in 2021 vs 2020. *JAMA Neurology*. https://doi.org/10.1001/jamaneurol.2022.3881

38. Castelli, J. M., Rearte, A., Olszevicki,, S., Voto, C., Del Valle Juarez, M., Pesce, M., Iovane, A. N., Paz, M., Chaparro, M. E., Buyayisqui, M. P., Belén Markiewicz, M., Landoni, M., Giovacchini, C. M., & Vizzotti, C. (2022, November 30). Effectiveness of mRNA-1273, BNT162b2, and BBIBP-CorV vaccines against infection and mortality in children in Argentina, during predominance of delta and omicron COVID-19 variants: test negative, case-control study. *BMJ, 379*, e073070. https://doi.org/10.1136/bmj-2022-073070

39. Delahoy, M. J., Ujamaa, D., Whitaker, M., O'Halloran, A., Anglin, O., Burns, E., Cummings, C., Holstein, R., Kambhampati, A. K., Milucky, J., Patel, K., Pham, H., Taylor, C. A., Chai, S. J., Reingold, A., Alden, N. B., Kawasaki, B., Meek, J., Yousey-Hindes, K., … Havers, F. P. (2021). Hospitalizations associated with COVID-19 among children and adolescents — COVID-NET, 14 states, March 1, 2020–August 14, 2021. *Morbidity and Mortality Weekly Report*, *70*(36), 1255–1260. http://dx.doi.org/10.15585/mmwr.mm7036e2

40. Messiah, S. E., Hao, T., DeSantis, S. M., Swartz, M. D., Talebi, Y., Kohl, H. W. I., Zhang, S., Valerio-Shewmaker, M., Yaseen, A., Kelder, S. H., Ross, J., Gonzalez, M. O., Wu, L., Padilla, L. N., Lopez, K. R., Lakey, D., Shuford, J. A., Pont, S. J., & Boerwinkle, E. (2022). Comparison of persistent symptoms following SARS-CoV-2 infection by antibody status in nonhospitalized children and adolescents. *The Pediatric Infectious Disease Journal*, *41*(10), e409-e417. https://doi.org/10.1097/INF.0000000000003653

41. Wanga, V., Gerdes, M. E., Shi, D. S., Choudhary, R., Dulski, T. M., Hsu, S., Idubor, O. I., Webber, B. J., Wendel, A. M., Agathis, N. T., Anderson, K., Boyles, T., Chiu, S. K., Click, E. S., Da Silva, J., Dupont, H., Evans, M., Gold, J. A. W., Haston, J., … Siegel, D. A. (2021). Characteristics and clinical outcomes of children and adolescents aged <18 years hospitalized with COVID-19 — Six hospitals, United States, July–August 2021. *Morbidity and Mortality Weekly Report*, *70*(5152), 1766–1772. http://dx.doi.org/10.15585/mmwr.mm705152a3

42. Lutrick, K., Rivers, P., Yoo, Y. M., Grant, L., Hollister, J., Jovel, K., Khan, S., Lowe, A., Baccam, Z., Hanson, H., Olsho, L. E. W., Fowlkes, A., Caban-Martinez, A. J., Porter, C., Yoon, S., Meece, J., Gaglani, M., Burns, J., Mayo Lamberte, J., … Burgess, J. L. (2021). Interim estimate of vaccine effectiveness of BNT162b2 (Pfizer-BioNTech) vaccine in preventing SARS-CoV-2 infection among adolescents aged 12–17 years — Arizona, July–December 2021. *Morbidity and Mortality Weekly Report*, *70*(5152), 1761–1765. http://dx.doi.org/10.15585/mmwr.mm705152a2

43. Levy, M., Recher, M., Hubert, H., Javouhey, E., Fléchelles, O., Leteurtre, S., & Angoulvant, F. (2022). Multisystem inflammatory syndrome in children by COVID-19 vaccination status of adolescents in France. *JAMA*, *327*(3), 281-283. https://doi.org/10.1001/jama.2021.23262

44. Nygaard, U., Holm, M., Hartling, U. B., Glenthøj, J., Samsø Schmidt, L., Brit Nordly, S., Thaarup Matthesen, A., von Linstow, M.-L., & Espenhain, L. (2022). Incidence and clinical phenotype of multisystem inflammatory syndrome in children after infection with the SARS-CoV-2 Delta variant by vaccination status: A Danish nationwide prospective

cohort study. *The Lancet Child & Adolescent Health*, *6*(7), 459-465. https://doi.org/10.1016/S2352-4642(22)00100-6

45. Chang, J. C., & Son, M. B. F. (2022). When vaccine adverse event reporting generates hope, not fear. *The Lancet Child & Adolescent Health*, *6*(5), 281-282. https://doi.org/10.1016/S2352-4642(22)00061-X

46. Fleming-Dutra, K. E., Britton, A., Shang, N., Derado, G., Link-Gelles, R., Accorsi, E. K., Smith, Z. R., Miller, J., Verani, J. R., & Schrag, S. J. (2022). Association of prior BNT162b2 COVID-19 vaccination with symptomatic SARS-CoV-2 infection in children and adolescents during Omicron predominance. *JAMA*, *327*(22), 2210-2219. https://doi.org/10.1001/jama.2022.7493

47. Yousaf, A. R., Cortese, M. M., Taylor, A. W., Broder, K. R., Oster, M. E., Wong, J. M., Guh, A. Y., McCormick, D. W., Kamidani, S., Schlaudecker, E. P., Edwards, K. M., Creech, C. B., Staat, M. A., Belay, E. D., Marquez, P., Su, J. R., Salzman, M. B., Thompson, D., Campbell, A. P., & MIS-C Investigation Authorship Group. (2022). Reported cases of multisystem inflammatory syndrome in children aged 12–20 years in the USA who received a COVID-19 vaccine, December, 2020, through August, 2021: A surveillance investigation. *The Lancet Child & Adolescent Health*, *6*(5), 303-312. https://doi.org/10.1016/S2352-4642(22)00028-1

48. Tan, S. H. X., Cook, A. R., Heng, D., Ong, B., Lye, D. C., & Tan, K. B. (2022). Effectiveness of BNT162b2 vaccine against Omicron in children 5 to 11 years of age. *The New England Journal of Medicine*, *387*, 525-532. https://doi.org/10.1056/NEJMoa2203209

49. Price, A. M., Olson, S. M., Newhams, M. M., Halasa, N. B., Boom, J. A., Sahni, L. C., Pannaraj, P. S., Irby, K., Bline, K. E., Maddux, A. B., Nofziger, R. A., Cameron, M. A., Walker, T. C., Schwartz, S. P., Mack, E. H., Smallcomb, L., Schuster, J. E., Hobbs, C. V., Kamidani, S., … Randolph, A. G. (2022). BNT162b2 protection against the Omicron variant in children and adolescents. *The New England Journal of Medicine*, *386*, 1899-1909. https://doi.org/10.1056/NEJMoa2202826

50. Lin, D.-Y., Gu, Y., Xu, Y., Zeng, D., Wheeler, B., Young, H., Khan Sunny, S., & Moore, Z. (2022). Effects of vaccination and previous infection on Omicron infections in children [Supplementary appendix]. *The New England Journal of Medicine*, *387*, 1141-1143. https://doi.org/10.1056/NEJMc2209371

51. Cohen-Stavi, C. J., Magen, O., Barda, N., Yaron, S., Peretz, A., Netzer, D., Giaquinto, C., Judd, A., Leibovici, L., Hernán, M. A., Lipsitch, M., Reis, B. Y., Balicer, R. D., & Dagan, N. (2022). BNT162b2 vaccine effectiveness against Omicron in children 5 to 11 years of age. *The New*

England Journal of Medicine, *387*, 227-236. https://doi.org/10.1056/NEJMoa2205011

52. Dorabawila, V., Hoefer, D., Bauer, U. E., Bassett, M. T., Lutterloh, E., & Rosenberg, E. S. (2022). Risk of infection and hospitalization among vaccinated and unvaccinated children and adolescents in New York after the emergence of the Omicron variant. *JAMA*, *327*(22), 2242-2244. https://doi.org/10.1001/jama.2022.7319

53. Klein, N. P., Stockwell, M. S., Demarco, M., Gaglani, M., Kharbanda, A. B., Irving, S. A., Rao, S., Grannis, S. J., Dascomb, K., Murthy, K., Rowley, E. A., Dalton, A. F., DeSilva, M. B., Dixon, B. E., Natarajan, K., Stenehjem, E., Naleway, A. L., Lewis, N., Ong, T. C., … Verani, J. R. (2022). Effectiveness of COVID-19 Pfizer-BioNTech BNT162b2 mRNA vaccination in preventing COVID-19–associated emergency department and urgent care encounters and hospitalizations among nonimmunocompromised children and adolescents aged 5–17 years — VISION Network, 10 States, April 2021–January 2022. *Morbidity and Mortality Weekly Report*, *71*(9), 352-358. http://dx.doi.org/10.15585/mmwr.mm7109e3

54. Shi, D. S., Whitaker, M., Marks, K. J., Anglin, O., Milucky, J., Patel, K., Pham, H., Chai, S. J., Kawasaki, B., Meek, J., Anderson, E. J., Weigel, A., Henderson, J., Lynfield, R., Ropp, S. L., Muse, A., Bushey, S., Billing, L. M., Sutton, M., … COVID-NET Surveillance Team. (2022). Hospitalizations of children aged 5–11 years with laboratory-confirmed COVID-19 — COVID-NET, 14 States, March 2020–February 2022. *Morbidity and Mortality Weekly Report*, *71*(16), 574-581. http://dx.doi.org/10.15585/mmwr.mm7116e1

55. Miller, A. D., Yousef, A. R., Bornstein, E., Wu, M. J., Lindsey, K., Melgar, M., Oster, M. E., Zambrano, L. D., & Campbell, A. P. (2022). Multisystem inflammatory syndrome in children during severe acute respiratory syndrome coronavirus 2 (SARS-CoV-2) Delta and Omicron variant circulation - United States, July 2021-January 2022. *Clinical Infectious Diseases*, *75*(Supplement 2), S303-S307. https://doi.org/10.1093/cid/ciac471

56. and Prevention. (2022, December 8). *Updates on multisystem inflammatory syndrome in children (MIS-C): Epidemiology, case definition, and COVID-19 vaccination* [PowerPoint Presentation; slide 54]. U.S. Department of Health and Human Services. https://emergency.cdc.gov/coca/ppt/2022/120822_slides.pdf

57. Vergales, J., & Gandhi, M. (2021, November 3). The childhood vaccine debate ignores a crucial point: Kids aren't supposed to die. *Time*. https://time.com/6113220/why-kids-should-get-COVID-19-vaccine/

58. Hammond, J. R. (2020, January 24). *NY Times deceives about the odds of dying from measles in the US*. Children's Health Defense. https://childrenshealthdefense.org/news/ny-times-deceives-about-the-odds-of-dying-from-measles-in-the-us/

59. America's Frontline Doctors. (2021, May 21). *Physicians group files motion to halt use of COVID vaccines in children*. The Defender: Children's Health Defense News & Views. https://childrenshealthdefense.org/defender/americas-frontline-doctors-files-motion-halt-COVID-vaccines-children/

60. Lavine, J. S., Bjornstad, O., & Antia, R. (2021). Vaccinating children against SARS-CoV-2. *BMJ*, *373*, n1197. https://doi.org/10.1136/bmj.n1197

61. Gorski, D. (2020, January 27). Harassment: The price of defending science-based medicine. *Respectful Insolence*. https://www.respectfulinsolence.com/2020/01/27/harassment-defending-science-based-medicine/

62. Prasad, V. [@VPrasadMDMPH]. (2021, January 13). *Let me be perfectly clear: children DO NOT NEED a sars-cov-2 vaccine before they are permitted to return to normal* [Tweet]. Twitter. https://twitter.com/VPrasadMDMPH/status/1349427724834664448

63. Prasad, V. (2021, February 3). Kids don't need COVID-19 vaccines to return to school. *STAT*. https://www.statnews.com/2021/02/03/kids-dont-need-COVID-19-vaccines-to-return-to-school/

64. and Prevention. (n.d.). *Influenza-associated pediatric mortality* [Interactive dataset]. U.S. Department of Health and Human Services. Retrieved December 3, 2022, from https://gis.cdc.gov/grasp/fluview/pedfludeath.html

65. and Prevention. (n.d.). *COVID data tracker: New admissions of patients with confirmed COVID-19, United States: Aug 01, 2020 - Dec 02, 2022* [Interactive dataset]. U.S. Department of Health and Human Services. Retrieved December 2, 2022, from https://COVID.cdc.gov/COVID-data-tracker/#new-hospital-admissions

66. Damania, Z. (Host). (2021, February 4). Should we vaccinate kids for COVID? & more [Video podcast episode]. In *ZDoggMD: Slightly funnier than placebo*. https://zdoggmd.com/vinay-prasad-7/

67. Pegden, W., Prasad, V., & Baral, S. (2021, May 7). COVID vaccines for children should not get emergency use authorization. *The BMJ Opinion*. https://blogs.bmj.com/bmj/2021/05/07/COVID-vaccines-for-children-

should-not-get-emergency-use-authorization/

68. Wallach, T. [@md_wallach]. (2022, July 21). *Honestly @ucsf I do not see how you reasonably maintain an association with someone this unprofessional* [Tweet; image attached]. Twitter. https://twitter.com/md_wallach/status/1550229581285695491

69. Ioannidis, J. P. A. (2020, March 17). A fiasco in the making? As the coronavirus pandemic takes hold, we are making decisions without reliable data. *STAT*. https://www.statnews.com/2020/03/17/a-fiasco-in-the-making-as-the-coronavirus-pandemic-takes-hold-we-are-making-decisions-without-reliable-data/

70. Ioannidis, J. P. A. (2020, April 17). *Perspectives on the pandemic* [Episode 4; video podcast interview transcript]. The Press and the Public. https://www.thepressandthepublic.com/post/perspectives-on-the-pandemic-iv

71. Claus, P. (2020, June 27). *Up to 300 million people may be infected by COVID-19, Stanford guru John Ioannidis says*. Greek Reporter. https://greekreporter.com/2020/06/27/up-to-300-million-people-may-be-infected-by-COVID-19-stanford-guru-john-ioannidis-says/

72. Kher, S. (2021, December 12). Our ability to block COVID infections, even with vaccines, is short-lived: Dr Sunetra Gupta. *Times of India*. https://timesofindia.indiatimes.com/home/sunday-times/all-that-matters/our-ability-to-block-COVID-infections-even-with-vaccines-is-short-lived-dr-sunetra-gupta/articleshow/88228611.cms

73. Menchaca, M. (2022, March 23). Former Trump COVID-19 adviser cites vaccine 'safety concerns' in UT address. *Austin American-Statesman*. https://www.statesman.com/story/news/2022/03/23/scott-adams-ut-austin-falsely-claims-vaccines-safety-concerns-children/7124582001/

74. Atlas, S. W. (2020, June 23). *The doctor is in: Scott Atlas and the efficacy of lockdowns, social distancing, and closings* [Interview transcript]. Hoover Institution. https://www.hoover.org/research/doctor-scott-atlas-and-efficacy-lockdowns-social-distancing-and-closings-1

75. Høeg, T. B., McBride, L., Krug, A., & Gandhi, M. (2021, May 26). It's time for children to finally get back to normal life. *The Washington Post*. https://www.washingtonpost.com/opinions/2021/05/26/its-time-children-finally-get-back-normal-life/

76. Mandrola, J. [@drjohnm]. (2020, December 29). *No, Young Adults Should Not Live in Fear from #COVID19 A rebuttal to a research letter in JAMA. WIth @andrewfoy82* [Tweet; thumbnail link to article]. Twitter.

https://twitter.com/drjohnm/status/1343906972861669376

77. Mandrola, J. [@drjohnm]. (2021, March 10). *Ky has vaccinated about 1 in 3 older people. CT has done even better. The vaccine squelches severe cases Millions* [Tweet]. Twitter. https://twitter.com/drjohnm/status/1369820360791711744

78. Mandrola, J. [@drjohnm]. (2021, April 23). *You know there is a diff discussion here. -for the vast majority of at-risk adults mRNA vaccines turn SARS-CoV-2 into* [Tweet]. Twitter. https://twitter.com/drjohnm/status/1385704101799989258

79. Mandrola, J. [@drjohnm]. (2021, April 23). *Why is this wrong thinking? I don't really think folks have considered how amazingly protective the mRNA vaccines are for* [Tweet; thumbnail link to tweet]. Twitter. https://twitter.com/drjohnm/status/1385705128381009926

80. Damania, Z. (Host). (2021, April 14). Focused protection for COVID [Video podcast episode]. In *ZDoggMD: Slightly funnier than placebo*. https://zdoggmd.com/jay-bhattacharya-2/

81. Damania, Z. (Host). (2021, May 24). Least wrong about COVID? [Video podcast episode]. In *ZDoggMD: Slightly funnier than placebo*. https://zdoggmd.com/marty-makary-3/

82. Krug, A., & Prasad, V. (2022, February 2). *Should we let children catch Omicron? Restrictions in schools must never return*. UnHerd. https://unherd.com/2022/02/should-we-let-children-catch-omicron/

83. Bhattacharya, J. (2021, May 11). *The Ingraham Angle* [Video interview transcript]. Fox News. https://www.foxnews.com/transcript/ingraham-dems-are-super-spreaders-of-fear-false-information-and-hypocrisy

84. Kulldorff, M. (2022, March 8). *Should I vaccinate my child against COVID?* Brownstone Institute. https://brownstone.org/articles/should-i-vaccinate-my-child-against-COVID/

85. Ladapo, J. A. [@FLSurgeonGen]. (2022, March 8). *As Surgeon General, I cannot recommend that healthy children receive the COVID-19 vaccine. When their overall risk is low, &* [Tweet]. Twitter. https://twitter.com/FLSurgeonGen/status/1501330123856891907

86. Ladapo, J. A. [@FLSurgeonGen]. (2022, October 29). *Parents, don't hold your breath… CDC & FDA abandoned their posts. Keep sticking with your intuition and keep those COVID* [Tweet]. Twitter. https://twitter.com/FLSurgeonGen/status/1586327074712604672

87. Prasad, V. [@VPrasadMDMPH]. (2021, May 8). *Vast majority of kids recover quickly from SARS cov 2. And after all adults are vaccinated their risk of COVID* [Tweet; thumbnail link to tweet]. Twitter. https://twitter.com/vprasadmdmph/status/1391196541705097224

88. Prasad, V. [@VPrasadMDMPH]. (2022, July 21). *Here is the risk to kids from this NEJM paper I've blown up the risk of hospitalization Getting O2 while* [Tweet; image attached; thumbnail link to tweet]. Twitter. https://twitter.com/vprasadmdmph/status/1550196543528898561

89. Jennifer Margulis. (2022, May 16). In *RationalWiki*. https://rationalwiki.org/wiki/Jennifer_Margulis

90. Palfreman, J. (Writer & Director) (Director). (2010, April 27). The vaccine war (Season 28, Episode 8) [TV series episode]. In D. Fanning & M. Sullivan (Executive Producers), *Frontline*. Public Broadcasting Service (PBS). https://www.pbs.org/wgbh/frontline/documentary/vaccines/transcript/

91. GMI Reporter. (2018, October 26). The Unreported health benefits of measles. *GreenMedInfo*. https://greenmedinfo.com/blog/unreported-health-benefits-measles

92. Messenger, S. (2012). *Melanie's marvelous measles*. Trafford Publishing.

93. Feder Ostrov, B. (2021, September 28). *Conspiracy theory doctor surrenders medical license*. CalMatters. https://calmatters.org/health/2021/02/conspiracy-theory-doctor-surrenders-medical-license/

94. Cowan, T. (2018). *Vaccines, autoimmunity, and the changing nature of childhood illness*. Chelsea Green Publishing.

95. G. D. (2013, November 7). #783: Suzanne Humphries. *Encyclopedia of American Loons*. http://americanloons.blogspot.com/2013/11/783-suzanne-humphries.html

96. Humphries, S. (n.d.). The benefits of having a natural measles infection. *Association of Natural Health*. Retrieved December 2, 2022, from http://www.aonh.org/Blogs/Details/3

97. Brogan, K. (n.d.). Vaccination: Your body. Your baby. Their flu. *Kelly Brogan, MD*. https://www.kellybroganmd.com/blog/vaccination-your-body-your-baby-their-flu

98. Columbia University's Mailman School of Public Health. (2020, May 27). Low vaccination rates and 'measles parties' fueled 2019 measles outbreak in NYC: Study is a wake-up call for the potential of another such outbreak, as vaccination rates plummet during

the COVID-19 pandemic. *ScienceDaily*. www.sciencedaily.com/releases/2020/05/200527181329.htm

99. Bosman, J. (2019, March 21). Remember chickenpox parties? Kentucky governor says he let his 9 children get the virus. *The New York Times*. https://www.nytimes.com/2019/03/21/us/kentucky-governor-chickenpox.html

100. Howard, J. (2022, February 11). Should an infectious disease epidemiologist comment on child vaccination? Yes! *Science-Based Medicine*. https://sciencebasedmedicine.org/unkind-largely-unqualified-and-highly-judgmental/

101. Sharff, K. (2022, October 1). Reflections of an infectious disease physician: Where COVID-19 and my personal world collide. *Sensible Medicine*. https://sensiblemed.substack.com/p/reflections-of-an-infectious-disease

102. Prasad, V. (2022, October 1). I am going to mask because I want to get fewer colds & other flawed ideas. *Vinay Prasad's Observations and Thoughts*. https://vinayprasadmdmph.substack.com/p/i-am-going-to-mask-because-i-want

103. Evans, C., & Knox, C. C. (2022, December 8). *"Tripledemic" of flu, RSV and COVID-19 strains hospitals, worries doctors as cases spike*. CBS News. https://www.cbsnews.com/news/tripledemic-flu-rsv-COVID-19-strains-hospitals-worries-doctors-cases-spike/

104. National Cancer Institute. (2022, September 12). *HPV and cancer*. U.S. Department of Health and Human Services. https://www.cancer.gov/about-cancer/causes-prevention/risk/infectious-agents/hpv-and-cancer

105. Soldan, S. S., & Lieberman, P. M. (2023). Epstein–Barr virus and multiple sclerosis. *Nature Reviews Microbiology*, *21*, 51-64. https://doi.org/10.1038/s41579-022-00770-5

106. Holley, P. (2021, November 23). Doctors gave her a choice: Let COVID-19 kill her child, or amputate his limbs. *Texas Monthly*. https://www.texasmonthly.com/news-politics/COVID-19-child-rare-condition/

107. Salcedo, A. (2021, June 9). A doctor falsely told lawmakers vaccines magnetize people: 'They can put a key on their forehead. It sticks.' *The Washington Post*. https://www.washingtonpost.com/nation/2021/06/09/sherri-tenpenny-magnetized-vaccine-ohio/

108. Tenpenny, S. (2007, September 3). *Who are the real charlatans?* EzineArticles. https://ezinearticles.com/?Who-Are-the-real Charlatans?&id=715162

109. Shaffer, B. (2015, April 24). First they came for the anti-vaxxers. *Age of Autism*. https://www.ageofautism.com/2015/04/first-they-came-for-the-anti-vaxxers-by-bretigne-schaffer.html

110. Iannelli, V. (2018, April 15). *When was the last measles death in the United States?* Vaxopedia. https://vaxopedia.org/2018/04/15/when-was-the-last-measles-death-in-the-united-states/

111. Autism Action Network. (n.d.). *USA take action: Stop FDA approval of Moderna COVID shots for toddlers*. VoterVoice. Retrieved December 2, 2022, from https://votervoice.net/AUTISMACTION/Campaigns/93654/Respond

112. Makary, M. (2021, June 10). Think twice before giving the COVID vax to healthy kids — Based on the data to date, there's no compelling case for it right now. *MedPage Today*. https://www.medpagetoday.com/opinion/marty-makary/93029

113. FAIR Health. (2020, November 11). *Risk factors for COVID-19 mortality among privately insured patients* [PDF file]. https://s3.amazonaws.com/media2.fairhealth.org/whitepaper/asset/Risk%20Factors%20for%20COVID-19%20Mortality%20among%20Privately%20Insured%20Patients%20-%20A%20Claims%20Data%20Analysis%20-%20A%20FAIR%20Health%20White%20Paper.pdf

114. Makary, M. (2021, July 19). The flimsy evidence behind the CDC's push to vaccinate children. *Wall Street Journal*. https://www.wsj.com/articles/cdc-COVID-19-coronavirus-vaccine-side-effects-hospitalization-kids-11626706868

115. Makary, M., & Saphier, N. (2021, March 29). The case for vaccinating kids against COVID-19. *The Day*. https://www.theday.com/op-ed/20210329/the-case-for-vaccinating-kids-against-COVID-19/

116. American Academy of Pediatrics & Children's Hospital Association. (2022, January 13). *Children and COVID-19: State data report*. https://downloads.aap.org/AAP/PDF/AAP%20and%20CHA%20-%20Children%20and%20COVID-19%20State%20Data%20Report%201.13.22%20FINAL.pdf

117. Coscetti, A., & Nexstar Media Wire. (2020, November 6). *Parents say 5-year-old daughter who died from COVID-19 was 'perfectly healthy'*. WFLA News Channel 8. https://www.wfla.com/community/health/coronavirus/parents-say-5-year-old-daughter-who-died-from-COVID-19-was-perfectly-healthy/

118. Doran, E. (2021, January 2). *4-year-old CNY boy who died of COVID complications had been healthy: 'I lost my miracle baby'*. Syracuse.com.

https://www.syracuse.com/coronavirus/2021/01/4-year-old-cny-boy-who-died-of-COVID-complications-had-been-healthy-i-lost-my-miracle-baby.html

119. *Child under 10 with no underlying conditions dies from COVID*. (2021, April 26). AP News. https://apnews.com/article/health-nursing-homes-coronavirus-ef2b3a7b554cc7252e96674e021e1c50

120. Nelson, J. (2020, July 20). *Child COVID-19 victim was 9 months old, had no underlying conditions*. Bring Me The News. https://bringmethenews.com/minnesota-news/child-COVID-19-victim-was-9-months-old-had-no-underlying-conditions

121. *Child with no underlying conditions is latest COVID-19 death in Hamilton County*. (2021, December 1). WRCB. https://www.wrcbtv.com/story/42283572/child-with-no-underlying-conditions-is-latest-COVID19-death-in-hamilton-county

122. Lynch, J., & Waldrop, T. (2020, August 6). *A 7-year-old boy in Georgia died of COVID-19, the youngest victim in the state*. CNN. https://www.cnn.com/2020/08/06/us/georgia-boy-COVID-19-death/index.html

123. *Kimora "Kimmie" Lynum, 9, is youngest COVID-19 victim in Florida*. (2020, July 27). ABC7 New York. https://abc7ny.com/9-year-old-girl-dies-coronavirus-kimora-kimmie-lynum-kimmie-putnam-county/6336608/

124. Moseley, M. (2020, April 25). *5-year-old daughter of Detroit first responders dies from coronavirus complications*. ABC News. https://abcnews.go.com/US/year-daughter-detroit-responders-dies-coronavirus-complications/story?id=70256558

125. Nagy, L. (2021, May 7). *15-year-old dies of COVID-19 just 2 days after diagnosis*. ABC7. https://abc7.com/15-year-old-teen-COVID19-diagnosis-dies-COVID-illinois/10593603/

126. Bixler, D., Miller, A. D., Mattison, C. P., Taylor, B., Komatsu, K., Peterson Pompa, X., Moon, S., Karmarkar, E., Liu, C. Y., Openshaw, J. J., Plotzker, R. E., Rosen, H. E., Alden, N., Kawasaki, B., Siniscalchi, A., Leapley, A., Drenzek, C., Tobin-D'Angelo, M., Kauerauf, J., … Pediatric Mortality Investigation Team. (2020). SARS-CoV-2–associated deaths among persons aged <21 years — United States, February 12–July 31, 2020. *Morbidity and Mortality Weekly Report*, *69*(37), 1324-1329. http://dx.doi.org/10.15585/mmwr.mm6937e4

127. Cook, L., & Hickey, M. (2022, January 8). *NY officials plead COVID vaccinations after pediatric hospitalizations jump 700%*. PIX11. https://pix11.com/news/coronavirus/ny-officials-plead-vaccinations-after-pediatric-hospitalizations-for-COVID-jump-700/

128. Hobbs, C. V., Woodworth, K., Young, C. C., Jackson, A. M., Newhams, M. M., Dapul, H., Maamari, M., Hall, M. W., Maddux, A. B., Singh, A. R., Schuster, J. E., Rowan, C. M., Fitzgerald, J. C., Irby, K., Kong, M., Mack, E. H., Staat, M. A., Cvijanovich, N. Z., Bembea, M. M., … Randolph, A. G. (2022). Frequency, characteristics and complications of COVID-19 in hospitalized infants. *The Pediatric Infectious Disease Journal, 41*(3), e81-e86. https://doi.org/10.1097/INF.0000000000003435

129. Prasad, V. (2021, December 5). Risk of hospitalization, severe disease, and mortality due to COVID-19 in Kids. *Vinay Prasad's Observations and Thoughts*. https://vinayprasadmdmph.substack.com/p/risk-of-hospitalization-severe-disease

130. American Cancer Society. (2019, February 12). *Survival rates for childhood leukemias*. https://www.cancer.org/cancer/leukemia-in-children/detection-diagnosis-staging/survival-rates.html

131. @Mangs@mastodon.lol [@Mangalang1]. (2021, July 20). *Can you please explain to me personally how my child's life, with a pre-existing condition, is less valuable and her* [Tweet]. Twitter. https://twitter.com/Mangalang1/status/1417604576778276872

132. *Number of intubated children with COVID-19 at MUSC increasing*. (2021, September 14). Live 5 News. https://www.live5news.com/2021/09/14/number-intubated-children-with-COVID-19-musc-increasing/

133. Torrago, L. [@Loretta_Torrago]. (2021, July 20). *These Tweets from @MonicaGandhi9 & @tracybethhoeg are shameful. 1. The zero mortality rate is based on a sample of THREE* [Tweet; attached photo]. Twitter. https://twitter.com/loretta_torrago/status/1417611796576358402?s=11

134. Badash, D. (2021, July 23). *GOP senator dismisses deaths of 400 children from COVID after assuming they all had 'underlying conditions'*. The New Civil Rights Movement. https://www.thenewcivilrightsmovement.com/2021/07/gop-senator-dismisses-deaths-of-400-children-from-COVID-after-assuming-they-all-had-underlying-conditions/

135. Carlson, T. (2021, July 19). *Tucker Carlson Tonight* [Video transcript]. Fox News. https://www.foxnews.com/transcript/tucker-democrats-claim-that-were-in-a-pandemic-of-the-unvaccinated-is-simply-untrue

136. Joseph Ladapo. (2022, December 23). In *Wikipedia*. https://en.wikipedia.org/w/index.php?title=Joseph_Ladapo&oldid=1129132958

137. Florida Department of Health. (2022, March 8). *Florida Department*

of Health issues new guidance regarding COVID-19 vaccination recommendations for children. Florida Health. https://www.floridahealth.gov/newsroom/2022/03/20220308-FDOH-COVID19-vaccination-recommendations-children.pr.html

138. Hodgson, I. (2022, March 11). COVID researchers: Florida 'cherry-picked' our work in kid vaccine recommendation. *Tampa Bay Times*. https://www.tampabay.com/news/health/2022/03/11/COVID-researchers-say-florida-cherry-picked-facts-in-child-vaccine-advice/

139. Pettypiece, S. (2022, June 16). *Florida is the only state that hasn't ordered COVID vaccines for kids under 5*. CNBC. https://www.cnbc.com/2022/06/16/florida-is-the-only-state-that-hasnt-ordered-COVID-vaccines-for-kids-under-5.html

140. American Academy of Pediatrics. [@AmerAcadPeds]. (2020, December 1). *Using the fireplace more as temperatures drop this winter? Here are tips on smoke detectors and how to prepare your* [Tweet; image attached]. Twitter. https://twitter.com/AmerAcadPeds/status/1333788775705575428

141. Mason, A. (2019, February 4). Measles scare tactics hurt us all. *GreenMedInfo*. https://greenmedinfo.com/blog/measles-scare-tactics-hurt-us-all

142. Gibson, K. (2021, February 3). *Tip-over TVs and furniture have killed 450 children since 2000*. CBS News. https://www.cbsnews.com/news/furniture-tipover-deaths-2000-2019/

143. Children's Health Defense. (2021, June 14). *Top ten reasons not to let your child get a COVID shot*. https://childrenshealthdefense.org/child-health-topics/known-culprits/vaccines-culprit/top-ten-reasons-not-to-let-your-child-get-a-COVID-shot/

144. Goldstick, J. E., Cunningham, R. M., & Carter, P. M. (2022). Current causes of death in children and adolescents in the United States. *The New England Journal of Medicine, 386*, 1955-1956. https://www.nejm.org/doi/full/10.1056/nejmc2201761

145. Kogan, V., & Prasad, V. (2022, January 26). *COVID testing of asymptomatic students doesn't make kids safer.* Slate. https://slate.com/technology/2022/01/COVID-testing-asymptomatic-students.html

146. and Prevention. (2022, October 7). *Drowning facts*. U.S. Department of Health and Human Services. https://www.cdc.gov/drowning/facts/index.html

147. and Prevention. (2022, October 14). *Child passenger safety: Get the facts*. U.S. Department of Health and Human Services. https://www.cdc.gov/transportationsafety/child_passenger_safety/cps-factsheet.html

148. National Center for Education Statistics. (2022). Violent deaths at school and away from school and school shootings. *Condition of Education*. Retrieved December 3, 2022, from U.S. Department of Education, Institute of Education Sciences. Retrieved December 2, 2022, from https://nces.ed.gov/programs/coe/indicator/a01

149. Choo, E. [@choo_ek]. (2021, October 12). *It's odd to see comparisons between children and older adults, as if the health indicators and expectations are the same* [Tweet]. Twitter. https://twitter.com/choo_ek/status/1447943035325538304

150. Ogbe, V. (2022, February 10). *'She loved with all her heart' Knoxville parents speak about the loss of their 7-year-old to COVID-19*. WKRN. https://www.wkrn.com/news/tennessee-news/she-loved-with-all-her-heart-knoxville-parents-speak-about-the-loss-of-their-7-year-old-to-COVID-19/

151. *Unvaccinated 7-year-old dies 72 hours after testing positive for COVID-19*. (2022, February 19). Newsroom Panama. https://www.newsroompanama.com/news/unvaccinated-7-year-old-dies-72-hours-after-testing-positive-for-COVID-19

152. Rogers, T. (2021, November 5). *Pfizer COVID vaccine fails risk-benefit analysis in children 5 to 11*. The Defender: Children's Health Defense News & Views. https://childrenshealthdefense.org/defender/fda-pfizer-COVID-vaccine-risk-benefit-analysis-nntv-children/

153. Howard, J. (2022, February 5). 1,200 is more than 6. *Science-Based Medicine*. https://sciencebasedmedicine.org/1200-is-more-than-6/

154. Burn-Murdoch, J. [@jburnmurdoch]. (2022, January 31). *And as many have said, we must also remember COVID is much more transmissible than flu, so even though its* [Tweet; thumbnail link to tweet]. Twitter. https://twitter.com/jburnmurdoch/status/1488084585527324672

155. Pirzada, K. [@KashPrime]. (2022, September 19). *You can see flu mortality estimates from the CDC from the last 'normal' flu season, 2018-2019. It is obvious that* [Tweet; thumbnail link to table data]. Twitter. https://twitter.com/KashPrime/status/1572041722384846854

156. Wsbgnl. [@wsbgnl]. (2022, August 18). *US pediatric COVID hospital admissions and deaths by month* [Tweet; infographic attached]. Twitter. https://twitter.com/wsbgnl/status/1560177856893710336

157. Faust, J. (2022, June 5). Pediatric COVID-19 versus influenza: further thoughts and statistics. *Inside Medicine*. https://insidemedicine.bulletin.com/pediatric-COVID-19-versus-influenza-further-thoughts-and-statistics

158. Jones, J. (2021, November 2). *Epidemiology of COVID-19 in children Aged 5 –11 years* [Slideshow presentation to ACIP meeting]. and Prevention. https://www.cdc.gov/vaccines/acip/meetings/downloads/slides-2021-11-2-3/03-COVID-Jefferson-508.pdf

159. Shein, S. L., Carroll, C. L., Remy, K. E., Rogerson, C. M., McCluskey, C. K., Lin, A., & Rotta, A. T. (2022). Epidemiology and outcomes of SARS-CoV-2 infection or multisystem inflammatory syndrome in children vs influenza among critically ill children. *JAMA Network Open*, *5*(6), Article 2217217. https://doi.org/10.1001/jamanetworkopen.2022.17217

160. Kulldorff, M. (2020, August 8). Herd immunity is still key in the fight against COVID-19. *The Spectator*. https://www.spectator.co.uk/article/herd-immunity-is-still-key-in-the-fight-against-COVID-19

161. The White House 45 Archived. [@WhiteHouse45]. (2020, August 15). *Dr. Scott Atlas: "We know that the risk of the disease is extremely low for children, even less than that* [Tweet; video attached]. Twitter. https://twitter.com/WhiteHouse45/status/1294665940127428609

162. Mandrola, J. [@drjohnm]. (2020, September 27). *As @VPrasadMDMPH and @dr_dmorgan discuss, the risk to children is greater from influenza than #COVID19. Telling graphic they had there* [Tweet; infographic attached]. Twitter. https://twitter.com/drjohnm/status/1310300707338293249

163. Daugherty, E. H. (2021, May 4). *Q&A: Dr. Lucy McBride '95 on COVID-19, risk, and mental health*. Princeton Alumni Weekly. https://paw.princeton.edu/article/qa-dr-lucy-mcbride-95-COVID-19-risk-and-mental-health

164. Høeg, T. B., Prasad, V., & Gandhi, M. (2021, May 12). American kids can wait. *The Atlantic*. https://www.theatlantic.com/ideas/archive/2021/05/vaccinate-adults-in-india-before-american-children/618849/

165. Hill, Z. K. (2021, July 21). Stanford doc Jay Bhattacharya calls vaccine mandates 'unethical,' says patients can choose. *Newsweek*. https://www.newsweek.com/stanford-doc-jay-bhattacharya-calls-vaccine-mandates-unethical-says-patients-can-choose-1611938

166. Atlas, S. W. (2021, September 22). *The Atlas Society asks Scott Atlas*

[Video interview]. YouTube. https://www.youtube.com/watch?v=rqI_gleskTM

167. Kulldorff, M., & Bhattacharya, J. (2021, November 6). *The six major fails of Anthony Fauci*. Brownstone Institute. https://brownstone.org/articles/the-six-major-fails-of-anthony-fauci/

168. Kulldorff, M. (2021, December 17). *Vaccines save lives*. Brownstone Institute. https://brownstone.org/articles/vaccines-save-lives/

169. Høeg, T. B., & Prasad, V. (2022, February 8). We're pro-vaccine but can't support California lawmaker's school COVID vaccine mandate. *SFGATE*. https://www.sfgate.com/politics-op-eds/article/California-vaccine-mandate-schools-COVID-omicron-16832461.php?utm_source=dlvr.it&utm_medium=twitter

170. Ioannidis, J. P. A. (2022). The end of the COVID-19 pandemic. *European Journal of Clinical Investigation*, *52*(6), Article 13782. https://doi.org/10.1111/eci.13782

171. Kulldorff, M., Gupta, S., & Bhattacharya, J. (2020, October 4). *The Great Barrington Declaration*. https://gbdeclaration.org/

172. Urgency of Normal. (2022, May 18). *Children, COVID, and the urgency of normal: the under 5 edition*. https://www.urgencyofnormal.com/s/Children-COVID-and-the-Urgency-of-Normal-The-Under-Age-5-Edition.pdf

173. Prasad, V. [@VPrasadMDMPH]. (2022, February 27). *Of course for children COVID and flu have always been comparable We never upended their life over flu* [Tweet; thumbnail link to tweet]. Twitter. https://twitter.com/VPrasadMDMPH/status/1498159887573872640

174. Newman, K. (2019, February 7). Schools are closing amid flu outbreaks. *USNews.com*. https://www.usnews.com/news/national-news/articles/2019-02-07/schools-close-hospitals-restrict-visitors-amid-flu-outbreaks

175. Freedman, D. [@dfreedman7]. (2022, February 3). *Those comparing COVID in children to flu in children really seem to forget that pediatricians were encouraging flu vaccines in* [Tweet]. Twitter. https://twitter.com/dfreedman7/status/1489442198814867463

176. Guarino, B. (2017, January 10). Cleveland Clinic doc pens viral screed against vaccines, peers call it 'post-truth medicine'. *The Washington Post*. https://www.washingtonpost.com/news/morning-mix/wp/2017/01/10/cleveland-clinic-doc-pens-viral-screed-against-vaccines-peers-call-it-post-truth-medicine/

177. Fox, M. (2017, April 3). *Most kids who died of flu weren't vaccinated, study finds*. NBC News. https://www.nbcnews.com/health/health-news/most-kids-who-died-flu-weren-t-vaccinated-study-finds-n742046

178. Mackay, M. (2021, August 10). *Mom regrets not getting her 13-year-old vaccinated as Delta variant surges*. KTHV. https://www.thv11.com/article/news/i-wish-i-wouldve-made-better-choices-for-her-arkansas-mom-regrets-not-getting-her-child-vaccinated/91-f6d38e7e-883e-4c98-a3f9-00f5f52e8bac

179. Mackay, M. (2021, October 29). *Arkansas teenager finally home after 16 week battle against COVID-19 in hospital*. KTHV. https://www.thv11.com/article/news/arkansas-teen-home-following-battle-against-COVID/91-b8a3b629-8a5c-4e8a-9011-2b29ec6b3a59

180. Ji, S. (2018, October 26). Measles transmitted by the vaccinated, gov. researchers confirm. *GreenMedInfo*. https://greenmedinfo.com/blog/measles-transmitted-vaccinated-gov-researchers-confirm

181. Woolf, S. H., Chapman, D. A., & Lee, J. H. (2021). COVID-19 as the leading cause of death in the United States. *JAMA*, *325*(2), 123-124. https://doi.org/10.1001/jama.2020.24865

182. Yamaguchi, L. (2022, February 3). *FDA used 'critically flawed' risk-benefit analysis to 'justify' COVID vaccines for children*. The Defender: Children's Health Defense News & Views. https://childrenshealthdefense.org/defender/fda-risk-benefit-analysis-COVID-vaccines-children/

183. Chakrabarti, M., & Chang, J. (2021, May 11). *What to know about kids and COVID vaccines*. WBUR. https://www.wbur.org/onpoint/2021/05/11/should-kids-be-vaccinated

184. Pezzullo, A. M., Axfors, C., Contopoulos-Ioannidis, D. G., Apostolatos, A., & Ioannidis, J. P. A. (2022, October 13). *Age-stratified infection fatality rate of COVID-19 in the non-elderly informed from pre-vaccination national seroprevalence studies*. Medrxiv. https://doi.org/10.1101/2022.10.11.22280963

185. The COVKID Project. (n.d.). *COVID-19 Deaths Dashboard* [Interactive dataset]. Retrieved December 4, 2022, from https://www.covkidproject.org/deaths

186. American Academy of Pediatrics Wisconsin Chapter. (2019, May 8). *Drowning prevention social media storm May 23 – #DrowningPrevention*. https://www.wiaap.org/drowning-prevention-social-media-storm-may-23-drowningprevention/

187. Mandrola, J., & Foy, A. (2020, December 29). No, young adults should not live in fear from coronavirus. *Dr John M.* https://www.drjohnm.org/2020/12/no-young-adults-should-not-live-in-fear-from-coronavirus/

188. Prasad, V. [@VPrasadMDMPH]. (2021, May 8). *Every death is tragic In April 2021, 19 kids died of COVID19 in a country of 330 million; Is that* [Tweet; image attached]. Twitter. https://twitter.com/VPrasadMDMPH/status/1391043307648655365

189. Levinovitz, A. (2021, September 29). How the phrase 'natural immunity' misleads us about real risks and dangers. *The Washington Post.* https://www.washingtonpost.com/outlook/2021/09/29/natural-immunity-public-health/

190. Brogan, K. (n.d.). Can pharma improve on nature? HPV vaccine vs natural infection. *Kelly Brogan, MD.* https://www.kellybroganmd.com/blog/can-pharma-improve-nature-hpv-vaccine-vs-natural-infection

191. Iannelli, V. (2019, April 29). *Should I stop calling chickenpox and measles diseases?* Vaxopedia. https://vaxopedia.org/2019/04/29/should-i-stop-calling-chickenpox-and-measles-diseases/

192. Makary, M. (2021, September 15). Natural immunity to COVID is powerful. Policymakers seem afraid to say so. *The Washington Post.* https://www.washingtonpost.com/outlook/2021/09/15/natural-immunity-vaccine-mandate/

193. Makary, M. (2021, June 8). The power of natural immunity. *Wall Street Journal.* https://www.wsj.com/articles/the-power-of-natural-immunity-11623171303

194. Makary, M. (2022, January 26). The high cost of disparaging natural immunity to COVID: Vaccines were wasted on those who didn't need them, and people who posed no risk lost jobs. *Wall Street Journal.* https://www.wsj.com/articles/the-high-cost-of-disparaging-natural-immunity-to-COVID-vaccine-mandates-protests-fire-rehire-employment-11643214336

195. Makary, M. [@MartyMakary]. (2022, June 12). *Natural immunity wins again. New England Journal study: natural immunity "protection was higher than that conferred after the same time* [Tweet; thumbnail link to article]. Twitter. https://twitter.com/MartyMakary/status/1536112474113683459

196. Makary, M. (2021, March 24). Herd immunity is near, despite Fauci's denial: His estimate that it'll take a 70% to 85% vaccination rate ignores those who have already been infected. *Wall Street Journal.* https://www.wsj.com/articles/herd-immunity-is-near-despite-faucis-denial-

11616624554?mod=e2fb

197. Wiley, T. L. (2021, September 1). August 12, 2021 vaccines- mandates-children's immunity. *Wiley Chiropractic Group P.C. Blog*. https://www.wileychiropracticgroup.com/blog/320002-august-12-2021-vaccines-mandates-childrens-immunity

198. Makary, M. (2021, February 18). We'll have herd immunity by April: COVID cases have dropped 77% in six weeks. Experts should level with the public about the good news. *Wall Street Journal*. https://www.wsj.com/articles/well-have-herd-immunity-by-april-11613669731

199. Makary, M. (2021, December 16). *Dr. Makary on 'Kilmeade Show': Omicron fear fueling a 'second pandemic of lunacy'* [Video interview]. Fox News. https://www.foxnews.com/media/omicron-COVID-fear-pandemic-lunacy-makary-kilmeade

200. Wall, J. (2022, January 2). *Updated science: Omicron called 'nature's vaccine' by Johns Hopkins professor Dr. Marty Makary*. TAPinto. https://www.tapinto.net/towns/hazlet-and-keyport/sections/health-and-wellness/articles/updated-science-omicron-called-nature-s-vaccine-by-johns-hopkins-professor-dr-marty-makary

201. Mathieu, E., Ritchie, H., Rodés-Guirao, L., Appel, C., Giattino, C., Hasell, J., Macdonald, B., Dattani, S., Beltekian, D., Ortiz-Ospina, E., & Roser, M. (2020). *Coronavirus pandemic (COVID-19)* [Interactive dataset]. Our World in Data. Retrieved December 14, 2022, from https://ourworldindata.org/COVID-deaths

202. Makary, M. (2022, June 10). Why America doesn't trust the CDC. *Newsweek*. https://www.newsweek.com/why-america-doesnt-trust-cdc-opinion-1713145

203. Makary, M. (2022, June 23). *CDC recommends COVID-19 vaccines for babies, kids under 5. Here are 6 things parents need to know*. Fox News. https://www.foxnews.com/opinion/cdc-recommends-COVID-19-vaccines-babies-kids-under-5-6-things-parents-need-know

204. *Dr. Makary questions data being used by FDA to authorize COVID vaccines for young kids*. (2022, June 15). Fox News. https://www.foxnews.com/media/dr-makary-questions-data-fda-authorize-COVID-vaccines-young-kids

205. Cifu, A., & Prasad, V. (2022, July 26). A pro-con debate: Should doctors encourage healthy kids 11 and under be vaccinated against COVID-19? *Sensible Medicine*. https://sensiblemed.substack.com/p/a-pro-con-debate-should-doctors-encourage

206. Prasad, V. [@VPrasadMDMPH]. (2021, June 23). *Myocarditis cont. ACIP slides are up. First, let us all remember cases are FALLING PRECIPITOUSLY The benefit side of the* [Tweet; thumbnail link to infographic]. Twitter. https://twitter.com/VPrasadMDMPH/status/1407743348719316993

207. Haslett, C. (2022, October 6). *86% of kids under 17 have antibodies from a past COVID infection, CDC data shows*. ABC News. https://abcnews.go.com/Health/86-kids-17-antibodies-past-COVID-infection-cdc/story?id=91106508

208. Mensah, A. A., Campbell, H., Stowe, J., Seghezzo, G., Simmons, R., Lacy, J., Bukasa, A., O'Boyle, S., Ramsay, M. E., Brown, K., & Ladhani, S. N. (2022). Risk of SARS-CoV-2 reinfections in children: A prospective national surveillance study between January, 2020, and July, 2021, in England. *The Lancet Child & Adolescent Health*, *6*(6), 384-392. https://doi.org/10.1016/S2352-4642(22)00059-1

209. Fang, S.-f., Liu, N., & Du, H.-w. (2022). Correspondence: BNT162b2 COVID-19 vaccine in children 5 to 11 years of age [Letter to editor]. *The New England Journal of Medicine*, *386*, 604-606. https://doi.org/10.1056/NEJMc2118775

210. Gorski, D. (2010, March 29). "Vaccines didn't save us" (a.k.a. "vaccines don't work"): Intellectual dishonesty at its most naked. *Science-Based Medicine*. https://sciencebasedmedicine.org/vaccines-didnt-save-us-intellectual-dishonesty-at-its-most-naked/

211. West, E. (2022, January 5). *A tribute to Raymond Obomsawin*. The Defender: Children's Health Defense News & Views. https://childrenshealthdefense.org/defender/tribute-raymond-obomsawin/

212. Prasad, V. (2022, July 22). Kids vaccine is low risk either way. *Vinay Prasad's Observations and Thoughts*. https://vinayprasadmdmph.substack.com/p/kids-vaccine-is-low-risk-either-way

213. Sheldrick, K. [@K_Sheldrick]. (2022, July 22). *I have read the piece. There are different ways to express data. Hospitalisation per infection, risk per child per year* [Tweet]. Twitter. https://twitter.com/K_Sheldrick/status/1550676976280543233

214. Panthagani, K. [@kmpanthagani]. (2022, July 23). *A case study in graphs that crush my soul, and why appropriate axes (and axis labels) are the lifeblood of* [Tweet; multi-tweet thread]. Twitter. https://twitter.com/kmpanthagani/status/1550992928008454149

215. Flanary, W. E. [@DGlaucomflecken]. (2022, July 22). *Hello Dr.*

Prasad, you may have missed this tweet from @K_Sheldrick . It's possible you already blocked him for disagreeing with [Tweet; image attached]. Twitter. https://twitter.com/DGlaucomflecken/status/1550549698770964480

216. Bystrianyk, R. (2019, March 1). Measles: The new red scare. *GreenMedInfo*. https://greenmedinfo.com/blog/measles-new-red-scare

217. and Prevention. (2020, November 5). *Measles history*. U.S. Department of Health and Human Services. https://www.cdc.gov/measles/about/history.html

218. Gargano, J. W., Wallace, M., Hadler, S. C., Langley, G., Su, J. R., Oster, M. E., Broder, K. R., Gee, J., Weintraub, E., Shimabukuro, T., Scobie, H. M., Moulia, D., Markowitz, L. E., Wharton, M., McNally, V. V., Romero, J. R., Keipp Talbot, H., Lee, G. M., Daley, M. F., & Oliver, S. E. (2021). Use of mRNA COVID-19 vaccine after reports of myocarditis among vaccine recipients: Update from the Advisory Committee on Immunization Practices — United States, June 2021. *Morbidity and Mortality Weekly Report*, *70*(27), 977-982. http://dx.doi.org/10.15585/mmwr.mm7027e2

219. *Number of intubated children with COVID-19 at MUSC increasing*. (2021, September 14). Live 5 News. https://www.live5news.com/2021/09/14/number-intubated-children-with-COVID-19-musc-increasing/

220. Greene, L. (2022, August 18). The COVID centrist MD to antivax pipeline. *Back to the Vax*. https://backtothevax.com/f/the-COVID-centrist-md-to-antivax-pipeline

221. Saphier, N., & Makary, M. (2021, November 8). Should you vaccinate your 5-year-old? *Wall Street Journal*. https://www.wsj.com/articles/should-vaccinate-children-COVID-19-infection-natural-immunity-vaccine-mandate-coronavirus-11636384215

222. and Prevention. (n.d.). *Coronavirus Disease 2019 (COVID-19)-Associated Hospitalization Surveillance Network (COVID-NET)*. U.S. Department of Health and Human Services. Retrieved December 4, 2022, from https://www.cdc.gov/coronavirus/2019-ncov/COVID-data/COVID-net/purpose-methods.html

223. Havers, F. P., Whitaker, M., Self, J. L., Chai, S. J., Daily Kirley, P., Alden, N. B., Kawasaki, B., Meek, J., Yousey-Hindes, K., Anderson, E. J., Openo, K. P., Weigel, A., Teno, K., Monroe, M. L., Ryan, P. A., Reeg, L., Kohrman, A., Lynfield, R., Como-Sabetti, K., … COVID-NET Surveillance Team. (2021). Hospitalization of adolescents aged 12–17

years with laboratory-confirmed COVID-19 — COVID-NET, 14 states, March 1, 2020–April 24, 2021. *Morbidity and Mortality Weekly Report, 70*(23), 851-857. http://dx.doi.org/10.15585/mmwr.mm7023e1

224. Pfeiffer, M. B. (2022, August 1). *5 facts to consider before vaccinating kids for COVID.* The Defender: Children's Health Defense News & Views. https://childrenshealthdefense.org/defender/COVID-vaccine-kids-facts/

225. Brauser, D. (2021, April 22). COVID-19 linked to new-onset epileptic seizures. *Medscape.* https://www.medscape.com/viewarticle/949769

226. Pasquel, F. J., Messler, J., Booth, R., Kubacka, B., Mumpower, A., Umpierrez, G., & Aloi, J. (2021). Characteristics of and mortality associated with diabetic ketoacidosis among US patients hospitalized with or without COVID-19. *JAMA Network Open, 4*(3), Article 211091. https://doi.org/10.1001/jamanetworkopen.2021.1091

227. Malhotra, A., Sturgill, M., Whitley-Williams, P., Lee, Y.-H., Esochaghi, C., Rajasekhar, H., Olson, B., & Gaur, S. (2021). Pediatric COVID-19 and appendicitis: A gut reaction to SARS-CoV-2? *The Pediatric Infectious Disease Journal, 40*(2), e49-e55. https://doi.org/10.1097/INF.0000000000002998

228. Henderson, E. (2022, October 17). *Asymptomatic COVID could potentially cause more complications in trauma patients.* News Medical. https://www.news-medical.net/news/20221017/Asymptomatic-COVID-could-potentially-cause-more-complications-in-trauma-patients.aspx

229. COVID-NET: COVID-19-Associated Hospitalization Surveillance Network. (n.d.). *Laboratory-Confirmed COVID-19-Associated Hospitalizations* [Interactive dataset]. and Prevention: U.S. Department of Health & Human Services. Retrieved December 4, 2022, from https://gis.cdc.gov/grasp/COVIDnet/COVID19_3.html

230. Bystrianyk, R. (2014, October 8). Measles and measles vaccines: 14 things to consider. *GreenMedInfo.* https://greenmedinfo.com/blog/measles-and-measles-vaccines-14-things-we-consider

231. Høeg, T. [@TracyBethHoeg]. (2021, April 2). *The same trend continues in Israel. As of yesterday, just over 60% of the population has received the first dose* [Tweet; Thumbnail to infographic]. Twitter. https://twitter.com/TracyBethHoeg/status/1378010361933176840

232. Høeg, T. [@TracyBethHoeg]. (2021, April 2). *Clarification, my saying there does not appear to be a need to vaccinate kids to reach herd immunity does *not** [Tweet]. Twitter. https://twitter.com/

TracyBethHoeg/status/1378063992757751812

233. Høeg, T. [@TracyBethHoeg]. (2021, August 5). *Fascinating. Looking at the @CDCgov 's COVID-NET, you see that it has been the 0-4 year olds driving up COVID hospitalization* [Tweet; infographic attached]. Twitter. https://twitter.com/TracyBethHoeg/status/1423370987127689218

234. Mandrola, J. [@drjohnm]. (2021, August 6). *Super-interesting observation [backhand index pointing down]* [Tweet; thumbnail link to tweet]. Twitter. https://twitter.com/drjohnm/status/1423750912758145031

235. Summers, D. [@WFKARS]. (2021, August 8). *Medical tidbit: there are tests that can be run and resulted in the span of minutes to differentiate RSV from* [Tweet]. Twitter. https://twitter.com/WFKARS/status/1424367776882384901

236. Hart, J. [@justin_hart]. (2021, September 7). *That's likely RSV - not COVID* [Tweet]. Twitter. https://twitter.com/justin_hart/status/1435454960024518662

237. Horne, Z., Powell, D., Hummel, J. E., & Holyoak, K. J. (2015, August 3). Countering antivaccination attitudes. *Proceedings of the National Academy of Sciences of the United States, 112*(33), 10321-10324. https://doi.org/10.1073/pnas.1504019112

238. Pittman, A. (2021, September 29). *16-year-old dies of COVID-19 after school ends mask mandate due to declining cases*. Mississippi Free Press. https://www.mississippifreepress.org/16400/16-year-old-student-dies-after-school-ends-mask-mandate-citing-declining-cases/

239. Long, C. (2021, September 9). *Florida dad regrets not getting COVID vaccine after 15-year-old daughter's death*. WAVY.com. https://www.wavy.com/COVID-19-vaccine/florida-dad-regrets-not-getting-COVID-vaccine-after-15-year-old-daughters-death/

240. Huntsman, A. (2022, February 21). *Their 17-year-old grandchild died of COVID-19. Now, a Cleveland couple urges teens to get vaccinated.* Ideastream. https://www.ideastream.org/news/their-17-year-old-grandchild-died-of-COVID-19-now-a-cleveland-couple-urges-teens-to-get-vaccinated

241. Vargas, A. (2021, December 15). *"Our missing stars": New foundation honoring Teresa Sperry and other children who have died from COVID-19*. 13NewsNow.com. https://www.13newsnow.com/article/news/local/mycity/suffolk/missing-stars-foundation-teresa-sperry-children-died-COVID-19/291-3de8d490-73dc-4c17-90f7-9a78086753b6

242. Our Missing Stars. (n.d.). *About*. Retrieved December 6, 2022, from https://ourmissingstars.org/about

243. Torrago, L. [@Loretta_Torrago]. (2022, February 19). *When @JuliaRaifman sent @drlucybmcbride this Tweet, McBride's response was: "Fear & shame aren't motivating." Imagine the parents reading that their baby* [Tweet; image attached]. Twitter. https://twitter.com/Loretta_Torrago/status/1495239220218241041

244. Ladhani, S. [@ShamezLadhani]. (2022, April 8). *Maybe it's just me, but as a parent and paediatrician, I think putting up the names & pictures of children who* [Tweet]. Twitter. https://twitter.com/ShamezLadhani/status/1512483678282481666

245. Olsen, S. (2022, February 8). *9-month-old baby marks Miller County's first child COVID-19 death*. KOMU. https://www.komu.com/news/COVID19/9-month-old-baby-marks-miller-countys-first-child-COVID-19-death/article_741f917e-852f-11ec-96de-930038965fd3.amp.html

246. McAlpine, A. [@AlastairMcA30]. (2022, April 9). *When you've been minimizing the risk of COVID-19 for kids, seeing kids who've died is harmful to your narrative. But* [Tweet]. Twitter. https://twitter.com/AlastairMcA30/status/1512850738048868354

247. Sperry, N. [@nksperry]. (2022, April 9). *As a parent of 1 of the children that have died from COVID, Im proud her name Teresa is shared* [Tweet]. Twitter. https://twitter.com/nksperry/status/1512771789105283076

248. Sperry, N. [@nksperry]. (2022, April 10). *A public apology to not only me but other families that have had to bury their child due to COVID* [Tweet; image attached]. Twitter. https://twitter.com/nksperry/status/1513173982769520647

249. Brogan, K. (n.d.). *Vaccines and brain health* [Pamphlet]. Retrieved December 7, 2022, from https://s3.amazonaws.com/kajabi-storefronts-production/sites/53102/themes/3164472/downloads/GOa48MFUSxm489azNLKl_Vaccines_Brain_Health.pdf

250. Ministry of Health. (2021, June 2). *Surveillance of myocarditis (inflammation of the heart muscle) cases between December 2020 and May 2021 (including)* [Press release; translation]. Government of Israel. https://www.gov.il/en/departments/news/01062021-03

251. Chua, G. T., Kwan, M. Y. W., Chui, C. S. L., Smith, R. D., Cheung, E. C. L., Ma, T., Leung, M. T. Y., Tsao, S. S. L., Kan, E., Ng, W. K. C., Chan, V. C. M., Tai, S. M., Yu, T. C., Lee, K. P., Wong, J. S. C., Lin, Y. K., Shek, C. C., Leung, A. S. Y., Chow, C. K., … Ip, P. (2022). Epidemiology

of acute myocarditis/pericarditis in Hong Kong adolescents following Comirnaty vaccination. *Clinical Infectious Diseases*, *75*(4), 673-681. https://doi.org/10.1093/cid/ciab989

252. Husby, A., Hansen, J. V., Fosbøl, E., Theisson, E. M., Madsen, M., Thomsen, R. W., Sørensen, H. T., Andersen, M., Wohlfahrt, J., Gislason, G., Torp-Pedersen, C., Køber, L., & Hviid, A. (2021). SARS-CoV-2 vaccination and myocarditis or myopericarditis: Population based cohort study. *BMJ*, *375*, e068665. https://doi.org/10.1136/bmj-2021-068665

253. Pillay, J., Gaudet, L., Wingert, A., Bialy, L., Mackie, A. S., Paterson, D. I., & Hartling, L. (2022). Incidence, risk factors, natural history, and hypothesised mechanisms of myocarditis and pericarditis following COVID-19 vaccination: Living evidence syntheses and review. *BMJ*, *378*, e069445. https://doi.org/10.1136/bmj-2021-069445

254. Thurner, L., Kessel, C., Fadle, N., Regitz, E., Seidel, F., Kindermann, I., Lohse, S., Kos, I., Tschöpe, C., Kheiroddin, P., Kiblboeck, D., Hoffmann, M.-C., Bette, B., Carbon, G., Cetin, O., Preuss, K.-D., Christofyllakis, K., Bittenbring, J. T., Pickardt, T., … Klingel, K. (2022). IL-1RA antibodies in myocarditis after SARS-CoV-2 vaccination. *The New England Journal of Medicine*, *387*, 1524-1527. https://doi.org/10.1056/NEJMc2205667

255. Shimabukuro, T. (2022, June 14). *Update on myocarditis following mRNA COVID-19 vaccination*. Vaccines and Related Biological Products Advisory Committee: U.S. Food and Drug Administration. https://www.fda.gov/media/159228/download

256. American Heart Association News. (2022, September 6). *Myocarditis from COVID-19 booster rare, but risk highest among teen boys, young men*. https://www.heart.org/en/news/2022/09/06/myocarditis-from-COVID-19-booster-rare-but-risk-highest-among-teen-boys-young-men

257. American Academy of Pediatrics. (n.d.). *Children and COVID-19 vaccination trends: AAP analysis of data posted by the Centers of Disease Control and Prevention as of August 31, 2022*. Retrieved December 12, 2022, from https://downloads.aap.org/AAP/PDF/Child%20Vaccinations%20Report%20US%20Cumulative%20and%20Weekly%20Aug%2031%20revised.pdf

258. Yasuhara, J., Masuda, K., Aikawa, T., Shirasu, T., Takagi, H., Lee, S., & Kuno, T. (2022). Myopericarditis after COVID-19 mRNA vaccination among adolescents and young adults: A systematic review and meta-analysis. *JAMA Pediatrics*. https://doi.org/10.1001/jamapediatrics.2022.4768

259. Samimisedeh, P., Afshar, E. J., Hassani, N. S., & Rastad, H. (2022).

Cardiac MRI findings in COVID-19 vaccine-related myocarditis: A pooled analysis of 468 patients. *Journal of Magnetic Resonance Imaging*, *56*(4), 971-982. https://doi.org/10.1002/jmri.28268

260. Khan, Z., Pabani, U. K., Gul, A., Muhammad, S. A., Yousif, Y., Abumedian, M., Elmahdi, O., & Gupta, A. (2022). COVID-19 vaccine-induced myocarditis: A systemic review and literature search. *Cureus*, *14*(7), Article 27408. https://doi.org/10.7759/cureus.27408

261. Ling, R. R., Ramanathan, K., Tan, F. L., Tai, B. C., Somani, J., Fisher, D., & MacLaren, G. (2022). Myopericarditis following COVID-19 vaccination and non-COVID-19 vaccination: A systematic review and meta-analysis. *The Lancet Respiratory Medicine*, *10*(7), 679-688. https://doi.org/10.1016/S2213-2600(22)00059-5

262. Dionne, A., Sperotto, F., Chamberlain, S., Baker, A. L., Powell, A. J., Prakash, A., Castellanos, D. A., Saleeb, S. F., de Ferranti, S. D., Newburger, J. W., & Friedman, K. G. (2021). Association of myocarditis with BNT162b2 messenger RNA COVID-19 vaccine in a case series of children. *JAMA Cardiology*, *6*(12), 1446-1450. https://doi.org/10.1001/jamacardio.2021.3471

263. Marshall, M., Ferguson, I. D., Lewis, P., Jaggi, P., Gagliardo, C., Collins, J. S., Shaughnessy, R., Caron, R., Fuss, C., Corbin, K. J. E., Emuren, L., Faherty, E., Hall, K., Di Pentima, C., Oster, M. E., Paintsil, E., Siddiqui, S., Timchak, D. M., & Guzman-Cottrill, J. A. (2021). Symptomatic acute myocarditis in 7 adolescents after Pfizer-BioNTech COVID-19 vaccination. *Pediatrics*, *148*(3), Article 2021052478. https://doi.org/10.1542/peds.2021-052478

264. Woo, W., Kim, A. Y., Yon, D. K., Lee, S. W., Hwang, J., Jacob, L., Koyanagi, A., Kim, M. S., Moon, D. H., Jung, J. W., Choi, J. Y., Jung, S. Y., Eun, L. Y., Lee, S., Shin, J. I., & Smith, L. (2022). Clinical characteristics and prognostic factors of myocarditis associated with the mRNA COVID-19 vaccine. *Journal of Medical Virology*, *94*(4), 1566-1580. https://doi.org/10.1002/jmv.27501

265. Diaz, G. A., Parsons, G. T., Gering, S. K., Meier, A. R., Hutchinson, I. V., & Robicsek, A. (2021). Myocarditis and pericarditis after vaccination for COVID-19. *JAMA*, *326*(12), 1210-1212. https://doi.org/10.1001/jama.2021.13443

266. Jain, S. S., Steele, J. M., Fonseca, B., Huang, S., Shah, S., Maskatia, S. A., Buddhe, S., Misra, N., Ramachandran, P., Gaur, L., Eshtehardi, P., Anwar, S., Kaushik, N., Han, F., Chaudhuri, N. R., & Grosse-Wortmann, L. (2021). COVID-19 vaccination–associated myocarditis in adolescents. *Pediatrics*, *148*(5), Article 2021053427. https://doi.org/10.1542/

peds.2021-053427

267. Montgomery, J., Ryan, M., Engler, R., Hoffman, D., McClenathan, B., Collins, L., Loran, D., Hrncir, D., Herring, K., Platzer, M., Adams, N., Sanou, A., & Cooper, L. T., Jr. (2021). Myocarditis following immunization with mRNA COVID-19 vaccines in members of the US military. *JAMA Cardiology*, *6*(10), 1202-1206. https://doi.org/10.1001/jamacardio.2021.2833

268. Rosner, C. M., Genovese, L., Tehrani, B. N., Atkins, M., Bakhshi, H., Chaudhri, S., Damluji, A. A., de Lemos, J. A., Desai, S. S., Emaminia, A., Flanagan, M. C., Khera, A., Maghsoudi, A., Mekonnen, G., Muthukumar, A., Saeed, I. M., Sherwood, M. W., Sinha, S. S., O'Connor, C. M., & deFilippi, C. R. (2021). Myocarditis temporally associated with COVID-19 vaccination. *Circulation*, *144*(6), 502-505. https://doi.org/10.1161/CIRCULATIONAHA.121.055891

269. Mevorach, D., Anis, E., Cedar, N., Hasin, T., Bromberg, M., Goldberg, L., Parnasa, E., Dichtiar, R., Hershkovitz, Y., Ash, N., Green, M. S., Keinan-Boker, L., & Alroy-Preis, S. (2022). Myocarditis after BNT162b2 vaccination in Israeli adolescents. *The New England Journal of Medicine*, *386*, 998-999. https://doi.org/ 10.1056/NEJMc2116999

270. Nygaard, U., Holm, M., Bohnstedt, C., Chai, Q., Schmidt, L. S., Hartling, U. B., Petersen, J. J. H., Thaarup, J., Bjerre, J., Vejlstrup, N. C., Juul, K., & Stensballe, L. G. (2022). Population-based incidence of myopericarditis after COVID-19 vaccination in Danish adolescents. *The Pediatric Infectious Disease Journal*, *41*(1), e25-e28. https://doi.org/10.1097%2FINF.0000000000003389

271. Witberg, G., Barda, N., Hoss, S., Richter, I., Wiessman, M., Aviv, Y., Grinberg, T., Auster, O., Dagan, N., Balicer, R. D., & Kornowski, R. (2021). Myocarditis after COVID-19 vaccination in a large health care organization. *The New England Journal of Medicine*, *385*, 2132-2139. https://doi.org/10.1056/NEJMoa2110737

272. Mouch, S. A., Roguin, A., Hellou, E., Ishai, A., Shoshan, U., Mahamid, L., Zoabi, M., Aisman, M., Goldschmid, N., & Yanay, N. B. (2021). Myocarditis following COVID-19 mRNA vaccination. *Vaccine*, *39*(29), 3790-3793. https://doi.org/10.1016/j.vaccine.2021.05.087

273. Larson, K. F., Ammirati, E., Adler, E. D., Cooper, L. T. J., Hong, K. N., Saponara, G., Couri, D., Cereda, A., Procopio, A., Cavalotti, C., Oliva, F., Sanna, T., Ciconte, V. A., Onyango, G., Holmes, D. R., & Borgeson, D. D. (2021). Myocarditis after BNT162b2 and mRNA-1273 vaccination. *Circulation*, *144*(6), 506-508. https://doi.org/10.1161/CIRCULATIONAHA.121.055913

274. Truong, D. T., Dionne, A., Muniz, J. C., McHugh, K. E., Portman, M. A., Lambert, L. M., Thacker, D., Elias, M. D., Li, J. S., Toro-Salazar, O. H., Anderson, B. R., Atz, A. M., Bohun, C. M., Campbell, M. J., Chrisant, M., D'Addese, L., Dummer, K. B., Forsha, D., Frank, L. H., … Newburger, J. W. (2021). Clinically suspected myocarditis temporally related to COVID-19 vaccination in adolescents and young adults: Suspected myocarditis after COVID-19 vaccination. *Circulation*, *145*(5), 345-356. https://doi.org/10.1161/CIRCULATIONAHA.121.056583

275. Patone, M., Lei, X. W., Handunnetthi, L., Dixon, S., Zaccardi, F., Shankar-Hari, M., Watkinson, P., Khunti, K., Harnden, A., Coupland, C. A. C., Channon, K. M., Mills, N. L., Sheikh, A., & Hippisley-Cox, J. (2022). Risks of myocarditis, pericarditis, and cardiac arrhythmias associated with COVID-19 vaccination or SARS-CoV-2 infection. *Nature Medicine*, *28*, 410-422. https://doi.org/10.1038/s41591-021-01630-0

276. Lai, F. T. T., Chan, E. W. W., Huang, L., Cheung, C. L., Chui, C. S. L., Li, X., Wan, E. Y. F., Wang, C. K. H., Chan, E. W. Y., Yiu, K. H., & Wong, I. C. K. (2022). Prognosis of myocarditis developing after mRNA COVID-19 vaccination compared with viral myocarditis. *Journal of the American College of Cardiology*, *80*(24), 2255-2265. https://doi.org/10.1016/j.jacc.2022.09.049

277. Varma, S. K., Horton, A. E., Taylor, A. L., Ditchfield, M. R., Hope, S. A., & Rao, S. J. V. (2022). Myocarditis after COVID-19 mRNA vaccination in Australia. *The Medical Journal of Australia*, *217*(5), 260-261. https://doi.org/10.5694/mja2.51657

278. Witberg, G., Magen, O., Hoss, S., Talmor-Barkan, Y., Richter, I., Wiessman, M., Aviv, Y., Grinberg, T., Shiyovich, A., Schamroth-Pravda, N., Auster, O., Dagan, N., Birk, E., Balicer, R., & Kornowski, R. (2022). Myocarditis after BNT162b2 vaccination in Israeli adolescents. *The New England Journal of Medicine*, *387*, 1816-1817. https://doi.org/10.1056/NEJMc2207270

279. Mansanguan, S., Charunwatthana, P., Piyaphanee, W., Dechkhajorn, W., Poolcharoen, A., & Mansanguan, C. (2022). Cardiovascular manifestation of the BNT162b2 mRNA COVID-19 vaccine in adolescents. *Tropical Medicine and Infectious Disease*, *7*(8), 196. https://doi.org/10.3390/tropicalmed7080196

280. Naveed, Z., Li, J., Spencer, M., Wilton, J., Naus, M., Velásquez García, H. A., Otterstatter, M., & Janjua, N. Z. (2022). Observed versus expected rates of myocarditis after SARS-CoV-2 vaccination: A population-based cohort study. *Canadian Medical Association Journal*, *194*(45), E1529-E1536. https://doi.org/10.1503/cmaj.220676

281. Mevorach, D., Anis, E., Cedar, N., Hasin, T., Bromberg, M., Goldberg, L., Levi, N., Perzon, O., Magadle, N., Barhoum, B., Parnassa, E., Dichtiar, R., Hershkovitz, Y., Green, M. S., Ash, N., Keinan-Boker, L., & Alroy-Preis, S. (2022). Myocarditis after BNT162b2 COVID-19 third booster vaccine in Israel. *Circulation, 146*(10), 802-804. https://doi.org/10.1161/CIRCULATIONAHA.122.060961

282. Goyal, M., Ray, I., Mascarenhas, D., Kunal, S., Sachdeva, R. A., & Ish, P. (2022). Myocarditis post SARS-CoV-2 vaccination: A systematic review. *QJM: An International Journal of Medicine*, hcac064. https://doi.org/10.1093/qjmed/hcac064

283. Gao, J., Feng, L., Li, Y., Lowe, S., Guo, Z., Bentley, R., Xie, C., Wu, B., Xie, P., Xia, W., Ma, S., Liu, H., Guo, X., Uy, J. P. N., Zhou, Q., Wazir, H., & Sun, C. (2022). A systematic review and meta-analysis of the association between SARS-CoV-2 vaccination and myocarditis or pericarditis. *American Journal of Preventative Medicine*. Advanced online publication. https://doi.org/10.1016/j.amepre.2022.09.002

284. Kracalik, I., Oster, M. E., Broder, K. R., Cortese, M. M., Glover, M., Shields, K., Creech, C. B., Romanson, B., Novosad, S., Soslow, J., Walter, E. B., Marquez, P., Dendy, J. M., Woo, J., Valderrama, A. L., Ramirez-Cardenas, A., Assefa, A., Campbell, M. J., Su, J. R., … Basavaraju, S. V. (2022). Outcomes at least 90 days since onset of myocarditis after mRNA COVID-19 vaccination in adolescents and young adults in the USA: A follow-up surveillance study. *The Lancet Child & Adolescent Health*, *6*(11), 788-789. https://doi.org/10.1016/S2352-4642(22)00244-9

285. American Heart Association. (2022, August 22). *Myocarditis risk significantly higher after COVID-19 infection vs. after a COVID-19 vaccine*. https://newsroom.heart.org/news/myocarditis-risk-significantly-higher-after-COVID-19-infection-vs-after-a-COVID-19-vaccine

286. Block, J. P., Boehmer, T. K., Forrest, C. B., Carton, T. W., Lee, G. M., Ajani, U. A., Christakis, D. A., Cowell, L. G., Draper, C., Ghildayal, N., Harris, A. M., Kappelman, M. D., Ko, J. Y., Mayer, K. H., Nagavedu, K., Oster, M. E., Paranjape, A., Puro, J., Ritchey, M. D., … Gundlapalli, A. V. (2022). Cardiac complications after SARS-CoV-2 infection and mRNA COVID-19 vaccination - PCORnet, United States, January 2021-January 2022. *Morbidity and Mortality Weekly Report*, *71*(14), 517-523. https://doi.org/10.15585/mmwr.mm7114e1

287. Voleti, N., Reddy, S. P., & Ssentongo, P. (2022). Myocarditis in SARS-CoV-2 infection vs. COVID-19 vaccination: A systematic review and meta-analysis. *Frontiers in Cardiovascular Medicine*, *9*, 951314. https://doi.org/10.3389/fcvm.2022.951314

288. McMurray, J. C., May, J. W., Cunningham, M. W., & Jones, O. Y. (n.d.). Multisystem inflammatory syndrome in children (MIS-C), a post-viral myocarditis and systemic vasculitis — A critical review of its pathogenesis and treatment. *Frontiers in Pediatrics*, *8*, 626182. https://doi.org/10.3389/fped.2020.626182

289. Sanil, Y., Misra, A., Safa, R., Blake, J. M., Eddine, A. C., Balakrishnan, P., Garcia, R. U., Taylor, R., Dentel, J. N., Ang, J., Cashen, K., Heidemann, S. M., Bauerfield, C., Sethuraman, U., Farooqi, A., Aggarwal, S., & Singh, G. (2021). Echocardiographic indicators associated with adverse clinical course and cardiac sequelae in multisystem inflammatory syndrome in children with coronavirus disease 2019. *Journal of the American Society of Echocardiography*, *34*(8), 862-876. https://doi.org/10.1016/j.echo.2021.04.018

290. Sperotto, F., Friedman, K. G., Son, M. B. F., VanderPluym, C. J., Newburger, J. W., & Dionne, A. (2021). Cardiac manifestations in SARS-CoV-2-associated multisystem inflammatory syndrome in children: A comprehensive review and proposed clinical approach. *European Journal of Pediatrics*, *180*, 307-322. https://doi.org/10.1007/s00431-020-03766-6

291. Belhadjer, Z., Méot, M., Bajolle, F., Khraiche, D., Legendre, A., Abakka, S., Auriau, J., Grimaud, M., Oualha, M., Beghetti, M., Wacker, J., Ovaert, C., Hascoet, S., Selegny, M., Malekzadeh-Milani, S., Maltret, A., Bosser, G., Giroux, N., Bonnemains, L., … Bonnet, D. (2020). Acute heart failure in multisystem inflammatory syndrome in children in the context of global SARS-CoV-2 pandemic. *Circulation*, *142*(5), 429-436. https://doi.org/10.1161/CIRCULATIONAHA.120.048360

292. Patel, T., Kelleman, M., West, Z., Peter, A., Dove, M., Butto, A., & Oster, M. E. (2022). Comparison of multisystem inflammatory syndrome in children–related myocarditis, classic viral myocarditis, and COVID-19 vaccine-related myocarditis in children. *Journal of the American Heart Association*, *11*(9), Article 024393. https://doi.org/10.1161/JAHA.121.024393

293. American Academy of Pediatrics. (2021, June 23). *Statement following CDC ACIP meeting from nation's leading doctors, nurses and public health leaders on benefits of vaccination*. https://services.aap.org/en/news-room/news-releases/aap/2021/statement-following-cdc-acip-meeting-from-nations-leading-doctors-nurses-and-public-health-leaders/

294. Mercola, J. (2022, January 7). *Children at risk for lifelong health problems from COVID vaccine*. The Defender: Children's Health Defense News & Views. https://childrenshealthdefense.org/defender/children-risk-lifelong-health-problems-COVID-vaccine/

295. Prasad, V. (2021, December 26). UK now reports myocarditis stratified by age & sex after vaccine or Sars-cov-2: Nature Medicine paper revisited: And it is shocking. *Vinay Prasad's Observations and Thoughts*. https://vinayprasadmdmph.substack.com/p/uk-now-reports-myocarditis-stratified

296. Prasad, V. (2022, January 19). *We need to talk about the vaccines: Public debate on side-effects is being censored*. UnHerd. https://unherd.com/2022/01/we-need-to-talk-about-the-vaccines/

297. Prasad, V. [@VPrasadMDMPH]. (2022, February 4). *No one says "vaccine induced myocarditis is mostly mild" like someone who just saw a graph that 20% of people* [Tweet; thumbnail link to tweet]. Twitter. https://twitter.com/VPrasadMDMPH/status/1489784991961608197

298. Prasad, V. [@VPrasadMDMPH]. (2021, September 13). *This infographic from BBC is terrific It is clear that the second dose brings WAY more hospitalizations from myocarditis than* [Tweet; infographic attached]. Twitter. https://twitter.com/vprasadmdmph/status/1437536062633431041

299. *Granville County mourns death of teen to COVID-19*. (2021, August 17). ABC11. https://abc11.com/teen-COVID-death-matthew-kirby-dirtbags-baseball-child-deaths/10957635/

300. Damania, Z. (Host). (2021, December 4). Omicron panic, natural immunity, fluvoxamine, & more [Episode 4; video podcast]. In *ZDoggMD: Slightly funnier than placebo*. https://zdoggmd.com/vpzd-4/

301. Prasad, V. [@VPrasadMDMPH]. (2021, January 13). *The virus meanwhile is *thank god* not that bad for most healthy kids, on par with seasonal influenza Even the* [Tweet]. Twitter. https://twitter.com/VPrasadMDMPH/status/1349427728953565189

302. Mandrola, J., Foy, A., & Prasad, V. (2021, May 14). Setting the record straight: There is no 'COVID heart'. *STAT*. https://www.statnews.com/2021/05/14/setting-the-record-straight-there-is-no-COVID-heart/

303. Prasad, V. [@VPrasadMDMPH]. (2020, December 30). *It's right to fault this headline; & news-stories of anaphylaxis after vaccination; Both are rare events & don't change fact vaccine* [Tweet; thumbnail link to article]. Twitter. https://twitter.com/VPrasadMDMPH/status/1344387754885406720

304. Prasad, V. [@VPrasadMDMPH]. (2020, December 30). *I'm not sure; perhaps some anecdotes should not be covered by the news. Someone who gets all the COVID vaccines* [Tweet]. Twitter. https://twitter.com/VPrasadMDMPH/status/1344396114414292993

305. Prasad, V. [@VPrasadMDMPH]. (2022, September 24). *6. We are living in a mad world, where a speculative anecdote in an older person with cancer is the* [Tweet]. Twitter. https://twitter.com/VPrasadMDMPH/status/1573803006054629376

306. Prasad, V. [@VPrasadMDMPH]. (2021, June 23). *I don't think people realize the damage continuing to push 2 doses in young men will do. It is beyond COVID* [Tweet]. Twitter. https://twitter.com/VPrasadMDMPH/status/1407743380507938817

307. Olmstead, S. C. (2022, June 23). *Media, health officials should 'Just tell the truth' about COVID shots for kids, physician says*. The Defender: Children's Health Defense News & Views. https://childrenshealthdefense.org/defender/COVID-shots-kids/

308. Koka, A. (2022, August 10). CNN myocarditis fact check by a cardiologist (me). *The Health Care Blog*. https://thehealthcareblog.com/blog/2022/08/10/cnn-myocarditis-fact-check-by-a-cardiologist-me/

309. Mandrola, J. [@drjohnm]. (2021, January 1). *This is EXACTLY why I promote robust critical appraisal of medical evidence. If you spent 2020 promoting fear-mongering howler-science (eg* [Tweet; thumbnail link to tweet]. Twitter. https://twitter.com/drjohnm/status/1345004816037249029

310. Mandrola, J. (2021, July 1). Vaccine-induced myocarditis concerns demand respect, not absolutism. *Medscape*. https://www.medscape.com/viewarticle/954038

311. Mandrola, J. [@drjohnm]. (2021, September 7). *I don't like the view 'contrarians' but yes, by being open and transparent and nuanced and humble, trust is increased.* [Tweet]. Twitter. https://twitter.com/drjohnm/status/1435211089990520836

312. Mandrola, J. [@drjohnm]. (2021, June 24). *As a cardiologist, I liken calling myocarditis 'mild' to the saying about 'minor' surgery. Minor surgery is surgery on someone* [Tweet; thumbnail link to tweet]. Twitter. https://twitter.com/drjohnm/status/1408166862626623489

313. Makary, M. (2021, December 27). *1/7,000 boys age 15-25 develop myocarditis after their second COVID vaccine dose* [Audio interview]. PodClips. https://podclips.com/c/pRzAbF

314. Makary, M. [@MartyMakary]. (2021, November 9). *Based on the data of kids w/ NO comorbid, an estimated 0-10 kids 5-11 have ever died of COVID VS* [Tweet]. Twitter. https://twitter.com/MartyMakary/status/1458090106976362498

315. Høeg, T. B., Krug, A., Stevenson, J., &Mandrola, J. (2021, September 8). *SARS-CoV-2 mRNA vaccination-associated myocarditis in children ages 12-17: A stratified national database analysis*. Medrxiv. https://doi.org/10.1101/2021.08.30.21262866

316. Stevenson, J. (2020, September 7). *A response to the viral "6%" post about COVID deaths*. Rational Ground. https://rationalground.com/a-response-to-the-viral-6-post-about-COVID-deaths/

317. Ault, A. (2021, September 15). COVID vaccine preprint study prompts Twitter outrage. *Medscape*. https://www.medscape.com/viewarticle/958778

318. Krug, A., Stevenson, J., & Høeg, T. B. (2022). BNT162b2 vaccine-associated myo/pericarditis in adolescents: A stratified risk-benefit analysis. *European Journal of Clinical Investigations*, *52*(5), Article 13759. https://doi.org/10.1111/eci.13759

319. and Prevention. (n.d.). *Vaccine adverse event reporting system (VAERS)*. U.S. Department of Health and Human Services. https://www.cdc.gov/vaccinesafety/ensuringsafety/monitoring/vaers/index.html

320. Goodman, M. J., & Nordin, J. (2006). Vaccine adverse event reporting system reporting source: A possible source of bias in longitudinal studies. *Pediatrics*, *117*(2), 387-390. https://doi.org/10.1542/peds.2004-2687

321. Freedman, D. (2021, September 12). Peer review of a VAERS dumpster dive. *Science-Based Medicine*. https://sciencebasedmedicine.org/peer-review-of-a-vaers-dumpster-dive/

322. Goldberg, D. (2021, September 10). *Although the scientific question that is being address is an important one, I have concerns about the methodology used to* [Comment to preprint article "SARS-CoV-2 mRNA vaccination-associated myocarditis in children ages 12-17: A stratified national database analysis"]. Medrxiv. https://www.medrxiv.org/content/10.1101/2021.08.30.21262866v1#comment-5529896348

323. Dreier, N. (2021, February 25). *10-year-old boy has hands, legs amputated after MIS-C, COVID-19 diagnosis*. Action News Jax. https://www.actionnewsjax.com/news/trending/10-year-old-boy-has-hands-legs-amputated-after-mis-c-COVID-19-diagnosis/2A7Q2NUKHVBBNBXETE5IOLOG2I/

324. Prasad, V. [@VPrasadMDMPH]. (2021, September 8). *Rate of cardiac adverse event after vax dose 2 in boys aged 12-15 is...... A Bombshell finding from dream team* [Tweet; thumbnail link to pre-print article]. Twitter. https://twitter.com/vprasadmdmph/status/1435807967345987587

325. McAdams, A. (2021, September 28). *'A devastating shock': UNCW student dies due to COVID-19 complications, funeral arrangements in place*. WBTV. https://www.wbtv.com/2021/09/27/devastating-shock-uncw-student-brain-dead-due-COVID-19-complications-mother-pleads-young-people-get-vaccinated/

326. Hviid, A., Stellfeld, M., Wohlfahrt, J., & Melbye, M. (2003). Association between thimerosal-containing vaccine and autism. *JAMA*, *290*(13), 1763-1766. https://doi.org/10.1001/jama.290.13.1763

327. Lee, B. Y. (2022, November 22). New 'Died Suddenly' film pushes unfounded depopulation claims about COVID-19 vaccine. *Forbes*. https://www.forbes.com/sites/brucelee/2022/11/22/new-died-suddenly-film-pushes-unfounded-depopulation-claims-about-COVID-19-vaccine/?sh=22f8511749d0

328. Høeg, T. B. [@TracyBethHoeg]. (2022, August 9). *[Flag: Thailand] Stunning prospective study from Thailand Of 301 13-18 year olds following dose 2 pfizer 18% had abnormal EKG post vax* [Tweet; infographic attached]. Twitter. https://twitter.com/tracybethhoeg/status/1557039855304990721

329. Prasad, V. (2022, August 13). What does the Thailand myocarditis study teach us? Taking safety signals seriously is imperative; the US CDC & others have failed to do that. *Vinay Prasad's Observations and Thoughts*. https://vinayprasadmdmph.substack.com/p/what-does-the-thailand-myocarditis

330. Koka, A. (2022, August 10). Vaccine myocarditis update from Thailand. *Dr. Anish Koka's Newsletter*. https://anishkokamd.substack.com/p/vaccine-myocarditis-update-from-thailand

331. Han, F. (2022, August 13). COVID-19 vaccination and myocarditis: another preprint. *Science-Based Medicine*. https://sciencebasedmedicine.org/COVID-19-vaccination-and-myocarditis-another-preprint/

332. Cirer-Sastre, R., Legaz-Arrese, A., Corbi, F., López-Laval, I., Puente-Lanzarote, J., Hernández-González, V., & Reverter-Masià, J. (2019). Effect of training load on post-exercise cardiac troponin T elevations in young soccer players. *International Journal of Environmental Research and Public Health*, *16*(23), 4853. https://doi.org/10.3390/ijerph16234853

333. Ramoğlu, M. G., Karagözlü, S., Bayram, Ö., Bakhtiyarzada, J., Aydin, A., Vatansever, G., Özdemir, H., Tekin, D., Uçar, T., Çiftçi, E., & Tutar, E. (2022). The role and efficacy of routine high-sensitivity troponin T screening in paediatric COVID-19. *Cardiology in the Young*, *32*(3), 472-476. https://doi.org/10.1017/S1047951121005199

334. Guner Ozenen, G., Akaslan Kara, A., Kiymet, E., Boncuoglu, E., Sahinkaya, S., Cem, E., Yilmaz Celebi, M., Kacar, P., Gulderen, M., Uras, M., Muhtar Yılmazer, M., Murat, M., Mese, T., Agin, H., Bayram, N., & Devrim, İ. (2022). The evaluation of troponin I levels and myocarditis in children with COVID-19: A pediatric single-center experience. *Pediatric Cardiology*. Advance online publication. https://doi.org/10.1007/s00246-022-03017-5

335. Dufort, E. M., Koumans, E. H., Chow, E. J., Rosenthal, E. M., Muse, A., Rowlands, J., Barranco, M. A., Maxted, A. M., Rosenberg, E. S., Easton, D., Udo, T., Kumar, J., Pulver, W., Smith, L., Hutton, B., Blog, D., & Zucker, H. (2020). Multisystem inflammatory syndrome in children in New York State. *The New England Journal of Medicine*, *383*, 347-358. https://doi.org/10.1056/NEJMoa2021756

336. Brogan, K. (n.d.). CDC: You're fired. Autism coverup exposed. *Kelly Brogan, MD*. https://www.kellybroganmd.com/blog/cdc-youre-fired-autism-coverup-exposed

337. Makary, M. [@MartyMakary]. (2022, September 27). *Last yr, the NEJM described a 22-yr-old that died from vax-induced myocarditis & I've heard of many more cases* [Tweet]. Twitter. https://twitter.com/MartyMakary/status/1574760794209882114

338. Makary, M. (2022, February 27). The CDC – which is withholding information – has a hidden agenda. *New York Post*. https://nypost.com/2022/02/27/the-cdc-has-a-hidden-agenda-when-it-comes-to-COVID-vaccines/

339. Martinez, C. (2022, October 24). *COVID-19 surges linked to spike in heart attacks*. Cedars-Sinai. https://www.cedars-sinai.org/newsroom/COVID-19-surges-linked-to-spike-in-heart-attacks/

340. Prasad, V. [@VPrasadMDMPH]. (2022, July 10). *the wisest comment that few appreciate* [Tweet]. Twitter. https://twitter.com/VPrasadMDMPH/status/1546258736489979904

341. Walensky, R. (2021, June 24). *CDC director weighs in on risk of myocarditis from COVID-19 vaccine* [Video interview]. ABC News. https://abcnews.go.com/GMA/News/video/cdc-director-weighs-risk-myocarditis-COVID-19-vaccine-78460627

342. U.S. Food and Drug Administration. (2021, December 8). *CBER assessment of a single booster dose of the Pfizer-BioNTech COVID-19 Vaccine (0.3 mL) administered to individuals 16 to 17 years of age after completion of a primary vaccination series with the Pfizer-BioNTech COVID-19 Vaccine or COMIRNATY* [Review memorandum]. U.S.

Department of Health and Human Services. https://www.fda.gov/media/154869/download

343. Prasad, V. (2021, November 4). *Doctors must be honest with parents about unknown risks of COVID-19 emergency vaccine*. Yahoo! News. https://www.yahoo.com/news/doctors-must-honest-parents-unknown-100213768.html
344. Emery, D. (2016, August 4). *Wisconsin girl dies as a result of receiving Gardasil HPV vaccine*. Snopes.com. https://www.snopes.com/fact-check/girl-dies-gardasil-hpv-vaccine/

345. Howard, J. (2021, May 10). Should COVID-19 vaccines be administered to children under an emergency use authorization? *Science-Based Medicine*. https://sciencebasedmedicine.org/COVID-19-vaccine-children-under-an-emergency-use-authorization/

346. Pegden, W. (2021, June 23). Weighing myocarditis cases, ACIP failed to balance the harms vs benefits of 2nd doses. *Medium*. https://medium.com/@wpegden/weighing-myocarditis-cases-acip-failed-to-balance-the-harms-vs-benefits-of-2nd-doses-d7d6b3df7cfb

347. Bennett, C., & Jones, B. (2021, June 23). *CDC investigating recent death of Saginaw teen days after receiving COVID-19 vaccine*. Mid-Michigan Now. https://nbc25news.com/news/local/cdc-investigating-recent-death-of-saginaw-teen-days-after-receiving-COVID-19-vaccine

348. Camp, T. (2022, February 9). *Probe shows no link between COVID-19 vaccine and death of 13-year-old Saginaw County boy*. ABC12. https://www.abc12.com/coronavirus/probe-shows-no-link-between-COVID-19-vaccine-and-death-of-13-year-old-saginaw/article_d20e2248-853c-11ec-a796-fff441e21fb4.html

349. Høeg, T. B. [@TracyBethHoeg]. (2022, February 9). *I believe this is the 1st confirmed post-vax myocarditis death in the US: "Because he wanted to take his classes* [Thumbnail link to article]. Twitter. https://twitter.com/TracyBethHoeg/status/1491510131879649281

350. Howard, J. [@19joho]. (2022, February 9). *It's a tragedy, but not closely related to the vaccine. The coroner can't even pronounce myocarditis and has to look* [Tweet; thumbnail link to audio recording]. Twitter. https://twitter.com/19joho/status/1491552792535867399

351. Høeg, T. B. [@TracyBethHoeg]. (2022, February 9). *I agree. This case and autospy for a 22 year old South Korean is more clear cut* [Tweet; thumbnail link to article]. Twitter. https://twitter.com/TracyBethHoeg/status/1491586239681626119

352. Redshaw, M. (2022, February 25). *8-year-old boy dies of MIS 7 days after Pfizer vaccine, VAERS report shows*. The Defender: Children's Health Defense News & Views. https://childrenshealthdefense.org/defender/vaers-cdc-8-year-old-boy-dies-pfizer-vaccine/

353. Redshaw, M. (2021, June 24). *13-year-old Michigan boy dies 3 days after second dose of Pfizer vaccine, aunt says 'moral, ethical, health' questions need answers*. The Defender: Children's Health Defense News & Views. https://childrenshealthdefense.org/defender/13-year-old-jacob-clynick-dies-pfizer-vaccine-myocarditis/

354. Menge, M. (2022, September 7). *55% of babies, toddlers had 'systemic reaction' after COVID vaccine, CDC survey shows*. The Defender: Children's Health Defense News & Views. https://childrenshealthdefense.org/defender/babies-toddlers-systemic-reaction-COVID-vaccine-cdc-et/

355. Research Office. (n.d.). *What is the Institutional Review Board (IRB)?* Oregon State University. Retrieved December 28, 2022, from https://research.oregonstate.edu/irb/frequently-asked-questions/what-institutional-review-board-irb

356. Torjesen, I. (2015, May 12). Drug development: The journey of a medicine from lab to shelf. *The Pharmaceutical Journal*. https://pharmaceutical-journal.com/article/feature/drug-development-the-journey-of-a-medicine-from-lab-to-shelf

357. *How much does a clinical trial cost?* (2020, January 2). Sofpromed. https://www.sofpromed.com/how-much-does-a-clinical-trial-cost

358. National Institute of Allergy and Infectious Diseases (NIAID). (2020, June 20). *Bulletin -- NIH clinical trial evaluating hydroxychloroquine and azithromycin for COVID-19 closes early*. U.S. Department of Health and Human Services. https://www.niaid.nih.gov/news-events/bulletin-nih-clinical-trial-evaluating-hydroxychloroquine-and-azithromycin-COVID-19

359. Walter, E. B., Talaat, K. R., Sabharwal, C., Gurtman, A., Lockhart, S., Paulsen, G. C., Barnett, E. D., Muñoz, F. M., Maldonado, Y., Pahud, B. A., Domachowske, J. B., Simões, E. A. F., Sarwar, U. N., Kitchin, N., Cunliffe, L., Rojo, P., Kuchar, E., Rämet, M., Munjal, I., … Gruber, W. C. (2022). Evaluation of the BNT162b2 COVID-19 vaccine in children 5 to 11 years of age (Supplementary material: Protocol). *The New England Journal of Medicine*, *386*, 35-46. https://www.nejm.org/doi/suppl/10.1056/NEJMoa2116298/suppl_file/nejmoa2116298_appendix.pdf

360. Schmidt, C. (2017). The struggle to do no harm in clinical trials: What

lessons are being learnt from studies that went wrong? *Nature, 552*, S74-S75. https://doi.org/10.1038/d41586-017-08705-4

361. Gorski, D. (2021, November 8). What the heck happened to The BMJ? *Science-Based Medicine*. https://sciencebasedmedicine.org/what-the-heck-happened-to-the-bmj/
362. Christian, J. (n.d.). The new Gardasil: Is it right for your daughter? *Kelly Brogan, MD*. https://www.kellybroganmd.com/blog/new-gardasil

363. Lehtinen, M., Paavonen, J., Wheeler, C. M., Jaisamrarn, U., Garland, S. M., Castellsagué, X., Skinner, S. R., Apter, D., Naud, P., Salmerón, J., Chow, S.-N., Kitchener, H., Teixeira, J. C., Hedrick, J., Limson, G., Szarewski, A., Romanowski, B., Aoki, F. Y., Schwarz, T. F., … Dubin, G. (2012). Overall efficacy of HPV-16/18 AS04-adjuvanted vaccine against grade 3 or greater cervical intraepithelial neoplasia: 4-year end-of-study analysis of the randomised, double-blind PATRICIA trial. *The Lancet Oncology, 13*(1), 89-99. https://doi.org/10.1016/s1470-2045(11)70286-8

364. NCI Staff. (2020, October 14). *Study confirms HPV vaccine prevents cervical cancer*. National Cancer Institute. https://www.cancer.gov/news-events/cancer-currents-blog/2020/hpv-vaccine-prevents-cervical-cancer-sweden-study

365. NCI Staff. (2020, October 14). *Large study confirms HPV vaccine prevents cervical cancer*. National Cancer Institute: Division of Cancer Epidemiology and Genetics. https://dceg.cancer.gov/news-events/news/2020/hpv-vaccine-sweden

366. Brogan, K. (n.d.). Truth out: Gardasil vaccine coverup exposed. *Kelly Brogan MD*. https://www.kellybroganmd.com/blog/truth-out-gardasil-coverup-documents-exposed

367. Howard, J., & Reiss, D. (2018). The anti-vaccine movement: A litany of fallacy and errors. In A. B. Kaufman & J. C. Kaufman (Eds.), *Pseudoscience: The conspiracy against science* (pp. 195-219). The MIT Press. https://doi.org/10.7551/mitpress/10747.003.0013

368. Kulldorff, M. (2022, May 6). *The triumph of natural immunity*. Brownstone Institute. https://brownstone.org/articles/the-triumph-of-natural-immunity/

369. Bienen, L., & Høeg, T. B. (2022, July 5). *The CDC is breaking trust in childhood vaccination: With its unscientific push to vaccinate all infants and toddlers against COVID, the agency will harm vaccine uptake for more significant diseases*. Tablet Magazine. https://www.tabletmag.com/sections/science/articles/cdc-is-endangering-childhood-vaccination-progress

370. *Our team: Dr. Tracy Høeg*. (2022, May 19). Northern California Orthopaedic Associates. https://www.norcalorthoassociates.com/team/hoeg.php

371. Lei, J., Ploner, A., Elfström, M., Wang, J., Roth, A., Fang, F., Sundström, K., Dillner, J., & Sparén, P. (2020). HPV vaccination and the risk of invasive cervical cancer. *The New England Journal of Medicine*, *383*, 1340-1348. https://doi.org/10.1056/NEJMoa1917338

372. Prasad, V. [@VPrasadMDMPH]. (2022, July 21). *yes, nice paper from the germans on MISC yesterday. Honestly still not sure vaccination lowers the risk of mis-c, but* [Tweet]. Twitter. https://twitter.com/VPrasadMDMPH/status/1550203802887720960

373. Prasad, V. [@VPrasadMDMPH]. (2022, August 28). *It Is Now Undeniable [backhand index pointing down] Vaccine can cause more Myocarditis in Men Under 40 Than COVID-19; Just OUT! Patrone Circ* [Tweet; infographic attached]. Twitter. https://twitter.com/vprasadmdmph/status/1564088565524357120

374. Patone, M., Mei, X. W., Handunnetthi, L., Dixon, S., Zaccardi, F., Shankar-Hari, M., Watkinson, P., Khunti, K., Harnden, A., Coupland, C. A. C., Channon, K. M., Mills, N. L., Sheikh, A., & Hippisley-Cox, J. (2022). Risk of myocarditis after sequential doses of COVID-19 vaccine and SARS-CoV-2 infection by age and sex. *Circulation*, *146*(10), 743-754. https://doi.org/10.1161/CIRCULATIONAHA.122.059970

375. McDonald, J. (2022, July 22). *Posts misleadingly omit critical data supporting COVID-19 vaccines for youngest kids*. FactCheck.org. https://www.factcheck.org/2022/07/scicheck-posts-misleadingly-omit-critical-clinical-trial-data-supporting-COVID-19-vaccines-for-littlest-kids/

376. Gilbert, P. B., Donis, R. O., Koup, R. A., Fong, Y., Plotkin, S. A., & Follmann, D. (2022). A COVID-19 milestone attained — A correlate of protection for vaccines. *The New England Journal of Medicine*, *387*, 2203-2206. https://doi.org/10.1056/NEJMp2211314

377. Makary, M. [@MartyMakary]. (2022, June 14). *"Inferred through "immunobridging" young adult data from another study?? This is statistical acrobatics, which appears to be done to achieve* [Tweet]. Twitter. https://twitter.com/MartyMakary/status/1536800260932222976

378. and Prevention. (2022, June 27). *ACIP evidence to recommendations for use of Moderna COVID-19 vaccine in children ages 6 months – 5 years and Pfizer-BioNTech COVID-19 vaccine in children ages 6 months – 4 years under an emergency use authorization.* U.S. Department of Health and Human Services. https://www.cdc.gov/vaccines/acip/recs/grade/

COVID-19-moderna-pfizer-children-vaccine-etr.html

379. U.S. Food and Drug Administration. (2022, November 22). *EUA 27034 - Emergency use authorization of Pfizer-BioNTech COVID-19 vaccine and Pfizer-BioNTech COVID-19 vaccine, bivalent, reissued on October 12, 2022, under Section 564 of the Federal Food, Drug, and Cosmetic Act (FDCA) (21 U.S.C. 360bbb-3)* [EUA amendment notification letter]. U.S. Department of Health and Human Services. https://www.fda.gov/media/163486/download

380. Hause, A. M., Marquez, P., Zhang, B., Myers, T. R., Gee, J., Su, J. R., Parker, C., Thompson, D., Panchanathan, S. S., Shimabukuro, T. T., & Shay, D. K. (2022). COVID-19 mRNA vaccine safety among children aged 6 months–5 years — United States, June 18, 2022–August 21, 2022. *Morbidity and Mortality Weekly Report*, *71*(35), 1115-1120. http://dx.doi.org/10.15585/mmwr.mm7135a3

381. Kennedy, R. F., Jr. (2018, December 29). The HPV debacle: Suppressing inconvenient evidence. *GreenMedInfo*. https://greenmedinfo.com/blog/hpv-debacle-suppressing-inconvenient-evidence

382. Belluz, J. (2017, December 1). *Why Japan's HPV vaccine rates dropped from 70% to near zero*. Vox. https://www.vox.com/science-and-health/2017/12/1/16723912/japan-hpv-vaccine

383. Simms, K. T., Hanley, S. J. B., Smith, M. A., Keane, A., & Canfell, K. (2020). Impact of HPV vaccine hesitancy on cervical cancer in Japan: A modelling study. *The Lancet Public Health*, *5*(4), E223-E234. https://doi.org/10.1016/S2468-2667(20)30010-4

384. Nevradakis, M. (2022, January 28). *Fauci says kids under 5 might need 3 shots, as Sweden says benefits don't outweigh risks for young kids*. The Defender: Children's Health Defense News & Views. https://childrenshealthdefense.org/defender/fauci-kids-under-5-might-need-3-shots/

385. Whittaker, R., Greve-Isdahl, M., Bøås, H., Alnes Buanes, E., & Veneti, L. (2022). COVID-19 hospitalization among children <18 years by variant wave in Norway. *Pediatrics*, *150*(3), Article 2022057564. https://doi.org/10.1542/peds.2022-057564

386. Ji, S. (2014, March 14). Should you trust 'The Daily Beast' about vaccines? *GreenMedInfo*. https://greenmedinfo.com/blog/should-you-trust-daily-beast-about-vaccines

387. *When should you get a polio vaccination?* (n.d.). Washington State Department of Health. Retrieved December 29, 2022, from https://doh.

wa.gov/you-and-your-family/immunization/diseases-and-vaccines-can-prevent-them/polio-0/when-should-you-get-polio-vaccination

388. and Prevention. (2022, September 6). *Diphtheria, tetanus, and whooping cough vaccination: What you should know*. U.S. Department of Health and Human Services. https://www.cdc.gov/vaccines/vpd/dtap-tdap-td/public/index.html

389. National Center for Immunization and Respiratory Diseases. (2016, November 30). *Clinician FAQ: CDC recommendations for HPV vaccine 2-dose schedules* [Information letter CS HCVG15-PTT-106]. and Prevention. https://www.une.edu/sites/default/files/provider2dose.pdf

390. Pfizer. (2021, October 21). *Pfizer and BioNTech announce phase 3 trial data showing high efficacy of a booster dose of their COVID-19 vaccine* [Press release]. https://www.pfizer.com/news/press-release/press-release-detail/pfizer-and-biontech-announce-phase-3-trial-data-showing

391. Moreira, E. D., Kitchin, N., Xu, X., Dychter, S. S., Lockhart, S., Gurtman, A., Perez, J. L., Zerbini, C., Dever, M. E., Jennings, T. W., Brandon, D. M., Cannon, K. D., Koren, M. J., Denham, D. S., Berhe, M., Fitz-Patrick, D., Hammitt, L. L., Klein, N. P., Nell, H., … Jansen, K. U. (2022). Safety and efficacy of a third dose of BNT162b2 COVID-19 vaccine. *The New England Journal of Medicine*, *386*, 1910-1921. https://doi.org/10.1056/NEJMoa2200674

392. Barda, N., Dagan, N., Cohen, C., Hernán, M. A., Lipsitch, M., Kohane, I. S., Reis, B. Y., & Balicer, R. D. (2021). Effectiveness of a third dose of the BNT162b2 mRNA COVID-19 vaccine for preventing severe outcomes in Israel: An observational study. *The Lancet*, *398*(10316), 2093-2100. https://doi.org/10.1016/S0140-6736(21)02249-2

393. Flynn, H. (2022, January 31). *Why Omicron is SARS-CoV-2's biggest 'evolutionary leap' yet*. Medical News Today. https://www.medicalnewstoday.com/articles/why-omicron-is-sars-cov-2s-biggest-evolutionary-leap-yet

394. Mueller, B., & Lutz, E. (2022, May 31). During the Omicron wave, death rates soared for older people. *The New York Times*. https://www.nytimes.com/2022/05/31/health/omicron-deaths-age-65-elderly.html

395. Andrews, N., Stowe, J., Kirsebom, F., Toffa, S., Sachdeva, R., Gower, C., Ramsay, M., & Lopez Bernal, J. (2022). Effectiveness of COVID-19 booster vaccines against COVID-19-related symptoms, hospitalization and death in England. *Nature Medicine*, *28*, 831-837. https://doi.org/10.1038/s41591-022-01699-1

396. Menni, C., May, A., Polidori, L., Louca, P., Wolf, J., Capdevila, J.,

Hu, C., Ourselin, S., Steves, C. J., Valdes, A. M., & Spector, T. D. (2022). COVID-19 vaccine waning and effectiveness and side-effects of boosters: A prospective community study from the ZOE COVID Study. *The Lancet Infectious Diseases*, *22*(7), 1002-1010. https://doi.org/10.1016/S1473-3099(22)00146-3

397. Abu-Raddad, L. J., Chemaitelly, H., Ayoub, H. H., Al-Mukdad, S., Yassine, H. M., Al-Khatib, H. A., Smatti, M. K., Tang, P., Hasan, M. R., Coyle, P., Al-Kanaani, Z., Al-Kuwari, E., Jeremijenko, A., Kaleeckal, A. H., Latif, A. N., Shaik, R. M., Abdul-Rahim, H. F., Nasrallah, G. K., Al-Kuwari, M. G., … Bertollini, R. (2022). Effect of mRNA vaccine boosters against SARS-CoV-2 Omicron infection in Qatar. *The New England Journal of Medicine*, *386*, 1804-1816. https://doi.org/10.1056/NEJMoa2200797

398. Arbel, R., Hammerman, A., Sergienko, R., Friger, M., Peretz, A., Netzer, D., & Yaron, S. (2021). BNT162b2 vaccine booster and mortality due to COVID-19. *The New England Journal of Medicine*, *385*, 2413-2420. https://doi.org/10.1056/NEJMoa2115624

399. Bar-On, Y. M., Goldberg, Y., Mandel, M., Bodenheimer, O., Freedman, L., Alroy-Preis, S., Ash, N., Huppert, A., & Milo, R. (2021). Protection against COVID-19 by BNT162b2 booster across age groups. *The New England Journal of Medicine*, *385*, 2421-2430. https://doi.org/10.1056/NEJMoa2115926

400. Muhsen, K., Maimon, N., Mizrahi, A. Y., Boltyansky, B., Bodenheimer, O., Hillel Diamant, Z., Gaon, L., Cohen, D., & Dagan, R. (2022). Association of receipt of the fourth BNT162b2 dose with Omicron infection and COVID-19 hospitalizations among residents of long-term care facilities. *JAMA Internal Medicine*, *182*(8), 859-867. https://doi.org/10.1001/jamainternmed.2022.2658

401. Thompson, M. G., Natarajan, K., Irving, S. A., Rowley, E. A., Griggs, E. P., Gaglani, M., Klein, N. P., Grannis, S. J., DeSilva, M. B., Stenehjem, E., Reese, S. E., Dickerson, M., Naleway, A. L., Han, J., Konatham, D., McEvoy, C., Rao, S., Dixon, B. E., Dascomb, K., … Ong, T. C. (2022). Effectiveness of a third dose of mRNA vaccines against COVID-19–associated emergency department and urgent care encounters and hospitalizations among adults during periods of Delta and Omicron variant predominance — VISION network, 10 states, August 2021–January 2022. *Morbidity and Mortality Weekly Report*, *71*(4), 139-145. http://dx.doi.org/10.15585/mmwr.mm7104e3

402. Accorsi, E. K., Britton, A., Fleming-Dutra, K. E., Smith, Z. R., Shang, N., Derado, G., Miller, J., Schrag, S. J., & Verani, J. R. (2022). Association between 3 doses of mRNA COVID-19 vaccine and

symptomatic infection caused by the SARS-CoV-2 Omicron and Delta variants. *JAMA*, *327*(7), 639-651. https://doi.org/10.1001/jama.2022.0470

403. McConeghy, K. W., White, E. M., Blackman, C., Santostefano, C. M., Lee, Y., Rudolph, J. L., Canaday, D., Zullo, A. R., Jernigan, J. A., Pilishvili, T., Mor, V., & Gravenstein, S. (2022). Effectiveness of a second COVID-19 vaccine booster dose against infection, hospitalization, or death among nursing home residents — 19 States, March 29–July 25, 2022. *Morbidity and Mortality Weekly Report*, *71*(39), 1235-1238. http://dx.doi.org/10.15585/mmwr.mm7139a2

404. Oliver, S. (2022, September 1). *Evidence to recommendations framework: Bivalent COVID-19 vaccine booster doses* [Presentation]. and Prevention. https://www.cdc.gov/vaccines/acip/meetings/downloads/slides-2022-09-01/08-COVID-oliver-508.pdf

405. Prasad, V. [@VPrasadMDMPH]. (2022, October 22). *The CDC director getting COVID-19 one month after bivalent booster is a reminder that she doesn't know what* [Tweet; thumbnail link to article]. Twitter. https://twitter.com/VPrasadMDMPH/status/1583886777646870528

406. Surie, D., DeCuir, J., Zhu, Y., Gaglani, M., Ginde, A. A., Douin, D. J., Talbot, H. K., Casey, J. D., Mohr, N. M., Zepeski, A., McNeal, T., Ghamande, S., Gibbs, K. W., Files, D. C., Hager, D. N., Ali, H., Taghizadeh, L., Gong, M. N., Mohamed, A., … IVY Network. (2022). Early estimates of bivalent mRNA vaccine effectiveness in preventing COVID-19–associated hospitalization among immunocompetent adults aged ≥65 years — IVY Network, 18 states, September 8–November 30, 2022. *Morbidity and Mortality Weekly Report*, *71*(5152), 1625-1630. http://dx.doi.org/10.15585/mmwr.mm715152e2

407. Tenforde, M. W., Weber, Z. A., Natarajan, K., Klein, N. P., Kharbanda, A. B., Stenehjem, E., Embi, P. J., Reese, S. E., Naleway, A. L., Grannis, S. J., DeSilva, M. B., Ong, T. C., Gaglani, M., Han, J., Dickerson, M., Fireman, B., Dascomb, K., Irving, S. A., Vazquez-Benitez, G., … Link-Gelles, R. (2022). Early estimates of bivalent mRNA vaccine effectiveness in preventing COVID-19–associated emergency department or urgent care encounters and hospitalizations among immunocompetent adults — VISION network, nine states, September–November 2022. *Morbidity and Mortality Weekly Report*, *71*(5152), 1616-1624. http://dx.doi.org/10.15585/mmwr.mm715152e1

408. Diane M. Harper. (n.d.). *Diane M. Harper, M.D., M.P.H., M.S. | Family Medicine | Michigan Medicine*. Michigan Medicine: University of Michigan. Retrieved December 29, 2022, from https://medicine.umich.edu/dept/family-medicine/diane-m-harper-md-mph-ms

409. Attkisson, S. (2009, August 19). *Gardasil researcher speaks out*. CBS News. https://www.cbsnews.com/news/gardasil-researcher-speaks-out/

410. Michigan Medicine. (2018, June 8). *NCI statement on cervical cancer prevention draws on leadership from Family Medicine faculty*. University of Michigan. https://medicine.umich.edu/dept/family-medicine/news/archive/201806/nci-statement-cervical-cancer-prevention-draws-leadership-family-medicine-faculty

411. Krause, P., Gruber, M. F., & Offit, P. A. (2021, November 29). We don't need universal booster shots. We need to reach the unvaccinated. *The Washington Post*. https://www.washingtonpost.com/outlook/2021/11/29/booster-shots-universal-opinion/

412. Gutman-Wei, R. (2022, January 11). Should teens get a booster for Omicron? Third shots for adolescent boys and young men were already a hard sell. Then came Omicron. *The Atlantic*. https://www.theatlantic.com/health/archive/2022/01/should-teens-get-booster-omicron/621222/

413. Redshaw, M. (2021, September 1). *2 top FDA vaccine officials resign, raising questions about pressure from White House to approve boosters*. The Defender: Children's Health Defense News & Views. https://childrenshealthdefense.org/defender/2-top-fda-regulators-resign-white-house-approve-boosters/

414. Redshaw, M. (2022, July 7). *Paul Offit: It 'felt like the fix was in' before FDA panel voted to reformulate COVID booster shots*. The Defender: Children's Health Defense News & Views. https://childrenshealthdefense.org/defender/dr-paul-offit-COVID-vaccine-mandate/

415. Prasad, V. [@VPrasadMDMPH]. (2022, January 11). *WOW! Paul Offit advised his own son not to get boosted [backhand index pointing down times 3] A man who made vaccines is saying this. Hard* [Tweet; thumbnail link to article]. Twitter. https://twitter.com/vprasadmdmph/status/1481003046893088769

416. Makary, M., & Høeg, T. B. (2022, July 14). *U.S. public health agencies aren't 'following the science,' officials say: 'People are getting bad advice and we can't say anything*. The Free Press for Free People. https://www.commonsense.news/p/us-public-health-agencies-arent-following?

417. Offit, P. (2020, March 2). *Dr. Paul Offit: Why the coronavirus will be hard to contain* [Video interview]. Amanpour & Co. https://www.pbs.org/wnet/amanpour-and-company/video/dr-paul-offit-why-coronavirus-will-be-hard-to-contain/

418. Damania, Z. (Host). (2021, October 11). The truth about myocarditis,

kids, boosters, natural immunity, & more [Video podcast episode]. In *ZDoggMD: Slightly funnier than placebo*. https://zdoggmd.com/paul-offit-7/

419. WRAL Investigates. (2022, December 27). *One expert recommends parents avoid latest booster vaccine for healthy children*. WRAL. https://www.wral.com/coronavirus/one-expert-recommends-that-parents-avoid-latest-booster-vaccine-for-healthy-children/20642043/

420. Pierce, C. A., Herold, K. C., Herold, B. C., Chou, J., Randolph, A., Kane, B., McFarland, S., Gurdasani, D., Pagel, C., Hotez, P., Cobey, S., & Hensley, S. E. (2022). COVID-19 and children. *Science*, *377*(6611), 1144-1149. https://doi.org/10.1126/science.ade1675

421. Associated Press. (2022, July 14). *25 million kids missed routine vaccinations because of COVID: About 25 million children worldwide have missed out on routine immunizations against diseases like diptheria, tetanus and pertussis*. ABC News. https://abcnews.go.com/Lifestyle/wireStory/25-million-kids-missed-routine-vaccinations-COVID-86852559

422. Seither, R., Laury, J., Mugerwa-Kasujja, A., Knighton, C. L., & Black, C. L. (2022). Vaccination coverage with selected vaccines and exemption rates among children in kindergarten — United States, 2020–21 school year. *Morbidity and Mortality Weekly Report*, *71*(16), 561-568. http://dx.doi.org/10.15585/mmwr.mm7116a1

423. Daley, J. (2020, July 8). Vaccinations have sharply declined nationwide during the COVID-19 pandemic: Rates of childhood immunization have fallen across the U.S., raising the risk of vaccine-preventable disease outbreaks. *Scientific American*. https://www.scientificamerican.com/article/vaccinations-have-sharply-declined-nationwide-during-the-COVID-19-pandemic/

424. Gorski, D. [Orac]. (2022, May 27). Radical COVID-19 antivax sentiment is metastasizing to childhood vaccines: COVID-19 has radicalized the antivaccine movement. Unfortunately, that radicalization is metastasizing to encompass all vaccines. *Respectful Insolence*. https://www.respectfulinsolence.com/2022/05/27/radical-COVID-19-antivax-sentiment-is-metastasizing-to-childhood-vaccines/

425. Defender Staff. (2022, August 12). *A COVID silver lining? More parents than ever questioning 'routine' childhood vaccines*. The Defender: Children's Health Defense News & Views. https://childrenshealthdefense.org/defender/parents-questioning-routine-childhood-vaccines-COVID/

426. Fox, M. (2015, July 2). *Washington woman is first U.S. measles death*

in 12 years. NBC News. https://www.nbcnews.com/health/health-news/woman-dies-measles-first-us-death-12-years-n385946

427. Forman, H. [@thehowie]. (2022, August 7). *Oncologist who has invested much of his time to undermining faith in vaccines and vaccine data now surprised that people* [Tweet; image attached]]. Twitter. https://twitter.com/thehowie/status/1556332687304146949

428. Howard, J. (2022, July 29). "Natural immunity" stans forget babies will always be vulnerable to COVID. *Science-Based Medicine*. https://sciencebasedmedicine.org/obviously/

429. Kekatos, M. (2022, August 8). *CDC sends team to New York to investigate polio case: The case was detected in an unvaccinated 20-year-old man*. ABC News. https://abcnews.go.com/Health/cdc-sends-team-york-investigate-polio-case/story?id=88095468

430. Novella, S. (2022, August 3). The return of Polio: Once again we lose the chance to eradicate polio, but the goal still remains relatively close. *Science-Based Medicine*. https://sciencebasedmedicine.org/the-return-of-polio/

431. Henry, J. (2022, July 21). *First US case of polio in nearly a decade is an Orthodox Jewish man*. Jewish Telegraphic Agency. https://www.jta.org/2022/07/21/ny/first-us-case-of-polio-in-nearly-a-decade-is-an-orthodox-jewish-man

432. Mole, B. (2019, May 14). Andrew Wakefield, others hold anti-vaccine rally amid raging measles outbreaks: Again, anti-vaxxers prey on communities hit by outbreak. *Ars Technica*. https://arstechnica.com/science/2019/05/andrew-wakefield-others-hold-anti-vaccine-rally-amid-raging-measles-outbreaks/

433. Rogers, K. (2019, September 25). *Measles outbreak that sickened 312 in Rockland County, New York, declared over*. CNN. https://www.cnn.com/2019/09/25/health/measles-outbreak-over-rockland-county-ny

434. *All London children aged one to nine to be offered polio vaccine dose after more virus found in sewers*. (2022, August 10). Yahoo! News. https://ca.news.yahoo.com/london-children-aged-one-nine-115000391.html

35. Prasad, V. (2021, December 24). *UK does not advise vaccines for 5-11 year olds, while the US starts to mandate them*. Brownstone Institute. https://brownstone.org/articles/uk-does-not-advise-vaccines-for-5-11-year-olds-while-the-us-starts-to-mandate-them/

436. Howard, J. (2022, August 12). Can COVID vaccines travel in space and time? *Science-Based Medicine*. https://sciencebasedmedicine.org/space-and-time/

437. Sun, L. H. (2022, December 26). Growing vaccine hesitancy fuels measles, chickenpox resurgence in U.S.: Anti-vaccine sentiment has increased since the pandemic, driven by politicization around the coronavirus vaccine. *The Washington Post*. https://www.washingtonpost.com/health/2022/12/26/vaccine-hesitancy-measles-chickenpox-polio-flu/

438. Gorski, D. (2022, May 9). The "12% efficacy" myth from the "Pfizer data dump": The latest slasher stat about COVID-19 vaccines. *Science-Based Medicine*. https://sciencebasedmedicine.org/the-12-gambit-the-latest-slasher-stat-about-COVID-19-vaccines/

439. Children's Health Defense Team. (2021, November 1). *WATCH: Sen. Johnson holds expert panel on COVID vaccine injuries, federal vaccine mandates*. The Defender: Children's Health Defense News & Views. https://childrenshealthdefense.org/defender/nov-2-sen-ron-johnson-cdh-COVID-vaccine-injuries-federal-mandates/

440. Doshi, P. (2020, November 26). Pfizer and Moderna's "95% effective" vaccines—let's be cautious and first see the full data. *The BMJ Opinion*. https://blogs.bmj.com/bmj/2020/11/26/peter-doshi-pfizer-and-modernas-95-effective-vaccines-lets-be-cautious-and-first-see-the-full-data/

441. Doshi, P. (2021, January 4). Peter Doshi: Pfizer and Moderna's "95% effective" vaccines—we need more details and the raw data. *The BMJ Opinion*. https://blogs.bmj.com/bmj/2021/01/04/peter-doshi-pfizer-and-modernas-95-effective-vaccines-we-need-more-details-and-the-raw-data/

442. Fraiman, J. (2022, April 2). *A physician's plea for exemption: Full text*. Brownstone Institute. https://brownstone.org/articles/a-physicians-plea-for-exemption-full-text/

443. Fraiman, J., Erviti, J., Jones, M., Greenland, S., Whelan, P., Kaplan, R. M., & Doshi, P. (2022, September 9). *Serious adverse events of special interest following mRNA vaccination in randomized trials*. SSRN. https://papers.ssrn.com/sol3/papers.cfm?abstract_id=4125239

444. Grimes, D. R. [@drg1985]. (2022, September 2). *and you know what makes it so much worse? Even AFTER they tortured the data, they didn't even get a* [Tweet; infographic attached]. Twitter. https://twitter.com/drg1985/status/1565658000978845702

445. Baden, L. R., El Sahly, H. M., Essink, B., Kotloff, K., Frey, S., Novak, R., Diemert, D., Spector, S. A., Rouphael, N., Creech, C. B., McGettigan, J., Khetan, S., Segall, N., Solis, J., Brosz, A., Fierro, C., Schwartz, H.,

Neuzil, K., Corey, L., … Zaks, T. (2021). Efficacy and safety of the mRNA-1273 SARS-CoV-2 vaccine (Supplementary material: Protocol). *The New England Journal of Medicine*, *384*, 403-416. https://www.nejm.org/doi/suppl/10.1056/NEJMoa2035389/suppl_file/nejmoa2035389_protocol.pdf

446. Polack, F. P., Thomas, S. J., Kitchin, N., Absalon, J., Gurtman, A., Lockhart, S., Perez, J. L., Pérez Marc, G., Moreira, E. D., Zerbini, C., Bailey, R., Swanson, K. A., Roychoudhury, S., Koury, K., Li, P., Kalina, W. V., Cooper, D., Frenck, R. W., Jr., Hammitt, L. L., … Gruber, W. C. (2020). Safety and efficacy of the BNT162b2 mRNA COVID-19 vaccine (Supplementary material: Protocol). *The New England Journal of Medicine*, *383*, 2603-2615. https://www.nejm.org/doi/suppl/10.1056/NEJMoa2034577/suppl_file/nejmoa2034577_protocol.pdf

447. Arora, R. (2022, September 1). *New study of Pfizer, Moderna data suggests vaccine harm outweighs benefit*. The Epoch Times. https://www.theepochtimes.com/new-study-of-pfizer-and-moderna-data-suggests-vaccine-harm-outweighs-benefit_4703419.html

448. Kulldorff, M. (2022, July 3). *Are the COVID mRNA vaccines safe?* Brownstone Institute. https://brownstone.org/articles/are-the-COVID-mrna-vaccines-safe/

449. Ladapo, J. A. [@FLSurgeonGen]. (2022, September 2). *New study published in #Vaccine shows concerning rate of serious adverse events after mRNA vaccination, but estimates are limited b/c* [Tweet; thumbnail link to article]. Twitter. https://twitter.com/FLSurgeonGen/status/1565701396971900936

450. Prasad, V. [@VPrasadMDMPH]. (2022, September 14). *This is exactly what I think. Older, vulnerable people likely to have net gain. Younger, healthy people entirely uncertainty and* [Tweet]. Twitter. https://twitter.com/VPrasadMDMPH/status/1570071823177613312

451. Chandler, K. (2021, August 23). *Though young and healthy, unvaccinated father dies of COVID*. KKTV. https://www.kktv.com/2021/08/23/though-young-healthy-unvaccinated-father-dies-COVID/

452. California Senate Bill 277. (2022, April 27). In *Wikipedia*. https://en.wikipedia.org/w/index.php?title=California_Senate_Bill_277&oldid=1084883482

453. Graham, J. (2017, May 18). Vaccination law passed after 2014 Disneyland measles outbreak increased immunizations in Orange County. *Orange County Register*. https://www.ocregister.com/2017/05/15/more-orange-county-schools-have-herd-immunity-after-state-vaccination-law-

inspired-by-disneyland-measles-outbreak/

454. Najera, R. F. (2017, January 11). Anti-vaccine activist Robert F. Kennedy Jr. claims to head Trump vaccine panel. *HistoryOfVaccines.org*. https://historyofvaccines.org/blog/anti-vaccine-activist-robert-f-kennedy-jr-claims-to-head-trump-vaccine-panel

455. Nagourney, A. (2022, March 1). Robert Kennedy Jr.'s crusade against COVID vaccine anguishes family: Robert F. Kennedy Jr. has risen to become a major figure in the vaccine resistance movement. Those close to him say it's "heartbreaking". *The New York Times*. https://www.nytimes.com/2022/02/26/us/robert-kennedy-COVID-vaccine.html

456. Bhattacharya, J. [@DrJBhattacharya]. (2022, March 30). *There was never any scientific basis for the idea that vaccinated people do not "carry the virus." This false idea* [Tweet; thumbnail link to video]. Twitter. https://twitter.com/DrJBhattacharya/status/1509222618934616065

457. Bhattacharya, J. (2021, October 21). *What happened: Dr. Jay Bhattacharya on 19 months of COVID* [Interview]. Hoover Institution. https://www.hoover.org/research/what-happened-dr-jay-bhattacharya-19-months-COVID-1

458. Gooch, K. (2022, February 17). *Vaccination-related employee departures at 55 hospitals, health systems*. Becker's Hospital Review. https://www.beckershospitalreview.com/workforce/vaccination-requirements-spur-employee-terminations-resignations-numbers-from-6-health-systems.html

459. Bardosh, K., Krug, A., Jamrozik, E., Lemmens, T., Keshavjee, S., Prasad, V., Makary, M. A., Baral, S., & Høeg, T. B. (2022, December 5). COVID-19 vaccine boosters for young adults: A risk benefit assessment and ethical analysis of mandate policies at universities. *Journal of Medical Ethics*. Advanced online publication. https://doi.org/10.1136/jme-2022-108449

460. Bardosh, K., Krug, A., Jamrozik, E., Lemmens, T., Keshavjee, S., Prasad, V., Makary, M. A., Baral, S., & Høeg, T. B. (2022, December 12). *COVID-19 vaccine boosters for young adults: A risk-benefit assessment and five ethical arguments against mandates at universities*. SSRN. https://papers.ssrn.com/sol3/papers.cfm?abstract_id=4206070

461. Malhi, S. (2022, September 18). COVID shots for young kids arrived in June. Few have received them. *The Washington Post*. https://www.washingtonpost.com/health/2022/09/18/kids-coronavirus-vaccine/

462. Calarco, J. (2021, October 25). 'There's almost no incentive at all

to give him the vaccine.' *The New York Times*. https://www.nytimes.com/2021/10/25/opinion/COVID-vaccine-kids-parents.html

463. Howard, J. (2022, May 6). Pediatric hepatitis, a medical Rorschach test. *Science-Based Medicine*. https://sciencebasedmedicine.org/pediatric-hepatitis-a-medical-rorschach-test/

464. *Texas teen who survived COVID-19 after double lung transplant asks others to get COVID vaccine: 17-year-old spent 5 months in hospitals across Texas, including ones in San Antonio, Houston*. (2021, June 12). ABC7 New York. https://abc7ny.com/COVID-vaccine-COVID-19-texas/10780753/

465. and Prevention. (2023, January 3). *Multisystem inflammatory syndrome in children (MIS-C): Information for healthcare providers about talking with families and caregivers*. U.S. Department of Health and Human Services. https://www.cdc.gov/mis/mis-c/hcp/provider-families.html

466. Salisbury, D. (2023, January 17). *Children with COVID and another viral illness more likely to have severe outcomes, study shows*. MLive.com. https://www.mlive.com/public-interest/2023/01/children-with-COVID-and-another-viral-illness-more-likely-to-have-severe-outcomes-study-shows.html

467. Watanabe, A., Kani, R., Iwagami, M., Takagi, H., Yasuhara, J., & Kuno, T. (2023). Assessment of efficacy and safety of mRNA COVID-19 vaccines in children aged 5 to 11 years: A systematic review and meta-analysis. *JAMA Pediatrics*, Advance online publication. https://doi.org/10.1001/jamapediatrics.2022.6243

468. Prasad, V. (2022, October 19). Heart scars & kids with myocarditis: Dr. Vinay Prasad on mRNA and CDC's advisory committee on immunization practices (ACIP) vote w/ Dr. Kelly Victory [audio podcast interview]. In *Ask Dr. Drew*. https://drdrew.com/2022/heart-scars-kids-with-myocarditis-dr-vinay-prasad-on-mrna-and-cdcs-advisory-committee-on-immunization-practices-acip-vote-w-dr-kelly-victory-ask-dr-drew/

469. Anderson, E. J., Campbell, J. D., Creech, C. B., Frenck, R., Kamidani, S., Munoz, F. M., Nachman, S., & Spearman, P. (2021). Warp speed for Coronavirus disease 2019 (COVID-19) vaccines: Why are children stuck in neutral? *Clinical Infectious Diseases, 73*(2), 336-340. https://doi.org/10.1093/cid/ciaa1425

470. File: Anti-vaccination protest near Leicester clock tower, October 2021.jpg. (2022, July 16). *Wikimedia Commons, the free media repository*. Retrieved from https://commons.wikimedia.org/w/index.php?title=File:Anti-vaccination_protest_near_Leicester_clock_tower,_

October_2021.jpg&oldid=674785627

471. File: Measles Canada 1924-2018.png. (2022, July 23). *Wikimedia Commons, the free media repository*. Retrieved from https://commons.wikimedia.org/w/index.php?title=File:Measles_Canada_1924-2018.png&oldid=677065401

472. File: Salk March of Dimes poster.jpg. (2021, October 6). *Wikimedia Commons, the free media repository*. Retrieved from https://commons.wikimedia.org/w/index.php?title=File:Salk_March_of_Dimes_poster.jpg&oldid=595961901

473. File: Allan Warner, photograph of two boys with smallpox (Atlas of Clinical Medicine, Surgery, and Pathology, 1901) (cropped).jpg. (2022, May 14). *Wikimedia Commons, the free media repository*. Retrieved from https://commons.wikimedia.org/w/index.php?title=File:Allan_Warner,_photograph_of_two_boys_with_smallpox_(Atlas_of_Clinical_Medicine,_Surgery,_and_Pathology,_1901)_(cropped).jpg&oldid=655954396

474. Prasad, V., & Mandrola, J. (2023, January 25). *The epidemic of #DiedSuddenly*. The Free Press. https://www.thefp.com/p/the-epidemic-of-diedsuddenly

475. Howard, J. [@19joho]. (2023, January 25). *Wait, is this minimizing myocarditis? That's impossible.* [Tweet; image attached]. Twitter. https://twitter.com/19joho/status/1618415222779445248

476. Høeg, T. [@TracyBethHoeg]. (2022, September 11). *Sounds like UK may no longer recommend COVID vax to non high risk kids <11 Here 👇 Nordic counties' vax policies* [Tweet; images attached]. Twitter. https://twitter.com/TracyBethHoeg/status/1569131107203031040

477. Arbel, R., Peretz, A., Sergienko, R., Friger, M., Beckenstien, T., Yaron, S., Hammerman, A., Bilenko, N., & Netzer, D. (2023, January 3). *Effectiveness of the bivalent mRNA vaccine in preventing severe COVID-19 outcomes: An observational cohort study*. Preprints with The Lancet, Preprint article. https://papers.ssrn.com/sol3/papers.cfm?abstract_id=4314067

478. Lin, D.-Y., Xu, Y., Gu, Y., Zeng, D., Wheeler, B., Young, H., Sunny, S. K., & Moore, Z. (2023, January 25). Effectiveness of bivalent boosters against severe Omicron infection. *The New England Journal of Medicine*, Advanced online publication. https://doi.org/10.1056/NEJMc2215471

479. Kuehn, B. M. (2022). Cardiac complications more common after COVID-19 than vaccination. *JAMA, 327*(20), 1951. https://doi.

org/10.1001/jama.2022.8061

480. Prasad, V. [@VPrasadMDMPH]. (2021, April 2). *media's breathless coverage of MIS-C and variants has been a disservice* [Tweet]. Twitter. https://twitter.com/VPrasadMDMPH/status/1378182052088999940

481. File: Measles US 1938-2019.png. (2022, July 23). *Wikimedia Commons, the free media repository*. Retrieved from https://commons.wikimedia.org/wiki/File:Measles_US_1938-2019.png

482. Makary, M. (2021, December 24). *The Ingraham Angle* [Video interview transcript]. Fox News. https://www.foxnews.com/transcript/the-ingraham-angle-on

Conclusion

1. Ioannidis, J. P. A. (2020, April 17). *Perspectives on the pandemic* [Episode 4; video podcast interview transcript]. The Press and the Public. https://www.thepressandthepublic.com/post/perspectives-on-the-pandemic-iv

2. Kaiser Family Foundation. (2022, December 22). *Global COVID-19 tracker – Updated as of December 22*. https://www.kff.org/coronavirus-COVID-19/issue-brief/global-COVID-19-tracker/

3. Mathieu, E., Ritchie, H., Rodés-Guirao, L., Appel, C., Giattino, C., Hasell, J., Macdonald, B., Dattani, S., Beltekian, D., Ortiz-Ospina, E., & Roser, M. (2020). *Coronavirus pandemic (COVID-19)* [Interactive dataset]. Our World in Data. Retrieved December 14, 2022, from https://ourworldindata.org/COVID-deaths

4. Bach, K. (2022, August 24). *New data shows long COVID is keeping as many as 4 million people out of work*. Brookings Institution. https://www.brookings.edu/research/new-data-shows-long-COVID-is-keeping-as-many-as-4-million-people-out-of-work/

5. Children's Health Defense. (2022, January 20). *CHD and Robert F. Kennedy, Jr. to join thousands on January 23 for the defeat the mandates rally in Washington, DC*. Yahoo Finance. https://www.yahoo.com/now/chd-robert-f-kennedy-jr-152200484.html

6. Martin, R. (2021, December 30). *The dishonest doctors who were Fox News' most frequent medical guests in 2021: These 10 guests made nearly 700 combined appearances on Fox this year – and often spread medical misinformation on-air.* Media Matters for America. https://www.mediamatters.org/fox-news/dishonest-doctors-who-were-fox-news-most-frequent-medical-guests-2021-0

7. Risen, J. (2022, October 10). *The Right's anti-vaxxers are killing Republicans: Since COVID-19 vaccines arrived, the gap in so-called excess deaths between Republicans and Democrats has widened, a new study says*. The Intercept. https://theintercept.com/2022/10/10/COVID-republican-democrat-deaths/

8. Walach, H., Weikl, R., Prentice, J., Diemer, A., Traindl, H., Kappes, A., & Hockertz, S. (2021, June 30). Experimental assessment of carbon dioxide content in inhaled air with or without face masks in healthy children: A randomized clinical trial. *JAMA Pediatrics*. https://doi.org/10.1001/jamapediatrics.2021.2659 (Retraction published July 16, 2021, *JAMA Pediatrics, 175*(9), Article 213252, https://doi.org/10.1001/jamapediatrics.2021.3252)

9. Oransky, I. (2021, July 2). *Journal retracts paper claiming two deaths from COVID-19 vaccination for every three prevented cases*. Retraction Watch. https://retractionwatch.com/2021/07/02/journal-retracts-paper-claiming-two-deaths-from-COVID-19-vaccination-for-every-three-prevented-cases/

10. Schraer, R., & Goodman, J. (2021, October 6). *Ivermectin: How false science created a COVID 'miracle' drug*. BBC News. https://www.bbc.com/news/health-58170809

11. Offord, C. (2020, October 1). The Surgisphere scandal: What went wrong? *The Scientist*. https://www.the-scientist.com/features/the-surgisphere-scandal-what-went-wrong--67955

12. Rabin, R. C. (2020, June 15). Scientists question validity of major hydroxychloroquine study: Experts demanded verification of data and methods used in a study of drugs to treat COVID-19. The study suggested the drugs might have increased deaths. *The New York Times*. https://www.nytimes.com/2020/05/29/health/coronavirus-hydroxychloroquine.html

13. *Retracted coronavirus (COVID-19) papers*. (n.d.). Retraction Watch. Retrieved December 30, 2022, from https://retractionwatch.com/retracted-coronavirus-COVID-19-papers/

14. World Health Organization (WHO) [@WHO]. (2020, March 8). *FACT: #COVID19 is NOT airborne. The #coronavirus is mainly transmitted through droplets generated when an infected person coughs, sneezes or* [Tweet; infographic attached]. Twitter. https://twitter.com/who/status/1243972193169616898

15. Select Subcommittee on the Coronavirus Crisis. (2022, October). *"It was compromised": The Trump administration's unprecedented campaign to control CDC and politicize public health during the coronavirus crisis* [Staff report]. U.S. House of Representatives. https://coronavirus.house.gov/sites/democrats.coronavirus.house.gov/files/2022.10.17%20The%20Trump%20Administration%E2%80%99s%20Unprecedented%20Campaign%20to%20Control%20CDC%20and%20Politicize%20Public%20Health%20During%20the%20Coronavirus%20Crisis.pdf

16. Schwartz, B. (2022, September 7). *Dr. Oz owns shares of companies that supply hydroxychloroquine, a drug he has backed as a COVID treatment*. CNBC. https://www.cnbc.com/2022/09/07/dr-oz-has-ties-to-hydroxychloroquine-companies-as-he-backs-COVID-treatment.html

17. Damania, Z. (n.d.). *Join The ZPac Supporter Tribe!* ZDoggMD. https://zdoggmd.com/supporters/

Index

Symbols

A

B

C

D

E

F

G

H

I

J

K

N

O

P

Q

R

S

Acknowledgements

This book would not exist without Drs. David Gorski and Steven Novella. I am enormously thankful to them for trusting me with a regular spot at *Science Based Medicine*. I had no idea I had so much to say, and they recognized that before I did. I am also thankful for all they've taught me over the years about the importance of critical thinking in medicine. We can all learn something by thinking about why smart people fall for fads like cupping. Dr. Gorski is mentioned frequently in this book, but I could have credited him with some insight on nearly every page. He's been doing this for decades and taught me everything I needed to know to write this book. Some people disappointed me during this pandemic. Drs. Gorski and Novella did not.

I am also thankful to the countless other healthcare workers who recognized the dangers of medical misinformation, both before and during the pandemic. Providing accurate information isn't always an easy thing to do, knowing your most likely reward is ugliness on social media and nasty e-mails to your boss. You certainly won't get a promotion for it. However, it's important to let the public know that the loudest, most confident voices are not always the most reliable.

I am grateful to Mallory Harris for her many helpful suggestions. Noah Louis-Ferdinand wrote an excellent discussion of the Great Barrington Declaration that greatly informed my own thinking, and I appreciate his comments on this book as well. Dorit Reiss has been a friend and teacher for years. Thank you, Dorit, for your help and advocacy. Thanks to Michael Lewis for inviting me on his podcast and writing the foreword to this book.

A special thanks to Cindy Harlow for her tireless editing prowess and many suggestions to improve the manuscript. Every writer should be lucky enough to have someone like her. She can be reached here: c_harlow@hughes.net.

Thanks to Patricia Thompson and the team at Redhawk Publications for taking a chance with this book. I knew after our first conversation you were all my kind of people.

There are probably three people in the world who have read all of my articles on *Science Based Medicine*. I am grateful to my parents for their love and support at every step of the way. In addition to being the perfect quarantine partner, my wife Robin offered me advice and encouragement throughout. It was her idea to put my thoughts together into a book, and though I ignored her advice to make it short and sweet, it would not exist without her. And though they have yet to read a word of anything I've ever written, my teenage children, Sadie and Judah, didn't roll their eyes too hard at their father's incessant dinner table blathering.

About the Author

Dr. Jonathan Howard is an Associate Professor of Neurology and Psychiatry at NYU Langone Health and the Chief of Neurology at Bellevue Hospital.

He is the author of *Cognitive Errors and Diagnostic Mistakes: A Case-Based Guide to Critical Thinking in Medicine* as well as several textbooks in neurology.

For additional information, visit jonathanhowardmd.com and check ScienceBasedMedicine.org for other articles written by the author. Questions or comments? E-mail Dr. Howard at wewanttheminfected@gmail.com.

Made in the USA
Las Vegas, NV
25 May 2023

72499382R00330